D1596878

POISONOUS PLANTS OF THE
UNITED STATES AND CANADA

PRENTICE-HALL BIOLOGICAL SCIENCE SERIES

William D. McElroy and Carl P. Swanson, *Editors*

BIOCHEMICAL SYSTEMATICS,* by Ralph E. Alston and B. L. Turner
CLASSIC PAPERS IN GENETICS, by James A. Peters
EXPERIMENTAL BIOLOGY, by Richard W. Van Norman
FOUNDATIONS OF EXPERIMENTAL EMBRYOLOGY, by Benjamin H. Willier
    and Jane M. Oppenheimer
MECHANISMS OF BODY FUNCTIONS, by Dexter M. Easton
MILESTONES IN MICROBIOLOGY, by Thomas D. Brock
PAPERS ON HUMAN GENETICS, by Samuel H. Boyer, IV
POISONOUS PLANTS OF THE UNITED STATES AND CANADA, by John M. Kingsbury
PRINCIPLES OF BIOLOGY, by Neal D. Buffaloe
SELECTED BOTANICAL PAPERS, by Irving W. Knobloch
SELECTED PAPERS ON VIROLOGY, by Nicholas Hahon
A SYNTHESIS OF EVOLUTIONARY THEORY, by Herbert H. Ross

Concepts of Modern Biology Series

BEHAVIORAL ASPECTS OF ECOLOGY,* by Peter H. Klopfer
MOLECULAR BIOLOGY: GENES AND CHEMICAL CONTROL OF LIVING CELLS, by
    J. M. Barry

Foundations of Modern Biology Series

ADAPTATION, by Bruce Wallace and A. M. Srb
ANIMAL BEHAVIOR, by Vincent Dethier and Eliot Stellar
ANIMAL DIVERSITY, by Earl D. Hanson
ANIMAL PHYSIOLOGY, by Knut Schmidt-Neilsen
THE CELL, by Carl P. Swanson
CELL PHYSIOLOGY AND BIOCHEMISTRY, by William D. McElroy
CHEMICAL BACKGROUND FOR THE BIOLOGICAL SCIENCES, by Emil H. White
GROWTH AND DEVELOPMENT, by Maurice Sussman
HEREDITY, by David M. Bonner and Stanley E. Mills
THE LIFE OF THE GREEN PLANT, by Arthur W. Galston
MAN IN NATURE, by Marston Bates
THE PLANT KINGDOM, by Harold C. Bold

* These titles are also in the Prentice-Hall International Series in Biological Science. Prentice-Hall, Inc.; Prentice-Hall International, United Kingdom and Eire; Prentice-Hall of Canada, Ltd., Canada.

POISONOUS PLANTS OF THE UNITED STATES AND CANADA

by

John M. Kingsbury

Professor of Botany
New York State College of Agriculture

and

Lecturer in Phytotoxicology
New York State Veterinary College

Cornell University

Prentice-Hall, Inc.
Englewood Cliffs, New Jersey

PRENTICE-HALL INTERNATIONAL, INC., LONDON
PRENTICE-HALL OF AUSTRALIA, PTY., LTD., SYDNEY
PRENTICE-HALL OF CANADA, LTD., TORONTO
PRENTICE-HALL OF INDIA (PRIVATE) LTD., NEW DELHI
PRENTICE-HALL OF JAPAN, INC., TOKYO

SB617
. K5

Library of Congress Catalog Card Number: 64-14394

Current printing (last digit):

13   12   11   10   9   8   7   6   5

Printed in the United States of America

68501-C

Dedicated to the memory of
Ray Ethan Torrey

Nous voulons bien croire à l'existence de plantes absolument malfaisantes, créées peut-être à seule fin de mettre en relief le mérite de celles qui nous rendent des services, mais ces plantes absolument malfaisantes sont bien rares.

PIERRE JOIGNEAUX

Le Livre de la Ferme et des Maisons de Campagne. Paris, 1865

ACKNOWLEDGMENTS

This book owes its existence in large measure to the hundreds of persons who made the thousands of decisions that have resulted in the almost unmatched excellence of Cornell's libraries for the subject here reviewed. I am more specifically indebted to the staffs of the Albert R. Mann Library of the Colleges of Agriculture and Home Economics, the Roswell P. Flower Library of the Veterinary College, and the University (Olin) Library, and especially to Helen Krebs and Mia Reinap, for help, advice, and services frequently beyond the strict call of duty in obtaining the thousands of references that were reviewed.

In a different way, but none the less directly, this book is the result of the pioneering efforts of my predecessor, Walter C. Muenscher, who developed the subject at Cornell and authored the text which has been standard for a generation. I am indebted to Minnie W. Muenscher for many courtesies and for making Professor Muenscher's materials available. It was her wish that the excellent illustrations prepared for the former text be carried forward in this, and with gracious permission of The Macmillan Company, they appear in this volume in tribute to Professor Muenscher.

Hospitality and invaluable local advice, generously given, have contributed immeasurably to the success of collecting trips for poisonous plants of the West and Southwest. I am particularly indebted in this way to Wayne Binns, W. T. Huffman, Bruno Klinger, and Omer Sperry. William T. Gillis, John M. King, and Richard Pohl have read the entire manuscript and each has offered many helpful criticisms. Abraham Krikorian has double checked the chemical formulas and Richard Hart has shared his knowledge. Remaining errors are the author's who would appreciate learning of them. The section on poison ivy (*Toxicodendron*) and related dermatitis plants was contributed by William T. Gillis who has made a special study of this subject.

All photographs used in the book, unless credited otherwise, were made by the author. Color photographs, though often especially instructive, are not ordinarily possible due to the high cost involved. Use of color for four photographs illustrating this book was made possible by a monetary grant from Merck Sharp & Dohme Research Laboratories. All line drawings not credited to The Macmillan Company are used by courtesy of Cornell Extension Bulletin #538.

Finally, I am indebted in a way not easily recorded, to my colleagues in the Departments of Botany, Pathology, Medicine and Obstetrics, and in the L. H. Bailey Hortorium, all of whom I have bothered with questions from time to time; to cooperative secretaries on whom I have placed imperious demands; to the publisher (especially in the person of John Riina) who has made the project easier than it might have been; and to my wife who encouraged it.

CONTENTS

INTRODUCTION

This book is intended as a reference for the physician and veterinarian who must deal with practical problems posed by poisonous plants, as a text for the medical and veterinary student, and as an introduction to the scattered literature for the person of whatever background, who desires to investigate poisonous plants. It should prove of value also to those interested in physiologically active compounds in plants.

Geographically it includes, as far as determinable, all plants known to have poisoned livestock or human beings in the continental United States and Canada. Hawaiian plants have been included as far as practical. A few plants not yet known to have caused poisoning in North America have been included on the basis of well-established histories of toxicity on other continents.

Botanically it includes the toxic members of all groups of plants except bacteria.

Toxicologically it includes all plants which have caused loss of life and in which toxicity has been traced or may reasonably be traceable to a particular component producing an identifiable or potentially identifiable deleterious reaction in one or more species of animal when taken into the body under natural circumstances. Plants containing medicinal compounds, overdoses of which are toxic, have been excluded unless the plant itself has also caused poisoning. Syndromes associated with particular plants which appear caused solely by deficiency of a nutritional factor in the plant have been excluded. Syndromes associated with particular plants which appear best interpreted as digestive upsets have been included only if it seems probable that upset in digestion may be traced to a particular characteristic or component of the plant.

This survey has been drawn from the literature. Information concerning poisonous plants of North America is found in unusually diverse sources. Many of the original references to toxicity of plants which stand behind current accounts are bibliographically, historically, or physically difficult to locate. For this reason, more than usual effort has been spent to identify original sources of information for the reader. The intention of the reference citations is to provide the interested reader or potential researcher with access to the entire toxicological literature concerning any poisonous plant of the United States or Canada. This does not mean that the references here presented are complete in themselves; frequently it has been possible to cite review papers, the bibliographies of which have not been repeated. North American literature has been searched extensively. European and other foreign literature has not been searched as exhaustively, but major foreign compendia have been employed to locate important material suitable for inclusion. Undoubtedly, useful references have been overlooked. The author will be indebted to persons who call such to his attention.

The author has learned of many cases of poisoning by telephone or letter, by newspaper account, or in other similar ways. Although some of these might have added significantly to our knowledge of poisonous plants, it has seemed the prudent and responsible course to exclude them (for the most part) from this book. Information has qualified for inclusion here only on the basis of reports published by scientific (as opposed to popular) press.

This book is not complete. Literally hundreds of species of plants additional to the ones discussed here have at one time or in one place or another, had a reputation of toxicity. In most cases the reputation is poorly founded or entirely undocumented. Plants have been included in this discussion, with rare exception, only if their toxicity has been reliably established by clear circumstantial or experimental evidence. Each year additional species of plants are discovered to be toxic. The absence of a plant from this book does not necessarily imply, therefore, that it is harmless.

A survey can be no better than the literature from which it is drawn. In the literature of poisonous plants it has been common practice to carry forward particular information from publication to publication, without reference either to the immediate or to the original source, thus obscuring the validity of the information. Effort has been made here to identify and evaluate sources in extracting from them the discussions presented and liberal use has been made of reference citations. In addition, the chapter on history of knowledge of poisonous plants is included so that the reader may form his own evaluation.

The physician may find this book apparently directed mainly toward the requirements of the veterinarian. The original impetus for its preparation came from need of a text for use in the course on poisonous plants taught in the New York State Veterinary College at Cornell University, but emphasis on animal poisoning is a true reflection of emphasis in the literature. Animal poisoning by plants is more frequent and usually more susceptible to investigation than is human poisoning. Experimental investigations have been directed from the point of view of the veterinarian.

The bulk of this book consists of autonomous descriptions of individual poisonous plants arranged alphabetically by scientific name, within botanical families taxonomically arranged. The classificational scheme used for the Divisions Pteridophyta and Spermatophyta is that of Lyman Benson (*Plant Classification* D. C. Heath and Co., Boston, 1957) which is a basically conservative representation of natural relationships among plants as currently understood.

The discussion of each major plant generally follows the outline: scientific name, common name(s), description, distribution and habitat, poisonous principle, toxicity, symptoms and lesions, and conditions of poisoning. Descriptions have been written with the intention of enabling a person to decide with certainty whether a suspected plant in hand is or is not the one described. Unavoidable specialized botanical and pathological terminology has been employed for precision and brevity. Definitions of these standard terms may be found in the glossaries of appropriate botanical or medical texts and dictionaries. In most cases, figures for toxicity have been converted uniformly into per cent of animal's weight of green plant necessary to produce a given toxic effect. Frequently a figure for average weight of breed has been employed in the absence of specified weight in the original source. Resulting toxicity figures should, therefore, be regarded only as rough approximation, reliable only within a degree of magnitude.

"For all practical purposes, treatment of poisoning by plants is symptomatic and supportive; no generally accepted antidotal agents are available." (Statement from the National Clearinghouse for Poison Control Centers, U.S. Public Health Service. September, 1958.) The same is true for treatment of animals. In the rare cases where specific antidotal agents are useful in treatment of identified poisonings, attention has been directed to them in the text, but no attempt has been made to indicate exact use.

Effective investigation of poisoning by plants usually involves the expert abilities of a number of specialists in relatively unrelated fields—physiology, pathology, biochemistry, botany, and others. Only rarely have these varied professional talents been assembled in experimental programs. Knowledge of poisonous plants in the United States and Canada, especially in the eastern portions, is poor. Physicians and veterinarians are understandably reluctant to publish cases dealing with poisonous plants since their education and professional experience rarely gives them necessary familiarity with the botanical side of the problem. Nevertheless, it is mainly through the appearance of well-documented, reliably established case histories in appropriate journals that information may be gathered about particular poisonous plants. This book will serve a useful purpose if it stimulates interest in the unresolved problems of poisonings by plants, furthers investigations by providing access to the literature, and encourages publication of appropriate cases.

KNOWLEDGE OF POISONOUS PLANTS IN THE UNITED STATES AND CANADA[1]

Introduction

Information found in current compilations dealing with poisonous plants of the United States represents an accumulation of specific items of knowledge, a few of which reach back to the time before written records were used. A continuum may be traced in this accumulation along the familiar lines of development of Western civilization, in which the scientific experimental approach is a relatively recent innovation. In many cases, repeated citation from ever newer sources clothes an item of information with unjustified authority. It is often difficult to determine what is soundly founded and what is less so. For example, experiment station bulletins on poisonous plants rarely represent the product of original research, yet sources of information are usually not cited. As one attempts to trace an item of information into older literature he is faced with additional problems. Difficulties of availability are compounded by obscure references to ancient literature that require professional bibliographic knowledge to identify.

I believe that compilers dealing with poisonous plants have often felt an obligation to carry a plant into newer literature even though uncertain of the original authority. This carry-over serves the useful function of drawing attention to the plant, but many perpetuate error, and may appear

[1] This chapter was published originally under the same title in *Economic Botany*, 15: 119–130, 1961. Reference numbers in this chapter apply to a separate list given at the end of the chapter, and not to the general list of references at the end of the book.

to validate what was established on tenuous evidence. This review sets forth the general nature of sources available to persons who first gathered information on poisonous plants of the United States, and upon whose original compilations the more recent are based.

Foundations in Western Tradition

The observation that knowledge of poisonous principles preceded agrarian civilization is curious yet logical. Hunters used poisons on their weapons to bring down game in the time before crops came under cultivation. Accurate observations of plants which might be employed in this manner, and in the healing art, had great value and were accumulated over the centuries. In the Western tradition, Dioscorides' manuscript "Of Medicinal Matters" (30) represents the pre-eminent compilation of supposed active properties of plants to the first century A.D. Even Dioscorides had trouble with his sources. Speaking of the asclepiads, he states, "But they have transmitted the powers of medicines and their examination cursorily, not estimating their efficacy by experience, but by vain prating about the cause, having lifted up each medicine to a heap of controversy: and besides this they have recorded one thing by mistake for another . . . ," and of one particular asclepiad, "And in the face of plain evidence he sets down many such falsehoods, which are tokens that he acquired his information not by his own observation, but had it only from the false relation of hearsay."

Many centuries elapsed before a work dealing specifically with poisonous plants appeared. The herbals—both the manuscripts of the Greek and Roman eras and the printed volumes of the period of the reawakening— served as the repository of comments on the poisonous nature of plants. Little is gained by close examination of the period between Dioscorides and the birth of the scientific method other than to establish that, during this time when much other knowledge fell into disuse, poisoning became truly an art. Practitioners developed, jealously guarded, and carefully transmitted secrets of poisonous compounds. Extraneous ingredients or procedures were introduced into recipes further to obscure the identity of the toxic principle, but were thus to some extent introduced also into contemporary literature. The flavor of the times has been captured by reviewers such as Blyth (6), Kobert (37), and Lewin (39).

The printed herbal appeared around 1470 and its era lasted for about two centuries (2). Dioscorides was translated from Latin into English in 1652–1655 by John Goodyer (30). Many herbals were based upon or made frequent reference to this work. In the process of the occasional attempt to equate plants of Northern Europe with those of Dioscorides, additional confusion occurred. Only gradually did erroneous information and superstition give way to contemporary observation. The herbals were succeeded in one direction by works dealing with medicinal and useful plants and in another by floras. In both, the poisonous nature of particular plants was frequently mentioned. Such references, for example, are not infrequent in the voluminous writings of Linnaeus. Compilations limited to poisonous plants, animals, and minerals made their appearance at about the beginning of the eighteenth century. These are divisible into two categories—those concerned with the results, causes, and treatment of poisoning (toxicologies) and those presenting an enumeration and description of poisonous plants and other poisonous substances.

European Publications Dealing with Poisonous Plants—
The Eighteenth Century
The subject-index cards of the library of the United States Department of Agriculture (62), relatively comprehensive for the period and subject in question, list more than a score of works in Latin, French, English, and German published during the seventeenth and eighteenth centuries which dealt exclusively with poisonous plants or other poisonous substances. Several were learned papers on relatively narrow subjects—for example, the classic work of J. J. Wepfer, 1679, *Cicutae Aquatica, Historia et Noxae* (66),[2] but more often they were compendia.

The following eighteenth century works deserve brief note. In 1701 Melchoir Friccius, a physician of Ulm, published a *Tractus de virtute venenorum medica* (24), and in 1710, *Paradoxa de venenis* (25). Richard Mead in 1702 published *A Mechanical Account of Poisons in Several Essays* (43) which set forth an ingenious explanation of the mechanisms of poisoning. In 1765 appeared Lieutaud's *Synopsis Univ. Praxeos Medicae* (41) in two volumes. This in the original and in translation became a standard reference for physicians, the second volume being a text on the materia medica.

Johann Frederick Gmelin's *Abhandlung von den giftigen Gewächsen* (26) published in 1775 and in a second, expanded edition in 1805; *Allgemeine Geschichte der Pflanzengifte* (27) in 1777, second edition in 1803; and *Allgemeine Geschichte der Gifte* in 1776 and 1777 (28, 29) were particularly influential. The first gives insight into knowledge of the times. In its preface the author states that he has been encouraged to publish in his native tongue the lectures which he had prepared in Latin for the Roman Imperial Academy of Natural Sciences (probably similar to or the same as those published as *Diss. de materia toxicorum hominis vegetabilium simplicium in medicamentum convertenda,* Tübingen, 1765). His information was drawn largely from earlier literature. Cases of poisoning in human beings are cited with particular attention to poisonings

[2] This work is cited by several of the early authors on poisonous plants. A translation of part of it may be found in a paper by Jacobson (36).

resulting from injudicious use of plant-derived medicines. Attention is given also to the effects of poisonous plants on animals. The book follows an organization that is still commonly used. A brief treatment of general aspects of poisoning is followed by individual discussions of 56 species in 30 genera:

Aconitum lycoctonum, A. napellus, Actaea spicata, Aethusa cynapium, Agaricus muscarius, Anemone nemorosa, A. pulsatilla, A. ranunculoides, Arum maculatum, Asarum europaeum, Atropa belladonna, Bryonia alba, Caltha palustris, Chaerophyllum bulbosum, C. sylvestre, C. temulum, Chenopodium hybridum, Cicuta virosa, Clematis flammula, C. vitalba, Colchicum autumnale, Conium maculatum, Daphne mezereum, Datura stramonium, D. tatula, Digitalis purpurea, Euphorbia amygdaloides, E. chamaesyce, E. cyparissias, E. esula, E. exigua acuta, E. helioscopia, E. paralias, E. peplus, E. platyphyllos, E. sylvatica, E. verrucosa, Helleborus foetidus, Hyoscyamus niger, Lolium temulentum, Mercurialis perennis, Pedicularis palustris, Polygonum hydropiper, Ranunculus acris, R. aquatilis, R. arvensis, R. bulbosus, R. ficaria, R. flammula, R. lingua, R. platanifolius, R. sceleratus, Sium latifolium, Solanum dulcamara, S. nigrum vulgare, Veratrum album. (All species named by Linnaeus.)

Several of these plants would not be included in such a work today. In Gmelin's later works the number of species considered was greatly augmented.

Nine years later, Pierre Bulliard published a slightly more extensive treatise, *Histoire des plants vénéneuses et suspectes de la France.* In the second edition (1798) (10), eighty-six species of poisonous plants, in fifty-four genera,

Aconitum, Actaea, Aethusa, Anemone, Aristolochia, Arum, Asarum, Asclepias, Atropa, Betonica, Bryonia, Chelidonium, Cicuta, Clematis, Colchicum, Conium, Cyclamen, Daphne, Datura, Digitalis, Euphorbia, Evonymus, Genista, Gladiolus, Gratiola, Hedera, Helleborus, Hyoscyamus, Iris, Juniperus, Lobelia, Lolium, Menyanthes, Momordica, Nigella, Oenanthe, Ononis, Paeonia, Papaver, Paris, Pedicularis, Phellandrium, Polygonum, Prunus, Ranunculus, Rhinanthus, Rhus, Ruta, Secale, Sedum, Solanum, Taxus, Veratrum, Agaricus,

are listed and discussed. Compared with Gmelin, more extensive treatment is given to symptoms, effects, and antidotes. Two additional publications of that century, Plenck's *Toxicologia, seu doctrina de venenis et antidotis* (51), 1785, and Woodville's *Medical Botany* (70), three volumes and supplement, 1790 to 1794, were much consulted. A passage from the latter provides insight into the condition of literature of that time. "It is a lamentable truth, that our experimental knowledge of many of the herbacious simples is extremely defective; for as writers on the

Materia Medica have usually done little more than copy the accounts given by their predecessors, the virtues now ascribed to several plants are wholly referable to the authority of Dioscorides."

The preceding were learned works intended for use by physicians and educated laity. It was important, too, that the public be informed about dangerous plants. In the common schools, two works of J. C. A. Mayer (55) appearing between 1798 and 1800, were employed. They serve as an index to the plants then considered most dangerous in Germany, namely, *Cicuta virosa, Datura stramonium, Conium maculatum, Hyoscyamus niger, Atropa belladonna, Aethusa cynapium, Ranunculus sceleratus, Solanum nigrum, Daphne mezereum,* and *Lolium temulentum.* Mayer's death prevented publication of another volume to have included *Sium latifolium, Anemone pratensis, Digitalis purpurea, Colchicum autumnale, Oenanthe fistulosa,* and *Oenanthe napellus.*

European Publications Dealing With Poisonous Plants—
The Nineteenth Century

European literature on medicinal or useful plants in general, and on poisonous plants in particular, increased geometrically during the nineteenth century. It is possible to mention only a few of the most outstanding works that discussed poisonous plants.

M. J. B. Orfila, who has been called (6) the "Father of Toxicology," was widely known in his time as a chemist and as the author of several texts. He investigated the chemistry of toxic substances, including those found in plants, performing hundreds of experiments. His *Traité des Poisons tirés des Règnes minéral, végétal et animal,* published in two volumes in 1814 and 1815 (47), presented results of his experiments and observations in cases of poisoning in human beings. The dog served as his chief experimental animal. To obtain experimental results it was often necessary to prevent vomition by ligating the esophagus. This rather drastic procedure undoubtedly was responsible for symptoms which in some cases he ascribed to the toxicity of the plant in question. He attempted to trace the route and site of accumulation of the poisonous substance and to recover it from the tissues, an approach not previously used. His works are organized on the basis of the characteristics of the poisonous substances. Waller's translation (49) treats poisonous plants under the categories of acrid poisons, narcotic poisons, and narcotic-acrid poisons. Orfila reported experiments demonstrating the toxicity of some forty-five species of plants. About as many again are included on the basis of references from other literature. An American edition of the English translation was published in 1817 (48). The following quotation is from the translator's preface:

Every physiological and chemical question, however futile, or practically useless, has engaged the attention, nay become the mania of European physiologists, the English and the French, as well as the Italians and
the Germans; but until lately none had devoted himself to the numerous
affectations produced by poisons. . . . For the practitioners in the United
States, to throw into one register the fatal cases by poison for one year,
what an awful reproach would it cast upon deficiency of practice in this
particular! . . . The work of Dr. Orfila is considered to be of more importance to the physicians of the United States than it can be to those of
any other country, because we are less capable of producing such a work
than almost any other nation, older than ourselves.

I have an anonymous booklet dated Dresden, 1815, and entitled *Giftbüchlein oder Abbildung und Beschreibung der in Deutschland wachsenden
Giftpflanzen* (1). It was obviously intended to familiarize the lay public
with the most dangerous poisonous plants. Although almost contemporary,
it is more extensive than Mayer's *Einheimische Giftgewächse* and includes
all the plants which Mayer published except *Lolium temulentum*. In addition are listed *Physalis alkekengi, Euphorbia esula, Solanum dulcamara,
Colchicum autumnale,* five species of *Ranunculus, Anemone pratensis,
Anemone nemorosa, Cynoglossum officinale, Paris quadrifolia, Aconitum
napellus,* and *Digitalis purpurea.* The twenty-four colored illustrations are
botanically faithful and better than some in current publications of similar
purpose.

Brandt, Phoebus, and Ratzeburg's *Abbildung und Beschreibung der in
Deutschland wild wachsenden und in Gärten im Freien ausdauernden Giftgewächse* (7) appeared in 1838. This served as a primary reference for at
least two of the more influential authors later to appear on the American
scene. It is given prominent mention by Pammel in his *Manual of Poisonous
Plants* (50) of 1911. A charge card in the copy of the *Abbildung* possessed
by the Library of the United States Department of Agriculture indicates that
the book was in the hands of V. K. Chesnut (see later) during the years he
was concerned with poisonous plants. The first volume of the *Abbildung,*
the work of Brandt and Ratzeburg, is a revised, expanded edition of a work
by the same authors that appeared in 1834. It deals with phanerogamous
plants. The second volume, by Phoebus, deals with cryptogamous plants and
was not preceded by an earlier edition. The section concerning phanerogamous plants discusses only fifty-six species,

*Aconitum, Aethusa, Anemone, Arum, Atropa, Caltha, Cicuta, Colchicum,
Conium, Coronilla, Cyclamen, Cynanchum, Daphne, Datura, Digitalis,
Euphorbia, Fritillaria, Gratiola, Helleborus, Hyoscyamus, Juniperus,
Lactuca, Ledum, Lolium, Mandragora, Narcissus, Nerium, Oenanthe, Pap-
aver, Paris, Pulsatilla, Ranunculus, Rhus, Scopolina, Sium, Solanum,
Taxus, Veratrum,*

but treats them rather fully. Many species found in Gmelin and/or Bulliard are omitted, although these sources are frequently cited for the plants listed. Orfila is, perhaps, most frequently used. A strong botanical emphasis is reflected in extensive botanical characterization of families, genera, and species, and in listing of synonymy. A discussion of poisonous principle accompanies each plant and includes reference to articles in journals of the time dealing with chemistry and physics. Usually the space devoted to discussion of toxicity of the plant is much less than that devoted to botanical matters.

Berge and Riecke's *Giftpflanzen-Buch* (4), published in 1845, also served as an important source for later investigators. It provides an excellent vantage point for consideration of the literature of poisonous plants at mid-nineteenth century and is particularly useful because it contains well-identified references for each plant discussed and is more extensive than the work by Brandt and Ratzeburg. Organized as a catalog, it uses subdivisions commonly employed in current works on poisonous plants: synonyms, common names, distribution and habitat, time and duration of flowering, properties of the active principle, optionally a brief treatment of the use in medicine, and a list of literature citations. Literature on the materia medica has always been greater than that restricted to plants from the point of view of their toxic capacities alone. Medical accidents contributed much to the knowledge of poisonous principles in plants. Berge and Riecke placed considerable reliance on works on the materia medica for their toxicological information. Discussion of 178 noncryptogamous species in this work represents a great increase over earlier authors. This increase is due in large part to the inclusion of species from areas such as the East Indies, the West Indies, South America, and Africa, where active exploration was taking place.

The work of the nineteenth century most frequently cited in later publications is the book of Charles Cornevin, *Des Plantes Vénéneuses et des Empoisonnements qu'elles déterminent* (20), published in 1887. Cornevin, professor at L'École National Vétérinaire, presents in this volume a small amount of experimental work as well as material meticulously collated from many sources. He treats 338 species of noncryptogamous plants. Some of the large increase represented in this figure is attributable to additional plants described as toxic from other parts of the world, but much appears to be due to citation of additional species, often without clear substantiation, in genera previously known as toxic. One gains the impression that he added many species to his lists on the basis of relationship rather than evidence. He visualized plants as containing many interacting active principles which might modify the characteristic physiology of the individual principle as extracted. He was concerned with the distribution of the toxic principle or principles in the plant; lability in cooking, drying, and similar influences; chemistry of the toxic principle; factors affecting the development and strength of the toxic principle in various plants; and the like. This publication was the first to emphasize the veterinary point of view regarding toxicity of plants to animals.

European Knowledge of Poisonous Plants—Summary

Knowledge of poisonous plants in Europe is seen to have developed directly from recorded observations by Greek and Roman writers, recollected and amplified during the period of the printed herbal. The herbals reflected interest in the distribution, relationships, and usefulness of plants. Floras, works on the materia medica, and pharmacopoeias developed from herbals. Lastly, works devoted solely to poisonous plants appeared. The eighteenth century saw an attempt to place information on poisonous plants in the public domain by bringing it from Latin into languages of common use. The information itself stemmed from a great variety of observations, but chiefly from observations of accidental cases of poisoning and from the results of overuse of plants as medicinal "simples." The eighteenth century, with pioneers such as Priestley, Lavoissier, Berthollet, and Scheele, was the period when chemistry as a science was born, and chance observation began to give way to experimental investigation. In the study of poisonous plants this development was reflected first in Orfila's experimental approach. For a complete picture of information concerning particular poisonous plants in the eighteenth and nineteenth centuries it would be necessary to refer to floras, toxicologies, works on poisonous plants, works on the materia medica, and learned papers in journals. Of these, the most reflective of the state of knowledge are those devoted solely to poisonous plants. In comparing the major works cited above (Gmelin, 1775; Bulliard, 1798; Berge and Riecke, 1845; and Cornevin, 1887) two conclusions stand out. First, the number of species considered poisonous increased many fold during this period. Secondly, each author dropped from consideration a significant number of species treated by those before him.

Such, in brief, was the information available by 1900 to persons interested in poisonous plants in the United States.

Development of Experimental Agriculture and
Veterinary Medicine in the United States

The inception of chemistry as a science in the United States may be traced to Priestley's arrival here in 1794. At about the same time, courses in chemistry, botany, and geology were introduced by the leading colleges. Jefferson's administration, which began in 1801, did much to promote the cause of science in the still young country and opened the door to an experimental approach in agriculture. But the experimental approach was not forthcoming for several decades for reasons associated with the exigencies of pioneering, clearing of the land, the westward movement, wars and unsettled political conditions, and—most important—for the reason that the landowners were not convinced of the value of such an effort. The Department of Agriculture was founded in 1862. In the same year federal aid (Morrill Land Grant Act) was made available to the states to further agricultural education, which was practically nonexistent at that time. The necessity for experimentation was felt almost immediately wherever a program for agricultural education was developed. Federal agricultural experimentation commenced in 1855 (in the Patent Office) but was greatly expanded after the organization of the Department of Agriculture. The early appointees were trained for, and worked in, entomology, chemistry, and botany. The first state-college appointees were similarly educated (35, 60).

In the United States investigations of poisonous plants have been concerned primarily with their effects on animals. These studies required the application of veterinary skills. The 1850's saw attempts at the establishment of veterinary colleges, associations, and journals. The first veterinary college successful in graduating students was the New York College of Veterinary Surgeons (private) which enrolled its initial class in 1864–5. Veterinary instruction commenced in the land-grant agricultural colleges of New York (Cornell), Illinois, and Massachusetts in 1868. The early students in these institutions served as a major source for veterinary personnel in the wide variety of programs subsequently established under federal and state auspices (40, 69).

Early Literature

Early reports of poisonings caused by plants in this country are heterogeneous. For example, in 1842, H. S. Randall described (54) a gangrenous disease of cattle in the area around Cortland, New York, and astutely observed that it might be caused by ergot because of its similarity to ergot-caused gangrene of human beings in Europe. It is interesting to note that he published in an English veterinary journal because none was then available in the United States. The disease in man known as milk-sickness, more recently shown to be caused by consumption of milk from cattle poisoned by ingestion of *Eupatorium,* may be traced back in the United States to the early 1820's (46). However, it cannot really be considered a part of the literature of poisonous plants at that time because its etiology remained unknown for many years and was still in dispute as late as 1900. In 1854, F. P. Porcher published a paper in which he discussed poisonous and useful cryptogamous plants of the United States (52). His information on toxic qualities of the plants discussed was drawn almost entirely from European sources. This paper was expanded into a book in 1857.

A short paper by W. W. Bailey (3) appeared in 1873 in which were discussed fifteen genera of plants poisonous by ingestion and a few others producing dermatitis. Unfortunately he cited no references. It is impossible to tell how much of his information came from domestic sources, personal observation, or elsewhere. Other cases reported in early years included poisoning of livestock by *Euphorbia,* by molds on grain, and by algae. Both loco poisoning and selenium poisoning were recognized in the West but were the subject of considerable confusion until later.

Questions concerning poisonous plants came with increasing frequency to veterinary departments at state colleges and to the United States Department of Agriculture. Investigations resulting from requests of the United States Department of Agriculture for aid in problems concerning poisonous plants are recorded in early Department Reports. The department botanist made several determinations of suspected plants, and the chemist analyzed many for toxic compounds (19, 63–65).

Ergotism in Kansas, 1884

In 1884 a crisis of considerable dimension drew public attention to poisonous plants and initiated a formal program of investigations by the Department of Agriculture. A cattle disease, characterized by sloughing of the hoofs and other symptoms, was reported from Kansas in that year. A local veterinarian diagnosed it as the highly contagious foot and mouth disease. Substance was given his diagnosis by the fact that foot and mouth disease was then extant in the Northeast, having been brought in by diseased cattle imported from Europe. The imminence in Kansas of a quarantine on cattle, at that time the primary resource of the state, caused great public excitement (21, 22). Several eminent veterinarians were detailed by the Army Veterinary Service, by various state governments, and by the Canadian government to investigate the situation, and conflicting reports soon appeared (23, 33, 34, 38). The Bureau of Animal Industry had just been organized in the Department of Agriculture. From it, M. R. Trumblower was sent to make an investigation (61). As a result of increasing public concern, D. E. Salmon, just-named chief of the Bureau, also investigated (57, 58). The correct diagnosis of non-infectious ergotism made by Salmon and several others eventually prevailed, and the incident served dramatically to emphasize the problems that poisonous plants could raise.

Investigations on Poisonous Plants, 1884–1900

Various other problems concerning poisonous plants came almost immediately under investigation, and the literature increased tremendously between 1884 and 1900. Part of the increase may be traced to the influence of the Hatch Act (1887) under which federal funds were made available to the states in support of agricultural experimentation. The problems investigated included ergotism and several other diseases of suspected fungal etiology (reflecting the contemporary interest in microorganisms); higher fungi; loco poisoning (certain species of *Astragalus* and *Oxytropis*); crotalism or "bottom disease" (*Crotalaria spp.*); larkspur (*Delphinium spp.*);

water hemlock (*Cicuta spp.*); the toxicity of sorghums (*Sorghum vulgare* Pers.); lupines (*Lupinus spp.*); death camas (*Zigadenus spp.*); castor bean (*Ricinus communis* L.); bitterweed (*Helenium autumnale* L.); sleepy grass (*Stipa robusta* Scribn.); and mechanical injury of stock caused by various plants, especially squirrel-tail grass (*Hordeum jubatum* L.); All of these problems occurred in, or were investigated by, states west of the Mississippi River between 1884 and 1900. Of the 21 states in that area, 16 had published on problems involving poisonous plants before 1900 and all but three by 1903. In sharp contrast were the states east of the Mississippi. Here, experiment-station investigations of particular problems appear to be limited to the single investigation of toxicity of wild cherry (*Prunus spp.*) by the New Hampshire station (45). Only a few additional plants received investigation under other auspices in the East.

Several review papers appeared in the period 1884 to 1900. Those appearing in states west of the Mississippi (5, 67, 68) were concerned largely with western poisonous plants and with the dissemination of information obtained in this country. On the other hand, review papers appearing in the East (31, 32, 56), while derived partially from local case histories, also drew heavily on European sources. Millspaugh's *American Medicinal Plants,* published in 1887 (44), is well documented with references and may be used as an index to the medical literature of the time. It derived much information from European and American compendia preceding it, and from case histories reported from various countries. Two later review papers dealing with poisonous plants in the United States were compiled in large part from this work (9, 59).

Federal Investigations on Poisonous Plants

It is not possible to trace the lines of investigation that have been pursued under various auspices in the United States since 1900 and that have resulted in the publication of several thousand articles. Instead, a brief survey of the investigations carried on by the United States Department of Agriculture may serve as an example of activity during this period. In 1894 V. K. Chesnut, a chemist, was hired as assistant botanist in the Division of Botany (which became in 1901 the Bureau of Plant Industry) to work exclusively on problems involving poisonous plants. This event marks the inception of organized federal concern with poisonous plants which has continued to the present. Botanists, chemists, and veterinarians have been cooperatively associated in the work from the beginning, although the program has been reorganized with various changes in administration of the Department of Agriculture. Chesnut's reports (11–18), widely distributed, contain a synthesis of information from the literature with an on-the-spot survey of the problems of poisonous plants in the West (chiefly in Montana at the request and with the cooperation of the Montana

Experiment Station) and a small amount of experimental work. His retiring presidential address to the Chemical Society of Washington (17) discusses the state of knowledge of the chemistry of poisonous principles in plants at that time. He continued with the Department until 1904, doing some work in Washington similar to that done in Montana. In 1905 the Division of Drug and Poisonous Plant Investigations was created in the Bureau of Plant Industry. Despite this relationship, many of the early reports are to be found in the Reports of the Bureau of Animal Industry. A field station was established in 1905 at Hugo, Colorado, in cooperation with the Colorado Agricultural Experiment Station. Work, primarily with loco, was carried on here for four years. A second station was established during the same period at Imperial, Nebraska, with the cooperation of the Nebraska Experiment Station. From 1909 to 1911 a station was maintained at Gunnison National Forest (Colorado), cooperatively with the Forest Service, for the investigation of larkspur. Work was done also on lupine and water hemlock. The station was moved to Greycliff, Montana, for investigations of lupine and death camas from 1912 to 1914. In 1915, investigations on poisonous plants were transferred to the Pathology Division of the Bureau of Animal Industry. A permanent and more convenient station was established that year, under the new administration, in the Fishlake National Forest near Salina, Utah. Many problems, but particularly oak, loco, and milkweed, were attacked there. Prominent names in federal investigations of poisonous plants at these stations include C. D. Marsh, A. C. Crawford, A.B. Clawson, W. W. Eggleston, Hadleigh Marsh, J. F. Couch, and W. T. Huffman. In 1955 the Salina station was closed and the experimental work moved to Logan, Utah, under the direction of Dr. Wayne Binns.

Conclusions

This review leads to some interesting conclusions. From experimental investigations more is known about poisonous plants of the West than the East in the United States. Of the three major reasons for this, the most important, in the writer's opinion, is that the West was settled concurrently with the development of facilities for and interest in agricultural experimentation in the United States. Farmers of the settled East, on the other hand, had developed, by experience, empirical husbandry practices which on the whole prevented mass loss of stock to unknown poisonous plants, such as occurred in the West. Secondly, the similarity of the flora of the East to that of Europe made it possible for easterners to use information from European works on poisonous plants. The flora of the West includes many plants not found in such works. Finally, the problem of poisonous plants is greater in the West than in the East, both in number of poisonous species and in severity of poisoning.

These generalizations require modification for the southeastern states, in which investigational activity has greatly increased in the last decade or two, largely in response to increased interest in cattle, poultry, and potentially useful agricultural by-products such as citrus seed meal.

An analysis of sources of information from which plants have been designated as poisonous in the United States shows that only about a third are so designated from experimental investigations performed in this country. The proportion rises to nearer two-thirds if to the former are added those considered poisonous from reports of cases in the United States. The rest are listed on the basis of information not obtained in this country, and of these a significant proportion must be traced into the literature of the nineteenth century for substantiation.

This has both advantages and disadvantages. On the one hand, European findings do not always apply here. For example, in the case of lupine, which has caused serious loss in the western United States, recent domestic publications of reputation carry the observation that icterus is a characteristic symptom or most prominent in lupine poisoning. This statement was originally derived from European literature of the late 1800's; it was valid in Europe but is not valid in the United States. Supposedly a fungus which occurs on European lupine, but not here, accounts for the difference. On the other hand, there is much to be said for maintaining a name on the roles of poisonous plants, even though the original source of information is old and not domestic. The following case, from the author's experience, is an example. In Ithaca, N.Y., a serious case of poisoning in a child was traced to ingestion of several berries from *Daphne mezereum.* Although relatively common, this plant does not appear to have been reported toxic on experimental evidence or clear case history anywhere within the United States. In fact some of the currently cited figures for its toxicity may be traced to Orfila (1814). The plant itself is mentioned by Dioscorides. In this instance, because *Daphne mezereum* was listed in the current work available to the physician involved, the drastic treatment for plant poisoning was undertaken and the child made a satisfactory recovery.

Literature Cited

1. Anonymous. *Giftbüchlein oder Abbildung und Beschreibung der in Deutschland wachsenden Giftpflanzen.* Beger, Dresden, 3te Aufl. 1815.

2. Arber, A. *Herbals, Their Origin and Evolution.* Cambridge University Press, England. 1912.

3. Bailey, W. W. Our Poisonous Plants. *Amer. Nat.,* **7:** 4–13. 1873.

4. Berge, F., and V. A. Riecke. *Giftpflanzen-Buch.* Hoffman, Stuttgart. 1845.

5. Bessey, C. E. Popular Descriptions of Some Harmful Plants. Iowa Agr. Coll., Dept. Botany, *Bull.,* November 1884: 111–118; 130–132. 1884.

6. Blyth, A. W. *Poisons, Their Effects and Detection.* Wm. Wood & Co., New York. Vol. 1. 1885.

7. Brandt, J. F., P. Phoebus, and J. T. C. Ratzeburg. *Abbildung und Beschreibung der in Deutschland wild wachsenden und in Gärten im Freien ausdauernden Giftgewächse.* Hirschwald, Berlin. 1838.

8. British Museum, The. *Catalogue of Printed Books, 1881–1900.* Edward Brothers, Ann Arbor. 1946.

9. Brooks, W. P. Poisonous Plants. *Trans. Mass. Hort. Soc. 1893* (Pt. 1): 123–144. 1893.

10. Bulliard, P. *Histoire des Plants Vénéneuses et Suspectes de la France.* A. J. Dugour, Paris. 2me. ed., 1798.

11. Chesnut, V. K. Some Common Poisonous Plants. USDA, *Ybk. Agr. 1896:* 137–146. 1896.

12. Chesnut, V. K. *Abrus* Poisoning. *Asa Gray Bull.,* **5:** 35–36. 1897.

13. Chesnut, V. K. Principal Poisonous Plants of the United States. USDA, Div. Bot., *Bull.* 20. 1898.

14. Chesnut, V. K. Thirty Poisonous Plants of the United States. USDA, *Farmer's Bull.* 86. 1898.

15. Chesnut, V. K. Preliminary Catalog of Plants Poisonous to Stock. USDA, Bur. Anim. Ind., *Ann. Rept.,* **15:** 387–420. 1898.

16. Chesnut, V. K. Some Poisonous Plants of the Northern Stock Ranges. USDA, *Ybk. Agr. 1900:* 305–324. 1900.

17. Chesnut, V. K. Problems in the Chemistry and Toxicology of Plant Substances. *Science,* **15:** 1016–1028. 1902.

18. Chesnut, V. K., and E. V. Wilcox. The Stock Poisoning Plants of Montana. USDA, Div. Bot., *Bull.* 26. 1901.

19. Collier, P. (Note on Loco.) USDA, *Rept. 1878:* 134. 1878.

20. Cornevin, C. *Des Plantes Vénéneuses et des Empoisonnements qu'elles déterminent.* Firmin-Didot, Paris. 1887.

21. Editorial. Foot and Mouth Disease. *Am. Vet. Rev.,* **8:** 20–22. 1884.

22. Editorial. Outbreak in Kansas. *Am. Vet. Rev.,* **8:** 78–79. 1884.

23. Faville, G. C. The Outbreak in Kansas. *Am. Vet. Rev.,* **8:** 53–58. 1884.

24. Friccius, Melchior. . . . *Tractus de Virtute Venenorum Medica, in quo . . . Probatur Venena Interne et Externe Usurpata non esse Noxia.* . . . Ulm, 1701. (See ref. 8.)

25. Friccius, Melchior. *Paradoxa de Venenis.* . . . Augustae Vindelicorum, Augsburg. 1710. (See ref. 8.)

26. Gmelin, J. F. *Abhandlung von den giftigen Gewächsen.* Stettin, Ulm. 1775.

27. Gmelin, J. F. *Allgemeine Geschichte der Pflanzengifte.* Raspe, Nürnberg. 1777.

28. Gmelin, J. F., *Allgemeine Geschichte der Gifte*. Weygand, Leipzig. 1776.

29. Gmelin, J. F. *Allgemeine Geschichte der Gifte*. Raspe, Nürnberg. 1777. (See ref. 37 and 62.)

30. Gunther, R. T. *The Greek Herbal of Dioscorides*. Hafner, New York. 1959.

31. Halsted, B. D. Poisonous Plants in New Jersey, a Preliminary Report. New Jersey Agr. Expt. Sta., *Ann. Rept. 1894:* 401–419; *1895:* 351–355. 1894–5.

32. Halsted, B. D. The Poisonous Plants of New Jersey. New Jersey Agr. Expt. Sta., *Bull.* 135. 1899.

33. Holcomb, A. A. Foot and Mouth Disease in Kansas. *Am. Vet. Rev.,* **8:** 13–18. 1884.

34. Hopkins, J. J. The Outbreak in Kansas. *Am. Vet. Rev.,* **8:** 59–61. 1884.

35. Houck, U. G. *The Bureau of Animal Industry*. Publ. by the Author, Washington, D.C. 1924.

36. Jacobson, C. A. Water Hemlock (*Cicuta*). Nevada Agr. Expt. Sta., *Tech. Bull.* 81. 1915.

37. Kobert, R. *Lehrbuch der Intoxikationen*. Bd. 1. Ferdinande Enke, Stuttgart. 1902.

38. Law, J. Report on the Recent Cattle Disease in Kansas. *Am. Vet. Rev.,* **8:** 199–211; 285–297; 331–341. 1884.

39. Lewin, L. *Die Gifte in der Weltgeschichte*. Julius Springer, Berlin. 1920.

40. Liautard, A. History and Progress of Veterinary Medicine in the United States. *Am. Vet. Rev.,* **1:** 5–19. 1877.

41. Lieutaud, J. *Synopsis Univ. Praxeos Medicae*. 2 vol. Amsterdam & Leipsig. 1775. (See ref. 42.)

42. Lieutaud, J. Synopsis of the Universal Practice of Medicine. Transl. by E. A. Atlee. Ed. & Rich. Parker, Philadelphia, 1816. (Vol. 1 only.)

43. Mead, R. A Mechanical Account of Poisons in Several Essays. R. South, London. 1702. (See ref. 62.)

44. Millspaugh, C. F. *American Medical Plants*. 2 vol. Boericke & Tafel, New York. 1887.

45. Morse, F. W., and C. D. Howard. Poisonous Properties of Wild Cherry Leaves. New Hampshire Agr. Expt. Sta., *Bull.* 56: 113–123. 1898.

46. Moseley, E. L. *Milk Sickness Caused by White Snakeroot*. Publ. jointly by the Author and the Ohio Acad. Sci., Bowling Green. Ohio. 1941.

47. Orfila, M. J. B. *Traité des Poisons tirés des Règnes minéral, végétal et animal. . . .* 2 tom. Paris. 1814–15. (See ref. 8.)

48. Orfila, M. J. B. *A General System of Toxicology or a Treatise on Poisons Found in the Mineral, Vegetable and Animal Kingdoms. . . .* Transl. by J. G. Nancrede. M. Carey & Son, Philadelphia. 1817.

49. Orfila, M. J. B. *A General System of Toxicology, or a Treatise on Poisons. . . .*

Trans. from the 2nd corrected French ed. by J. A. Waller. 2 vol. Cox, Butterworth and Burgess, London. 1819.

50. Pammel, L. H. *A Manual of Poisonous Plants.* Torch Press, Cedar Rapids, Iowa. 1911.

51. Plenck, J. J. *Toxicologia, seu Doctrina de Venenis et Antidotis.* Graeffer, Vienna, 1785. (See ref. 53.)

52. Porcher, F. P. On the Medicinal and Toxicological Properties of the Cryptogamic Plants of the United States. *Trans. Am. Med. Assoc.,* **7**: 167–284. 1854.

53. Pritzel, G. A. *Thesaurus Literaturae Botanicae.* F. A. Brockhaus, Leipsig. 1872.

54. Randall, H. S. An Account of a Gangrenous Disease among Cattle in the United States. *Veterinarian,* **15**: 622–625. 1842.

55. Rautenberg, L. E. J. C. A. Mayer's *Einheimische Giftgewächse* (1789–1801). *Jour. Soc. Bibliogr. Nat. Hist.,* **3**: 325–327. 1958.

56. Rusby, H. H. The Poisonous Plants of the Vicinity of New York. *J. Alumni Assoc. Col. Pharm. City of New York.* December 1895. (Seen as reprint.)

57. Salmon, D. E. Enzootics of Ergot. USDA, *Rept.* 1884: 212–252. 1884.

58. Salmon, D. E. Report of the Chief on Enzootics of Ergotism. USDA, Bur. Anim. Ind., *Ann. Rept.,* **1**: 175–214. 1884.

59. Selby, A. D. Poisonous Plants. *J. Columbus Hort. Soc.,* **8**: 119–128.

60. True, A. C. A History of Agricultural Experimentation and Research in the United States 1607–1925. USDA, *Misc. Publ.* 251. 1937.

61. Trumblower, M. R. Ergotism among Cattle in Kansas. USDA, Bur. Anim. Ind., *Ann. Rept.,* **1**: 310–320. 1884.

62. United States Department of Agriculture, Library. *Botany Subject Index.* Microprinting Company, Boston. 1958.

63. Vasey, G. Plants Poisonous to Cattle in California. USDA, *Rept. 1874:* 159–160. 1874.

64. Vasey, G. Report of the Botanist. USDA, *Rept, 1884:* 123–136. 1884.

65. Vasey, G. Johnson Grass in Montana. USDA, *Rept. 1885:* 74–75. 1885.

66. Wepfer, J. J. *Historia Cicutae Aquaticae.* Potuliet, Lugduni Batavorum (Leiden). 3rd ed., 1733.

67. Wilcox, E. V. List of Plants of Known or Suspected Poisonous Properties which Grow within the State. Montana Agr. Expt. Sta., *Bull.,* **22**: 51–53. 1899.

68. Williams, T. A. Some Plants Injurious to Stock. South Dakota Agr. Expt. Sta., *Bull.* 33. 1893.

69. Williams, W. L. Veterinary Science in Agricultural Colleges and Experiment Stations. *Am. Vet. Rev.,* **16**: 422–439. 1892.

70. Woodville, W. *Medical Botany.* 3 vol. & suppl. James Phillips, London. 1790–1794.

POISONOUS PRINCIPLES

A variety of compounds produced in or absorbed by plants may cause toxic reactions when ingested by animals. Commonly recognized natural toxic principles include the following:

Alkaloids
Polypeptides
Amines
Glycosides—glucosides
   Cyanogenetic (nitrile) glycosides
   Goitrogenic substances
   Irritant oils
   Coumarin glycosides
   Steroid and triterpenoid glycosides
    Cardiac glycosides
    Saponins
Oxalates
Resins or resinoids

Phytotoxins (Toxalbumins)
Mineral poisonings
   Copper, lead, cadmium, fluorine, manganese
   Nitrogen
    Nitrites—nitrates
    Nitrosos
    Gaseous oxides of nitrogen
   Selenium
   Molybdenum
Compounds causing photosensitivity
   Primary photosensitization
   Hepatogenic photosensitization

Sometimes the poisonous principle is less easily categorized. A number of species of plants contain a toxic substance unique to each (e.g., hydroquinone in *Xanthium*). Some syndromes, whose etiology is now unknown, but which are associated with particular plants, may turn out to be the result of absence of a necessary factor in the diet rather than presence of a toxic one. Even if one may (somewhat arbitrarily) exclude such plant-associated syndromes from a discussion of poisonous plants, he cannot exclude deficiency syndromes directly related to the presence of a plant-produced "anti-factor" in the diet (e.g., thiaminase in *Pteridium*).

A large and miscellaneous group of plants contains toxic principles whose nature is not yet fully understood, or produce injury in an entirely me-

chanical fashion. A few plants contain two or more toxic principles which
are not in the same chemical group (e.g., a liver toxin and potentially toxic
nitrate levels in *Tribulus*). In many cases, the chemical definitions of the
groups named above are not on parallel grounds, and characteristics which
identify a given moiety as a member of one may not exclude its concurrent
membership in another. One of the best examples of this is the toxic principle solanine found in species of *Solanum* (nightshades, etc.). It is a

solanose   solanidine

glycoside because of the presence in it of a sugar residue (solanose). It is
considered among the alkaloids because on hydrolysis it yields the alkamine
solanidine which fits the definition of an alkaloid and is physiologically
active. Solanidine bears chemical relationship (indicated in boldface) to
the basic structure of sterols, so that solanine may be considered to belong
to the steroid glycosides. Finally, its physical characteristics are those of a
saponin.

Not all compounds occurring in each of the groups named above are
toxic. Some alkaloids, for example, produce no significant physiological
reaction. Therefore, chemical detection of one or another of these classes of
compounds in a particular plant neither establishes the toxicity of that plant
nor, if the plant is known to be toxic on other evidence, does it serve
necessarily to identify the source of toxicity.

In the following, each of the categories of toxic compounds listed above
is briefly characterized, with emphasis on the characteristics of greatest
importance for those studying the poisonous effects of plants.

Alkaloids

Historically, alkaloids (lit. "alkali-like") are those products of chemical
analysis of plants which are not true bases (alkalis) but share certain
chemical similarities with them. They are basic in reaction and form salts
with acids. Generally insoluble in water but extractable in organic solvents,

they occur as crystalline solids (a few as liquids) in pure form, and in plants they are most often found as a soluble organic acid-alkaloid salt. They are almost universally bitter in taste.

Some geographic or taxonomic surveys indicate (1085, 1688, 1689) that alkaloids may be present in 5 to 10 per cent of plant species. They are particularly common in some plant families (e.g., *Leguminosae, Amaryllidaceae*); rare in others. More than five thousand alkaloids have been characterized to some extent and given names. Alkaloids of similar structure are commonly found in closely related plants. Occasionally the same alkaloid may be detected in species of no immediate relationship [e.g., nicotine in *Nicotiana* (tobacco), *Lycopodium* (princess pine), and *Equisetum* (horsetail)].

Most alkaloids produce a strong to very strong physiological reaction when introduced into an animal; a few produce no reaction. In most cases activity is effected primarily via the nervous system by a mechanism at best poorly understood. Lesions are absent. Some types of alkaloids, however, produce completely different syndromes. For example, the pyrrolizidine alkaloids cause severe liver damage. The reaction may be quite specific for a given alkaloid in a given organism, yet may vary considerably both with different alkaloids in the same animal or with the same alkaloid in different animals.

The major research interest in alkaloids is engendered by their importance in medicine and in human toxicology. The molecular structure is known for several hundred and a few have been synthesized. They are seen to be a heterogeneous assemblage of complex basic compounds containing nitrogen, usually in heterocyclic and/or aromatic ring structure. Not all such compounds can be termed alkaloids. A few similar substances of animal origin, for example, are usually excluded by definition, and so are compounds answering the above description which may be found as normal intermediaries in metabolic pathways of plants and animals. Classically, alkaloids have been identified by more or less specific color reactions in spot tests with certain reagents. Recently, chromatography, electrophoresis, and similar techniques have proved fruitful in their separation and identification. Use of these newer techniques has made obsolete many of the results (and names of compounds) associated with earlier methods. The name of a compound derived from the generic or specific name of a plant from which it has been extracted (e.g., robinine from *Robinia pseudoacacia*) often gives a false sense of knowledge. Such names are no more useful than the degree to which the compound so named has been chemically and physiologically characterized—sometimes not at all.

The alkaloid content of a plant usually varies little with ecological factors such as nature of the growing season, climate, and availability of water. When present in a plant, alkaloids are frequently distributed throughout its structures. Any part may be dangerous to livestock. The amount of an alkaloid may differ considerably with variety in cultivated plants. Their role in the plant has been variously ascribed. A view commonly held is that they represent not particularly selective evolutionary "eddies" in plant nitrogen metabolism.

The accompanying tables give a list of toxic alkaloids and of the poisonous plants that contain them.

TYPES OF ALKALOIDS AND POISONOUS PLANTS WHICH CONTAIN THEM
BASIC CONFIGURATIONS

Tropane

Atropa	belladonna
Datura	Jimson weed
Hyoscyamus	henbane

Pyrrolizidine

Crotalaria	rattlebox, crotalaria
Echium	viper's bugloss
Heliotropium	heliotrope
Senecio	groundsel, senecio

Pyridine

Conium	hemlock, poison hemlock
Lobelia	Indian tobacco
Nicotiana	tobacco

Isoquinoline

Argemone	prickly poppy
Chelidonium	celandine poppy
Corydalis	fitweed
Dicentra	dutchman's breeches
Papaver	poppy
Sanguinaria	bloodroot

Indole

Claviceps	ergot
Gelsemium	Carolina jessamine
Hippomane (?)	manchineel
Peganum	African rue

Quinolizidine

Baptisia	false indigo
Cytisus	Scotch broom
Laburnum	goldenchain, laburnum
Lupinus	lupine, bluebonnet
Sophora	mescalbean, frijolito

Steroid Alkaloids
  (a) Solanum type (solanidine)
    (see also steroid glycosides, p. 30)

Lycopersicon tomato
Solanum potato, nightshades

  (b) Veratrum type (veratramine)   *Amianthium*   (?)   staggergrass
                                       Veratrum   false hellebore
                                         Zigadenus   death camas

Polycyclic Diterpenes (delphinine)

Aconitum monkshood
Delphinium larkspur

POISONOUS PLANTS CONTAINING UNCHARACTERIZED OR INCOMPLETELY
CHARACTERIZED ALKALOIDS (EXCLUDING ALGAE AND FUNGI)

Allium	onion
Buxus	box
Ervatamia	crape jasmine
Festuca	fescue
Fritillaria	fritillaria
Gloriosa	glory lily
Ornithogalum	star-of-Bethlehem
Taxus	yew

Colchicine from *Colchicum,* though chemically known, does not fit any of the above categories.

Significant amounts of alkaloid nitrogen oxides have been detected in some plants (e.g., *Senecio, Lupinus*). The contribution of these compounds to the toxicity of the plant is not yet fully known, but some at least are toxic.

The poisonous principle of *Astragalus* has been stated (584) to be of alkaloidal nature. Some members of this genus are selenium accumulators. Others (together with species of *Oxytropis*) are responsible for the nervous disease of horses, sheep, and cattle called "loco." This syndrome has long been known in the West where it has caused serious loss of life in livestock. It has been investigated at length yet in many ways is still enigmatic. It is this syndrome which has been associated with the presence of alkaloids in the plants producing it, but later work (524, 585) has left the identity of the toxic compound in doubt.

Polypeptides and amines

Considering the large number and great variety of organic molecules containing nitrogen which are formed in plants, it is perhaps surprising that toxicity is in general (excluding cyanide) limited to the alkaloids. Among the rare exceptions are a small number (so far) of polypeptides and amines. Certain algae (e.g., *Microcystis,* a bluegreen alga), fungi (e.g., *Amanita,* a mushroom) and higher plants (e.g., *Blighia sapida,* akee) contain toxic peptides. *Phoradendron flavescens* contains amines (phenylethylamine, tyramine) which are credited (279) with toxic action. Ergot (*Claviceps*) alkaloids are accompanied with amines which may be partially responsible for the toxicity of the sclerotia. N-methyl-*beta*-phenylethylamine is the toxic principle of *Acacia berlandieri* (guajillo), and more than one toxic compound in species of *Lathyrus* appears to be related to *beta*-cyano-L-alanine.

Glycosides

Glycosides are compounds which yield one or more sugars and one or more other compounds (aglycones) when hydrolzyed *in vitro* by dilute mineral acids or *in vivo* by enzymes. The term *glucoside* has often been used synonymously with *glycoside,* and this practice continues. Critical usage reserves the term glucoside for that particular kind of glycoside in which the sugar component is glucose. Purified glycosides are usually bitter, colorless, crystalline solids. Glycosides are much more widely distributed in the plant kingdom than are alkaloids. Many are nontoxic (e.g., several of the common nonphotosynthetic plant pigments).

Glycoside sugars include a number of common pentoses and hexoses. Glucose is often found. On the other hand, in some glycosides (e.g., cardiac glycosides) sugars of unique structure have been discovered.

$$
\begin{array}{c}
CHO \\
| \\
CH_2 \\
| \\
HC-OCH_3 \\
| \\
HCOH \\
| \\
HCOH \\
| \\
CH_3
\end{array}
$$

cymarose
(3-methyl digitoxose)

Toxicity is a function of the aglycone component, or of part of it. A great variety of compounds serve as aglycones in glycosides. Toxic glycosides include cyanogenetic (nitrile) glycosides, goitrogenic substances, irritant oils, coumarin glycosides, and steroid (cardiac and saponic) glycosides.

The amount of a particular glycoside elaborated in a plant depends not only on intrinsic factors such as genetics, part of plant, age of plant, and sometimes even sex of plant, but also to a large degree on extrinsic factors such as climate, moisture supply, and soil fertility. Glycosides perform a variety of functions in the plant economy (1073).

Cyanogenetic (nitrile) glycosides

Glycosides which yield hydrocyanic acid (HCN) upon hydrolysis are termed *cyanogenetic* or *cyanophoric*. The glycoside amygdalin, represented on page 24, is one of the most common. It is found in many members of the *Rosaceae*. The intact glycoside is not toxic (354). The violent toxicity of the compound is caused solely by its HCN component, acting as a free molecule after hydrolysis. Little free HCN is found in healthy, actively growing

Amygdalin

$+ H_2O \rightarrow$

$+ C_6H_{12}O_6$

$+ \downarrow H_2O$

HCN +

Benzaldehyde

Mandelonitrile

$+ C_6H_{12}O_6$

plants. Free cyanide is toxic to plant tissues (161). In natural circumstances, hydrolysis is brought about by enzymatic action in the plant (354) or animal (1125). An unknown mechanism blocks or inhibits reaction between enzyme and substrate in healthy plants. The frequently observed higher content of free HCN in wilted, frosted, or stunted plants may result from the joining of plant enzyme and cyanogenetic glycoside caused by these conditions, with resulting release of free HCN. Ruminant animals seem to be more susceptible to HCN poisoning from plants of equal cyanogenetic potential than are monogastric animals and the human being, for the reason that the microflora of the rumen provokes, and ruminal *p*H encourages, greater enzymatic breakdown than that accomplished in nonruminants. Enzyme from the plant is not necessary (325). In ruminants absorption into the bloodstream takes place directly from the rumen. HCN is a small molecule and is rapidly absorbed and readily excreted by several routes. Much is eliminated simply in breathing. Chronic HCN poisoning as it is known in human beings is rare in animals.

A number of factors must be considered in determining whether cyanide poisoning may be expected to take place. They include cyanogenetic potential of the plant, amount of free HCN in the plant before ingestion, size and kind of subject, speed of ingestion, and speed of release of HCN during digestion. Cyanide is highly reactive and, during digestion, may enter reactions which prevent its absorption by the blood. Thus, the kind of ingesta present in the digestive tract, and the degree of wetness, are important. The amount of ingesta is significant in its diluent effect on entering cyanide. Speed of excretion or detoxification within the body is obviously to be considered in estimating whether a toxic level of HCN will develop in the blood.

There is little difference between toxic and lethal blood HCN levels. Two milligrams HCN per pound of animal per hour is close to the minimum lethal dose, and as a rule of thumb, plants which contain more than 20 mg of HCN per 100 g can be considered potentially dangerous (1125). The well-known picrate test for cyanide has been adapted for easy field use on plant or stomach-content samples by Burnside (214, 215).

Filter-paper strips dipped in an aqueous solution containing 5 per cent Na_2CO_3 and 0.5 per cent picric acid (shelf life not over four months) are allowed almost to dry, then are suspended in a test tube over a sample (rumen contents, minced liver, or shredded plant material), to which has been added a few drops of chloroform or dilute acetic acid, and are incubated at 30–35°C. (as under the arm). A positive result is indicated by a color change from yellow to red or maroon. The speed and intensity of this reaction may be used as an approximation of the amount of cyanide present. In some cases a color change may be detected almost immediately, but a negative test may not be assumed until after three hours have passed without change. It must be remembered that this test is sufficiently delicate to detect cyanide concentrations well below the toxic level.

Hydrocyanic acid acts by inhibiting the action of the porphyrin enzyme cytochrome oxidase. This enzyme is a terminal respiratory catalyst linking atmospheric oxygen with metabolic respiration. Thus, HCN poisoning constitutes asphyxiation at the cellular level. The ability of the blood to carry oxygen is unimpaired (of diagnostic importance). Death usually follows ingestion of a lethal dose within 15 min to a few hours (613). Experimentally, it has been possible (207) to protect an animal against up to three times the minimum lethal dose of HCN by prompt injection of sodium thiosulfate and sodium nitrite, but sufficiently prompt treatment is usually unavailable. Sodium nitrite is used to convert some of the blood's hemoglobin to methemoglobin (see nitrate poisoning, p. 38). Methemoglobin combines preferentially with cyanide in competition with the respiratory enzyme cytochrome oxidase. Sodium thiosulfate converts some cyanide (including that from dissociation of cyanmethemoglobin) into the relatively nontoxic and stable thiocyanate (677). The amount of nitrite injected is critical, since sufficient unaltered hemoglobin must remain to carry a necessary minimum amount of oxygen to the tissue; otherwise nitrite poisoning will result (299, 300, 360, 361). Experiments with mice (1157) have shown hydroxo-cobalamin (B_{12a}) effective in cyanide poisonings. Large amounts of this molecule, which combines preferentially with the cyanide radical, may be safely used.

There is evidence (326) that dextoxification of cyanide in the body is a rapid and effective process. Thiocyanides are formed in the liver with sulfur from amino acids and other sulfur donors. Sheep, by this mechanism, can detoxify at least 2 mg HCN per kilogram body weight per hour.

In gross aspect, symptoms of cyanide poisoning consist primarily of early stimulation of respiration, rapidly changing to dyspnea, excitement, gasping, staggering, paralysis, prostration, convulsions, coma, and death. The mucous membranes of mouth and eye may present evidence of congestion. It is sometimes possible to detect a characteristic odor (of benzaldehyde from breakdown of the aglycone of certain cyanogenetic glycosides) in the ingesta if the subject is examined immediately.

The content of cyanogenetic glycoside in a given wild plant or crop may vary widely with a number of external conditions. This variation has been explored most thoroughly in the case of sorghum. Factors such as climate, season, amount of rainfall, fertilization, and stage of growth are influencing. Heritable strain differences are important in sorghum. Hay made from some plants may be dangerous when cut but may become safe in time, possibly through volatilization of its HCN content.

Cyanide was first detected in plants in 1803. The early history of knowledge of cyanogenetic compounds in plants has been reviewed by Robinson (1350).

PLANTS WITH CYANOGENETIC POTENTIAL

Acacia greggii	catclaw
Bahia oppositifolia	bahia
Cercocarpus spp.	mountain mahogany
Florestina tripteris	florestina
Glyceria striata	fowl mannagrass
Holcus lanatus	velvet grass
Hydrangea spp.	hydrangea
Linum spp.	flax
Lotus corniculatus	birdsfoot trefoil
Manihot esculenta	cassava
Phaseolus lunatus	lima bean
Prunus spp.	cherries
Pyrus malus	apple
Sorghum spp.	sudan grass, Johnsongrass, etc.
Stillingia treculeana	queen's delight
Suckleya suckleyana	poison suckleya
Trifolium repens	white clover
Triglochin spp.	arrowgrass
Vicia sativa	vetch seed
Zea mays	maize, corn

Goitrogenic substances

A number of natural substances are known which prevent the thyroid from accumulating inorganic iodide normally, thus inhibiting formation of the thyroid hormone. Included are thiouracil, thiourea, cyanides, and sulfonamides. Two additional compounds, thiocyanates and L-5-vinyl-

2-thiooxazolidone, have been isolated from plants which have caused stock loss with symptoms of hypothyroidism. Both occur in the plant as glycosides.
    Starting in 1928 with the report (271) of goiter produced in rabbits fed

thiooxazolidone

on cabbage (*Brassica oleracea* var. *capitata* L.), a list of plants of diverse relationships with goitrogenic capacity has developed. Literature reviews may be found in papers of Greer and Astwood (654) and Nordfeldt *et al.* (1181).
    In 1949 the goitrogenic factor in a number of species of *Brassica* was found to be L-5-vinyl-2-thiooxazolidone. This compound has been isolated from the following species of the genus *Brassica:* kale (*B. oleracea* var. *acephala* DC.), Brussels sprouts (*B. oleracea* var. *gemmifera* Zenker), broccoli (*B. oleracea* var. *botrytis* L.), rape (*B. napus* L.), and kohlrabi (*B. caulorapa* Pasq.). It can be removed or detoxified in rape seed meal by hot water extraction. Its major effects can be countered by adding the appropriate amount of iodinated protein to the diet (1181).
    The loss of lambs with acute goiter in iodine-deficient areas of New Zealand has been traced to linseed meal fed the ewes over the period of their pregnancy. It was postulated, following experimental evidence of Blakely and Coop (133), that HCN released from the cyanogenetic glycoside linamarin is detoxified in the liver by coupling with sulfur, forming thiocyanates. Thiocyanate is excreted slowly. It is an iodine-responsive goitrogen, suppressing accumulation of iodine in the thyroid. Its effects may be counteracted by iodine therapy.
    Thiooxazolidone and thiocyanate cause hyperplastic enlargement of the thyroid and symptoms of hypothyroidism. Most stock loss has been associated with lambs from ewes which were fed a plant or plant product containing a goitrogenic factor. The ewes themselves may show few signs of hypothyroidism, although greater or lesser enlargement of the thyroid may be observed on post mortem examination. A large fraction of the lambs may be born dead, or if not, will be poorly developed, listless, and seemingly disinterested in nursing. Enlarged thyroids may be palpated and are distinctly obvious upon post mortem examination (1443).
    Rape and white mustard (*Brassica hirta* Moench.) have been grown commercially for an oil which may be extracted from their seeds. During World War II, when extensive acreages were grown in Canada, Germany, and in Scandinavian and other countries, the seed meal residue was fed

to various classes of stock. In small percentages, it caused little trouble. Experiments have been conducted to establish a practical method for detoxification to allow larger percentages to be utilized. Reviews by Allen and Dow (19) and Nordfeldt *et al.* (1181) may be consulted. In the case of poultry, a residual goitrogenic effect may be utilized constructively to produce slightly heavier birds on less feed (1603).

PLANTS CONTAINING GOITROGENIC COMPOUNDS

Beta vulgaris var. *cicla*	chard
Brassica caulorapa*	kohlrabi
Brassica hirta*	white mustard seed
Brassica napus*	rape seed or meal
Brassica nigra*	black mustard seed
Brassica oleracea var. *acephala**	kale
var. *botrytis**	broccoli
var. *capitata**	cabbage
var. *gemmifera**	brussels sprouts
var. *napobrassica**	rutabaga
Brassica pekinensis*	Chinese cabbage
Brassica rapa*	turnip root
Glycine max	soybean
Linum usitatissimum	flax

   * Taxonomic treatment of commercial members of the *Cruciferae* varies. The treatment used here is that found in L. H. Bailey, *Manual of Cultivated Plants* (New York: The Macmillan Co., 1949).

   Additional food plants in the *Cruciferae, Rosaceae, Umbelliferae,* and other families have been found (654) capable of inhibiting the uptake of radioactive iodine in the human being.

Irritant Oils

MUSTARD OILS. The pungent, sharp taste characteristic of mustard preparations is derived from mustard oils. These compounds are found in greatest amount in the seeds of various *Cruciferae*. A variety of volatile and fixed oils are separated on crude analysis. They exist in the plant in glycosidic combination, being freed upon enzymatic breakdown of the glycoside. For example, black mustard (*Brassica nigra*) seeds contain the glucoside, sinigrin, which is hydrolyzed to yield glucose, allyl *iso*thiocynate (a mustard oil), and potassium hydrogen sulfate in the presence of the enzyme myrosinase. The glycosidic precursor is nonirritant, while the mustard oil derived from it is a vesicant oil capable of serious injury to animal tissue if ingested in quantity or concentration.

   Research into the sulfur-containing fractions of various *Cruciferae* has revealed that the mustard oils are *iso*thiocyanates. The two best known and most common are allyl *iso*thiocyanate and 3-butenyl *iso*thiocyanate.

$$CH_2=CH-CH_2-N=C=S \qquad\qquad CH_2=CH-CH_2-CH_2-N=C=S$$

allyl *iso*thicocyanate   3-butenyl *iso*thiocyanate

The *iso*thiocyanate content of black mustard has been shown to be allyl *iso*thiocyanate. Rape seed (*Brassica napus*), on the other hand, contains at least three *iso*thiocyanates, of which the most prominent is 3-butenyl *iso*thiocyanate. An attempt has been made to correlate specific mustard-oil content with species, variety, and chromosome number in the genus *Brassica*. However, of fifteen species and varieties examined, the only generalization that could be made with assurance was that the majority contain allyl *iso*thiocyanate either alone or mixed with additional *iso*thiocyanates; some contain none. The toxicity of allyl *iso*thiocyanate has been established (1289). Cattle are killed by ingestion of about 0.001 per cent of the animal's weight of oil.

The *iso*thiocyanates chemically are closely related to the goitrogenic sulfur-containing compounds also found in various *Cruciferae*, but feeding tests have established (833) the nongoitrogenic nature of the *iso*thiocyanates.

PLANTS WHOSE MUSTARD-OIL CONTENT IS HELD RESPONSIBLE FOR SYMPTOMS OF GASTROENTERITIS PRODUCED IN STOCK

Armoracia lapathifolia	horseradish
Brassica hirta	white mustard
Brassica juncea	Indian mustard
Brassica kaber	charlock
Erysimum cheiranthoides	wormseed mustard
Raphanus raphanistrum	wild radish
Thlaspi arvense	fanweed

PROTOANEMONIN. Several genera in the buttercup family (*Ranunculaceae*) owe their irritant properties to the presence of an innocuous glycoside, ranunculin. Ranunculin readily breaks down to release the aglycone protoanemonin which is a volatile, strongly irritant, unstable oil. The chemistry of this reaction is discussed under *Ranunculus*.

PLANTS PRODUCING PROTOANEMONIN

Actaea spp. (probably)	baneberry
Anemone spp.	windflower
Caltha palustris	marsh marigold
Ranunculus spp.	buttercups

OTHER IRRITANT OILS. Not all irritant oils are glycosides. A wide variety of chemical compounds have the physical characteristics of irritant oils and are found, usually in relatively small amounts, among plants of diverse relationships. Oil of wintergreen (methyl salicylate) is an example. It is found in several members of the *Ericaceae* (heath family) and *Betulaceae* (birch family). Species in which such irritant oils may have accounted for, or contributed to, toxicity include *Glechoma hederacea* (gill-over-the-ground) and *Chenopodium ambrosioides* (wormseed).

Coumarin glycosides
There are several glycosides in the plant kingdom in which the aglycone is a modification of coumarin.

coumarin

Three are found in plants which produce poisonings. Aesculin and daphnin are found in *Aesculus* (horsechestnut, buckeyes) and *Daphne* respectively, but the degree to which they can be held responsible for the toxicity of these genera is not clear.

The sweetclovers (*Melilotus alba, M. officinalis*) contain a coumarin derivative which under certain conditions of spoilage in sweetclover hay polymerizes to form dicoumarol, a hemorrhagic agent. Both natural and synthetic dicoumarol reduce blood prothrombin level in similar fashion and cause the blood to become incapable of clotting.

Steroid glycosides and triterpenoid glycosides
A large number of glycosides, the aglycones of which are composed of cyclic chains of carbon atoms grouped in complex fashion, are found in the plant kingdom. For convenience, those interesting us may be divided into two groups on structural grounds. The *steroid glycosides* possess a sterol group in their structure (see structure of solanine, p. 18). The aglycones of *triterpenoid glycosides* contain 30 carbon atoms and also have polycyclic structure. Most members of both groups possess the physical characteristics by which saponins are recognized. The aglycones by themselves may have definite toxic characteristics, but the sugar portions of the molecules are important in altering or determining the activity of the intact glycoside. The sugars are especially important in increasing the solubility of the molecules.

Steroid glycosides may be further divided on physiological grounds into those which possess marked ability to stimulate the heart (cardiac glyco-sides) and those which do not. The saponic characteristics of the latter are emphasized in the name by which they are generally designated (saponic glycosides) and in the generic term applied to their aglycones (sapogenins), but, as pointed out above, they are not unique in possessing the charac-teristics of saponins.

CARDIAC GLYCOSIDES. Crude preparations from *Digitalis spp.* (foxglove) have long been used in medicine for their ability to strengthen the action of a weakened heart. The activity of these preparations comes from the presence in them of certain glycosides, the aglycones (genins) of which possess a particular steroid configuration. Cardioactivity is associated with

Oleandrin found in *Nerium oleander*

the presence and specific orientation of an unsaturated lactone ring and hydroxyl group (indicated in boldface in the formula) in the aglycone.

About 400 cardiac glycosides have been isolated and characterized. Most have come from genera in the *Scrophulariaceae* (figwort family), *Liliaceae* (lily family), and *Apocynaceae* (dogbane family). As yet none of the naturally occurring glycosides has been synthesized, nor have any synthetic steroid compounds approached the natural cardiac glycosides in potency. A large pharmacological literature exists on the action of these compounds. Rate of absorption from the digestive tract varies mark-edly among glycosides and is further influenced by the digestive milieu. In therapeutic amount, they act directly on heart musculature to increase the force of contraction in systole, and on its vagus innervation to decrease the rate of beat. The mechanism of these actions is unknown. Overdoses produce additional effects including nausea, dizziness, blurred vision, and diarrhea.

In most cases, a relation between the presence of cardiac glycosides and the specific toxicity of a plant species is suspected but has not been demonstrated. Toxicity figures have been established for several pharmacologically useful cardiac glycosides (1689).

POISONOUS PLANTS CONTAINING CARDIAC GLYCOSIDES

Adonis spp.	pheasants-eye
Apocynum spp.	dogbane
Convallaria majalis	lily-of-the-valley
Digitalis purpurea	foxglove
Nerium oleander	oleander
Thevetia peruviana	be-still tree
Urginea maritima	squill

SAPONINS. The noncardioactive steroid glycosides and the triterpenoid glycosides may be considered together under this term, since their saponic character seems to be the basis for much of their physiological activity. Saponins are large molecules which form a colloidal solution and produce a nonalkaline, soapy froth or foam when shaken in water. The discovery of steroid configuration in some saponins, suggesting potential value as precursors for sex and cortical hormones, led to extensive investigation which has resulted in a better understanding of this group of compounds (1639). Nevertheless, few of the plants in which toxicity has been attributed to the saponin content (see the accompanying table) has served as the subject of detailed toxicological investigation, and the general statements made here concerning saponins have not yet been shown to apply specifically to most of these plants.

Saponins occur in plants as amorphous glycosides in which the aglycone may be termed a sapogenin. Many different sapogenins exist and are widely scattered in the plant kingdom. The sugars associated with them in the glycosides include glucose, galactose, rhamnose, and arabinose.

Hederagenin, the triterpenoid aglycone of hederin found in *Hedera helix*

The saponin content of a particular plant species commonly varies with part of plant, season, and stage of growth. The physiological reaction which is believed to account for the toxicity of both triterpenoid and steroid saponins is the destruction of erythrocytes by lysis (1639). The hemolytic effect is apparently the result of reaction between saponin and cholesterol in the cell membrane, causing it to burst.

Saponins are not readily absorbed into the bloodstream through the uninjured digestive tract. To be toxic, therefore, they must possess, or be accompanied in the plant by a substance which possesses, irritant properties sufficient to injure the wall of the digestive tract and permit absorption. Under such circumstances the major symptoms and lesions are those of severe gastroenteritis. Saponins, by themselves, may contribute to gastrointestinal irritation. Administered parenterally, some saponins produce marked visceral vasodilation (443).

Poisonous Plants Containing Saponins

Agrostemma githago	corn cockle
Aleurites spp.	tung tree
Fagus sylvatica	beech
Hedera helix	English ivy
Linum neomexicanum	yellow pine flax
Medicago sativa	alfalfa
Phytolacca americana	pokeweed
Saponaria spp.	bouncing bet, cow cockle
Sesbania spp.	coffeeweed, rattlebox

Oxalates

Oxalic acid ingested as a chemical is corrosive to animal tissues which it reaches. Under natural conditions, however, oxalic acid is toxic not because of its acidity but because of the reactions of the oxalate ion. This is the only organic acid of plants which is toxic to livestock under natural conditions. It occurs in plants in the form of soluble (sodium and potassium) and insoluble (calcium) oxalates or acid oxalates.

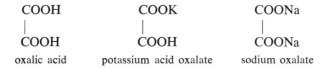

COOH	COOK	COONa
|	|	|
COOH	COOH	COONa
oxalic acid	potassium acid oxalate	sodium oxalate

Many plants contain small amounts of soluble oxalates; only a few have enough to be dangerous. Plants, such as *Rumex,* with sap pH of about 2, contain mostly acid oxalates; those, such as many *Chenopodiaceae* (goosefoot family), in which the pH is 5–6, contain mostly oxalate salts (1100). The content of soluble oxalates varies widely with season and location, reaching a maximum in late summer and fall. In *Halogeton,* soluble oxalates have reached 34.5 per cent of the dry weight of the plant (318).

Oxalate poisoning is fundamentally complex and poorly understood. The small natural amounts of insoluble oxalates in the diet are not absorbed and are excreted without effect. Soluble oxalates may be absorbed rapidly, especially in the nonruminant. Ruminants are relatively resistant to oxalate poisoning for reasons described below, yet most cases occurring under natural conditions involve cattle or sheep because of their feeding habits and management. Resistance of ruminants is owed to the capacity of the normally functioning rumen to alter chemically and detoxify soluble oxalates reaching it in the diet (1240). Evidence has been presented (1561) suggesting that detoxification accompanies reactions of oxalates in which carbonates and bicarbonates are formed.

Absorption of soluble oxalates into the bloodstream correlates directly with drop in level of ionic calcium in the serum. In one study (1616) ionic calcium was shown to have dropped to about 20 per cent of normal at time of death. Removal of calcium ion by precipitation produces effects which may be assigned not only to unavailability of calcium but also to imbalance in mono- and divalent cations and perhaps to pH changes. These include nervous symptoms, reduced coagulability of the blood, and acute nephritis. Drop in serum calcium is not so simple as it first appears. Its effects cannot be reversed by injection of calcium gluconate (120).

Probably of greater importance than the immediate effects of blood cationic imbalance are the consequences of the kidney's reaction to soluble oxalates in the circulation. Moderate amounts are readily excreted, but larger concentrations result in precipitation of oxalate crystals in the kidney tubules. Precipitates may take the form of small rhomboidal crystals, or of rosettes of crystals completely occluding the lumen of the tubule. In mild cases some tubules remain functional. In severe cases the lumena of almost all tubules are plugged and symptoms are those of renal insufficiency. Necrosis of epithelial cells occurs where they contact oxalate crystals; the remainder of the kidney tissue remains apparently healthy. Calculi may be formed in the urinary tract.

Both the amount of oxalate consumed and the time required for its consumption are important in determining whether a toxic level of oxalate will be reached in the blood. Less than one ounce of soluble oxalate is lethal to a sheep. Presence of food in the stomach reduces the rate of absorption. Less than 0.1 per cent of the animal's weight of oxalate is required to develop symptoms in a fasted animal. A total of several times these amounts may be ingested without untoward effect if taken in small amounts over a period of a day.

Ingestion by sheep of a toxic dose of plants containing soluble oxalates is followed, usually within 2 to 6 hours, by symptoms of dullness, colic, depression, dyspnea, prostration, and coma. Death intervenes about 10 hours after ingestion. Post mortem findings include excess fluid in abdominal and thoracic cavities, diffuse and petechial hemorrhages throughout the digestive tract and in the serous membrane about the (empty) heart, and emphysema of the lungs which also sometimes contain inspired ingesta. The cortex and medulla of the kidney, both dark red in color, are separated by a line of gray resulting from the accumulation of oxalate crystals in the uriniferous tubules.

Experiments at Utah (120, 319) have shown that immediate apparently beneficial results of calcium gluconate treatments for poisoning are not lasting, but that addition of calcium salts or calcium-rich feeds to the diet while trailing animals through dangerous range offers protection. Dicalcium phosphate fed free choice as 25 per cent of the usual salt ration seems to offer complete protection against the usual losses.

PLANTS WHICH MAY CONTAIN DANGEROUS AMOUNTS OF SOLUBLE OXALATES

Beta vulgaris	beet, mangold
Halogeton glomeratus	halogeton
Oxalis spp.	sorrel, soursob
Portulaca oleracea	purslane
Rheum rhaponticum	rhubarb
Rumex spp.	sorrel, dock
Salsola pestifer	Russian thistle
Sarcobatus vermiculatus	greasewood

Just as high calcium in the diet tends to limit oxalate absorption, so high oxalate intake tends to reduce sharply the amount of calcium absorbed from a diet containing adequate amounts. With laboratory animals it may be demonstrated (883) that spinach, under conditions of minimum adequate dietary calcium intake, can be fatal when fed in moderate amount over a period of time. Besides spinach (Spinacia oleracea), New Zealand spinach (Tetragonia expansa), Swiss chard (Beta vulgaris var. cicla), beet tops (Beta vulgaris), lamb's quarters (Chenopodium album), and pokeweed (Phytolacca americana), all of which contribute frequently or occasionally to the human diet, have been found to contain anhydrous oxalic acid at levels 10 per cent or greater of the dry weight of the plant. Oxalate-producing fungi may elevate the oxalate content of some moldy forages to potentially toxic levels (1694).

Crystals of calcium oxalate occur copiously in the tissues of some plants, especially in plants of the Araceae (arum family). It is generally believed (but also disputed) that the intense burning sensation and irritation which accompanies chewing such plants is brought about mechanically by the penetration of the crystals into the mucous membranes and to a lesser degree chemically by the salt itself.

PLANTS WHICH PRODUCE BURNING AND IRRITATION UPON CHEWING

Alocasia spp.	alocasia
Arisaema spp.	jack-in-the-pulpit
Caladium spp.	caladium
Calla palustris	wild calla
Colocasia spp.	elephants-ear
Dieffenbachia spp.	dumbcane
Philodendron spp.	philodendron
Symplocarpus foetidus	skunk cabbage
Xanthosoma spp.	caladium

Resins or resinoids

Certain active principles of considerable virulence found in some plants are classified as resins or resinoids. These terms group for convenience a heterogeneous assemblage of complex compounds, differing widely in chemistry but united on the basis of certain shared physical characteristics. Upon extraction, they are solid or semisolid substances at room temperature, are brittle, and are easily melted or burned. They are soluble in a number of organic solvents but insoluble in water and do not contain nitrogen.

The chemical structure of many resins is still unknown. In those cases where structure is conclusively established, the compound is reclassified into a more specific group.

Physiological activity of resins may be effected by direct irritation of nervous or muscle tissue and is sometimes quite specific. Plants of widely differing relationships may contain resins, but a few plant families are noted for content of the same or similar resins in their toxic members. Some species containing toxic resins are among the most dramatic poisoners of human beings as well as of animals.

PLANTS CONTAINING RESINOID PRINCIPLES

Asclepias spp.	milkweeds
Cannabis sativa	marihuana
Cicuta spp.	water hemlock
Kalmia spp.	laurel
Ledum spp.	Labrador tea
Leucothoe davisiae	laurel

Melia azedarach	chinaberry tree
Menziesia ferruginea	rustyleaf
Pieris japonica	Japanese pieris
Rhododendron spp.	laurel, rhododendron

Phytotoxins

Phytotoxins (also called toxalbumins) are protein molecules of high toxicity produced by a small number of plants. Few native plants elaborate them and those that do are rarely the cause of livestock loss. *Abrus precatorius* (precatory bean), however, is particularly dangerous to children because of the attractive nature of the seeds, the most dangerous part. Phytotoxins are large, complex molecules similar to bacterial toxins in structure and causing somewhat similar physiological reactions. Like bacterial toxins they act as antigens, eliciting an antibody response in the reacting subject. *In vitro,* phytotoxins cause agglutination of erythrocytes. This does not seem to be the basis of their extreme toxicity. It has been suggested (909) that they function *in vivo* as potent proteolytic enzymes, owing their toxicity to breakdown of critical natural proteins and accumulation of ammonia. True immunity can be produced through administration of immunizing doses of the phytotoxin in increasing strength. Passive immunity can be conferred by the injection of antisera. Antisera for phytotoxins are commercially unavailable because of the rarity of cases. Phytotoxins are nondialyzable, heat labile, and can be positively identified by precipitin reactions with sera containing known antibodies. Toxic castor-bean press cake can be made nontoxic simply by heating (290).

There is considerable variation in susceptibility to phytotoxins with species of animal and individual subject. The minimum lethal dose of ricin, the phytotoxin from castor bean, when administered by injection, may be as small as 0.00000001 per cent of an animal's weight; orally it is several hundred times less toxic. Unlike some bacterial toxins and venoms, phytotoxins are more or less readily absorbed through the wall of the digestive tract. Usually a distinct and characteristic lag period occurs between ingestion and appearance of symptoms. Symptoms largely are those associated with gastrointestinal irritation. Lesions consist of hemorrhagic gastrointestinal inflammation and edematous swelling in several organs.

PLANTS CONTAINING PHYTOTOXINS

Abrus precatorius	precatory bean
Aleurites fordii et spp.	tung tree
Jatropha curcas	barbadosnut
Ricinus communis	castor bean
Robinia pseudoacacia	black locust

Mineral poisonings

Copper, lead, cadmium, fluorine, manganese

Plants may be made toxic secondarily through deposition on their surfaces of certain minerals such as arsenic or fluorine (769) in the vicinity of particular industrial installations. Such situations are usually obvious and are not detailed here.

Less obvious are cases of copper poisoning from vegetation in areas where bordeaux mixture ($CuSO_4$) has been applied as a fungicide repeatedly for many years (1160), or in Australia from top dressing deficient soils with copper sulfate (1310). Some plants may have greater accumulating power for copper than others. Subterranean clover (*Trifolium subterraneum*), for example, accumulates copper to a potentially lethal level from some natural, high-copper soils in Australia and has caused loss (649). In similar fashion, the lead content of forage or other plants may reach toxic levels at the edges of heavily travelled highways (238). Its source is the tetraethyl lead used in modern gasolenes. Cadmium is taken up in vegetables and other plants, especially from soils heavily fertilized with commercial superphosphate in which it is an impurity. It accumulates in the mammalian body, with possibly deleterious result in large amount (1418). The African plant *Dichapetalum toxicarium* contains poisonous levels of fluorine (as fluoro-oleic acid) (1264). Some evidence suggests that this plant accumulates and concentrates fluorine from the soil.

Also, often obscure are instances in which forage becomes toxic by virtue of mineral imbalance or deficiency. Deficiency of manganese in the forage fed pregnant cattle, if not rectified, results in the birth of deformed calves ("acorn calves") (469, 727). Deformity is caused by prenatal permanent contracture of skeletal musculature. The disease has been serious on some ranches of the northwestern United States.

Nitrogen

NITRATES—NITRITES. Poisoning by nitrate in plants or compounds elaborated from it has been known in this country since the late nineteenth century but has become increasingly complex. Many crop plants (especially oat hay, corn, and sorghum), vegetables and weeds [especially of the amaranth (*Amaranthaceae*), goosefoot (*Chenopodiaceae*), mustard (*Cruciferae*), composite (*Compositae*), and nightshade (*Solanaceae*) families] have been found to contain nitrates at a potentially toxic level. Several have been incriminated in cases of poisoning. Plants containing more than 1.5 per cent nitrate (as KNO_3, dry weight) may prove lethal to livestock (128, 163, 1552). Sublethal nitrate poisoning has been attributed (264) to ingestion of feed containing between 1.5 and 0.5 per cent. This type of poisoning is characterized in differing ways. Abortion is common. In other cases depression of lactation, discolored urine, digestive disturbances, and symptoms of vitamin A deficiency and hypothyroidism (1708) have been described (606, 1527, 1552) in various herds of cattle. Experiments with nitrates added to diets and with forages naturally high in nitrates indicate (164, 387, 817) that 0.05 per cent of an animal's weight is close to the minimum lethal dose in the ruminant. Hundreds of cattle and sheep have been lost in some parts of the United States and Canada in certain years (402, 885, 1552). Poisoning in nonruminants is less common.

Nitrate poisoning can be produced in animals by ingestion of nitrate fertilizers, machine oil, natural-well and pond water of high nitrate content, pickling brine and the like, as well as by plants and hay or silage made from them, and in human beings by foods improperly preserved with nitrates. A number of factors may influence the amount of nitrate contained in plants (169, 381, 885). Certain species of weeds and cultivated plants tend to accumulate moderately large concentrations of nitrates under given conditions. Horticultural varieties of crop plants may vary markedly in ability to accumulate. The content and form of nitrogen in the soil both before and after fertilization and, to a degree, the kinds and amounts of other ions present determine the capacity of the soil to supply nitrates to accumulating plants. Growth under drought conditions and lessened light tend to promote increased nitrate content. Nitrate accumulates in vegetative tissues. The grain (fruit) remains safe.

Treatment with the herbicide, 2,4-D, has been shown to produce two unexpected results (1507). First, a number of normally unpalatable weeds, such as pigweeds (*Amaranthus spp.*), ragweeds (*Ambrosia spp.*), and Jimson weed (*Datura stramonium*) become palatable. Second, the resulting upset in nitrogen metabolism in the plant may cause it to accumulate nitrate to a toxic level.

Both the brucine and diphenylamine tests for nitrates may be adapted for use by the veterinarian in the field (214, 261). For the latter, the test reagent is made by dissolving 500 mg diphenylamine in 20 ml water and adding concentrated sulfuric acid (carefully!) to make 100 ml. This stock solution should be stored in a brown bottle. It may be used without dilution to detect small amounts of nitrates or after dilution with an equal volume of 80 per cent sulfuric acid to serve for rough estimation of the presence or absence of physiologically dangerous amounts of nitrates. The development of a blue color (precipitate) within 30 minutes constitutes a positive test. The test may be used directly on plant tissues [samples must be representative since nitrate content may vary greatly among individual samples of the same plant materials (482)] or on rumen contents. It may be used with somewhat more precision as a spot test on filtered juices from these sources. If it becomes necessary to distinguish nitrites, the diazotization test may be applied. This has been adapted for veterinary use by Case (261). Tests better adapted for experimental work have been described by others (428, 1439).

In ruminant digestion, and less vigorously in monogastric animals, ingested nitrate is reduced in steps to ammonia (924). Several discrete reactions are involved. In the first, nitrite is formed from nitrate. Nitrite is about ten times as toxic as nitrate and is the most common immediate cause of poisoning in animals when nitrates are ingested.

Antibiotics which upset the rumen's capacity to convert nitrate to nitrite may temporarily and partially protect against nitrite accumulation in the blood of animals on high nitrate forage (484). Nitrite impairs the blood's ability to transport oxygen. Normal ferrous hemoglobin picks up oxygen in a chemically loose combination, releasing it easily to the tissues on demand. Nitrite causes oxidation of ferrous hemoglobin to ferric hemoglobin, termed methemoglobin, which cannot transport oxygen. This compound causes the blood to turn dark, chocolate-brown in color (diagnostic in nitrite poisoning). Death through asphyxiation (anoxia) occurs when the blood is no longer able to supply the oxygen demand of the body. The latter is partly dependent on activeness of the subject. Comatose animals may remain alive when 85 per cent of their hemoglobin has been converted to methemoglobin, whereas death has occurred in active animals at about 50 to 60 per cent conversion to methemoglobin (482). Symptoms of acute poisoning may be divided into two categories—those of anoxia and those associated with the pronounced vasodilatory and diuretic effect of nitrates. The latter (reduced blood pressure, increased cardiac activity, coma) can be countered by administration of vasoconstricting drugs (786). Anoxia is treated effectively by methylene blue (164, 786). This reducing agent causes ferric methemoglobin to change to ferrous hemoglobin, which again can carry oxygen. Tests for methemoglobin are available but must be applied without delay after death, since methemoglobin readily reverts to hemoglobin on standing (482, 748).

The gross symptoms of nitrite poisoning appear rapidly and include cyanosis, severe dyspnea, trembling, and weakness. Lesions include petechial hemorrhages and congestion in membranes of the respiratory and digestive systems. The most characteristic finding is the chocolate-brown discoloration of the blood (402).

Whether nitrite poisoning will occur depends upon the level of methemoglobin that is developed in the blood. This depends not only on the concentration of nitrates in the ingesta, but also on the speed of ingestion, the speed of the reaction forming nitrite, and the speed of reduction of nitrite to ammonia. In the complete ruminal reduction of nitrate to ammonia, the first step, reduction of nitrate to nitrite, is probably limiting

(1268). It has been found (387, 482, 786, 1268, 1397) that animals maintained on a nutritionally good diet have higher resistance to nitrate poisoning than animals maintained on a mediocre or starvation diet. It is probable that differences in populations of microorganisms and pH in the rumen, caused by differences in diet, in turn cause differences in the rates of the various reactions by which nitrites are formed and eliminated. Wide variations in the amount of methemoglobin produced by standard amounts of nitrate administered to different animals (381, 429, 1699) suggest that plasma nitrate level is a better index of exposure to nitrate than is its methemoglobin level (429).

Under certain circumstances nitrites may be ingested. It has been shown (1199, 1343) that bacterial denitrification from nitrate to nitrite may occur in haystacks under conditions of unusually high moisture. Corn grown under drought conditions may spontaneously contain appreciable levels of nitrites (261). Circumstances such as these predispose to poisoning, since the nitrite is available for absorption into the bloodstream immediately and totally upon ingestion.

The fetus is particularly sensitive to anoxia. Widespread abortion in beef and dairy herds in the Central States has been traced (1457, 1458, 1552, 1553) to ingestion of plants from unimproved, weedy, low-lying pastures whose soil was by nature high in nitrogen. Methemoglobin was detected in the blood of the dams. The aborted fetuses showed lesions suggestive of anoxia. Abortion with similar characteristics and fetus lesions could be produced by adding nitrate salts to the diet of pregnant cows. Almost one hundred species of weeds occurred on the dangerous pastures, but only a few gave strong positive reactions for nitrates when tested. Elimination of weeds together with adoption of practices that encouraged grass development on these lands greatly reduced the incidence of abortion. Occasional abortion in sheep also has been linked with ingestion of plants containing less-than-lethal concentrations of nitrates (259).

NITROSOS. Additional kinds of poisoning by various combinations of nitrogen have come to light. Nitrite (NO_2) can be reduced still further to a nitroso (NO) radical. Nitrosohemoglobin exhibits many of the color and toxicity characteristics of carbon monoxide hemoglobin. Nitrosohemoglobin poisoning may occur under natural conditions and is distinguishable from carbon monoxide poisoning by obvious differences in the source of the poisonous principle or by a simple test as detailed by Case (261). Extensive long-term losses of cattle over the years in the Central States with symptoms similar to those of nitrite poisoning, yet with normally colored blood (no methemoglobin), seem to be explained on this basis. It has been suggested (259) that high nitrate levels in forage may result in vitamin A deficiencies in the rations of sows or in the way they use or convert vitamin A from natural sources.

GASEOUS OXIDES OF NITROGEN. Abnormally high concentrations of nitrate in forage intended for silage lead to dangerous and even explosive (nitrocelluloses?) (261) fermentations in the silo. Bacterial denitrification of nitrates in an acid medium results in the production of nitrogen dioxide (NO_2), a toxic, heavy, yellow-brown gas. Other toxic nitrogen oxides (especially nitrogen tetroxide, N_2O_4) may be formed. The industrial safety standard for nitrogen dioxide is 10 ppm. Concentrations as high as 58,500 ppm have been measured (381) from some silos. One or two breaths of the gas at these concentrations results in acute poisoning in the human being ("silo-filler's disease"), with symptoms and lesions of pulmonary edema, emphysema, and in cases of somewhat longer duration, adenomatosis. It has been suggested (1430) that this type of poisoning in cattle may be caused by the evolution of toxic gases directly in the rumen. In some areas poisoning of human beings has been severe (1552).

A number of factors determine the outcome of high nitrite levels in plants used for silage. Toxic gases may be formed as described above, and dissipated in time so that eventually the silage is safe. Or the fermentation may not result in more than minor reduction in nitrate levels in the silage, which then causes typical nitrate poisoning when fed. The method of silage treatment with additives, if any, may influence nitrogen conversions within the silo to a marked degree (169).

PLANTS IN WHICH TOXIC CONCENTRATIONS OF NITRATES HAVE BEEN MEASURED

WEEDS			REFERENCES
Amaranthus spp.	pigweeds	Amaranthaceae	163, 299, 1668
Ammi majus	bishop's weed	Umbelliferae	1598
Amsinckia sp.	tarweed	Boraginaceae	104
——	bluegreen algae	(Cyanophyta)	261
Bidens frondosa	beggar-tick	Compositae	1598
Bromus catharticus	rescue grass	Gramineae	1598
Carduus sp.	plumeless thistle	Compositae	163, 299, 1668
Chenopodium spp.	pigweed, lamb's quarters	Chenopodiaceae	163, 299, 1668
Cirsium arvense	Canada thistle	Compositae	163, 299, 1668
Cleome serrulata	Rocky Mt. bee plant	Capparidaceae	1598
Conium maculatum	poison hemlock	Umbelliferae	1598
Convolvulus sp.	bindweed	Convolvulaceae	163, 299, 1668
Datura sp.	Jimson weed	Solanaceae	261
Echinochloa crusgalli	barnyard grass	Gramineae	261
Eleusine indica	goose grass	Gramineae	1598
Eupatorium perfoliatum	joe-pye weed	Compositae	1553
Eupatorium purpureum	thoroughwort	Compositae	1553
Euphorbia maculata	milk purslane	Euphorbiaceae	261
Franseria discolor	white ragweed	Compositae	163, 299, 1668

Gnaphalium purpureum	purple cudweed	Compositae	1598
Haplopappus venetus	Coast goldenbush	Compositae	1598
Helianthus annuus	wild sunflower	Compositae	163, 299, 1668
Kochia scoparia	fireball	Chenopodiaceae	163, 299, 1668
Lactuca scariola	prickly lettuce	Compositae	1598
Lygodesmia juncea	skeletonweed	Compositae	163, 299, 1668
Malva parviflora	cheeseweed	Malvaceae	1598
Melilotus officinalis	sweetclover	Leguminosae	1598
Montia perfoliata	miner's lettuce	Portulacaceae	1598
Panicum capillare	witchgrass	Gramineae	163, 299, 1668
Parkinsonia aculeata	horsebean	Leguminosae	1598
Plagiobothrys sp.	popcorn flower	Boraginaceae	1598
Polygonum spp.	smartweeds	Polygonaceae	261
Rafinesquia californica	California chicory	Compositae	1598
Rumex spp.	dock	Polygonaceae	163, 299, 1668
Salsola pestifer	Russian thistle	Chenopodiaceae	163, 299, 1668
Salvia reflexa	annual sage	Labiatae	836
Sambucus pubens	elder	Caprifoliaceae	1553
Silybum marianum	variegated thistle	Compositae	857
Solanum spp.	nightshades	Solanaceae	163, 299, 1668
Solidago spp.	goldenrods	Compositae	1553
Sonchus spp.	sow thistles	Compositae	163, 299, 1668
Sorghum halepense	Johnsongrass	Gramineae	261
Stellaria media	chickweed	Caryophyllaceae	261
Thelypodium lasiophyllum	mustard	Cruciferae	104
Tribulus terrestris	puncture vine	Zygophyllaceae	1598
Urtica procera	nettle	Urticaceae	1553
Verbesina encelioides	crownbeard	Compositae	1598

CROP PLANTS

Apium graveolens	celery	Umbelliferae	1318
Avena sativa	oat hay	Gramineae	163, 299, 1668
Beta vulgaris	beet and mangold	Chenopodiaceae	1395
Brassica napobrassica	rutabaga	Cruciferae	1598
Brassica napus	rape	Cruciferae	187
Brassica oleracea	broccoli, kale, etc.	Cruciferae	1598
Brassica rapa	turnip	Cruciferae	166
Cucumis sativa	cucumber	Cucurbitaceae	1598
Cucurbita maxima	squash	Cucurbitaceae	1598
Daucus carota	carrot	Umbelliferae	1598
Glycine max	soybean	Leguminosae	1598
Hordeum vulgare	barley	Gramineae	163, 299, 1668
Ipomoea batatas	sweet potato vines	Convolvulaceae	165
Lactuca sativa	lettuce	Compositae	1598
Linum usitatissimum	flax	Linaceae	1598
Medicago sativa	alfalfa	Leguminosae	261
Raphanus sativus	radish	Cruciferae	1598
Secale cereale	rye	Gramineae	1598
Sorghum vulgare	sudan grass	Gramineae	163, 299, 1668
Triticum aestivum	wheat	Gramineae	163, 299, 1668
Zea mays	corn	Gramineae	480, 1667

Selenium

Of plants which vary in toxicity with geological formation, those which take up selenium are by far the most important. Stock loss, now known to have been caused by ingestion of selenium, has been reported from as early as 1857, but sustained work to elucidate the causes dates only to 1932 (580, 581). Pathologies locally termed (inappropriately) blind staggers and alkali disease, as well as an acute poisoning syndrome, have since been shown to be caused by selenium ingestion. Major contributions to the study of the geology, geography, and biological implications of naturally occurring selenium deposits have come from the South Dakota and Wyoming Experiment Stations, the United States Department of Agriculture, and the late S. F. Trelease at Columbia University. Much has been learned, yet certain observations remain obscure and several gaps in information exist. The massive accumulation of data has been reviewed by Moxon and Rhian (1139) of the South Dakota group, Trelease and Beath (1591) (the latter of the Wyoming group), Anderson et al. (25) of the USDA., and Brown (181). The biological significance of selenium compounds has been reviewed by Shrift (1452), the chemistry of toxic selenium compounds by Painter (1212), the geology of selenium by Luttrell (995), and the potential use of selenium-accumulating plants by Beath (89).

The nonmetallic element selenium is found in various forms in soils and rocks of geological formations from Pennsylvanian to Recent, particularly the Cretaceous, in fifteen western states (89), Hawaii, and western Canada. Because of the small amounts of total selenium in soils, rarely exceeding 100 ppm,[1] determination of the form of selenium has been difficult. Some amounts of elemental selenium, and certain selenides, selenites, and selenates are present in varying ratio. Elemental selenium and the selenides are relatively insoluble. Some selenites and selenates are insoluble, others are soluble. These forms are originally of geologic origin, but physical, chemical, and perhaps biological forces cause some interconversion. Organic selenium compounds found in the soil are of biological origin. Some are soluble, some are not. Some native rocks contain up to 2 per cent selenium (89). The selenium content of soils varies from a trace to not more than 190 ppm. The majority of soils contain less than 5 ppm. More than 2 ppm is considered abnormally high.

The selenium content of a given plant is not a simple function of the selenium content of the soil. Selenium in acid soils is precipitated in a form unavailable to plants. The major factor influencing uptake of selenium from alkaline soils is its solubility. Soluble selenium usually represents less than half the total amount in such soils. The degree to which soluble selenium will be absorbed is in turn dependent, in ways not understood,

[1] ppm = parts per million.

on factors such as chemical form and quantities of other soil constituents, especially sulfur. These factors are more significant in the root-bearing soil horizon than at the soil surface and between which there may be a large difference. Seleniferous soils support range plants and in some areas forage and cereal crops. The latter situation poses a potential health hazard for human beings. Seleniferous areas now have been well mapped. They are usually characterized by large expanses of mildly seleniferous soils spotted with a few, small areas of high selenium content at the soil surface.

Plants show a remarkable and unexpected relationship to selenium in the soil. They accumulate it or they do not. The strength of selenium accumulation exhibited by some plants is considerable. The accumulators may be further divided into obligate and facultative species.

Obligate species seem to require selenium for proper growth and will be found *only* where there is selenium in the soil. For this reason they are termed *indicator plants* (93, 96) throughout the selenium literature, and have been useful in pointing to selenium-bearing geologic formations of potential toxicity. These plants invariably contain selenium during the greater part of their life cycle, and maximum tissue concentrations have been reported (1591) approaching 15,000 ppm. Their selenium content, determined by chemical analysis, can be used as a rough index of toxicity for the soil bearing them. Twenty-four species and varieties of *Astragalus* all species so far examined of *Xylorrhiza* (woody aster), all species examined of *Oonopsis* (goldenweed), and all species examined of *Stanleya* (prince's plume) have been found to be reliable selenium indicator plants. All of these are conspicuous elements in the areas where they occur. Obligate plants have the ability to extract selenium from shales and native rock debris, taking it from a chemical combination which is unavailable to most forage plants. There are some 300 American species in the genus *Astragalus*. Those accumulating selenium fall into genetically related groups which can be recognized as such by criteria other than selenium accumulation. Four species, *A. racemosus, A. bisulcatus, A. pectinatus,* and *A. pattersonii,* are most useful as indicators because they enjoy a wide geographic distribution and are particularly strong accumulators. One or more are found in Montana, North and South Dakota, Nebraska, Kansas, Oklahoma, Texas, Wyoming, Colorado, New Mexico, Idaho, Utah, Arizona, Nevada, and Western Canada. With the exception of California and Hawaii, these are all the states in which the selenium problem is found. *Astragalus preussii* is an indicator species of California.

The facultative species or, as commonly called, the *secondary selenium absorbers,* are not limited to soils containing selenium. They accumulate selenium when growing in seleniferous soils but, other conditions equal, grow just as well on soils containing no selenium. They are commonly the cause of stock poisoning, for among them are a number of genera (for example, *Aster, Atriplex, Sideranthus,* and *Machaeranthera*) that are grazed. On nonseleniferous soil, these genera may be palatable and valuable forage plants. Fortunately, increasing selenium content tends to make a given species increasingly unpalatable.

Most plants are nonaccumulators. However, any plant may passively take up selenium dissolved in the soil. The amount taken up will be small and will be determined by the amount available in the soil. Moderate amounts of selenium exert a markedly toxic effect in many plants, which are stunted or otherwise harmed. Within the genus *Astragalus,* some species (indicators) require, are stimulated by, and vigorously accumulate quantities of selenium. Others take it up only passively and are inhibited in growth or killed. Growing on the same seleniferous soil, the former species may contain several thousand parts per million, and the latter only a trace. The basis of the accumulatory power of obligate and facultative species is unknown. Some experimental results indicate that the accumulatory power is not to be correlated with any particular form of selenium in the soil; all kinds of available selenium are taken up in greater amount by an accumulator plant than by a nonaccumulator.

In summary, the amount of selenium in a given plant is determined by its selenium-accumulating power and the soil's selenium-supplying power. The former is determined, in turn, by the species of plant, its stage of growth, and its general vigor. The latter is determined by the form of selenium, its concentration in the root zone, and the amount and kind of other elements present. As a rough approximation, if the amount of selenium in an indicator species on a given soil is $100x$, then the amount in a facultative species will be of the order of magnitude of $10x$, and in a nonaccumulating species, of x. Five ppm selenium renders a plant potentially toxic. The higher amounts of selenium in plants can be detected by the characteristic garlicky odor which they impart.

Of the nonaccumulators, both native range plants and crop plants may occasionally build up toxic levels of selenium. A few natural soils contain high enough levels of soluble selenium to cause nonaccumulators growing on them to be potentially toxic (89). Such soils are found in limited areas of western South Dakota, northern Nebraska, northeast Wyoming, Hawaii, Alaska, and in a few other places. More important is the toxicity conferred upon nonaccumulators, especially cereal plants, through the action of converter plants. Both obligate and facultative species may act as converters. Selenium, extracted from native rock formations and concentrated by these plants, is returned to the soil upon leaf drop, by death of the accumulating plant, or when it is plowed under. The local concentration of soluble selenium compounds thus is increased to a point at which toxicity may be imparted to those nonaccumulating plants subsequently growing there. Native grasses and other plants growing within a few feet of a perennial converter plant thus may be made toxic. Entire fields of grain or crop plants may be made toxic if grown where a stand of converter plants was plowed under.

Animal disorders caused by ingestion of selenium are determined in part by the amount and form of the selenium ingested. Three basic syndromes are presented. Cattle, sheep, swine, horses, poultry and other animals may be poisoned; the form, severity, and frequency are in part determined by the different habits of the animals.

Acute selenium poisoning is produced by single massive doses. Obligate species, particularly of the genera *Astragalus* and *Xylorrhiza,* are usually responsible. This type of poisoning is not common. It may be duplicated with injection of inorganic selenium. Animals will not consume plants with high selenium content unless driven to it. Symptoms appear in a few hours to a day or two and consist of anorexia, depression, polyuria, dyspnea, coma, and death through respiratory and myocardial failure. The pulse is rapid and weak, sometimes undetectable. Lesions consist largely of acute passive congestion, severe enteritis, and widespread hemorrhage. The liver and kidney present early acute degenerative changes.

Two more or less chronic syndromes have been recognized. "Blind staggers" is usually found in animals, cattle especially, on range. It is the more acute of the two. The rather inappropriate name comes from the tendency of poisoned animals to wander aimlessly. Vision may or may not be faulty. The syndrome appears after a week or more during which animals have consumed native range plants of moderate (less than 200 ppm) selenium content. Termination often is abrupt. Wandering may be accompanied by excitement and by failure to distinguish fences or other immovable objects. Physiological blindness, possibly correlated with depressed levels of vitamins A and C, may occur. Terminally there is paralysis, weakness, dyspnea, cyanosis, and death through respiratory failure.

The second chronic syndrome, "alkali disease," usually appears in animals on forage or grain crops grown on seleniferous soils. This name is even more inappropriate, going back to the time when the disease was associated with alkaline soils or water. (This type of selenium poisoning must be distinguished from other syndromes given the same name which do not involve selenium.) Corn, wheat, barley, oats, grass and hay containing 5 to 40 ppm selenium, ingested over a period of a week to a month or more, produce symptoms largely different from those of blind staggers. Dullness, emaciation, and lameness are pronounced. The latter is the result of hoof deformity and erosion of the articulation surfaces of the long bones of the legs. A deep groove appears parallel to the coronary band of the hoof and opens as a crack. The hoof tissues distal to this

SELENIUM INDICATOR SPECIES OF ASTRAGALUS AND
THEIR DISTRIBUTION (AFTER 1591)

SPECIES	DISTRIBUTION
Astragalus albulus Woot. & Stand	Ariz., N.M.
A. argillosus Jones	Utah, Ariz.
A. beathii Porter	Ariz.
A. bisulcatus (Hook.) Gray	Alba., Sask., Man., Mont., N.D., Ida., Wyo., S.D., Nebr., Colo., Okla., Kans., N.M.
A. confertiflorus Gray	Wyo., Utah, Colo., Ariz., N.M.
A. crotalariae (Benth.) Gray	Calif., Nev., Ariz.
A. diholcos (Rydb.) Tidestrom	Wyo., Colo.
A. eastwoodae Jones	Utah
A. ellisiae Porter	N.M.
A. grayi Parry	Wyo., Mont.
A. haydenianus Gray	Wyo., Utah, Colo., Nev., N.M.
A. moencoppensis Jones	Utah, Ariz.
A. oocalycis Jones	Colo., N.M.
A. osterhouti Jones	Colo.
A. pattersoni Gray	Utah, Colo., Ariz., N.M., Tex., Nev.
A. pectinatus Dougl.	Alba., Sask., Man., Mont., N.D., S.D., Utah, Wyo., Colo., Kans.
A. Preussii Gray	Nev., Utah, Calif., Ariz., N.M.
A. racemosus Pursh	Alba., Mont., N.D., Wyo., S.D., Nebr., Utah, Colo., Kans., N.M., Okla., Tex.
A. recedens (Jones) Trelease and Beath	Colo., N.M.
A. sabulosus Jones	Utah, Ariz.
A. toanus Jones	Ida., Utah, Nev.

line slough off and new hoof is formed proximally. The process is painful and the old hoof tissue does not receive normal wear. As a result hooves become markedly deformed and bent forward, increasing the signs of lameness. The process may occur repeatedly. Animals so affected often graze from a kneeling position and are unable to obtain adequate nourishment or water. Death from starvation or thirst is not infrequent. The long hair, especially of the tail, drops out, and the animals are anemic.

Internal lesions are similar in both chronic syndromes. They include rumen stasis, more or less gastroenteritis, myocardial atrophy, and greater or lesser degenerative changes in liver and kidney. In long-standing cases the liver becomes truly cirrhotic. Myocardial insufficiency promotes passive congestion in the lungs together with degenerative changes resulting eventually in respiratory insufficiency and death. Rosenfeld *et al.* have described the pathology of each of the three syndromes in detail (1366).

The source of differences in chronic syndromes is not clear. It has been observed that the form of selenium in plants producing acute selenium poisoning and blind staggers is different in some ways from that in plants producing alkali disease. The former contain mostly soluble selenium compounds, while in the latter selenium is somehow bound into the protein fraction and is mostly insoluble. Certain indicator plants and forage crops contain organic selenium. Certain facultative species, on the other hand, contain varying amounts of inorganic selenium (94). A disease of cattle and sheep clinically indistinguishable from blind staggers has been recognized (835) in California, Colorado, Kansas, New York, Nebraska, Iowa, Wyoming, and Canada. It has been impossible either to reproduce this disease from suspected forage or to find a correlation with selenium intake. Termed "forage poisoning" or polioencephalomalacia, it is characterized by lesions of the central nervous system alone. Local areas of necrosis occur in the cerebral cortex, and lesions are found in the visual cortex. Experiments with sodium selenite on cattle (953) failed to produce the typical chronic syndrome in a majority of animals or to demonstrate the supposed cumulative effects of selenium. On the other hand definite signs of toxicity were obtained at certain levels, and two experimental animals developed symptoms and lesions of polioencephalomalacia. These observations and others (1599) lead to the realization that not all the aspects of selenium poisoning as it occurs under natural conditions have definitely been linked to the presence of selenium in the diet. Strong possibility exists that some of them, at least, may eventually be traced to the presence of other poisonous constituents of the vegetation involved.

Chromatographic separation and analysis of the selenium compounds in *Astragalus bisulcatus* has shown (1592) that the principal selenium compound is the selenium analog of methylcysteine, an amino acid nutritionally important in the formation of hair and horn. Some evidence suggests that selenium inactivates succinic dehydrogenase and perhaps other important dehydrogenases as well. Arsenic may act to counter this reaction (181).

Selenium in the diet has been associated with reduced hatchability, malformed embryos, and teratological chicks in poultry (242), with signs of toxicity in fish, (482), with malformed lambs, and with certain other syndromes, the latter on less-than-satisfactory evidence. The evidence concerning selenium poisoning in human beings in the United States and Canada is not conclusive. Since the 1930's researchers have been on the lookout for definite signs of poisoning in populations consuming cereal crops from seleniferous soils of the United States. Aside from questionable arthritis, none has been found. The practice of mixing grains from different fields and the relatively large dilution that grains receive in the normal diet make it unlikely that selenium intake in the human population would ever reach dangerous levels. Selenium content of hair may be used as a diagnostic aid in borderline cases of alkali disease (1198).

Nevertheless, seleniferous soils are a severe agricultural problem in some areas, and repeated selenium poisoning of animals from agricultural crops has put some farmers out of business and resulted in abandoned farms. Efforts to find additives to counter the effect of highly seleniferous feeds have had mixed success. Under some circumstances addition of organic and inorganic arsenic compounds, sulfur compounds, and protein supplements such as linseed meal to the diet have arrested or countered some or all of the effects of weakly or moderately toxic feedstuffs (599, 692, 693, 1110, 1337, 1367, 1391, 1452, 1491, 1633, 1634). But results have been erratic and nothing seems to be completely effective or specific.

It is worth noting in relation to the toxicity of selenium in amounts greater than 5 ppm that this element functions as a nutritional factor, the absence of which correlates with syndromes such as dietary liver necrosis in rats and swine, exudative diasthesis in fowl, and muscular dystrophy in sheep (781, 898).

PLANTS WHICH MAY ACCUMULATE SELENIUM

OBLIGATE OR INDICATOR

Astragalus, certain species	poisonvetches	Leguminosae
Stanleya, all species	prince's plume	Cruciferae
Oonopsis, all species	goldenweeds	Compositae
Xylorrhiza, all species	woody asters	Compositae

FACULTATIVE OR SECONDARY SELENIUM ABSORBERS

Aster spp.	aster	Compositae
Atriplex spp.	saltbushes	Chenopodiaceae
Castilleja spp.	paint brushes	Scrophulariaceae
Comandra pallida	bastard toadflax	Santalaceae
Grayia spp.	hop-sage	Chenopodiaceae
Grindelia spp.	gumweeds	Compositae
Gutierrezia spp.	snakeweed	Compositae
Machaeranthera spp.	tansy aster	Compositae
Penstemon spp.	beard tongue	Scrophulariaceae
Sideranthus spp.	ironweed	Compositae

Crops which have taken up toxic levels of selenium include corn, wheat, oats, barley, grass, and hay.

Molybdenum

Molybdenum is another mineral element occasionally found in soils in sufficient quantity to cause the vegetation supported by them to be toxic to livestock. The molybdenum content of a soil may determine a toxic effect in animals in two ways. Abnormally low molybdenum in soils of normal copper content supports forage which promotes copper accumulation in animals and eventual development of symptoms of copper poisoning—even death. Abnormally high molybdenum in soils of normal copper content results in forage which depletes the copper reserves of animals over a period of time and results in development of symptoms of copper deficiency. Soils of moderate molybdenum content but low copper content do likewise. Copper and molybdenum are antagonistic in animal nutrition, but this effect is not simple. It is influenced strongly by inorganic sulfate content of forage and to lesser degree by other dietary factors (421). It is not within the scope of this book to discuss simple deficiency diseases, even though forage-mediated. However, the well-recognized syndrome in cattle associated with soils of high molybdenum capacity is not exactly equivalent to copper deficiency and is associated selectively with particular kinds of forage which have greater accumulating capacity for molybdenum than others.

Molybdenum poisoning was first recognized in England (where it is called teartness), and has since been reported in this hemisphere in the San Joaquin Valley of California (74), in valleys at the edges of the Sierra Nevada Mountains of Nevada ("alkali disease") (1193), in the Everglades of Florida (886), and in Canada (388). Much work has been done with it in New Zealand where it is a relatively severe problem.

Under usual conditions soils containing more than 5 ppm molybdenum are considered potentially dangerous, but some organic soils (as in the Everglades) cause trouble at 3 ppm or less. A number of factors influence the uptake of molybdenum by plants. Poorly drained soils of high pH are more apt to be dangerous than others. Molybdenum in acid soils is largely or totally unavailable. As stated above, the availability of inorganic sulfate and copper in the forage partially determines its toxicity. Dietary sulfate level markedly influences the degree of retention of molybdenum in animal tissues. Signs of molybdenum toxicity can usually be prevented by addition of copper to the diet. In most areas of molybdenum toxicity, copper is particularly scarce in soils.

Analyses of vegetation in areas of molybdenum toxicity have shown that legumes in general have consistently and markedly greater molybdenum content than neighboring nonlegume plants. The accumulation of high levels of molybdenum by legumes is not injurious to the plants and often reaches maximum during periods of rainfall and lush growth. In some areas (of weakly or moderately toxic soils) poisoning may be controlled by cultivation of grass forage and pasturage rather than legumes.

Symptoms of molybdenum poisoning appear one to seven months after dangerous forage is continuously grazed and disappear promptly if affected animals are removed to safe vegetation. Well-cured hay is less dangerous than the green plants from which it was made. Nonruminants are relatively resistant to poisoning and are rarely involved in poisoning under natural conditions. Prominent symptoms in cattle include emaciation, scours, change in coat color, anemia, stiffness, reproductive difficulty, and occasionally death (74, 173, 388, 1672). Young animals are more seriously poisoned than mature stock. Coat color fading is considered (1193) the result of inability of tyrosinase to mediate the formation of melanin in the absence of copper. Anemia, noticed in some cases, may be the result of copper deficiency preventing formation of haem (850).

Treatment of animals with soluble copper compounds may be useful if the molybdenum content of the forage is below 100 ppm (1193). Copper glycinate (120 mg Cu per adult animal, subcutaneously) protects against moderate amounts of molybdenum in the forage for a period of 3 to 9 months.

Compounds causing photosensitivity

Under certain circumstances animals become hypersensitive to light. Hypersensitivity can be traced to the presence of a pigment in the peripheral circulation which is not normally found there. One of several different pigment molecules may be involved. While the gross clinical manifestations of hypersensitivity to light may be identical or nearly so, the nature or source of pigment may be quite unlike in particular cases. Similarity in consequences must not be allowed to mask dissimilarities in etiology.

Certain drugs and genetic or structural diseases result in the presence of photodynamic pigments in the circulation (and often in the urine or feces) in man and animals, but attention is given here only to photosensitivity directly related to ingestion of plants. Blum (138), Clare (284, 285), and Brown (180) have reviewed the extensive literature on photosensitization. The terminology of Clare is used in this summary.

A hypersensitive animal reacts to light with the development of erythema and pruritis followed by edematous suffusions and (usually) eventual necrosis of the skin in affected parts. The exact biochemical mechanism by which photosensitization is produced is not yet clear. The basic reaction is probably an oxidation enhanced by energy from incident light trapped and made chemically available by the photodynamic pigment. (Use of the term "pigment" may be inexact since it is possible that a substance may absorb effective radiation in the ultraviolet region of the spectrum and be photodynamic even though colorless.) There is some evidence to suggest that proteins (particularly the amino acids histidine, tryptophan, and tyrosine) form the substrate in which light-enhanced oxidations take place and that the observed changes in photosensitization are due to resulting cellular damage or alterations in permeability of the cell membrane.

The wavelengths of greatest absorption, and particularly the wavelengths at which the engendered reaction is greatest, can be used to characterize the light-absorbing substance. Plant-caused photosensitivity can be distinguished from true sunburn by differences in activating wavelengths. True sunburn is brought about by exposure to light in the short ultraviolet wavelengths (less than 3300 Å). Where investigated, photosensitivity has been shown to occur over a wider range of wavelengths at the blue end of the visible spectrum and in the longer ultraviolet, being more pronounced in the latter. Since ordinary window glass filters out the shorter wavelengths of ultraviolet, it may be used experimentally to separate sunburn from photosensitivity. An animal will not be sunburned by light passed through window glass but may be photosensitized by it.

In photosensitization the capillary walls become abnormally permeable in the surface beds where reaction takes place. Both light and the presence of a reactant substance in the peripheral circulation are required. Therefore, the reaction will occur only in areas of unpigmented or lightly pigmented skin which are not covered by a dense light-screening coat of hair. In classical photosensitization, white sheep are affected particularly about the head, and cattle on white or unpigmented areas of the skin, especially about the escutcheon, udder, and muzzle. Black-skinned animals are resistant, but may not prove immune to massive exposures.

Pathology is remarkably similar no matter what the source or chemical identity of the reactant pigment. In animals, restlessness is followed by reddening of the skin (erythema), which in turn is superseded by an edematous infusion under the skin of affected parts, caused by leakage of serum from the capillary beds. In severe cases serous seepage occurs through the skin. Necrosis follows, and in time varying amounts of skin slough off, depending upon the severity of photosensitization. In seriously affected sheep, lips may be lost and ears may be seriously deformed. Intense itching and rubbing trauma is commonly followed by secondary invasion of necrotic areas with bacterial infection. The photodynamic action, by itself, is rarely lethal, but deaths are frequent from starvation, other secondary effects, or from liver damage (see below). In sheep which recover, areas of affected skin do not grow further wool.

Photosensitivities may be divided into types on the basis of the nature of the photodynamic substance, and particularly its source. In photosensitizations caused by plants, the photodynamic substance may come directly and unchanged from the plant (Type I of Clare), or it may be a normal breakdown product in digestion usually eliminated by the liver (Type III of Clare). The former may be called *primary* photosensitivity, and the latter may be termed *hepatogenic* photosensitivity. Sometimes the latter is termed *ictrogenic* photosensitivity, since pronounced general icterus is a common symptom accompanying it.

Two plants occurring in North America have been shown to produce primary photosensitivity. Both were known as photosensitizers in Europe and had been early investigated before cases were reported here. *Hypericum perforatum* (St. Johnswort, or Klamath weed) is widely distributed as a common weed, particularly in the Northeast and the Northwest. *Fagopyrum sagittatum* (buckwheat) is a crop grown for its grain. The vegetation from either plant contains a pigment (not the same) which is absorbed through the intestinal wall, enters the circulation, is not eliminated by liver or kidney and, therefore, reaches the peripheral circulation. All symptoms produced by either of these plants are solely those of photo-sensitization. The photodynamic pigment in *Hypericum* has been identi-fied as a napthodianthrone derivative, and named hypericin. The pigment in *Fagopyrum,* fagopyrin, is likewise a derivative of napthodianthrone. Both may have colorless precursors in the plant and may exist in more than one (closely related) chemical form. Cases produced by ingestion of *Hypericum* are not common, and those produced by ingestion of buckwheat vegeta-tion are rare in this hemisphere. It is interesting to note that elimination of *Hypericum* has been the objective in one of the more publicized at-tempts at biological control (through use of insects of the genus *Chrysolina*).

Hypericin

Hepatogenous photosensitivity is an immediate result of liver dys-function. Much of the pioneering work leading to the present understand-ing of this syndrome was performed at the Onderstepoort Veterinary Station in South Africa and has been reviewed by Brown (180). Normally the liver eliminates in the bile a number of pigmented breakdown products of digestion which reach it through the portal circulation. In certain types of liver dysfunction or obstruction of the bile duct, these pigments reach the peripheral circulation. One of them, phylloerythrin (a normal breakdown product from chlorophyll) has been shown to be photodynamic and to cause photosensitivity (1589). It may prove to be the universal photo-dynamic pigment in this type of photosensitivity, or it may not.

Phylloerythrin

The primary lesion in hepatogenic photosensitization is the liver lesion. Plants which cause hepatogenic photosensitivity do so by producing liver dysfunction, since the photosensitizing pigment is a normal product of digestion. The poisonous principle is the liver toxin contained in the plant, and liver dysfunction is clinically the more important aspect of the disease. The identity of the liver toxin has only recently been established for a few of the plants which produce hepatogenic photosensitivity. In these (*Lippia, Lantana*) it is a polycyclic triterpene. It is unlikely that all photosensitivity-producing liver toxins will be chemically related, since several other types of liver toxins are already known (e.g., pyrrolizidine alkaloids in *Senecio* and other genera), and since it is reasonable to expect that nonexcretion of photodynamic pigments may accompany more than one type of liver lesion, although possibly to different degrees. Some evidence suggests (180) that the liver toxin (in *Tribulus*) functions by inhibiting or preventing both the conjugation of pigments which normally takes place before their excretion in the bile, and the excretory process itself. It is inability to eliminate pigmented molecules which causes the generalized icterus and intensely colored livers found in typical cases of hepatogenic photosensitization.

Much of the African work has been with *Tribulus terrestris*, which produces bighead ("Geeldikkop") in sheep. This plant (commonly called caltrop, or puncture vine) is found in several of the western states, but cases of photosensitization by it in the United States appear to be rare. The plant which produces the heaviest domestic loss by photosensitization is horse brush, *Tetradymia,* a common bushy plant of several of the western states. Typical bighead in sheep is produced within 16 to 24 hours after ingestion of a toxic dose. It is accompanied by liver damage, but neither the liver toxin nor the photodynamic pigment has been identified. If sufficient of the normally distasteful plant is ingested, death will follow within one day directly as a result of liver injury and without the development of symptoms of photosensitization.

Agave lecheguilla, the lechuguilla of the Southwest, produces photosensitization accompanied by liver damage. Certain experimental results indicate, nevertheless, that photosensitization may be caused directly by a pigment contained in the plant. *Nolina texana,* sacahuiste, also of the Southwest, produces liver damage in sheep, goats, and cattle which under certain circumstances is also accompanied by photosensitization. The buds, blooms, and mature fruits are the parts of the plants which are normally ingested. These contain no chlorophyll (hence do not give rise to phylloerythrin during digestion). If the animal ingests no chlorophyll from other sources, photosensitization does not follow, but it usually develops if the diet contains other green feed.

Some photosensitizations are associated with types of vegetation rather than with individual species of plants. Ingestion of water containing heavy concentrations of bluegreen algae (p. 60) has more than once resulted in well-defined lesions of photosensitivity of livestock. In Texas, Sperry *et al.* (1505) have associated photosensitivity of livestock with ingestion of pasture grasses, both native and cultivated, and have correlated the syndrome with periods of lush growth following seasonal rains.

PLANTS CAUSING PHOTOSENSITIZATIONS

PRIMARY

Fagopyrum sagittatum	buckwheat
Hypericum perforatum	St. Johnswort, Klamath weed

HEPATOGENIC

Agave lecheguilla	lechuguilla
Brassica napus	cultivated rape
Lantana spp.	lantana
Nolina texana	sacahuiste
Panicum spp.	panic-grasses
Tetradymia spp.	horsebrush
Tribulus terrestris	puncture vine

OTHER

Species of bluegreen algae	water bloom
Avena sativa	oats
Euphorbia maculata	milk purslane
Species of fungi	molds
Medicago sativa	alfalfa
Polygonum spp.	smartweeds
Kochia scoparia	summer cypress
Sorghum vulgare var. *sudanense*	sudan grass
Trifolium spp.	clovers
Vicia spp.	vetches

Mechanical injury

A number of plants may inflict injury to animals in a purely mechanical manner. Usually obvious, they receive little attention, but particular plants under particular circumstances have caused economic loss sufficient to have been treated in the veterinary literature (701).

Contact with nettle (*Urtica chamaedryoides* Pursh) has produced a syndrome in hunting dogs characterized by excessive salivation, pawing at mouth, emesis, respiratory distress, slow and irregular heart beat, and muscular weakness (405). The plant bears stinging hairs and contains toxicologically significant amounts of acetylcholine and histamine which could well account for the symptoms.

Some Plants Which Have Caused Mechanical Injury

Anemone patens	anemone	hairballs
Aristida spp.	poverty grasses	awns
Eremocarpus setegerus	turkey mullein	hairballs
Hordeum jubatum	squirreltail barley	barbed awns
Pisum sativum	pea straw hay	impaction
Rubus sp.	blackberry vines	lodged in nasal passages
Setaria lutescens	foxtail grass	mucous erosion from barbs
Stipa spp.	needle grasses	awns
Trifolium incarnatum	crimson clover	hairballs

Additional poisonous principles and syndromes

It is sometimes difficult to separate syndromes resulting from dietary deficiencies when an excess of a particular plant lacking some nutritional factor is given, from syndromes in which symptoms result from the presence of a particular toxic factor. The two come together in those instances in which plants contain a specific factor which antagonizes or makes unavailable a particular essential nutrient otherwise adequately supplied in the diet. One example is the antagonism of copper by forage high in molybdenum, discussed above. Others are more clear-cut. *Equisetum spp.* (horsetails), *Pteridium aquilinum* (bracken fern), and *Dryopteris felix-mas* (male fern), for example, have been shown to contain a thiaminase which brings about destruction of thiamine in the diet and produces the syndrome of avitaminosis B_1 in monogastric animals.

Toxemias resulting from digestive upsets after ingestion of a particular forage or plant-derived concentrate—often associated with an abrupt change in diet—are beyond the scope of this book. Such syndromes have occurred with corn, apples, crucifers, wheat, barley, and other cereal grains (659, 1295). In grass tetany and in certain syndromes resulting after ingestion of *Avena sativa* (oats), *Beta vulgaris* (beets and mangels), *Brassica napus* (rape forage), *Medicago sativa* (alfalfa), *Pyrus malus* (apple), and *Prosopis juliflora* (mesquite), the conditions may usefully be regarded as nutritional upsets brought about by an excess of a dietary factor normally present in moderate amount.

The poisoning of human beings from milk of poisoned animals is practically nonexistent in the United States for the following reasons: The usual mechanism for the elimination of toxic principles from the animal body is by action of the liver or kidneys, and in most cases toxic principles reach the milk in only minor amounts. Acutely poisoned animals usually either die or recover before many milking periods have elapsed, or milk flow may be reduced or completely stopped by the poisoning. Most dairy farmers discard milk from animals exhibiting obvious symptoms of any kind. As a generalization, it may be pointed out that unless a toxic principle is concentrated in the milk, or unless the human species is much more susceptible to being poisoned by a given principle than is the lactating animal, the normal human diet (containing other foods) insures that the total intake of a poisonous principle will be below the toxic level. Finally, the present practice of pooling milk not only from many cows in a herd but from many herds in a relatively wide geographic area, insures that if a poisonous principle is present, it will be diluted far below the level of toxicity to the human being.

Two kinds of poisonous principles in the past have caused poisoning in human beings from milk. In both situations, direct consumption of milk from a "family cow" was almost always involved. Low-grade poisonous principles with irritant action (such as volatile oils) may possibly cause the milk of animals ingesting them to become laxative, or, further, to produce gastric distress in the human being. Cases are rare, minor, and difficult to diagnose. In the second instance, a factor of more specific toxicity is concentrated in the milk. An example is the higher alcohol tremetol ($C_{16}H_{22}O_3$), which has been found in the closely related, but geographically widely separated, species *Haplopappus heterophyllus* (rayless goldenrod) and *Eupatorium rugosum* (white snakeroot). Since the symptoms of tremetol poisoning in cattle are slow to develop and not particularly distinctive at first, highly toxic milk may be produced and ingested. It is common for symptoms to appear in a suckling calf before they do in the parent.

Other unusual poisonous principles include the polyphenolic pigment gossypol in *Gossypium spp.* (cotton), unusual nitrogen compounds in *Indigofera endecaphylla* (creeping indigo), *Lathyrus* (sweet peas), and *Leucaena glauca* (koa haole), estrogenic factors in *Trifolium subterraneum* (subterranian clover), hydroquinone in *Xanthium strumarium* (cocklebur), and a higher unsaturated alcohol in *Cicuta spp.* (water hemlock).

The above discussion should not be allowed to leave a false impression. Much work remains to be done on the nature of toxic principles in plants. The list of species of plants definitely known toxic for which the toxic principle is unknown is longer than any of the lists given above.

ALGAE

DIVISION CYANOPHYTA
Class Myxophyceae—Pondscums, water blooms, plankton, etc.

Freshwater Algae

Thus far, only members of the bluegreen algae (Division Cyanophyta) have been found directly toxic in the freshwater environment.

DESCRIPTION, DISTRIBUTION, AND HABITAT. Bluegreen algae are common in almost any natural body of water. Poisoning results when certain species grow rapidly and become amassed in the water in great quantity. Such an accumulation ("bloom") is clearly visible as a green or bluish-green scum or paintlike dispersion on or in the upper layers of water. Only certain bloom-forming algae are bluegreens, and only certain bluegreen algae are toxic. Individual cells of these organisms are microscopic but they are collected into colonies, filaments or packets of filaments which may (in some cases) be visible to the naked eye as tiny, colored flecks or spots in the water.

Usually one or two organisms predominate in a bloom but several others are almost always present in greater or lesser amount. It is difficult, therefore, to identify with certainty the toxic member or members of such an association. This difficulty is compounded by the rapidity with which populations of algae change composition; by the time a collection reaches a person equipped to examine it for the algae, what is then in it may not be representative of what was present when it was collected and the latter may not represent the condition in the pond when poisoning took place. In many cases of poisoning associated with blooms, little or no attempt has been

made to obtain qualified identifications of the algae. The following list from
the literature is, therefore, tentative.

Anabaena flos-aquae (Lyngb.) DeBrébisson (incl. *A. lemmermannii* P.
  Richter)
Anabaena torulosa (Carm.) Lagerheim
Aphanizomenon flos-aquae (L.) Ralfs
Coelosphaerium kuetzingianum Naegeli
Gloeotrichia echinulata (J. E. Smith) P. Richter
Lyngbya birgei G. M. Smith
Microcystis (= *Polycystis*) *aeruginosa* Kuetz. *emend.* Elenkin [incl. *M. flos-
  aquae* (Wittr.) Kirchner and *M. toxica* Stephens]
Microcystis incerta Lemm.
Nostoc rivulare Kuetzing

Of these, *Anabaena flos-aquae, Aphanizomenon flos-aquae,* and *Microcystis aeruginosa* (in certain circles referred to as Annie, Fannie, and Mike)
have the greatest substantiation as toxic. All three are common in quiet,
nutrient-rich, warm waters throughout the world.

Under the microscope, individual plants consist of aggregations of cells
into colonies of regular (*Coelosphaerium*) or irregular outline (*Microcystis*), into separate filaments (*Lyngbya, Anabaena*), into packets of filaments (*Aphanizomenon*), or into gelatinous aggregations of filaments
(*Nostoc*). The cells may be uniform or certain of them may be different
in size, shape, or contents from the remainder. The cells are small, without nucleus, and usually blue-green in color. Contents may or may not be
homogeneous. Lack of nucleus separates these plants from all others with
the exception of bacteria. Presence of pigmentation separates them from all
but a few uncommon bacteria. Identification of genera and species of blue-
green algae requires the services of a specialist in the algae (phycologist). In
cases of suspected algal poisoning it is important to obtain material for
identification at the time of poisoning. If material cannot be examined immediately, it should be refrigerated. If it cannot be examined within 24 hours,
it should be preserved in 3 to 5 per cent formaldehyde.

POISONOUS PRINCIPLE. The many attempts to extract, purify, and identify
a toxic principle from natural blooms of bluegreen algae (1449, 1526,
1665) have suffered from the variable and changing composition of such
populations. Nevertheless, studies from natural materials have led to the
general realization that more than one toxic compound may be involved.
One toxic fraction is nonvolatile, heat stable, passes dialysis membranes, is
stable to drying, is soluble in some solvents (e.g., alcohol) and not in
others (e.g., benzene), and may be alkali labile.

A new approach was first reported in 1958 (805) in which colonies
of *Microcystis aeruginosa* were isolated from nature, treated in ways to
remove all other algae and most bacteria (it was impossible to remove all),

and cultured in large quantities. At least four different toxic factors were produced in these and similar cultures. One of them, called the fast-death factor, is algal in origin and has been identified as a cyclic polypeptide containing seven amino acids (aspartic, glutamic, D-serine, valine, ornithine, alanine, and leucine). This molecule is heat stable, dialyses slowly, and has moderate toxicity [LD_{50} (intraperitoneally in white mice) is 0.47 mg per kg]. The three other toxic factors are slower acting, bacterial in origin, and unidentified (126, 638).

TOXICITY, SYMPTOMS AND LESIONS. Toxicity of freshwater bluegreen algae has been reviewed by Davidson (400), Dillenberg and Dehnel (424), Fitch *et al.* (536), Gorham (638, 639), Ingram and Prescott (823), Olson (1203, 1204), Schwimmer and Schwimmer (1427), and Vinberg (1627). Extensive loss of life and severe sickness of livestock, pets, wild animals, and the human being has been associated with algal blooms in the northern half of the United States (also in Texas) and the southern provinces of Canada (151, 167, 400, 412, 424, 517, 533, 536, 624, 956, 963, 1082, 1188, 1203, 1294, 1317, 1438, 1526), and in many other countries of the world. Cattle, sheep, horses, swine, dogs, cats, fowl, geese, wild and domestic ducks, game and song birds, fish, rodents, and small game have been killed, some in large numbers.

It is probable that some of the poisonings associated with algal blooms were caused by botulism (*Clostridium* is commonly found in such blooms), from compounds such as hydoxylamine or hydrogen sulfide (1294) (toxic at least to fish) produced by the decay of large quantities of organic matter, or in fish by suffocation when blooms of algae deplete the oxygen in a natural body of water by respiration (at night) and by decay.

Most reports of algal poisoning agree in the following particulars. Poisoning appears rapidly; symptoms usually occur within 15 to 45 minutes after ingestion of a toxic dose. Poisoning proceeds rapidly and is severe; death is common, occurring in less than 24 hours, often within one or two hours. The usual sequence is nausea, vomition, abdominal pain, diarrhea, prostration, muscular tremors, dyspnea, cyanosis, general paralysis, convulsions, and death. Symptoms resulting from gastroenteritis are variable in severity and occasionally are absent. In the uncommon case in which death does not rapidly supervene, additional symptoms of blood in the feces, icterus, and typical photosensitization (p. 52) have been recorded (424, 956, 1535).

Few feeding experiments have been carried out with naturally occurring algal blooms, and oral toxicity is difficult to estimate. It is clear that toxicity varies greatly over periods as brief as a few hours and may disappear as quickly as it comes if the algal bloom is dissipated by waves, turbulence, or rapid decomposition. In one instance, six gallons of bloom administered to a

1000-lb Holstein cow by stomach tube resulted in death in 25 minutes (1526); in another 50 ml was lethal to a hen in 1½ hours.

Principal lesions fall into two categories. Lesions associated with gastroenteritis include inflammation of the digestive tract, increasing in severity toward the posterior end, sometimes hemorrhagic. The other principal lesions are those of acute general degenerative change in the cells of various organs, especially liver and kidney. The liver in poisoned animals is swollen and mottled with areas of yellow; the kidney shows signs of toxic tubular nephritis.

Gorham's purified fast-death factor produces congestion and hemorrhage in the liver of experimental animals (638). He suggests that the gastroenteric symptoms and lesions in natural cases are produced by bacterial toxins accompanying the fast-death factor.

The cases of poisoning by *Nostoc rivulare* (400) differ in some particulars from the above. The form of bloom also is different. This alga forms large mucilaginous or gelatinous masses of irregular outline which float in the surface water, and may collect to some depth in the water at the windward side of a pond.

The poisoning of human beings after drinking water from reservoirs with algal blooms or swimming in such ponds has been suggested several times (1203, 1583, 1619, 1627), the most conclusive cases being associated with blooms in Saskatchewan in 1959 (1438). Cases prior to these have been reviewed by Schwimmer and Schwimmer (1427). They consist of epidemic intestinal disorders in populations drinking from the same water supply, and of severe individual gastroenteritis after swimming in, and ingestion of, water containing a bloom. There is some evidence that the usual treatments of drinking water reduce the level of toxicity greatly (although they are not specific for the removal or inactivation of the toxic principle), and it is the rare combination of circumstances that will result in at most only slightly toxic water in municipal supplies.

Haff disease of peoples along the Baltic Coast, at first enigmatic, has now been associated with ingestion of fish and fish liver from waters supporting algal blooms (1627). A number of cases of dermatitis in human beings after contact with algae while swimming have been reviewed by Schwimmer and Schwimmer (1427).

CONDITIONS OF POISONING. It is clear that algal blooms have been responsible for extensive loss of life in livestock, pets, wild animals, and birds. The toxicity of such blooms results from one or more toxic fast-death factors produced in the cells of certain bluegreen algae, products of decomposition, and toxins produced by bacteria associated with the bloom. Studies have shown (638) that production of one fast-death factor is genetically and physiologically controlled. Not all strains of a toxic species form it, and rate of formation is markedly influenced by temperature. The fast-death factor accumulates in growing cells but is released into the water from old populations either through disintegration of the cells or by leakage through the cell wall. Level of toxicity in a bloom is greatest at this time, disappearing rapidly as the bloom decays or is dissipated.

Poisoning does not occur unless a dense bloom of toxic organisms has formed and the toxic material has been thus concentrated. Two factors lead to the formation of such blooms. They are the presence of good growing conditions (warm, sunny weather, ample nutrients) and a gentle, constant wind which blows across the water, drifting and collecting the organisms against the windward shore.

DIVISION CHLOROPHYTA
Class Chlorophyceae—Green algae
DIVISION CHLOROMONADOPHYTA
Class Chloromonadophyceae—Chloromonad flagellates, marine
plankton
DIVISION PYRROPHYTA
Class Dinophyceae—Dinoflagellates, marine plankton
DIVISION PHAEOPHYTA
Class Phaeophyceae—Brown algae, some seaweeds

Marine Algae

Toxic marine algae fall in the classes named above (which also have freshwater representatives) and in the bluegreen algae (one species).

Shellfish poisoning

Serious poisoning and death of pets, fowl (1087, 1098), livestock (1496), wild animals, and especially of human beings has occurred after ingestion of shellfish gathered from southern California to Alaska along the west coast or in the Bay of Fundy and the mouth of the St. Lawrence River (1567) on the east coast of North America. Paralytic shellfish poisoning has been reviewed by Edwards (476), Hutner and McLaughlin (813), Medcof *et al.* (1087), Meyer (1097), and Sommer and Meyer (1496, 1497). Hundreds of cases of severe poisoning and death of human beings have been recorded since the first observation of the disease on the West Coast in 1798. Intensive investigation was undertaken following an epidemic of poisoning by shellfish from the shores of California in 1927

(1098). It was soon established that shellfish poisoning (as here under-stood) is different from food poisoning from spoiled shellfish, and is caused by the presence of a specific toxic substance in healthy shellfish. Mussels, clams, scallops, and other molluscs and invertebrates (especially crabs) have been found on occasion to contain the toxic principle in dangerous amounts. Epidemics of shellfish poisoning on the East Coast, although less numerous than those of the West Coast, have likewise been investigated and the two have proved similar in all basic respects. In each, mollusc toxicity has been traced to a minute planktonic organism on which the mollusc feeds. This is the dinoflagellate *Gonyaulax*. Mollusc toxicity occurs during and immediately following periods of bloom of the dinoflagellate in which populations as great as several million cells per liter of seawater appear (1341). Toxicity of West Coast molluscs is associated with blooms of *Gonyaulax catenella* Whedon & Kofoid (1498) and of East Coast molluscs with blooms of *Gonyaulax tamarensis* Lebour (1087).

Dinoflagellates are minute, pigmented, flagellated, single-celled organisms which swim in the upper layers of oceanic waters as members of the plankton. Together with diatoms they constitute the major primary producers of the ocean. Because they are motile and may ingest particulate food, zoologists classify them among the flagellated protozoa. Because they contain photosynthetic pigments, botanists classify them among the algae and treat them as a division of the plant kingdom—Division Pyrophyta. With proper optical equipment, recognition of dinoflagellates is relatively easy, but identification of species is a matter for the expert. Dinoflagellates may be recognized by the possession of two flagella which are inserted at a single place laterally (in terms of the direction of motion) in the cell. One flagellum trails posteriorly, while the other encircles the cell more or less equatorially.

POISONOUS PRINCIPLE. The toxic principle in *Gonyaulax catenella* was first described as an alkaloid. Much effort has been expended in an attempt to learn the identity of the toxic compound (209, 364, 1341, 1401, 1402). Separation and purification of the toxic principle were accompanied by great difficulty. Data have accumulated slowly, however, which have established certain characteristics of the toxic molecule. It is a basic nitrogenous substance which is soluble in water and highly polar, insoluble in all lipid solvents, acid stable, alkaline labile, and dialyzable. Its composition as extracted is $C_{10}:H_{17}N_7O_2 \cdot 2HCl$. Successful axenic (bacteria-free) culture of the dinoflagellate (209) has made it possible to determine that the toxin is contained in the algal cell in the same form in which it is later toxic to the subject poisoned, and that there may be intrinsic variation in the amount of toxin formed in a given cell. Chemical studies indicate that the toxin in *Gonyaulax catenella* is identical with the toxin in *G. tamarensis*.

TOXICITY, SYMPTOMS, AND LESIONS. *Gonyaulax* toxin is a nerve poison somewhat like curare in its effects. The purified substance is extremely toxic to warm-blooded animals [$LD_{total} = 3$ to 4 μg per kilogram parenterally (1156)], and a lethal dose for the human being may be contained in, for example, less than a half dozen clams. It causes depression, often complete, of both peripheral nerve function and reflex transmission. It interferes directly with myocardial conduction and has an additional, similar effect through central nervous system action at the level of the brain. The result is cardiovascular collapse (1156).

Symptoms appear in the human being within a few minutes to 3 hours after ingestion of a toxic dose. Highly toxic shellfish may produce slight topical anesthesia about the lips and mouth on contact (148). Symptoms consist of numbness about the face and in the fingertips, "pins and needles" sensation at the lips, nausea (usually without vomiting because of paralysis), ataxia, thick speech, headache, and increasing general paralysis. Death usually occurs as a result of respiratory failure. Prognosis is excellent if the patient survives the first 24 hours. Artificial respiration is useful, and considerable success in animal experiments has been had (1156) with DL-amphetamine as an antidote.

Various animals, especially cats and poultry, have been poisoned from shellfish remains in garbage. Death is rapid and symptoms have rarely been observed.

Specific lesions have not been found in post mortem examinations. In experiments designed to establish chronic poisoning in laboratory animals (365), degenerative changes in the large nerve cells of the spinal cord and medulla have been described.

CONDITIONS OF POISONING. Molluscs depend on a more or less unselective filtering mechanism for obtaining their food. When toxic dinoflagellates are present in abundance they are filtered out of seawater by the molluscs, digested, and their toxin is accumulated in the tissues of the mollusc. For some reason the mollusc is immune to the toxin. The toxin is concentrated to different degrees in different tissues. Some molluscs concentrate it in the viscera, others in the siphon. The "white meat" of any mollusc is usually lowest in toxicity.

Toxicity of a particular mollusc population depends on presence, concentration, and intrinsic toxicity of a dinoflagellate bloom, selectivity of the species of mollusc, length of time over which the toxin has been concentrated by the mollusc, and speed of excretion of toxin. Blooms of toxic dinoflagellates are triggered by unknown hydrographic factors. They always occur in the warmer waters of summer months, but winter temperatures may influence the possibility of a bloom the following summer. Molluscs may contain toxic levels of the dinoflagellate poison within a day or two after a bloom appears. The rate at which toxicity is lost varies greatly with type of mollusc, but is slower than accumulation and usually requires a week to a month or sometimes longer for reduction below the dangerous level.

Blooms of dinoflagellates are related to rather precise characteristics of the environment. The blooms of *G. catenella* along the West Coast are quite random in time and location; they appear to be associated with upwelling of deeper water along the shore. The blooms of *G. tamarensis* of the East Coast have a predictable geographic pattern (148). They occur only in bays which are more or less open to the ocean.

Dinoflagellate blooms are often visible as areas of brownish or reddish water. The color comes from the large numbers of organisms present. Each dinoflagellate cell contains a complement of photosynthetic and other pigments. There is some evidence (1498) that as toxicity of a bloom increases, the color of the individual cells becomes more red and brown. It should be emphasized that many dinoflagellate blooms (of genera and species other than those named above) are nontoxic, and further that molluscs may accumulate dangerous levels of toxin from dinoflagellate populations which are not concentrated enough to impart color to the water.

Preparation and cooking of edible molluscs may result in greatly reduced toxicity in the product as consumed. In some cases, for example, the more highly toxic viscera are thrown away before cooking. In scallops danger rarely is present because only the adductor muscle, the least toxic part, is commonly eaten. Steaming tends to leach out much of the toxin into the broth. Rarely is all of the latter consumed. Cooking, by itself, tends to reduce toxicity. On the average, cooked molluscs have about one-third the toxicity of raw molluscs of the same original potency (1087). Frying seems especially destructive to toxin. Processing procedures of commercial canneries greatly reduce toxicity.

Nevertheless uncooked molluscs, as consumed by some people, and cooked and canned molluscs sometimes may still be dangerous. Governments of Canada and the United States for many years maintained testing and enforcement programs designed to keep toxic molluscs from being processed commercially (1072). These programs, which involve continuous checks on the toxicity of commercially exploited mollusc populations and on the toxicity of the product, have been entirely effective. For the protection of the person who digs molluscs for himself, seasonal or special prohibitions are imposed as necessary. Despite signs at the danger areas, other types of publicity, and in some instances actual patrol, from time to time some people ignore these warnings and are poisoned.

Red tides and poisoning of fish

Fish mortality associated with the presence of a conspicuous, red dinoflagellate bloom has been reported sporadically along the west coast of Florida from 1844 to the present. In some instances dead fish which have accumulated along the beaches have numbered in the millions (821). In addition to marine fish, turtles, barnacles, oysters, shrimp, crabs, dolphins, and other animals have been killed. Following a severe outbreak of poisoning in 1946 and 1947, intensive investigations were undertaken at a number of laboratories with the result that toxicity was soon associated with a previously undescribed species of dinoflagellate, *Gymnodinium brevis* Davis (403).

Little work has been done with the toxic principle in this species but a related dinoflagellate *G. veneficum* has been studied (2) in Britain. The toxic principle in the latter species appears to be different from the toxic principle associated with shellfish poisoning. It is nondialyzable. Some aspects of its action and its ability to depolarize membranes have been investigated (2).

Gymnodinium blooms are rapidly toxic to fish and other marine animals. In many cases fish have been observed to die almost immediately after swimming into an area of dinoflagellate concentration.

Gymnodinium brevis blooms near shore, together with onshore winds, provoke attacks of choking and coughing in the human population within a few miles of the shore. These manifestations have been traced to the presence in the air of small droplets of material which has apparently originated in the dinoflagellate cells. The effect is transitory and disappears as soon as the air changes.

Masses of decaying fish along beaches are in themselves a powerful stimulus to research designed to prevent or predict dinoflagellate blooms ("red tides"). Much work has been done to determine the combination of ecological factors which initiates the almost uninhibited population explosion found in blooms. The availability of phosphorus, once thought critically limiting, seems less important on the basis of later work (101).

Miscellaneous syndromes sometimes associated with marine algae

Many marine fish are poisonous when consumed by human populations, and much loss of life has occurred in various parts of the world. Certain types of fish poisoning present symptoms similar to those of shellfish poisoning. Some of these fish may feed on corals which contain algal cells as symbionts. The algal members of some corals turn into motile dinoflagellates when artificially released from their hosts. It has been suggested (813) that the source of fish toxicity in some instances therefore may be toxin-forming dinoflagellates in corals that serve as food for the fish.

Toxicities associated with other dinoflagellates

Evidence for toxicity along the shores of North America of the species of dinoflagellates named above is clear. Elsewhere other dinoflagellates have been associated with poisoning, and in some of the American blooms additional species have been present and may have contributed to the toxicity. Among marine planktonic organisms considered toxic for one reason or another (59) may be included the dinoflagellates, *Gonyaulax polyedra* Stein, *Gymnodinium splendens* Lebour, *Gymnodinium mikimotoi* Miyake & Kominani, *Cochlodinium catenatum* Okamura, *Pyrodinium phoneus* Woloszynska & Conrad, and *Exuviella baltica* Lohmann; the bluegreen *Trichodesmium spp.;* the chloromonad *Hornellia marina* Subrahmanyan; and the yellowgreen *Prymnesium parvum* Carter. The dinoflagellates are physiologically not yet well known, and it is likely that additional species will readily be found that form toxic compounds.

Toxicities associated with seaweeds

Larger seaweeds, particularly brown algae (Division Phaeophyta) have been fed as principal forage to farm animals under some circumstances, and commercial supplements made mostly from seaweeds have been advertised as beneficial in certain ways when added to the animal diet. On the basis of experience and experimentation (e.g., 588, 1067) no serious general harm exists in these practices, but, on occasion specific difficulties have been associated with seaweed diets. A disease in lambs, for example, from ewes which have fed heavily on seaweeds during pregnancy has been recognized (1215) in Iceland for many years. Disturbed coordination and paralysis is associated with demyelination confined to the cerebrum. The giant kelp of the Pacific [*Macrocystis pyrifera* (Turn.) Agardh], one of the brown algae used in feed supplements, also has been shown (673) to contain a moderately toxic principle.

FUNGI

Fungi may cause disease in three ways. They may be pathogenic, allergenic, or toxic. Toxic fungi constitute a heterogeneous assemblage of species which, alone or in symbiosis with the plant they parasitize, produce compounds having toxic effect when ingested by man or animals. Compared with pathogenic fungi, toxic fungi, the only group here reviewed, are poorly known. The poisonous nature of certain mushrooms is familiar to all. Less well recognized or understood are the toxic effects of a wide variety of molds, smuts, rusts, and other types of lower fungi.

Taxonomically, toxic species are found among the basidiomycetes, ascomycetes, and imperfect fungi. The positive identification of a species in most of these groups requires specialized knowledge and often involves culturing and microscopic examination.

In this book, fungus toxicoses have been divided into three major categories for ease of treatment. Higher fungi of characteristic structure, not requiring microscopic examination for recognition, have been grouped together under the term "mushrooms" and treated as separate genera. Ergot (*Claviceps*), with its characteristic and easily recognized sclerotium, is treated separately. Molds, smuts, and rusts present a different problem. In many reports, the fungus is not identified botanically and therefore cannot serve to identify the disease. Often the most characteristic element unifying the disease is its association with a particular type of feedstuff or forage. Thus, the disease caused by ingestion of fungus-infected barley grain is recognized as scabby barley disease. Poisonings of this type, in which the host is the most conspicuous botanical element, are treated elsewhere in this book under the generic name of the host. These include scabby barley (*Hordeum*), vulvovaginitis (*Zea*), smutty oats (*Avena*), fescue foot (*Festuca*), darnel poisoning (*Lolium*), goldenrod poisoning (*Solidago*), Bermuda grass poisoning (*Cynodon*), and toxic peanut meal (*Arachis*).

In other instances, neither the fungus nor the feedstuff involved can serve to identify the disease, the former being unknown and the latter varying. It is necessary to treat these syndromes, therefore, on the basis of characteristic symptoms and lesions. They are discussed below under "molds, smuts, and rusts."

The genera of fungi mentioned by name in this book may be classified as follows:

DIVISION PHYCOMYCOTA (algalike fungi; phycomycetes)
 CLASS PHYCOMYCETES
  Rhizopus
DIVISION ASCOMYCOTA (sac-fungi, ascomycetes)
 CLASS ASCOMYCETES

Claviceps	*Gyromitra*
Gibberella	*Monascus*

 CLASS LICHENES
  Parmelia
DIVISION BASIDIOMYCOTA (smuts, rusts, mushrooms; basidiomycetes)
 CLASS BASIDIOMYCETES

Amanita	*Lactarius*
Boletus	*Lepiota*
Clathrus	*Panaeolus*
Clytocybe	*Pholiota*
Coleosporium	*Psilocybe*
Coprinus	*Russula*
Entoloma	*Scleroderma*
Inocybe	*Tricholoma*

FUNGI IMPERFECTI (fungi lacking sexual stages necessary for proper classification in above categories)

Alternaria	*Paecilomyces*
Aspergillus	*Sclerotium*
Endoconidium	*Stachybotrys*

Molds, smuts, and rusts

Forage poisoning

The term "forage poisoning" appears to have been coined by Pearson in 1900 (617, 1254) but the etiological association of molded forage with the production of animal diseases occurred many years earlier (426). "Forage poisoning" has been used in a heterogeneous way in veterinary literature and has not become firmly attached to any specific syndrome. Because of this, and because of the broad spectrum of diseases to which

it might be applied, it has fallen into disuse. In general, in the older literature, it was used as a name for one or more of the situations described
below.

Historical review of livestock poisoning by molded feedstuffs, to 1930
As early as 1850 (643) diseases associated with, or caused by,
moldy feedstuffs were described in the veterinary literature. A large mass
of literature describing cases and reporting occasional positive experimental
feedings of suspected materials had accumulated by the early decades
of the twentieth century. Losses totaling tens of thousands of animals,
particularly cattle and horses, were described in the United States. Heterogeneity in reports prevented generalizations and frustrated a systematic
attack on the problem. In part this heterogeneity came out of actual heterogeneity in etiology. It is likely that some cases of stock loss were coinci-
dentally associated with ingestion of moldy feedstuffs when the real
cause of death was a pathogenic condition (374) or nitrate poisoning
(1064). Conditions which promote mold development on feedstuffs usually
encourage other deleterious changes. Botulism from spoiled silage thus was
confused with mold poisoning (646, 647, 1376, 1420, 1534). Simple
overeating may have accounted for some losses attributed to mold poisoning. Subtracting these, there remained a number of reports which could not
be so dismissed.

DISEASES. Most reports fell into one of two patterns, both commonly
associated with ingestion of moldy corn forage or silage. In one, usually
displayed in cattle, symptoms were those associated with severe gastroenteritis, followed by death. In the other, usually seen in horses, symptoms
were primarily nervous in character and more variable.

The term "cornstalk disease"[1] came to be applied generally to the
former, that is, poisoning of cattle from molded corn forage. In earlier
days it was the practice to harvest corn by hand-picking the ears, then to
pasture animals on the stalks. Horses on molded corn pasturage occasionally developed a disease which was considered to be identical with
cornstalk disease in cattle (1262).

The typical nervous disease in horses associated with the ingestion
of moldy forages, particularly corn, was given a variety of names including
cerebrospinal meningitis, cerebritis, leucoencephalitis, staggers, blind staggers, choking distemper, stomach staggers, acute hemorrhagic encephalitis,
moldy corn disease, and others. Excitement and paralysis were usually
described; other symptoms were variable. In some instances well-defined
necrosis and liquefaction in the brain or upper spinal column were found;

---

[1] The term "cornstalk disease" currently applies to a separate syndrome in cattle
in which corn of high nitrogen content produces toxic nitrosohemoglobin in the
blood. (See *Zea.*)

in others these lesions were absent. In some, liver and kidney damage were noted (1063). Some persons associated particular instances of cattle poisoning with this syndrome (1515).

Reviews of these two syndromes include those of Moore, 1896 (1124); Peters, 1898 (1262); Buckley, 1901, (196); Butler, 1902 (221); Nebraska Department of Animal Pathology, 1903 (419); Graham, 1913 (643); Mohler, 1914 (1114); and Eckles *et al.,* 1924 (472). Steyn in 1933 (1529) and 1934 (1533) provided the first comprehensive survey of fungus poisonings of animals and human beings in the world literature.

FUNGI INVOLVED. In the course of investigations into poisonings caused by molded feedstuffs, experimental feedings occasionally gave clear-cut positive results (221, 643, 1063, 1101, 1254, 1515). Identification of the principal fungus was sometimes obtained. Among the fungi found were species of *Penicillium* (426), *Aspergillus* (1063), and *Monascus* (1515). Toxicity of *Rhizopus* was suggested in some experiments (283). Despite these circumstantial incriminations of particular fungi, by 1924 no fungus cultures had yet been isolated which proved toxic by oral administration (283, 472). Sometimes a toxic principle is produced only by fungus and host together, as for example in the case of scabby barley. In such cases the toxic principle is produced by interaction of fungus and host over a specific portion of the host's life cycle. In the majority of cases where toxicity is associated with molds, however, it is probably caused by the fungus alone and should be found in cultures.

Livestock poisoning attributed to molded feedstuffs, since 1930

In 1930 virus equine encephalitis was recognized. In this disease, lesions of the brain are not found. Many cases of moldy feed poisoning in horses reported previous to 1930 may well have been virus encephalitis (1421), yet those cases in which brain lesions were described remained unexplained. Since that date several excellent investigations have penetrated deeply into the matter of moldy feed poisonings in various classes of stock. In the main, losses in cattle, horses, swine, and poultry are associated with moldy corn but other molded feeds have been incriminated in some instances. The toxicity of several species of fungi has been demonstrated beyond question. Two major syndromes may be recognized. The first is similar to, and may be identical with, the nervous disease of horses described on p. 72.

NERVOUS SYNDROME IN HORSES. In the winter of 1934–1935, severe loss of horses was experienced in the Central Plains states. It was estimated (644) that more than 5000 horses were lost in Illinois alone. Cases appeared first in September, reached a peak in November, and declined thereafter, disappearing by May (644, 1421). In the great majority of instances, death occurred in horses which had been receiving damaged corn or cornstalks. Locally the disease was termed forage poisoning, corn-stalk disease, cerebrospinal meningitis, staggers, moldy corn poisoning, leucoencephalitis, and acute hemorrhagic encephalitis. In recent years it has most generally been designated "moldy corn poisoning." It was re-produced experimentally both by placing sound animals in fields which had caused trouble (644) and by feeding molded corn to animals confined without pasturage (1421). In Illinois it was associated with the same climatic conditions, namely a dry summer followed by an unusually wet fall, which had characterized the two similar outbreaks in the preceding half century.

In experimental work duplicating natural conditions, two experimental animals succumbed 23 and 26 days respectively after being placed on suspected corn forage (644). Similarly in field cases the disease appeared to have a long incubation period and relatively acute termination (12). Symptoms were variable, depending upon the extent of central nervous system lesions. Graham (644) divided them into three clinical types: lethargic, nervous, and paralytic. This disease, in its variability, was clini-cally indistinguishable from virus encephalitis. The lesions, however, are characteristic, permitting positive diagnosis of moldy corn poisoning in horses as distinct from virus encephalitis and botulism (1420). The primary lesion consists of degenerative changes and liquefaction necrosis in the white matter of the brain. Graham (644) found this lesion in gross ex-amination of only 65 per cent of the 55 brains he dissected, but Schwarte, Biester, and others (115, 1421), upon microscopic examination of brains of animals suffering from moldy corn poisoning, invariably found some degenerative change. Attempts to isolate a virus or bacterium from areas of liquefaction in experimental cases were unsuccessful (115, 1421). Liver and kidney lesions were noted by Biester et al. (1421). Preliminary at-tempts to identify or determine the toxicity of particular fungi in these outbreaks were abortive and unsuccessful (115).

HEMORRHAGIC SYNDROME IN LIVESTOCK. During the drought years of the middle 1930's a hemorrhagic syndrome in cattle was recognized (12) which seemed related to the nervous syndrome of horses in the following ways. It occurred mostly in the same general area (north-central United States) at the same season (fall and winter) and was associated with the same forage (corn). The presence of fungi was not noted in reports of the hemorrhagic syndrome in cattle but seems likely. Cases were especially frequent when cattle were placed on immature, stunted, or frosted corn. The nervous syndrome of horses and the hemorrhagic syn-drome in cattle rarely, if ever, appeared in the same field, and usually in a given locality both diseases were not encountered in the same season.

Symptoms in the hemorrhagic disease of cattle appeared in a week or ten days after animals were placed on cornstalk pasturage, and subsided within a day or so if the herd was removed. Incidence was spotty, younger animals apparently being more susceptible. Symptoms consisted of incoordination, excitement, coma, and death, the period of symptoms lasting between 24 to 48 hours. Mortality in affected animals invariably approached 100 per cent. Post mortem lesions consisted mainly of petechial and ecchymotic hemorrhages throughout the body tissues. The liver was congested and slightly swollen.

In the decades following the 1930's further insight into hemorrhagic syndromes associated with fungi, in cattle, swine, and fowl, has been gained by investigations into two superficially quite different diseases of livestock. Both were first associated with fungi, almost simultaneously, in 1953.

Hyperkeratosis is a skin disease characterized externally in cattle primarily by epithelial overgrowth. This results in thickening of the skin and loss of hair, particularly on neck and shoulders (1194). It has been traced to ingestion of very small amounts of highly chlorinated napthalenes, present in wood preservatives and lubricating oils, the latter sometimes contaminating feed concentrates during milling or pelleting. Vitamin A deficiency was a sign in hyperkeratosis induced by chlorinated napthalene poisoning. Similar lesions can be experimentally reproduced by any measures which result in reduced vitamin A levels in the body.

In some instances of hyperkeratosis, chlorinated napthalenes could not be detected (246). Instead, moderate contamination of the feedstuffs with fungal growths was found (244, 245, 246, 247, 568, 569). Isolates, when grown on sterilized substrates, in some instances produced toxic substances which could be extracted both from the fungus and from the substrate material. Such extracts produced dermal reactions by contact and were toxic when given orally to various animals. The unextracted substrates used in these culture experiments proved acutely toxic.

Fungi isolated and proved toxic in this series of experiments included *Aspergillus chevalieri* (Mangin) Thom & Church, isolated from a feed concentrate, grown on sterile bread; *Aspergillus clavatus* Desm. isolated from feed pellets, grown on sterile whole corn; and *Aspergillus fumigatus* Fres., isolated from a nontoxic source and grown on sterile whole corn. Two of these three species when fed in relatively small amounts over several weeks (the third not so tested) produced some symptoms characteristic of bovine hyperkeratosis. In larger amount, all three produced an acute disease characterized by widespread internal hemorrhage and death within a week in most instances. Forgacs and Carll have termed this disease aspergillustoxicosis (567).

The second investigation resulting in the demonstration of toxicity of certain fungi, also reported in 1953 (217), was occasioned by heavy mortality in livestock on corn pasturage in Georgia, Florida, Alabama, and Missouri in the late summer and fall of 1952. Losses in swine ran into the thousands (56, 218) and losses were also noted in cattle (255, 1471). This, too, was a disease characterized by massive internal hemorrhaging (1335). In the original detailed report (1473), Sippel *et al.* described field and experimental cases in swine and cattle, giving pathology in some detail. They recognized acute and chronic conditions among the field cases in swine. In acute cases, animals died or were found dead after being sick not more than two days. Symptoms included depression, staggering, especially with weak hind quarters, anorexia, and pale or yellowish mucous membranes. Petechial and ecchymotic hemorrhages were found in some animals. These animals gave the appearance of having bled to death in their own tissues. In cases distinguished as chronic, symptoms included depression, stiffness of gait, anorexia, and "tucked up" appearance. Icterus and yellow fibrotic livers were the most prominent findings in post mortem examinations. Some hemorrhage was present in various locations, and the abdominal and thoracic cavities contained amounts of straw-colored fluid. Degenerative changes were observed on histopathological examination of various organs, especially liver and kidney.

Experimentally hand-shelled molded corn from an area where loss had occurred, fed at the rate of 1.25 lb per day to 40-lb pigs, caused mortality, with symptoms and lesions similar to those in acute field cases, after as little as three days.

Sippel and coworkers (1473) observed closely one outbreak in cattle. The first death occurred within three days after the herd had been placed on moldy corn which they ate ravenously. Several more deaths occurred over the next few days. Symptoms of depression and anorexia usually lasted from one to three days before death and were frequently accompanied by bloody diarrhea and bleeding from the nostrils. Lesions were essentially the same as those observed in pigs. Experimentally, 18 lb shelled corn fed to a 280-lb calf produced death on the third day. In this case the animal exhibited periods of nervous seizures. Case (255) has described disease in cattle associated with ingestion of moldy corn and production of hemorrhagic lesions in which nervous symptoms of excitement or lethargy were noted. His cases were confused by the presence of solanaceous weeds among the corn and high nitrate content in the forage.

From similarity, in production of hemorrhages, to sweetclover disease (see *Melilotus*) Sippel *et al.* (1473) examined and tested the blood of poisoned animals in various ways. Besides a raised icteric index in many instances, the only abnormal value found was diminution in plasma vitamin A. Prothrombin time was normal or almost so, distinguishing this condition from sweetclover poisoning.

Thirteen fungus isolates were made from corn used in the experimental work described above. These were grown on sterile substrates and tested for toxicity in work described by Sippel (1471) and by Burnside et al. (218). Of these, only two, *Penicillium rubrum* Stoll and *Aspergillus flavus* Link gave positive results for toxicity. Symptoms and lesions in swine fed substrate (sterile whole-grain corn) upon which *A. flavus* had been grown duplicated those in the field cases. Detailed histopathology is given by Burnside et al. (218). *Penicillium rubrum* substrate produced very rapid death with lesions of intense inflammation of the stomach and enteritis, together with lesions of liver and kidney detected upon microscopic examination. Severity of kidney damage appeared to be directly related to time of death, while extent of liver damage varied over wide limits.

The supernatant from water-soaked and ground corn substrate upon which *P. rubrum* had been grown proved toxic to the horse (1471), producing symptoms similar to those found in swine poisoned with *Aspergillus flavus*. In one instance extensive hemorrhage was observed in the cerebellum together with edema and necrosis, but no liquefaction necrosis of classical "moldy corn poisoning" of horses was observed. Likewise examination of several swine brains (1473) failed to show lesions of this type. The toxic principle experimentally was shown stable to heat (70° C) and to storage for two months in a cool dry place and was shown by the experiment cited above to be water soluble.

Of the thirteen fungal isolates in this study, nine proved to be strains of *A. flavus*. Only one of these was toxic. Three had the ability to depress plasma vitamin A level, but the toxic strain produced death before examination for plasma vitamin A content was possible. Forgacs and Carll have termed this disease moldy corn toxicosis (567).

When, in 1953, field cases were first correctly diagnosed, it was thought (1473) they were confined to animals placed on moldy corn of the "soft" kinds. Since that time cases have been diagnosed in animals on "hard" corns, on molded peanuts and oats, and have been suspected in animals on low-grade commercial concentrates (1471).

HEPATITIS X DISEASE IN DOGS. When moldy corn from an experimentally confirmed case of swine poisoning was fed experimentally to a dog, a syndrome was produced that differed in no important respect from naturally occurring "hepatitis X" of dogs. This syndrome was originally recognized in dogs in the same areas and at the same time that moldy corn poisoning was first diagnosed in swine. Symptoms and lesions in the dog are comparable with those of moldy corn poisoning in swine (56).

HEMORRHAGIC DISEASE IN POULTRY. In 1951–1952 in the peninsular portion of Delaware, Maryland, and Virginia area a hemorrhagic disease of poultry raised as broilers became economically significant and in subsequent years has become a major problem (366). Undoubtedly several diseases, of different etiology, producing a wide range of clinical characteristics are involved. Some fungi may be isolated at almost any time from poultry litter and feeds. The role of these fungi in producing toxic substances has been only partially described. Forgacs *et al.* in 1955 (566, 570, 571), from the similarity of lesions in poultry hemorrhagic disease to those they found in moldy feed poisoning in cattle, were prompted to examine feedstuffs and litter from broiler houses in which hemorrhagic disease was enzootic. They isolated eight strains of fungi in several genera which, when grown on scratch-grain substrates and fed as such, reproduced the symptoms and lesions characteristic of the natural disease. Symptoms consisted of depression, anorexia, failure to make normal gains, and death. Lesions included widespread internal hemorrhages, erosions of proventriculus and gizzard, and after the seventeenth day paleness of bone marrow with subsequent anemia. Other work has shown that hemorrhage is not always associated with hypoplastic bone marrow (1647). Fungi involved (567) included *Aspergillus clavatus* Desm., *A. flavus* Link, *A. glaucus* Link, *Penicillium citrinum* Thom, *P. purpurogenum* Stoll, *P. rubrum* Stoll, *Paecilomyces varioti* Bainier (= *Penicillium divaricatum* Thom), an unidentified species of *Alternaria,* and of *Penicillium.*

In natural outbreaks in broiler houses the disease usually appears when the birds are 4 to 12 weeks old. The highest incidence occurs at 4 to 7 weeks. The wetness of litter is a factor contributing to the appearance of the disease. Under usual conditions incidence is spotty, and recovery in the flock occurs spontaneously and without apparent cause.

Miscellaneous

Some fungi (*Aspergillus spp.* and *Penicillium spp.*) produce oxalates. Wilson has suggested (1694) with supporting experimental evidence, that some outbreaks of poisoning associated with moldy feeds, and appropriate symptoms and lesions, are the result of continued ingestion of moderately high oxalate levels and concomitant reduction in dietary calcium availability.

Several cases of pharyngeal paralysis in cattle following ingestion of spoiled grass or corn trench silage have been described by Gibbons (617). In some instances paralysis has become general, resulting in death after a few days.

Corn-grain substrate on which the ascomycete *Gibberella zeae* (Schw.) Petch (corn root-rot organism) has been grown is extremely toxic to rats (1111).

A disease of cattle characterized by severe pulmonary distress has been associated with ingestion of corn pasturage or sweet potatoes infected with an imperfect fungus of the genus *Sclerotium* (1115). This is a form genus maintained for fungi for which only the sclerotial and associated mycelial stages are known. Symptoms of severe dyspnea and anorexia appear quickly and usually terminate fatally within a week. Some subcutaneous emphysema may occur in the neck and shoulder regions. Lesions of the lung are those of pulmonary adenomatosis and pneumonia, varying in exact character with the duration of the disease. Impaction of the forestomach is present in all cases and mild gastroenteritis in many. Attempts to reproduce the disease experimentally were not successful.

Considerable work on fungal toxicoses has been performed in other countries, particularly in Russia, and Japan (1608), where human as well as animal poisoning has occurred. Other genera than those named above often have been incriminated. One, which causes a complicated, three-stage hemorrhagic syndrome in horses (atypically, one-stage) is caused by toxins produced by *Stachybotrys atra* Corda (= *Stachybotrys alternans* Bonorden) in the forage. For a review of stachybotryotoxicosis, see 567. Forgacs, following his interest in fungal toxicoses, obtained 40 strains of this species from a culture collection in the United States and tested them for toxicity in various ways (565). Although several showed activity of various types, only one was found which made a straw or oat substrate toxic to animals. Some strains, initially nontoxic, developed activity when cultured on appropriate media over several transfers. A single-stage hemorrhagic disease was produced in which prothrombin time was reduced. Hemorrhagic diseases caused by other fungi as described above do not share this characteristic.

The world literature on fungal toxicity has recently been reviewed by Ainsworth and Austwick (11) and Forgacs and Carll (567). A few reviews of the Russian work have appeared in English. One, easily available, is that of Mayer (1062). See also *The Merck Veterinary Manual* (1453).

Distinct from development of toxicity are changes in nutritive value when crop plants are heavily parasitized by fungi. For example, it has been shown (1111) that diplodia and fusarium rots of corn definitely lower the nutritive value of the grain and change its chemical composition. Also beyond the scope of this discussion is a disease associated with spoiled oat silage which has been found (652) to be caused by a listeric infection.

Ergot

> *Claviceps purpurea* (Fr.) Tul. (= *C. microcephala*)
> *Claviceps paspali* Stev. et Hall

Claviceps cinerea D. Griffiths
[See also *Festuca*]

COMMON NAME. The term "ergot" is used in two ways. It is applied as a common name for species of *Claviceps*. It is also used more precisely to refer to the sclerotium formed by *Claviceps purpurea* when infecting rye (*Secale cereale*). This is the ergot of commerce and medicine.

The use of ergot in childbirth and in controlling uterine hemorrhage goes back to the days of secret formulas and herb decoctions. Employment of ergot gradually spread during the Middle Ages as more persons learned of it, but it was not until the early 1800's that the "secret" became public property and was published together with recommended procedures and amounts for general use by physicians and midwives. Human poisoning traceable to ingestion of ergot in cereal grains has been recorded over several centuries; in the last 100 years human poisoning has declined but animal poisoning has occasionally been severe.

A voluminous literature has accumulated over the years through investigations of the biology of the fungus, its active principles, their physiology and toxicity, and indications for the use of ergot in medicine. It is here intended to treat only the toxicology of the fungus as it has been obtained by human beings and animals under natural conditions (ie., not as a drug). Reviews such as the following may be consulted for additional details: general, Barger (65) and Youngken (1712); history of ergot, Salmon (1381), Brown and Ranck (177), and Latour (903); the biology of the fungus, Weniger (1369); the chemistry of the alkaloids, Stoll (1547); the physiology of the alkaloids, Reynolds (1336); the nature of the disease in human beings, Latour (903) and in animals, Guilhon (664).

DESCRIPTION AND HABITAT. Species of the genus *Claviceps* are ascomycetous fungi of complex life cycle which parasitize the grains of various cultivated and wild grasses. Of the several species found in the United States, *Claviceps purpurea,* parasitizing cultivated rye, wheat (especially durum), barley, and a number of wild grasses, and *C. paspali,* parasitizing Dallis grass (*Paspalum dilatatum* Poir.), Argentine bahia grass (*Paspalum notatum* Flugge), and some others, and *C. cinerea* parasitizing tobosagrass [*Hilaria mutica* (Bukl.) Benth.] and galletagrass [*Hilaria jamesii* (Torr.) Benth.] are known to have caused disease. A list of the grasses which may become infected with various species of *Claviceps* may be found in Barger (65). Human poisoning has resulted from ingestion of ergot in uncleaned cereal grains, especially rye, or products made from them. Stock loss has resulted from ingestion of ergotized grasses from pasture, in hay, or in ergotized grain or grain screenings. Species of wild grasses mentioned in various publications as becoming heavily ergotized and therefore dangerous under natural conditions include the following:

Agropyron spp.	wheat grasses, quack grass	741, 1659, 1692
Agrostis alba	redtop	726, 1381
Bromus inermis	smooth bromegrass	1659
Calamagrostis spp.	reed grasses, bluejoint grass	1659, 1683, 1692
Elymus spp.	wild rye	741, 1381, 1510, 1683, 1692
Phalaris arundinacea	reed canarygrass	1692
Poa spp.	bluegrasses	1510, 1692

In many cases of ergotism, little attention has been given to identification of the grass. The recognition of ergotized grains suffices to assure the diagnosis.

Claviceps parasitizes only the ovary of the developing grass flower. Infection takes place at the time the grass flower opens. At first the fungus filaments ramify throughout all or part of the grass ovarial tissue, obtaining nutrients from it, and prevent development of the seed. Asexual spores (conidia) are formed in chains at the tips of filaments which reach the surface of the host tissue, and are shed in a drop of sticky exudate, the "honey dew" secreted by the host. Infection of additional grass heads takes place by insect transfer of conidia. No toxic substances are produced by the fungus up to this point in its life cycle. Simultaneously with the production of conidia, the continuously developing mat of filaments in the host tissue begins to become compact, to harden, and eventually to transform into a hard, pink or purplish structure which gradually replaces the grass grain. This grain-shaped mass varies in size from the same as, to three or four times larger than, the grain it replaces, depending mainly upon the species of grass. Its surface is irregularly fissured and its mass homogeneous and white upon sectioning. It is designated the sclerotium or ergot proper and constitutes the poisonous stage in the life cycle. Shed with the grass head, it overwinters, producing a second, sexual type of spore (ascospore) in small, mushroomlike outgrowths appearing on its surface in spring. The ascospore effects initial infection of the grass crop of the second season. Sclerotia are easily observed when present in cultivated cereal grasses or Dallis grass. In some of the small-seeded wild grasses they may be so tiny as to be just visible to the naked eye.

Claviceps may heavily infect one or another wild grass species in any part of the United States. Losses from *C. purpurea* have occurred from the northeastern and eastern states to the Rocky Mountains and in California, and from *C. paspali* in many of the southern states and from *C. cinerea* in Texas. Ergot occasionally causes crop loss of economic significance in the spring grain areas of Nebraska, the Dakotas, and Montana by reducing the yield and quality of grain. Grain containing 1 per cent sclerotia is considered (1336) dangerous for human consumption. Federal law prohibits use of grain containing more than 0.3 per cent ergot sclerotia by weight (422).

Growing seasons with high humidity promote heavier infestations. Because of the usefulness of ergot alkaloids, limited amounts of sclerotia are produced commercially in Europe (1547) using mechanical methods for promoting infection and for harvest. Most ergot used in the United States is obtained from these sources.

POISONOUS PRINCIPLE. Ergot contains a number of active and inactive alkaloids, amines, and other nitrogen-containing compounds. The active alkaloids are ergocryptine, ergocornine, ergocristine, ergotamine, ergosine, and ergonovine (1336). Of these, ergonovine and ergotamine are therapeutically most useful. The older term "ergotoxine" found in the literature refers to an alkaloidal complex which has since been resolved (1547) into three alkaloids (the first three of the list above). Ergometrine and ergobasine are synonyms for ergonovine, the name adopted by the American Medical Association.

Ergot alkaloids contain lysergic acid in combination with various amine-

lysergic acid

bearing structures (1547). Ergonovine is simplest, with one amine-bearing group attached to the lysergic acid moiety. Alkaloids like ergotamine are polypeptides with the lysergic acid moiety bearing two amino acid groups.

Ergot sclerotia from different geographic areas may produce different reactions. It appears that the relative amounts of the alkaloids may vary considerably (392), certain alkaloids occasionally being absent altogether. Ergot sclerotia infected with *Fusarium* (an imperfect fungus) are not uncommon in the United States and are rejected by pharmaceutical companies (422) for unsatisfactory activity. The specific physiological effect of particular ergot alkaloids is known in part (e.g., 809).

TOXICITY, SYMPTOMS, AND LESIONS. In gangrenous ergotism the majority of symptoms and lesions result from the ability of the ergot alkaloids to cause direct stimulation of smooth muscle. Medically, particular ergot alkaloids are used to provoke uterine contractions in labor. In poisoning, contraction of arteriole musculature and smooth muscle of the gastrointestinal tract are important in producing the characteristic symptoms and lesions.

Ingestion of small amounts of ergot daily over a period of several weeks to a few months results in chronic poisoning characterized by necrosis of tissues of the extremities. Dry gangrene of extremities is the classical ergotism of human populations. Epidemics of ergotism reached proportions of historical significance in certain European countries prior to 1800 and the disease was among the most dreaded. Occasional isolated outbreaks still occur in countries where control of cereal grain purity is not fully effective (593).

In cattle, the most common subject of ergot poisoning in America, two syndromes are produced, the gangrenous and the neurotropic or convulsive. Relatively large total amounts of ergotized grain or hay are involved in each, although daily intake of ergot sclerotia may be very small in gangrenous ergotism. Considerable loss of life has been recorded—in the Northeast prior to 1880 and in the Midwest to about 1900. In 1884 there was an outbreak in the Midwest (p. 10) which caused great excitement among cattlemen and threatened to disrupt the entire cattle industry when it was mistaken for foot and mouth disease, and gave the just-established Bureau of Animal Industry an opportunity to prove its worth. Salmon's (1381) discussion of gangrenous ergotism in cattle prepared at that time is still useful.

Few experiments have been made to determine the exact amount of ergot sclerotia necessary to produce lesions in cattle or the time to production of symptoms. In one (392), 100 g sclerotia per day for 11 days produced gangrenous ergotism in a cow (about 0.02 per cent of the animal's weight per day; 0.22 per cent total). In another closely observed case (944) cattle showed nervousness and stamping of feet after one week on ergotized prairie grass hay. Individual animals display wide variation in reaction to ergot alkaloids obtained by ingestion.

Ergot alkaloids in small daily doses cause vasoconstriction and predispose to thromboses with occlusion of circulation in the extremities. Most cases involve one or both hind feet. Lameness is followed by coldness and insensitivity of the affected areas. A greater extent of the leg, the tip of the tail, the tips of the ears, and even of the tongue may become gangrenous in more severe cases. In a typical case, a distinct, contricted band encircles the affected limb at the juncture between gangrenous and healthy tissues. A crack forms in this area, the continuing constriction of which effects disjunction of gangrenous from healthy tissues with a clean, readily healing surface. A certain amount of swelling and redness may be associated with these processes. Occasionally, instead of dry gangrene, some serum seeps from the gangrenous tissues and considerable secondary infection occurs. Disjunction usually occurs at a joint in cattle, causing loss of one or more bones of one or both digits. In extreme cases, necrosis may occur at any point distal to the upper third of the metatarsal or metacarpal. In this case, naked bone is exposed upon sloughing of the dead tissues.

Symptoms associated with involvement of the smooth musculature of the digestive system usually precede or accompany the above. They include nausea or vomition, evidences of abdominal pain, and constipation or diarrhea. In some cases the oral mucous membranes are inflamed or display shallow superficial erosions from $\frac{1}{4}$ to 1 inch in diameter (1381). Pregnant animals may abort.

Symptoms and lesions in the human being are similar. In mild cases only the nails are lost. Extreme cases result in the loss of the hands or feet and occasionally in gangerene of internal organs. Gastrointestinal discomfort and headache usually precede and accompany any of these lesions. Symptoms and lesions have been reviewed in detail by Latour (903).

Fowl are poisoned by unclean grain. The comb and beak are most commonly the parts which become gangrenous.

Convulsive ergotism in cattle and human beings appears to result from the ingestion of larger amounts of ergot per day. In addition to symptoms of gastrointestinal distress as in gangrenous ergotism, nervous symptoms are observed. The convulsive syndrome has been produced in cattle after ingestion of *Claviceps purpurea* (425) but is rare from this source. It occurs occasionally also in animals feeding on tobosagrass parasitized with *Claviceps cinerea* (434) but is much more common in the United States in animals pastured on Dallis grass or Argentine bahia grass parasitized with *Claviceps paspali*. Poisoning of stock by this species of fungus, which is not known to have poisoned human beings, was first reported (842) in 1915. Symptoms appear within 48 hours (737, 788) to a week (sometimes two) after animals have access to a heavy infestation. A steer developed nervous symptoms after nine days on ergotized Dallis grass in one feeding experiment (1459) during which he consumed about 10 per cent of his weight of ergotized grass.

First sign of convulsive ergotism is hyperexcitability. Animals distrust persons approaching them. This may be accompanied by belligerency in some and is followed by a stage in which trembling and incoordination are prominent. Exaggerated flexure of the forelimbs may be observed when the animals are made to run. A sudden stimulus, such as clapping one's hands, often provokes a quiescent animal to drop. Excited animals often fall while trying to run away. Death sometimes occurs at this stage of poisoning when animals are drowned while attempting to drink. Heart and pulse rates are greatly accelerated when the animals are excited. The appetite remains excellent as long as the animals maintain sufficient co-ordination to graze. Ultimately, in severe poisoning, periods of kicking are interspersed with periods of tetanic rigidity and opisthotonus (305). Animals removed from dangerous vegetation in the early stages of intoxication will recover within a few days. Death results in about a month's time through thirst or starvation in the cases of average severity (177) or may occur otherwise within three days in severely affected animals. Deleterious effects of excitement in an animal handled for treatment usually outweigh any beneficial effects of the treatment. Care should be taken to avoid undue excitement in moving animals from ergotized vegetation.

Horses and sheep as well as cattle have displayed the typical convulsive syndrome (305, 1456), although Wilcox (1683) has recorded also a somewhat different syndrome in horses. The convulsive syndrome in the human being is less common than the gangrenous but was recognized occasionally in early European epidemics of *C. purpurea* poisoning (903) and also more recently (593). Tremors of the extremities are followed by painful spasmodic convulsions of the whole body, often accompanied by delerium.

Gross necropsy findings in both the gangrenous and convulsive syndromes, other than the obvious lesions of gangrene, are meager and not characteristic. Degenerative changes in the central nervous system of sheep have been described histologically (305) after convulsive ergotism. It was postulated that the central nervous system lesions may have resulted from increased pressure of the cerebrospinal fluid such as is associated with hypovitaminosis A. Low body levels of vitamin A have been reported more than once in cases of ergotism.

Ergot poisoning in animals other than cattle is rare in comparison. On the basis of scanty information, it appears that the effects of ergot alkaloids may vary considerably with the class of livestock. Heavy loss of newborn pigs has been reported (1184) in Montana following use of a diet which consisted of moderately (to 1.0 per cent) ergotized grains, mostly barley. Experimental feedings following the natural outbreak established that sows obtaining even small amounts of ergot during pregnancy suffered lack of development of mammary glands and were without milk at parturition. This effect could be reversed if ergot was removed from the diet a few weeks before farrowing. Of more fundamental significance, it appeared that small amounts of ergot in the diet at any time during pregnancy contributed to the development of progeny weak or dead at birth and to premature farrowing. Experimental feeding of crude ergot to rats (1369) corroborates these observations. Reduction of milk production has also been reported in cattle.

In experiments with sheep fed ergot sclerotia from perennial rye grass (*Lolium perenne* L.) in New Zealand (393), typical gangrene of the extremities did not occur even at levels of ergot ingestion which produced death. Necrosis of the tip of the tongue was observed in two animals, but ulceration of various portions of the digestive tract was the most characteristic lesion observed upon post mortem. Extent of lesions did not seem closely dependent either upon level of sclerotia intake (between 0.0046 and 0.0196 per cent of the animal's weight daily) or total intake (0.022 per cent produced death in two days in one instance, whereas 3.0 per cent fed over 238 days did not in another). Production of lesions appeared to be due to direct contact with the ergot sclerotia in the digestive tract; injection of sclerotial extracts produced symptoms primarily of nervous origin.

CONDITIONS OF POISONING. Sclerotia may be obtained from headed grasses by animals on pasture, or in hay. Sclerotia of *Claviceps purpurea* may be obtained by animals when fed in contaminated grain or grain screenings. Since the potentialities of ergot sclerotia in grain are widely appreciated and the sclerotia of cereal grains are easily recognized, cases of this sort are practically nonexistent. The majority of cases of gangrenous ergotism have resulted from wild grass pastures and wild grass hay, especially in the prairies. Poisoning attributed to ergotized red top and quack grass has been reported in Ontario (1075). Cases may be expected to occur more frequently following humid summers when the fungus produces its heaviest infestation and growth. Horses are less apt to be poisoned because of their more selective feeding habits (1510). Gangrenous ergotism is currently rare in the United States but occasionally still is responsible for severe outbreaks (525). *Claviceps paspali* on Dallis grass has not yet been reported definitely to cause the gangrenous syndrome.

Convulsive poisoning by *Claviceps paspali* is currently a problem in several southern states. It usually results from pasturing of animals on headed Dallis grass and occurs in late summer or early fall. Hay made from such grass is potentially toxic and has produced cases in horses in winter (1456), but most sclerotia are dislodged and drop out of the hay as it is handled before being fed. Cattle do not dislike the sclerotia and when let into a pasture of headed Dallis grass may eat only the grass heads at first, thus obtaining a concentrated amount of sclerotia. Control of either type of poisoning can be effected by practices which utilize the forage before it heads out, or by clipping the heads as they form. Attempts to breed a strain of rye (*Secale*) resistant to ergot infection have not been successful, but the Mississippi Experiment Station has been successful in attempts to produce a resistant variety of *Paspalum*.

It is worth emphasizing that undergrazing, a practice opposite to that usually resulting in poisoning of animals by plants, in this instance has the opposite effect. It allows pasture grasses to develop inflorescences and become potentially dangerous (842, 1456).

Additional references for ergot include 47, 170, 177, 837, 1238.

Lichens

Parmelia molliuscula Ach. Lichen, ground lichen.

DESCRIPTION. Plant composed of gray-green, crisp (dry) or leathery (moist), flattened (straplike) expanses of tissue irregularly dissected, twisted and tangled into open masses a few inches in diameter; these unattached to any substratum, accumulating into windrows or masses under the influence of wind and absence of obstructions.

DISTRIBUTION AND HABITAT. Surface of soil, Nebraska to North Dakota, west into the Rocky Mountains.

POISONOUS PRINCIPLE. Usnic acid is present in this species. In feeding experiments (90, 801) typical symptoms were produced in laboratory animals fed an emulsion of usnic acid extracted from the lichen. The residue of lichen remaining after extraction was not toxic.

usnic acid

TOXICITY, SYMPTOMS, AND LESIONS. Feeding experiments with cattle and sheep have been performed by the United States Department of Agriculture at the Salina (Utah) experiment station (801), and by the Wyoming Agricultural Experiment Station (90, 97). These were prompted by cases observed on the range. It was found that *Parmelia* in the amount of 1 per cent of an animal's weight per day for five days is lethal. A single dose of 3.6 per cent of an animal's weight also is lethal. This is an amount larger than likely to be consumed at one time under natural conditions. Symptoms produced in feeding experiments were equivalent in all ways to those observed in range livestock.

Sheep and cattle are affected on range. Usually natural cases are mild. Symptoms in mild cases consist of ataxia, particularly in the hind legs. In severe cases posterior paralysis is followed by total paralysis of the extremities and the animal is unable to rise. Except in the most severe cases where depression is noted, the animal remains alert and the appetite is normal. Inability to obtain feed is, of course, a concomitant of paralysis.

No characteristic lesions have been found on post mortem examinations (97).

CONDITIONS OF POISONING. The lichen remains toxic throughout the year. Most cases of poisoning occur in the winter when other forage is scarce.

Other genera and species of lichen are utilized as livestock, wild-animal, and human emergency foodstuffs in the north. Several of these require cooking in water to remove mildly toxic principles before being suitable for human consumption (746).

Mushrooms

Compared with the total number of species of mushrooms, the poisonous ones are few. Nevertheless, the deadliness of some of the toxic ones has been recognized from very early times and has generated a large body of literature in many languages. The first report of mushroom poisoning in the United States appeared in 1871 (562). Much of the information that has been accumulated concerning mushroom toxicity is inaccurate and many mushrooms are undeservedly considered poisonous. Certain species with the general reputation in one country of being poisonous are among the prized edible species in another (1326). Reasons for inaccuracies are many. First, species determination is often difficult, and since poisonous and prized species frequently exist in the same genus there is ample opportunity for confusion to arise among them. Secondly, some evidence suggests that toxicity varies with ecological conditions under which the mushrooms have grown and with geographical location. Thirdly, in many cases, mushrooms which are poisonous raw are rendered nonpoisonous by cooking or drying. On the other hand nontoxic mushrooms, as with any food, may become unwholesome after cooking or storage, or may be harvested when old and partially decayed. Finally, it has been observed repeatedly that some persons can eat with impunity mushrooms which provoke poisoning in others (1479). Insight into the development of a body of knowledge concerning poisonous mushrooms may be gained from historical reviews such as those of Ford (562) and Ramsbottom (1319, 1320). The world literature has also been reviewed by Grossman and Malbin (662).

There exist a large number of popular "rules" for distinguishing between poisonous and harmless mushrooms. The persistence of these rules despite repeated authoritative public warnings against using them is surprising. No single rule, characteristic, or procedure exists (other than absolute identification of the mushroom in question) which allows a poisonous species to be distinguished from one that is not. One such "rule" states that if the skin can be peeled from the cap of a mushroom, it is nonpoisonous. The skin may easily be peeled from the cap of *Amanita muscaria,* one of the commonest poisonous mushrooms in the United States. Even more frequently encountered is the statement that a silver spoon or coin added to the pan in which mushrooms are cooked will darken if poisonous species are present. This is not so. *Amanita phalloides,* the most dangerous species in the United States, will not cause silver to darken, nor, is it believed, will any *fresh* mushroom. The application of this "rule" has resulted in human deaths in this hemisphere. It is common for certain fungi to be recognized in some areas as "mushrooms" and considered edible while others are termed "toadstools" and believed poisonous. In other places the terms are used synonymously without regard for supposed toxicity. The first usage has some basis in the fact that "toadstool" is a corruption of the German "Todesstuhl" meaning "death's stool."

Mushrooms are difficult to identify. Even the specialists are not in complete agreement. Unfortunately, one area of disagreement is the genus *Amanita,* which probably accounts for nine-tenths or more of all cases of lethal mushroom poisoning. More so than in other groups of plants, color differences are particularly useful in distinguishing species. Excellent color plates showing the characteristics of the poisonous mushrooms most likely to be encountered have been published by Pilat and Usak (1277), Ramsbottom (1319), Krieger (888), Murrill (1154), Wakefield (1634), and others. Volume two of A. H. Smith's treatise on mushrooms (1479) contains colored photographic transparencies and a viewer giving three-dimensional reproductions of 231 mushrooms in their natural habitats. Particular attention was given to depicting poisonous species in that work.

In cases of poisoning it is most important to obtain as quickly as possible a competent species determination. Prominently encountered in many cases is fear of death. It is desirable to reassure patients that although symptoms may appear grave, prognosis is good (except for *Amanita phalloides* and its close relatives).

The nature of toxic principles in mushrooms has been the object of much investigation since the latter half of the nineteenth century, but their exact chemistry has not lent itself to easy determination. Most of the work has been concerned with the toxic substances in the genus *Amanita,* although once particular substances have been characterized from that genus they have often been sought and found in other mushrooms. The toxic amanitas contain two different groups of poisonous compounds and produce two different syndromes.

In *Amanita phalloides* and its relatives, early German analyses were superceded by those of Ford and coworkers reported in a series of papers commencing in 1906 and reviewed by Ford in 1923 (562). They found a hemolytic substance in *Amanita phalloides* which they named amanitahemolysin. They were able to characterize it with a more or less accurate empirical formula but also showed that it was heat labile, was destroyed in digestion, and was not responsible for the major symptoms found in poisoning from *Amanita phalloides.* A second toxic fraction was isolated which proved capable of provoking symptoms and lesions in animals similar to those of *Amanita phalloides* poisoning in man. This they named amanitatoxin. Beginning in 1940 renewed efforts to determine the exact chemistry of these fractions were undertaken by the Wielands and coworkers in Germany. Their papers are cited and reviewed by Ramsbottom (1320). They crystallized three substances from amanita-toxin, which they named alpha and beta amanitine and phalloidine. Amanitine ($C_{30}H_{45(-47)}O_{12}N_7S$) constitutes more than half the total, is slow-acting, is responsible for the major symptoms, and produces hypoglycemia. It is a polypeptide containing an indole ring. Phalloidine ($C_{30}H_{39}O_9N_7S$) also is a polypeptide. It is more rapid in action, and produces degenerative changes in kidney, liver, and cardiac musculature. A clinical test for these substances has been described by Block *et al.* (136). It has been known for some years that animals may be immunized with increasing amounts of the toxic principle from *Amanita phalloides*. Advantage has been taken of this fact by the Institut Pasteur which has maintained a stock of antiphalloidian serum. Serum is effective if given when or shortly after symptoms of poisoning appear.

Choline and a similar molecule, muscarine, are found in *Amanita muscaria* (10, 1320). The physiological activity of these compounds is well known and is not equivalent to poisoning by the fungus. An alkaloid muscaridine, not yet structurally characterized, is also present and there may be additional physiologically active principles. The effects of muscarine are countered by atropine, and in earlier days administration of this drug was widely recommended in cases of poisoning. According to Ramsbottom (1319) and Ainsworth (10), treatment with atropine is contra-indicated unless the mushroom contains amounts of muscarine large enough to produce symptoms overshadowing those of other active principles, muscaridine especially. This may be true of American specimens of *Amanita muscaria* (10), but is not true of the English ones. Muscarine has been isolated from a number of other genera and species of fungi, but usually with little evidence to show that it is responsible for the syndrome produced in any case.

In the United States, mushrooms have produced numerous cases of loss of life in the human being, and several cases of livestock loss have been recorded. Mushroom poisoning in man in this country has been reviewed by Ford (562) and Fischer (534) and a record of deaths since 1924 is maintained by Buck (189). While many mushrooms may produce serious nervous symptoms or symptoms of gastroenteritis, *Amanita phalloides* and its close relatives account for almost all fatal cases of mushroom poisoning.

Various persons from time to time have attempted classifications of types of poisoning produced by ingestion of mushrooms. Ford (562), whose classification is frequently followed, divided poisonings into five distinct types. Some recent treatments (10, 1326) use three:

I. Fungi causing enteritis: *Entoloma lividum, Russula spp., Lactarius spp., Boletus santanus,* and others.
II. Fungi causing cell destruction: *Amanita phalloides* and close relatives, *Lepiota helveola, Gyromitra esculenta* (blood destruction), and others.

Amanita muscaria. Fly mushroom. Top: young stages; below: fully opened mushrooms. Use of this illustration has been made possible by the Merck Sharp & Dohme Research Laboratories.

III. Fungi with major effect on the nervous system: *Amanita muscaria, A. pantherina, Clitocybe spp., Inocybe spp.,* and others.

Amanita muscaria is used in certain areas of the world as an intoxicant or hallucinogenic material. Similar use has been made of several other species of mushrooms which are physiologically active but not toxic as used and therefore not treated here. Examples of this kind of activity may be found in the papers of Stein and others (1517, 1518, 1519). Fungi identified by the common name "mushroom" are mostly members of the Class Basidiomyceteae (basidiomycetes); a few belong in the Class Ascomyceteae (ascomycetes). The following are all basidiomycetes except *Gyromitra esculenta,* which is an ascomycete.

Mushroom poisoning in the human being

Amanita

According to Smith (1479) there are probably between 25 and 35 species of *Amanita* to be found in the United States, the exact number depending upon the particular author's interpretation of species. No good monograph of the genus has appeared. In this context it is difficult unequivocally to delineate the poisonous and edible species. No *Amanita* should be ingested unless the collector is *certain* of the species and that it is well known to be edible. The nontoxic species most commonly eaten are *Amanita caesarea* (Scop.) Pers., Caesar's mushroom, and *A. rubescens* Pers., the blusher.

Amanita phalloides (Bull.) Fr. Destroying angel, death cup, deadly amanita, white amanita

In some taxonomic works on the fungi (889, 1479), it is held that this species does not occur in North America. In others (521, 523) it is said to be common or even exceedingly abundant. This apparent contradiction arises from the fact that the species was originally described in Europe where it commonly has an olive or greenish color. This color form is not known to occur in the United States. Instead a number of other color forms from white to brownish are found, some of which are also known in Europe. Many mycologists consider that the different color forms are distinct species, separate from *A. phalloides.* On the other hand, they appear in general to have the toxic characteristics of *A. phalloides.* It is convenient here to treat them all as a single toxic entity under that name, recognizing however, that not enough evidence is at hand to demonstrate beyond doubt that all have absolutely equivalent toxic characteristics. This group includes those recognized by some as *A. verna,* (Bull.) Quel., *A. virosa* (Fr.) Quel., *A. bisporiger* Atk., and others.

DESCRIPTION. A fungus of the type recognized in the common terms, mushroom or toadstool, with stem and cap, the latter bearing gills on its under surface. Cap 2 to 5 in. broad, conical when young, usually flattopped or even slightly turned up at the edges when fully expanded; usually smooth and dry, but occasionally with a few thin scales of tissue adherent to the upper surface, surface color from white to greenish, yellowish, yellowish-brown to blackish-brown, sometimes slightly viscid when young or moist; gills *white* [they are distinctly brown or purple-brown in the *mature* edible field mushroom (*Psalliota campestris*)]. Stem white, 3 to 8 in. long, uniform in diameter or slightly tapering upward; *base distinctly bulbous* (base may be well buried in the ground—care should be taken that the entire mushroom is at hand before judging this characteristic); filled with a cottony material when young, hollow at maturity; upper extremity of the bulbous base characteristically prolonged upward in a free edge or membrane (volva) encircling the stem ("death's cup"); stem bearing a downward-hanging, membranous ring of tissue (annulus) a short distance beneath the cap. The relationship of the various parts of the developing mushroom is represented in the accompanying figure. Neither taste nor smell is obnoxious. (This description is general and covers the forms recognized as *A. verna*, *A. bisporiger*, and *A. virosa*.)

DISTRIBUTION AND HABITAT. The form recognized as *A. verna* is the most common. It is relatively smaller than the others and chalky white. It is frequently encountered throughout the United States and Canada with the exception, apparently, of the Pacific states and provinces. Amanitas of the phalloides group occur solitarily or in groups mostly in open woods, appearing from June to September. They are rarely found in lawns or meadow pastures.

POISONOUS PRINCIPLE. See above.

TOXICITY, SYMPTOMS, AND LESIONS. One or two mushrooms, cooked, have frequently caused human deaths. On record (425) is the case of a child killed by ingestion of one-third of a single cap. Many cases occur when one or two specimens are mixed in with others during collecting of edible mushrooms. The raw mushroom is probably more toxic than when cooked.

Symptoms are characteristic and well known. They have been repeatedly described in the medical literature (317, 425, 1610). The review by Fischer (534) may be consulted for several typical case histories. After eating a toxic or lethal amount of mushroom, the subject shows no symptoms for a period of 6 to 15, commonly about 10, hours (rarely to 40 hours). Symptoms appear in the form of a sud-

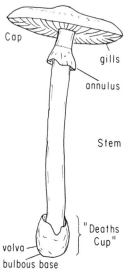

Fig. 1. Terminology of mushroom structure.

den, severe seizure of extreme abdominal pain, vomiting, and diarrhea. Blood, mucus, and undigested food appear in the vomitus and stools. Excessive thirst develops but is usually accompanied with anuria. Hemoglobinuria is absent. Paroxysms of pain and vomiting accompanied with cries or screams of pain alternate with periods of remission. Loss of strength occurs rapidly and is severe, resulting in prostration accompanied by pain-caused restlessness. Death may follow within 48 hours after ingestion of a large amount of fungus, but more typically the disease lasts 6 to 8 days in adults or 4 to 6 in children. After 2 or 3 days, jaundice, cyanosis, and marked coldness of the skin appear. Frequently there are lengthened periods of remission during which the prognosis appears good and the patient may attempt too much, followed by a further acute attack resulting in death. Death is commonly preceded by a period of coma and may or may not be accompanied terminally by convulsions. Frequently these symptoms are accompanied by others including abnormal pupillary reactions, and muscular cramps which may often have been caused by ingestion of additional toxic fungi mixed with the specimens of *Amanita phalloides* or its relatives. Mortality has variously been quoted from 50 per cent to 90 per cent. If recovery occurs, it requires about a month and is accompanied by liver enlargement.

Lesions include fatty degeneration and necrosis in liver and kidney. Cell destruction also occurs in other organs including endothelial cells of blood vessels, muscle cells, and cells of the central nervous system. Hemorrhagic enteritis is common, and hemorrhages may be found in other organs. The pathological picture in many respects resembles phosphorus poisoning.

Amanita muscaria (L.) Fr. Fly mushroom, fly agaric

DESCRIPTION. As *A. phalloides* except larger (cap 3 to 8 in. broad), bright yellow to orange red (sometimes pale brownish to almost white in deeply shaded locations), surface usually rough with white or yellowish wartlike scales (which may occasionally be rare or almost absent); gills and stem white to pale yellow; stem 4 to 8 in. long, ½ to 1 in. thick, regular above the base; base bulbous, its upper surface covered with one or more concentric rings of irregular tissue or scales (the remains of the volva which does not part freely from the stem in this species, therefore no "death's cup" is formed); annulus present or lost in older specimens. It is said (534) the taste is bitter and unpleasant.

DISTRIBUTION AND HABITAT. Throughout the United States in wooded areas, especially conifer forests, and occasionally in pastures especially where brushy. Common throughout the summer months with two periods of greatest abundance, spring or early summer and again after the end of dry summer conditions. In many places more common than the common edible mushroom (*Psalliota*). Found singly or in groups; sometimes in more or less regular circles (so-called "fairy-rings"). Yellow and orange forms predominate in northern and eastern parts of the country, red on the Pacific coast.

POISONOUS PRINCIPLE. See above.

TOXICITY, SYMPTOMS, AND LESIONS. Symptoms come on rapidly, are characteristic if other poisonous species have not been ingested at the same time, severe, yet rarely fatal. Within ½ to 3 hours, sometimes longer if the dose was small, the patient experiences increased secretions of salivary and lacrymal glands and others, perspiration, and severe gastrointestinal disturbances [latter sometimes absent (236)]. Copious watery diarrhea is almost universally present, usually accompanied by retching and vomiting. Breathing may be labored. Pupils rarely respond to light. Signs of auditory or visual hallucination (this species is prized for its hallucinogenic capacities on the Kamchatka Peninsula of Eastern Russia) or confusion accompany or supercede the digestive upset. In the rare lethal case, delerium is followed by convulsions, a comatose period, and death through respiratory failure. Usually, however, recovery follows within several hours in light cases which exhibit only gastric or mildly hallucinogenic signs. In somewhat more severe cases these may be followed by a period of several hours during which the patient experiences profound sleep from which he awakens without symptoms and often without memory of his ordeal. The severity of symptoms often depends upon the promptness with which vomiting relieves the patient of the offending material.

Only rarely have fatal cases been available for autopsy. Ford (562) reports significant lesions essentially absent.

Amanita pantherina (DC.) Fr. Panther mushroom, panther amanita.

DESCRIPTION. As *A. phalloides,* except: plant small and relatively squat, cap to 4 in. diameter, stem to 5 in. tall. Cap surface yellow, yellowish brown, or purplish brown; covered with persistent, regularly spaced and sized whitish warts or flecks of adherent tissue. Stem base bulbous, prolonged upward in one or two encircling, yet not greatly developed, lips (volva). Annulus prominent, frequently borne relatively low on the stem (to halfway down).

DISTRIBUTION AND HABITAT. Rare in the United States, but locally common west of the Cascade Mountains in Oregon and Washington. It is characteristically found in conifer woods and appears in spring and fall.

POISONOUS PRINCIPLE. Muscarine has been isolated. From the similarity of poisoning by this species with that by *A. muscaria,* it is generally assumed that *A. pantherina* contains additional poisonous principles similar to those in *A. muscaria* (see above).

TOXICITY, SYMPTOMS, AND LESIONS. While the death rate of poisoning from *A. muscaria* is very low in Europe, that from *A. pantherina* is significantly higher (10). Cases of poisoning in the United States have been reported occasionally since 1929 (189). Eight cases with one death occurring at Seattle, Washington in 1934 were described by Hotson (790, 791). In symptoms and other characteristics they agreed well with typical *Amanita muscaria* poisoning.

Other Poisonous Higher Fungi

Many additional species of higher fungi have bad reputations. For example, Ford (562) lists 80 species in 24 genera from the world literature as poisonous. Active principles have been isolated from a number of species where no cases of poisoning have been reported. It is likely that if all species of higher fungi were tested for toxicity the lists of poisonous fungi would be considerably longer. The wise person, therefore, not only avoids all species known to be poisonous, but also avoids species which are not known to be edible.

Below are listed species for which reports of accidental poisoning or other records indicate toxicity in the United States.

A number of species of *Amanita* other than those named above have reputations for toxicity. Some of these bad reputations may have been earned through confusion of nonpoisonous with poisonous species or through confusion arising from variation in taxonomic treatment. *Amanita pantherinoides* and *A. cothurnata* especially require comment. *Amanita pantherinoides,* named by Murrill and considered by him toxic (887), is considered synonymous with *A. pantherina* by others (791, 1479). *Amanita cothurnata* Atk. was observed by Murrill (1153) to kill flies that sucked at it, but in America this species is considered synonymous with *A. pantherina* by Ford (562). Alcoholic extracts of *Amanita verniformis* Murr. and *A. virosiformis* Murr. have been shown (321) toxic on injection into guinea pigs, producing some of the characteristics of *A. phalloides* poisoning.

Amanitopsis volvata (Pk.) Sacc. is stated by Krieger (889) to be fatal to rabbits and guinea pigs.

In the genus *Boletus,* several species are suspect. Plants of this genus look at first glance like mushrooms but bear pores rather than gills on the undersurface of the cap. *Boletus miniato-olivaceus* Frost var. *sensibilis* Pk. is recorded (246) as having produced poisoning in a group of five people. Within two hours after ingestion, vomition followed by purging was experienced. In the more severe cases there was some disturbance of vision. The flesh of this species (and of some others) turns blue immediately upon being handled.

Clathrus columnatus Bosc., the "lattice fungus," is a gasteromycete, or a gill-less form related to the common puffball. As it develops it bursts through its original skin, the expanded mass forming a basketlike net of coarse strands surrounding a large empty central area. This fungus has a marked disagreeable odor, but has been known (522) to produce convulsions and narcosis lasting many hours in a child who sampled it. It was also reported poisonous to hogs in North Carolina, producing death in 12 to 15 hours after being greedily sought out and eaten.

Clytocybe illudens (Schw.) Sacc. is common in the eastern United States characteristically growing from hardwood stumps. It is colored brilliantly orange-yellow, usually occurs in dense clumps in which the cap of one specimen spreads out over that of another, and has gills which are decurrent for a short distance down the stem. The gills are luminescent and are distinctly visible when the fungus is taken into a dark room. This species and two others, *C. sudorifica* Pk. and *C. morbifera* Pk., have produced known cases of poisoning, the former causing many cases each year (287, 523, 534, 851, 1256). Mild cases of *C. illudens* poisoning are characterized solely by vomition beginning within 2 hours and lasting for several hours. Poisoning by the other species also may be characterized by vomition, but this is accompanied by perspiration, salivation, more or less discomfort and purging. In reported cases no fatalities have occurred. Muscarine was identified in *C. illudens,* and the effects of extracts in frogs and turtles were studied by Clark and Smith (287).

Poisoning by *C. sudorifica* and *C. morbifera* has been reviewed by Jelliffe (831). The former usually produces, after a latent period of variable extent, excessive perspiration over the entire body unaccompanied by other symptoms or accompanied only by visual disturbance.

Coprinus atramentarius Fr., one of the common inky caps, has long been known in Europe (1320) to produce in certain individuals a peculiar reaction when followed by ingestion of alcohol. The face and often other parts of the body become purplish-red a short time after beer, wine, or other alcoholic beverage is taken following ingestion of the mushroom. The effect does not persist but may return with the next meal if an alcoholic beverage is again consumed. In producing a deleterious reaction with alcohol this plant is similar to the drug antabuse (tetraethylthiuram disulfide) used in treating alcoholism. Fischer (534) records symptoms of intoxication following ingestion of *Coprinus comatus* Fr., the shaggy mane, [but see (887)] generally considered one of the better edible species, and of cardiovascular disturbances from ingestion of *C. atramentarius,* in some cases at least, unaccompanied with alcoholic beverages.

Several species of the genus *Entoloma* are known poisonous in Europe. Two especially, *E. sinuatum* (Bull.) Quel. and *E. lividum* (Bull.) Sacc., have been the subjects of repeated reports (534). Rautavaara, in his attempt to remove unfounded and unsubstantiated names from the lists of poisonous fungi (1326), nevertheless retains *E. lividum* among "unconditionally poisonous." All entolomas bear pinkish gills and pink spores. There are few desirable edible mushrooms among those with pink spores so a safe rule in collecting is to discard any showing this characteristic. No cases of poisoning appear to have been reported in the United States.

Galerina venenata A. H. Smith was discovered and named (1480) as the result of a case of severe poisoning in two individuals in Portland, Oregon. It is a small, cinnamon-brown mushroom, not more than 1½ in. tall. The cap is almost flat at maturity, and less than 1½ in. in diameter. This species was found growing gregariously in a lawn in Portland, Oregon. The clinical report (662) of poisoning by this mushroom is one of the most detailed available. In both of two cases, symptoms did not appear until ten hours after ingestion. One case was light. It was produced by ingestion of a cupful of mushrooms, some of which was later eliminated by vomition. In this case the principal symptom was vomition lasting until the seventh day despite hospitalization.

The other case was much more severe. One and one-half cupfuls of mushroom were consumed and none was brought up in the vomitus. First symptoms were nausea, vomition, and diarrhea. Remission after partial recovery occurred in the hospital on the fourth day. The ileus became completely paralysed (not previously reported in mushroom poisoning) and the patient's condition began to deteriorate, despite continuous symptomatic treatment. Convulsions, coma, icterus, pulmonary edema, and other serious symptoms were displayed until the patient became moribund on the fifteenth day of hospitalization. Nevertheless the crisis was survived and the patient began slow recovery, during which he was disoriented with delusions and hallucinations for a period of several days. He was finally released on the forty-sixth day of hospitalization but required several additional weeks for complete recovery. Tests made during the period of illness showed severe gastrointestinal, genitourinary, hepatic, cardiovascular, and central nervous system injury.

The delay before appearance of symptoms in these cases is similar to that previously considered unique for *Amanita phalloides* poisoning.

Gyromitra esculenta Fr. (= *Helvella esculenta* Fr.) is a fleshy ascomycetous fungus closely related to, and in appearance much like, the highly prized morel (*Morchella esculenta* Fr.). The false morel or lorchel, as it is commonly called, bears a brownish or orange irregularly convoluted fleshy mass on a thick, somewhat fluted stem. The head, 1½ to 3½ in. in diameter, when loosely lobed looks somewhat like a piece of popcorn in general outline. In more tightly covoluted forms it resembles a brain. From its species name one would judge this fungus to be edible, and in fact it is so considered by many persons. It is extremely difficult to pin down the toxic characteristics of this species for it appears to be toxic in some places (as Germany) and not others (as France), safe when cooked (1320) or not so (415, 751), harmless to some even when raw while toxic to others, (751), and toxic to some on second ingestion when it was nontoxic on the first (414, 1320). Smith (1479) recommends it as a desirable edible fungus if caution is taken during the first experience with it. It is found in various parts of the United States and has caused a number of reported cases including fatalities (341, 415, 534, 751). A compound, highly soluble in water, named helvellic acid was isolated from this fungus in Germany before the turn of the present century. It was shown to be hemolytic, and to be destroyed by heating or drying. Since some cases have occurred with cooked material, it has more recently been assumed that a second toxic principle is present, lethal in itself if taken in sufficient quantity (10). In many cases symptoms characteristic of a hemolytic poisonous principle have been found. These were accompanied on post mortem examination by degenerative changes in liver and kidney. In other cases symptoms appear to be confined to vomition, diarrhea, and weakness (534, 751). Symptoms do not appear until 6 to 8 hours after ingestion of the fungus, and if the poisoning is severe may terminate fatally after a comatose period of varying duration.

At least one species of *Inocybe* has proven lethal in Europe (1320). In the United States there is a well-recorded case of poisoning near New York City in the family of a person who was both a physician and a mycologist (1152). The fungus involved was identified as *Inocybe infida* (Pk.) Earle. This species and *I. infelix* Pk., which has also been considered potentially poisonous (534, 889), are small whitish or slightly brownish mushrooms with no particularly distinctive characteristics. Fortunately they would usually be overlooked by the average collector because of their small size. The caps rarely reach an inch in diameter. Symptoms are similar to those of poisoning by *Amanita muscaria* and it has been generally assumed that the poisonous principle is similar. Some toxicological experiments with extracts have not borne this out (286).

The genus *Lepiota* contains several species—for example *L. procera,* the parasol mushroom—that are among the prized edible mushrooms. *Lepiota morgani* Pk., on the other hand, has caused considerable poisoning and some loss of life (276, 1654) in the United States. Several cases in the literature have been reviewed by Fischer (534). *Lepiota morgani* is among the largest mushrooms known. The cap when fully expanded is from 5 to 10 in. across. This species can be distinguished from all others when mature if the color of the spores is observed. Spores when first mature are bright green but later fade to dull green and finally to brownish-black. Cooked or raw it produces, sometimes after ingestion of as little as a cubic inch or less, symptoms of vomition followed by diarrhea. Symptoms appear in as little as an hour or less, and are accompanied by intense abdominal pain. Some persons seem to be immune to this species. Toxicity has also been ascribed to *L. naucinoides* Pk. by Dearness (414). This species is generally considered edible. Krieger suggests (889) that the statement of

L. naucinoides toxicity comes from misidentification. He claims it very similar to *L. schulzeri* (Kalchb.) Sacc. which he once collected for *L. naucinoides* and found to produce vomition from personal experience.

Four species of *Panaeolus* have been mentioned in the American literature as poisonous. These mushrooms are small, inconspicuous, of various habitats including lawns and beds of cultivated mushrooms, and in general appearance very much like the common inky-caps. They have black spores (like *Coprinus* and the cultivated mushroom). Cases have been described for *P. semiglobatus* (425), *P. papilionaceus* Fr. (562, 1622), and *P. venenosus* Murr. (1155) [= *P. papilionaceus* (562); = *P. subbalteatus* (Berk et Br.) Sacc. (1466)]. *Panaeolus camplanatus* (Fr.) Quel. was considered by Krieger (887) to be the true culprit in a case of poisoning ascribed to *Coprinus comatus*. Symptoms appear almost immediately in many instances. They are entirely nervous and consist of ataxia, disturbances of vision and other senses, hallucinations, some loss of volition, and exhilaration or depression. The event or parts of it may not be retained in the memory. Many of these effects are subjectively well described in the account by Verrill (1622). See also the account by Stein (1519) of the effects of a Mexican species. The effects wear off after several hours and the subject is then perfectly normal.

Pholiota autumnalis Pk., a small brownish mushroom of decaying wood, is the subject of a report by Peck (1257) of the death of two children. Cases have also been reported from Minnesota (534) and Michigan (562). It is one of the few brown-spored mushrooms which are poisonous, and because of its size and rather unacceptable texture is not likely to be collected for consumption.

Human fatalities have been reported (189) without details in northwestern United States from ingestion of a species of *Psilocybe*. This genus is composed of small, relatively inconspicuous mushrooms of difficult positive identification.

Scleroderma is related to the common edible puffballs, with subspherical fruiting structure, up to 6 in. in diameter. It differs from edible genera in possessing purple-colored flesh. *Scleroderma* is considered edible by some authors, but clearcut cases of poisoning are on record (1525). *Scleroderma aurantiacum* Pers., cooked, produced serious illness, while a "small bite" of *S. cepa* Pers. (raw) rendered the subject violently ill within 30 minutes. Symptoms included abdominal pain, nausea, weakness, parasthesias, sweating, and marked tetany. Vomition relieved the symptoms.

Fischer (534) describes a case in which symptoms of violent vomition developed in several persons an hour after ingestion of a mushroom which Atkinson considered and described as a new species, *Tricholoma venenatum* Atk. This fungus has not been taxonomically confirmed in later works.

Mushroom Poisoning in Animals

Only a few reports of mushroom poisoning in animals are found in the veterinary literature. In some cases no attempt to identify the mushroom was reported and in others identification was only approximate. In all cases where identification appears to have been reliably established the mushroom involved was a species of *Amanita*. Cattle were principally concerned; one case in the dog (1026) and two tentative cases in cats (1147) have been reported. In the cases of cattle poisoning, occurring in Louisiana (219, 1272), Georgia (212), and Michigan (28), it appears that animals were driven to consuming mushrooms by an abundance of them and a lack of any other feed. There is some evidence that after being thus accustomed to mushrooms cattle will seek them out (1272). In no case was it possible to determine either the amount consumed nor the time of appearance of symptoms.

Symptoms and lesions as reported are not in basic disagreement with symptoms and lesions known in human beings. *Amanita verna* (1272) produced severe gastric irritation, including ulceration and necrosis of the rectal mucosa, anus, vulval labia, together with rectal prolapse in some cases. Feces appeared normal in most instances but became matted about the base of the tail through failure of the poisoned animals to raise the latter in defecation, probably because of intense pain. Appetite likewise remained normal. In fatal cases convulsions preceded death. Necropsy disclosed petechial hemorrhages in liver and heart musculature and evidence of severe gastroenteritis.

Poisoning in cattle, apparently from ingestion of *Amanita muscaria* (212), caused excessive salivation, labored and rapid respiration, and bloody feces. In the dog (1026), symptoms included salivation, diarrhea, slow pulse, and protracted coma. Again the mushroom involved was most likely *A. muscaria*.

Additional references to mushroom toxicity include 286, 289, 637.

FERNS

DIVISION PTERIDOPHYTA—Spore-bearing plants
Class Pteropsida
Order Filicales—Ferns

Polypodiaceae

Dryopteris felix-mas (L.) Schott (= *Aspidium felix-mas*). Male fern
This handsome, widely distributed fern has been used as the source of a vermifuge. It is listed in some poisonous plants publications (507), but has not been the subject of an experimental demonstration of toxicity under natural conditions, nor of cases of stock loss. However, recently it has been shown (733) to contain thiaminase. See discussion under *Pteridium* and *Equisetum*.

Notholaena sinuata (Lag.) Kaulf. var. *cochisensis* (Goodding) Weath. Jimmy fern, cloak fern
DESCRIPTION. Evergreen, perennial, erect fern. Leaves (fronds) erect, about a foot in length, simple, once pinnately compound, narrow, arising in a clump from a short, woody rhizome; pinnae almost as wide as long, margins with 2 to 3 pairs of lobes, gray-green above, covered with brownish scales beneath. Sporangia on the back and margins of the photosynthetic pinnae. The plant folds in on itself when dry, reopening with rain.
DISTRIBUTION AND HABITAT. Dry, rocky hills and crevices, especially on limestone soils at elevations above 2000 ft. western Texas, Arizona, New Mexico, and Mexico.
POISONOUS PRINCIPLE. Unknown, excreted in the milk.
TOXICITY, SYMPTOMS, AND LESIONS. Knowledge of the poisonous properties of jimmy fern is based on the investigations of Mathews (1052, 1056) in Texas. The disease, which had been recognized for many years by

101

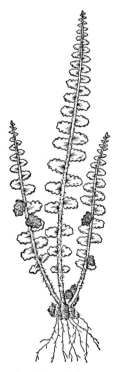

Fig. 2. *Notholaena sinuata* var. *crispa.* Habit of plant. Courtesy of The Macmillan Company.

ranchers, affects cattle, sheep, and goats on the range, but is of economic significance primarily as it affects sheep. The nervous syndrome produced by this fern is popularly termed "jimmies." Affected animals appear well and prosperous until exercised, either by being trailed or rounded up or in returning to water. Affected animals lag behind, usually displaying increasing incoordination of front and hind legs, and finally come to a stop with arched back. They then tremble violently, exhibit markedly increased respiration and heartbeat, and may become prostrated. If left alone, most recover after resting 15 to 30 minutes, regain their feet, and attempt to rejoin the band. Additional exercise usually brings on a second attack. Fatal attacks are not uncommon in severely poisoned animals or in those forced to continue moving while exhibiting symptoms. Characteristically, a fatally poisoned animal in its last attack takes three or four stilted steps, drops, gasps a few breaths, and dies almost immediately of respiratory paralysis. Attempts at artificial respiration under these circumstances have not been successful even though the heartbeat continues for a time.

Experimental feedings of jimmy fern to sheep duplicated the syndrome as found on the range. It was found that between 0.5 and 1.5 per cent of an animal's weight of the fern, green-weight basis, was necessary to provoke the nervous symptoms. Animals were walked for an hour each day to detect symptoms. In general, the typical syndrome developed 2 to 3 days after administration of the fern.

Although Mathews performed extensive histopathological examinations on animals killed by jimmy fern, he was unable to find any significant lesions. He found that the poisonous principle was stable to drying and that fern stored for several months remained toxic. On the range there was a tendency for pregnant ewes to show evidence of poisoning prior to other animals in the same flock. Both on the range and in experiments it could be determined that the poisonous principle was excreted in the milk, since occasionally typical symptoms appeared in suckling lambs before they were evident in the dam.

CONDITIONS OF POISONING. There are several species of *Notholaena* and several varieties of the species *sinuata*. Mathews observed that, on the range, toxicity seemed to be associated only with variety *cochisensis* even though in some areas there were more plants of the form recognized as the typical variety (var. *sinuata*) of the species. The typical variety was found in greater abundance on soils of igneous origin, while variety *cochisensis* was more common on limestone formations. In some places both could be found together. Mathews, using fern from such a location to eliminate the possibility of soil differences influencing toxicity, performed feeding experiments with both the typical variety and with variety *cochisensis*. He found that the typical variety was not toxic to sheep in amounts three times those necessary to provoke symptoms with variety *cochisensis*. He concluded that *N. sinuata* var. *sinuata* was not toxic.

Jimmy fern remains green and succulent after frost eliminates most other forage. It is not unpalatable. The poisonous principle is somewhat cumulative. This, coupled with the greater apparent susceptibility of pregnant animals, means that poisoning usually develops in mild form in early winter but becomes severe, resulting in considerable mortality in sheep, as the winter season progresses. Symptoms clear up between one and two weeks after animals cease to feed on the fern. Three-fourths or more of the animals in a flock may be affected. Mortality may approach 25 per cent Handling an affected flock may result in heavy mortality. This frequently occurs when the trouble is misdiagnosed and one or another treatment is attempted. Jimmy fern poisoning in cattle is rare, both because the range where the plant grows is more suited to sheep than cattle, and also because of an apparent greater ease of recovery in cattle. Incidence of poisoning in goat herds may be equivalent to that in sheep, but mortality is much lower because goats cannot be forced to exercise when seized with an attack. Horses are not known to be poisoned.

Notholaena distans has been suspected of producing a nervous syndrome in sheep in Australia.

Onoclea sensibilis L. Sensitive fern

DESCRIPTION. This perennial fern has separate, characteristic, vegetative and reproductive foliage. Vegetative fronds erect, green, once-pinnate, broadly triangular in general outline, 6 in. to 1½ ft tall; pinnae few, opposite; lower pinnae lanceolate, distinct and separate, grading upwards into pinnae that become mere lobes along the midvein; margins undulate. Reproductive fronds erect, stiff, deep brown, persistent; sporangia within globose structures (rolled pinnules) pinnately inserted on axes (pinnae) which, in turn, are inserted pinnately on the main axis. Vegetative and reproductive fronds borne on a horizontal perennating rhizome; vegetative fronds produced singly, reproductive fronds not produced every year by every plant.

DISTRIBUTION AND HABITAT. Open woods, thickets, meadows, and old pastures, throughout eastern North America from Florida and Texas to Manitoba and Labrador.

Fig. 3. *Onoclea sensibilis*. Sensitive fern. Photograph showing three fronds (leaves) and a fruiting stalk.

POISONOUS PRINCIPLE. Unknown.

TOXICITY, SYMPTOMS, AND LESIONS. Knowledge of the poisonous characteristics of this species rests entirely on limited experiments and field observations performed at the New Hampshire Agricultural Experiment Station (1642). The only uniform finding in investigations of complaints of nervous disorder in horses was the presence of large amounts of sensitive fern in the hay. A feeding experiment was undertaken with two horses. In one, symptoms of incoordination developed in 6 weeks on a diet composed entirely of hay containing about 17 per cent fern. The animal displayed increasing incoordination, became unable to grasp hay, went down and was sacrificed on the sixth day after the appearance of symptoms. Two principal lesions were found. The animal was icteric and the liver displayed cloudy swelling and fatty degeneration on microscopic examination. Of more significance to the symptoms observed were lesions in the nervous system. The brain was grossly edematous with blood-tinged fluid in the brain ventricles. Histologically it displayed edema and multiple hemorrhage with neuronal degeneration and invasion by Glial cells. The second experimental horse developed only transitory hyperesthesia even though continued on the *Onoclea* diet for several weeks after the death of the first horse.

Two heads from field cases were examined and displayed essentially the same brain lesions as found in the experimental horse. Symptoms reported in field cases were variable but basically nervous in character. Considerable variation in susceptibility and in amount of fern provoking symptoms among horses on the same diet was observed. Older horses were more sensitive than young, and symptoms were delayed or absent in those horses receiving exercise or grain or both.

Pteridium aquilinum (L.) Kuhn (= *Pteris aquilina* L.).
Bracken fern
Bracken is a variable genus of worldwide distribution. Many botanical varieties are recognized, of which several occur in the United States and Canada. Literature of England, Europe, Japan, Australia, the United States, and elsewhere makes it clear that many varieties of bracken produce equivalent poisoning. Therefore, in this work bracken is handled following conservative botanical treatment (1597) in which all kinds are considered as varieties of the single species, *Pteridium aquilinum*. The elevation by some botanists of varieties to species accounts for other species

Fig. 4. *Pteridium aquilinum*. Bracken fern. Frond (leaf), with details of leaf segment and sporangia lining under-surface of leaf margins. Photograph of frond. Drawing, courtesy of The Macmillan Company.

names for this plant sometimes encountered in literature on poisonous plants.

DESCRIPTION. Herbaceous perennial with stout blackish horizontal rhizome, often more than a yard in length. Leaves (fronds) scattered, erect, coarse, narrowly or broadly triangular, to 6 ft in height; pinnules (ultimate segments) oblong, entire in the apices of the pinnae, lobed toward the stalk. Reproduction by spores produced in sporangia lining the undersurface margins of the photosynthetic fronds when reproductive, covered by the narrow recurved edge of the leaf.

DISTRIBUTION AND HABITAT. Upland pastures, recently cleared lands, abandoned fields, and open woods, chiefly on dry, sandy, or gravelly soils, often in dense stands. Serious loss has occurred in the northeastern, southeastern, midwestern, and far western states.

POISONOUS NATURE. Ingestion of bracken, green or dry, produces entirely different syndromes in ruminants and monogastric animals.

POISONOUS PRINCIPLE. 1. *Monogastric Animals*. The enzyme thiaminase.

TOXICITY, SYMPTOMS, AND LESIONS. Bracken poisoning of horses was first reported in North America in 1917 (678) following severe loss of stock in British Columbia during the winter months of 1916. In all cases the horses were stabled and fed poor-quality, bracken-containing hay. A simple experiment with two horses, comparing the effect of bracken removed from hay with that of the hay remaining after bracken removal, established the toxicity of the bracken. Since that time the disease has been repeatedly recognized in Oregon, Washington, and British Columbia. Experimental feedings in that area and in England and observation of field cases has resulted in the syndrome being well characterized.

Feeding experiments (249, 507, 678, 680, 1348) have repeatedly established that a large amount of bracken is required to produce symptoms. For example, 792 lb bracken fed to a 1036-lb horse at 15 to 24 lb per day produced symptoms on the thirty-first day (1348). In general, ingestion of hay containing more than 20 per cent bracken produces symptoms in about one month. Symptoms first noted are loss of condition, loss of weight, and minor incoordination when forced to walk. Incoordination increases. Animals are disinclined to move, become lethargic, and stand with legs apart as though bracing themselves. They may assume a crouching attitude with arched back. Widespread muscular twitches develop into severe tremors and the animal is unable to remain standing. It may make violent attempts to regain its feet, usually inflicting injury upon itself in this process. Intoxication terminates in death following convulsions. Although the animal loses weight throughout the course of the poisoning, the appetite usually remains normal until symptoms become severe.

In some cases anorexia has been observed earlier (1348). Cardiac irregularities have been reported in experimental poisonings. Death occurs several days to several weeks (908) after onset of symptoms.

No significant gross lesions characteristic of the disease are found on post mortem examination. Examination of the blood, however, discloses a seriously lowered thiamine level, a markedly raised pyruvate concentration, and a diminution in platelet complement. Lowered red blood cell count and increase in leucocytes observed in one case (1348) may have been caused by secondary complications (507).

Therapy with massive doses of thiamine is dramatically successful in all but the terminal stages of intoxication. Marked improvement is noted within a day or two and recovery is complete within two to four days. Experimental horses suffering severe intoxication on a bracken diet, brought to normal by thiamine therapy, but continued on the same diet without further thiamine, again develop symptoms of bracken poisoning in three weeks to a month (507, 1348). Thiamine therapy at this juncture is again fully effective. Experimental case treatment has been mostly by injection. Oral treatment of cases also has been successful (249).

CONDITIONS OF POISONING. Most cases have occurred when horses were maintained on a poor to inadequate diet of hay containing large amounts of bracken. Some greedy horses have contracted bracken poisoning from ingestion of their bedding. In a very few instances, poisoning in horses has occurred following ingestion of green bracken on pasture (507, 679). There is some evidence (510) for variation in bracken thiaminase activity, but successful poisoning experiments with bracken from an area where bracken poisoning was unknown (249) have shown that all bracken should be considered potentially toxic.

THE THIAMINASE IN BRACKEN. The thiaminase activity in bracken was discovered in 1945 in an investigation of bracken toxicity to horses in Oregon (1663). In experiments with rats, it was observed that inclusion of bracken in the diet at 40 per cent allowed weight gains for 10 days, but was followed by decrease in weight, accompanied eventually with anorexia, emaciation, and polyneuritis, and death in about 30 days. These symptoms suggested thiamine deficiency. Treatment with thiamine brought dramatic improvement. Thiamine content of the feed without bracken was adequate for normal requirements. These results pointed to the presence of a thiamine-destroying substance in the bracken. Thiamine-destroying activity has been detected in the feces of poisoned rats (1571).

Further work by the same group and others (328, 331, 505, 510, 1163, 1571, 1663) has characterized this syndrome in rats more thoroughly. Some similarities exist between lesions found in the rat (a monogastric animal) and the cow (a ruminant), which have complicated investigations into the latter problem. Rats on a 40 per cent bracken diet develop bone-marrow lesions which result in thrombocytopenia and terminal leuco-penia and internal hemorrhaging. Thiamine therapy corrects this condition. Rats on raw bracken supplemented with massive thiamine therapy do not develop bone-marrow hypoplasia, yet an experimental diet deficient in thiamine alone does not produce it (328, 1163). This apparent contradic-tion has not yet been resolved. Rats on autoclaved bracken diet gain poorly but bone-marrow lesions do not develop (328).

Investigations of bracken thiaminase activity (510, 515, 516, 670, 671, 672, 859, 1648, 1663) have shown it to be brought about by a system consisting of a thermostable, dialyzable cofactor and thermolabile, nondialyz-able apoenzyme, which mediate a reaction:

$$P \cdot CH_2 \cdot T^+ + R \cdot NH_2 \longrightarrow P \cdot CH_2 \cdot NH \cdot R + T + H^+$$

where P = pyrimidine, T = thiazole, and $R \cdot NH_2$ represents the cofactor. A variety of aromatic amines have been found to act as cofactors in this reaction. Proline and pyridine are two that have been found in bracken. This reaction is similar to that mediated by an enzyme system found in a few fish and shellfish (such as carp which produces athiaminosis or Chastek disease when fed to foxes) and is different from a hydrolytic thiamine-splitting system found in certain bacteria. The bracken system is extractable in chloroform water, thermolabile, and of increasing activity from pH 2.0 to 5.5 or 6.5. The thiamine-destroying activity of crude bracken is mostly inactivated by steaming or boiling for 30 minutes. Equivalent dry heat produces much slower inactivation. Apparent residual thiaminase activity of autoclaved fern is caused by adsorption of thiamine. Inactivation of this kind may account for about 10 per cent of the total thiamine-inactivating capacity of raw bracken.

A few imperfectly described instances of suspected bracken poisoning in pigs have been reported (134, 1542) in England.

2. *Ruminants.* Sheep are more resistant than cattle to bracken poison-ing (511). Although sheep have been poisoned experimentally with the development of symptoms and lesions similar to those of bracken-poisoned cattle (1118, 1120, 1261), natural cases (556, 557) are rare and none has been reported in the United States.

Bracken poisoning in cattle was first described in the United States by Bosshart and Hagan (152) following losses in New York in 1917, 1918, and 1919. The disease, characterized by markedly elevated tempera-ture and multiple internal hemorrhages, was first supposed of bacterial etiology. Although cultures could be obtained from blood and various organs, known pathogens were not found. Persistence and careful observa-tion led Hagan to suspect bracken poisoning, which he then found had been recognized as a syndrome in cattle on experimental evidence by Stockman (1542) in England in 1917, and had been originally described earlier (1258, 1549).

The disease has undergone a great amount of investigation, particularly by English and French workers, and is now well characterized. It is one of the most striking syndromes to be seen by the veterinarian in the field. Reviews by Shearer (1448), Stamp (1511), Boddie (143), Evans and Evans (510), Muth (1161), Osebold (1209), Sippel (1469), Evans *et al.* (511) and Wagnon (1630) may be consulted.

TOXICITY, SYMPTOMS AND LESIONS. Ingestion of large amounts of bracken fronds over an extended period of time produces an acute disease of sudden onset, brief duration, and usually fatal termination. Many experimental poisonings of cattle with bracken, green or dried, have been performed (628, 683, 1261, 1448, 1542, 1543). In general, ingestion of an amount of bracken roughly equivalent to an animal's weight over a period ranging from one to three or even four months will result at the end of that time in overt symptoms followed by death in one to four days, or occasionally longer. Ingestion of more highly toxic green bracken may bring on symptoms in less than a month. Poisoning is slow to appear and instances are recorded (511) in which symptoms and death developed as much as eight weeks after animals had ceased to have access to bracken. Cattle have also been poisoned by rhizomes exposed by plowing (363). Rhizomes appear to have about five times the toxicity of fronds (521).

In the period before acute termination, cattle appear healthy and may gain weight. Young bracken has been shown (1119) to have nutritive value equivalent to good hay. A week or so before the appearance of serious symptoms a rough coat, listless attitude, and mucous discharge from nostrils and mouth may be observed. Elevated temperature usually appears first among the symptoms of the acute condition. Readings as high as 109°F have been recorded. They are usually not lower than 104°. As the acute syndrome progresses, blood appears in the feces and bleeding from the nostrils is common. These symptoms are accompanied by anorexia. Petechial hemorrhages may be observed in the mucous membranes of the orbit and elsewhere. Occasionally death is delayed for several days. In this case emaciation, haematuria, and rarely icterus may be observed.

Frequently, in young cattle, edematous swelling develops in the throat region (556, 948, 1469), causing roaring and difficulty in breathing with eventual death. Temperature is elevated, but externally visible signs of hemorrhage are absent. The edema may be brought about by a low plasma protein level (511).

Post mortem examination in typical cases discloses carcasses in which practically every organ appears as though "splashed" with hemorrhages varying from petechiae to ecchymoses and suffusions. As much as 2½ gallons of blood have been removed from the lumen of the large intestine

(152). Commonly, small to large ulcers are observed in the gastrointestinal tract. It is usually possible to isolate bacteria from the liver, infection of that organ having developed after invasion of the hepatic portal system by bacteria which gained entrance as the result of intestinal ulceration. Occasionally other parenchymatous organs may display bacterial infection, and in longer-standing instances necrotic patches of skin or other tissue may develop in various places.

The primary lesion, bone-marrow hypoplasia, was not detected until after the demonstration in 1947 (143, Schofield, cited in 511) of a blood dyscrasia in which the numbers of leucocytes and platelet elements are seriously lowered. Repeated examination of blood of poisoned ruminants since (363, 506, 742, 1163, 1208), has shown that the only change associated with production of hemorrhage is the serious thrombocytopenia; clotting and prothrombin values remain within normal limits while fibrinogen levels are raised. Leucopenia is undoubtedly responsible for making possible the terminal invasion of bacteria of the surface flora. It has been suggested (1164) that bacterial invasion is responsible for causing elevation in temperature, but no correlation has been found between temperature elevation and presence or absence of bacteria in the blood by others (511). The erythrocyte count remains within normal limits until the final hemorrhagic stage, when the number is reduced. It has been shown (1166) that failure in primary divisions of the blood-manufacturing elements in bone marrow is responsible for lowered counts in the leucocyte and thrombocyte series. The longer life of the erythrocyte may account for the fact that an erythropenia does not appear in the prehemorrhagic stages of the disease (1208). In terminal stages, heparin is released in abnormal amount into the blood stream suggesting involvement or destruction of mast cells (508).

POISONOUS PRINCIPLE. Following the demonstration of thiaminase in bracken, many persons (249, 1205, 1615) attempted treatment of bracken poisoning in ruminants with thiamine, with other members of the B vitamin group, and with natural substances rich in them, such as yeast, to no avail. It has been shown (511) that urine thiamine levels drop when cattle are placed on a bracken diet, and rumen liquor from such animals will bring on symptoms of thiamine deficiency when fed to rats (1271). On the other hand it is impossible to detect thiamine deficiency in the tissues of bracken-fed cattle. The following explanation has been postulated (511). Although bracken thiaminase is active in the rumen, microbial activity there resynthesizes thiamine from the products of the thiaminase-mediated breakdown. It has been shown (515) that the microfloral populations of the rumen are not significantly changed in numbers or composition in bracken poisoning. The products of thiamine breakdown are recombined within their cells by rumen bacteria. In this locale, thiamine cannot be reached by thiaminase, it is held, since the latter is a protein molecule incapable of passing the intact bacterial membrane. Analyses of rumen sludge from bracken-fed cattle shows it to have thiamine activity. In the course of passage into the abomasum, thiaminase is subject to attack and destruction by bacterial activity and increasingly acid pH, resulting, it is held, in thiaminase inactivation. As the thiamine-containing bacteria are digested, thiamine is made available to the animal in a milieu devoid of significant thiaminase activity. Experiments (1271) have shown also that cattle seem to have very low requirements for thiamine in their normal economy.

The poisonous activity of bracken towards cattle is reduced or eliminated by steaming the fern for an hour or longer (1261, 1569). Bracken ash is not toxic (Raafat thesis quoted in 742). Experiments (515) to determine whether a cofactor-pyrimidine moiety resulting from the thiaminase-mediated reaction may be the toxic factor suggested that such is not the case.

It has proven difficult to obtain by usual procedures extracts in which toxicity to ruminants is not absent or greatly reduced. Toxicity does not follow the thiaminase-protein fraction in dialysis and cold isoelectric precipitations (1570) and, in corroboration, *Equisetum arvense,* which contains an identical or similar thiaminase, even when fed in large amount, does not produce the typical symptoms of bracken poisoning in cattle (515). In separations, only the fraction containing the dialyzable molecules provoked symptoms and lesions characteristic of bracken poisoning in ruminants. Early attempts at water extraction of the dialyzable poisonous principle led to its inactivation. More recently it has been found possible (513) to obtain a water extract of high toxicity by mincing fresh green bracken into boiling water.

A variety of cyclic compounds, unrelated chemically, such as benzene, dinitrophenol, and others, bring about bone-marrow hypoplasia in human beings. It appears that a small molecule, yet unknown, produces symptoms and lesions, almost identical with those of bracken poisoning, in poisoning of cattle by trichloroethylene-extracted soybean-oil meal. In that much-studied syndrome, marked species sensitivity to the toxic principle has been demonstrated. Cattle, horses, and sheep may be poisoned, but goats and a variety of laboratory animals are insensitive. Whether these facts will prove useful in studying bracken poisoning remains to be seen.

TREATMENT. Bracken poisoning in cattle is similar to aplastic anemia in human beings. This condition may be brought about by a variety of agents including ionizing radiation. Bone-marrow extracts have been found useful in treating human patients suffering from aplastic anemia. The beneficial effect derives from stimulation of whatever undamaged tissue remains in the marrow to greatly increased activity. Attempts to determine the nature of the molecule responsible for this stimulating effect led to the recognition of batyl alcohol. This molecule appears to be a common constituent in the body's economy, having been isolated from a number of tissues and from red blood cells.

$$H_2C \cdot O \cdot CH_2(CH_2)_{16} \cdot CH_3$$
$$|$$
$$HCOH$$
$$|$$
$$H_2COH$$

batyl alcohol

Following this lead, Evans *et al,* in 1957 (514) reported a dramatic doubling in leucocytes and thrombocytes in four days following treatment of bracken-poisoned animals with batyl alcohol supported by antibiotic, antiheparin, and antihistamine therapy (508) as indicated. Evans *et al,* in a later communication (509) have reported the results of similar therapy in 27 cases. They were able to obtain a recovery rate of 80 per cent in this disease, which previously had been almost universally fatal. In their experience the treatment may be expected to work if the leucocyte count is not below 2000 and platelets not below 50,000 to 100,000 per mm^3.

A diagnostic method useful in detecting bracken poisoning has been described by Naftalin and Cushnie (1164, see also 216). It depends upon the fact that the clot formed in the blood of bracken-poisoned animals does not consolidate or retract after forming, as does the clot formed from normal blood. Ten ml venous blood is introduced into a graduated centrifuge tube which is closed with a cork through which a copper wire has been inserted. The copper wire is bent into a hook which is inserted well into the blood. The tube is incubated for two hours at 37°C. Clot retraction is measured as a function of the serum remaining when the clot is withdrawn. In blood from healthy animals the clot retracts and squeezes out serum, the amount of which may be expressed as per cent of original. Normal blood expresses between 40 and 70 per cent serum, while failure of the clot in blood from bracken-poisoned animals to retract results in readings between 40 and 0 per cent.

CONDITIONS OF POISONING. Loss of cattle to bracken poisoning in the United States has been reported from the Pacific Northwest (952), California (1209, 1630), the Midwest (1300), the Northeast (152, 681, 682, 683), and the Southeast (1469). The syndrome presents some of the characteristics of an infectious disease but outbreaks are widely scattered and usually involve only a few animals in a herd. Most cases occur in animals on pasture and cease with frost or a few weeks thereafter. Incidence is sporadic but greater in dry years when other forage is less available, especially toward the end of the pasture season. In California, cases frequently occur at the beginning of the pasture period when the bracken is just coming up and other green forage is still mostly absent. An unusual instance of poisoning has been reported in Britain (1656) in which animals on ample lush pasturage sought out bracken, apparently because of its fibrous nature. Bracken in hay may cause loss occasionally, and instances of loss in calves bedded on bracken have been recorded (271, 948). Bracken poisoning may easily be confused with a number of other hemorrhagic diseases. Sippel (1469) has described the essential points in establishing a differential diagnosis.

BOVINE HAEMATURIA. Widespread outbreaks of intermittent bovine haematuria in the northwestern United States and British Columbia have been correlated (661) with the distribution of bracken in that area. Work relating bracken more closely with this syndrome has been reported in Germany but is not altogether convincing (1197). Similar outbreaks of bovine haematuria have not been reported from other areas in North America where bracken is common.

Additional references on bracken toxicity include 576, 578, 900, 1165, 1468, 1470.

HORSETAILS

DIVISION SPHENOPHYTA—Spore-bearing plants
Class Sphenopsida
Order Equisetales

Equisetaceae

Equisetum arvense L. ⎱
Equisetum palustre L. ⎰ Horsetail, foxtail, rush

DESCRIPTION. Small herbaceous perennials, growing each season from deeply buried rhizomes. Aerial stems rushlike, jointed, hollow, and of harsh texture to the touch. Leaves reduced to scales, joined laterally, forming a short, cylindrical, papery sheath about the stem at each node. Secondary axes in whorls from the angles of the scale leaves. Stems and branches green, photosynthetic, often occurring in great numbers, the whole giving the appearance of a horse's tail, whence the common name. Reproduction by spores. Sporangia produced in a complex cone borne terminally on the vegetative axis in *E. palustre* or terminally in *E. arvense* on a colorless, specialized reproductive axis which appears and matures early in the spring before the vegetative sterile axis is produced. Other species of *Equisetum* are locally common. Mostly they may be recognized by the characteristics named above, but some species form an erect, rigid, unbranched, green, pencil-like stem.

DISTRIBUTION AND HABITAT. *Equisetum arvense* is common throughout the United States and Canada as a weed of moist fields and meadows, especially on sandy or gravelly soils, and on the sandy banks of road or railroad cuts. *Equisetum palustre* is found from Newfoundland across the northern United States and Canada into Alaska, making locally abundant stands in wet meadows, springy places, and on margins of streams and ponds.

POISONOUS PRINCIPLE. Silica, aconitic acid, palmitic acid, nicotine,

Fig. 5. *Equisetum arvense*. Horsetail. Photograph of a mature vegetative plant.

3-methoxypyridine, equisitine, palustrine (the last two are partially characterized alkaloids), and dimethylsulfone have all at one time or another been suggested as the toxic principle in *Equisetum* species (666, 797, 844, 933, 971). The heavy film of diatoms commonly found on *E. palustre* was once suggested, as were fungi, as the probable source of toxicity. Experiments have shown, however, that aconitic acid and the siliceous content of the plants are not responsible for the toxicity, that equisitine, although toxic to mice parenterally, cannot be held responsible for the major toxicity of the plant (861), and that dimethylsulfone is essentially nontoxic. None of the other suggested toxic factors listed above is currently believed the source of toxicity.

From the similarity of symptoms of equisetosis to those of bracken poisoning (*Pteridium*) in horses, several persons at about the same time suspected the presence of a thiamine-destroying substance in *Equisetum*. Experimental demonstrations of thiaminase activity in extracts of *Equisetum* and successful treatment of horses poisoned by *Equisetum* with thiamine

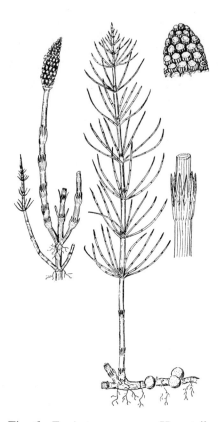

Fig. 6. *Equisetum arvense.* Horsetail.
Left, fruiting stalk appearing in early
spring; at center, vegetative axis appearing late and persisting through
the summer; at right, details of axis
node, and fruiting structure. Courtesy
of The Macmillan Company.

prove the presence of such a substance, but its chemistry is unknown (507,
563, 750, 936). By comparison with bracken poisoning in ruminants and
because of some difference in symptoms between the ruminant and nonruminant in horsetail poisoning, it is unlikely that thiaminase can account
for all the toxic effects.

TOXICITY, SYMPTOMS, AND LESIONS. Cases of *Equisetum* toxicity to
stock in the United States and Canada have been reported from time to time
since the late 1800's (183, 277, 660, 666, 750, 844, 936, 1231, 1338,
1339, 1524). Experimental investigations have been conducted by authorities at Vermont (844, 1338, 1339), and Canada (750, 936), and in
European countries (507, 515, 563, 787, 861, 933).

From all these reports it appears that there is a relationship between species of *Equisetum* and class of livestock poisoned. The largest number of reported cases concerns poisoning of horses by *Equisetum arvense* obtained in hay. In North America this is the sole, well-recorded form of *Equisetum* poisoning, although cases in sheep have been mentioned (277, 1339). The second most frequently recorded poisoning in the world literature is that of cattle by *E. palustre* (474, 563, 787, 861, 933). Both species have proven toxic to additional classes of livestock (563, 574, 861). *E. limosum* L. is considered toxic to livestock in Europe (563, 933) and *E. ramosissimum* Desf. has been shown toxic to sheep in South Africa (1533). Two additional species, *E. laevigatum* A. Br. and *E. hyemale* L., have been said (1383) to be poisonous in California.

Hay composed one-fifth or more of *Equisetum arvense* produces symptoms in horses in 2 to 5 weeks (666, 750, 928, 1339). Unthriftiness is followed by weakness, especially in the hind quarters, ataxia, and difficulty in turning. The appetite remains normal almost to the end. Attempts to work or exercise poisoned horses produce trembling and muscular exhaustion. Animals which become prostrated make nervous, anxious attempts to regain their feet. In later stages muscular rigidity and constipation may be noted (563). The pulse becomes rapid and weak and the extremities cold. Corneal opacity has been described in several cases diagnosed as horsetail poisoning (936).

In fatal cases death is preceded by quiescence and coma. Lesions are not specific. Removing the offending hay in the early stages of poisoning brings about rapid recovery. Treatment with massive doses of thiamine is effective in all but the final stage when the animal is prostrated. The blood-chemistry picture has been analyzed during the course of the disease by Forenbacher (563), who finds evidences of metabolic changes characteristic of thiamine deficiency.

Equisetum arvense is rarely, if ever, lethal to cattle. This is to be expected if the only toxic factor it contains is thiaminase. Experimental feedings to cattle of hay containing *E. arvense* of high thiaminase activity have been made in connection with studies on bracken toxicity (507). The sole result was production of marked loss in condition over a forty-day period.

According to Lott (936), bracken poisoning in horses may be distinguished from horsetail poisoning by the fact that the appetite is lost in the former and retained in the latter. (This does not agree with observations of bracken poisoning in horses by others.)

Poisoning of cattle by ingestion of *Equisetum palustre,* green or in hay, produces hyperexcitability, loss of condition, and muscular weakness accompanied with diarrhea and, in dairy animals, a dramatic decrease in milk flow. Change in diet provides rapid relief. Thiamine therapy has not been reported.

Symptoms in sheep experimentally poisoned with *Equisetum ramosissimum* included nervous weakness, staggering, and trembling (1533).

CONDITIONS OF POISONING. There are several anomalies in the current state of knowledge of horsetail poisoning which need further investigation. These relate to relative toxicity of various species of *Equisetum,* variation in apparent susceptibility and symptoms with class of stock, the apparent selective toxicity of the plant green or in hay, and the different nature of poisoning of ruminants by *Equisetum* compared with bracken. Explanations may reside in factors such as variation in the amount of toxic principle with stage of growth or other aspects of the environment, the presence, nature, relative effects, and relative amounts of more than one toxic principle, the feeding habits of particular classes of stock, and the physiology of ruminant vs. nonruminant.

Normally, sheep, goats, and horses are rarely poisoned by *E. palustre* although cattle frequently are. Cattle, sheep, and goats are rarely poisoned by *E. arvense* though horses frequently are. *E. palustre* may be poisonous green or in hay. *E. arvense* appears dangerous only in hay. The toxicity of the hay is not lost with age. Forsyth (514) records an instance in which hay, responsible for poisoning horses four months after cutting, was responsible for poisoning bullocks a full year later. The young green growth appears more dangerous than older growth (933). Finally, it has been found that horses may develop an appetite for *Equisetum arvense,* eating it from their bedding in preference to clean hay provided them (844), and that young animals may be more susceptible than old (1339).

Additional reference: 1323.

GYMNOSPERMS

DIVISION SPERMATOPHYTA—Seed-bearing plants
Class Conopsida—Gymnosperms
Order Pinales

Pinaceae

Pinus ponderosa Doug. ex Laws. Western yellow pine

DESCRIPTION. This pine tree may be recognized by its yellowish-green needles, 7 to 11 in. long, in groups of threes, and its subterminal, ovoid cones, 2½ to 6 in. long.

DISTRIBUTION AND HABITAT. Western yellow pine is the dominant forest member of coniferous forests at moderate elevations east of the Cascade Mountains, scattered elsewhere, California to British Columbia, east to Idaho and Rocky Mts.

POISONOUS PRINCIPLE. Unknown.

TOXICITY, SYMPTOMS, AND LESIONS. As early as 1927 (183) it was widely believed among ranchers of the northwestern United States and British Columbia that cattle browsing on needles and buds of the western yellow pine were predisposed to abortion, but it was not until 1952 that experimental proof (960) was available in support. During winter months cattle may consume quantities of fallen needles and will browse upon yellow pine slash, if available, even when other forage is ample. In the feeding experiment, 6 Hereford cattle were allowed fresh pine needles and buds free choice, while 6 others were forced to consume somewhat larger amounts by restricting other feed given them. In both cases a mineral and vitamin A supplement was given. During the winter the animals in both groups gained weight and showed no signs of nutritional deficiency throughout the experiment. Consumption of pine needles averaged 5.0 lb per head per day in the free-choice group, and 6.4 lb per head per day in the other group.

119

The pine needles and buds were collected fresh daily. Of the 12, only 3 gave birth to normal calves. The remainder experienced stillbirths or weak calves which died shortly after birth. Of these, a significant proportion were produced prematurely. These results have been confirmed by others (1600).

Experimental procedures with mice have resulted in the recognition of at least two toxic factors in yellow pine needles (21). One, soluble in water, depresses uterine weight, while the other, soluble in ether, is directly toxic.

CONDITIONS OF POISONING. Since cattle readily browse pine slash, lumbering operations should be suspended when bred cattle are present. The danger period for consumption is in the latter part of gestation (37). Pelleted pine needles lose their toxicity (1600).

Pinus taeda L. Loblolly pine

Loblolly pine is a light-reddish barked tree, with long needles in bundles of two or three, of the southeastern United States. Needles from this tree used as bedding have produced death after ingestion by cattle (1335).

Cupressaceae

Cupressus macrocarpa Hartw. Monterey cypress, macrocarpa

In North America this tree grows only on the Monterey Peninsula of California.

The same species grows in New Zealand, where it has been considered (959) the cause of an unusual pregnancy difficulty and abortion in cattle. In the instances cited (three outbreaks involving somewhat more than a dozen cows), abortion occurred two weeks to two months before term. The maternal cotyledons were found to be greatly enlarged and the fetal membranes were firmly adherent and dark in color. Severe, persistent, "almost frantic" straining occurred. The animals became weak, ataxic, or prostrated. In the absence of treatment, death soon followed.

Antihistamines, specifically promethazine hydrochloride, proved rapidly effective in relieving cotyledonary swelling and promoting passage of the fetal membranes. In all cases it was possible to demonstrate that cypress trees had recently been felled where the cattle had access to them and that the foliage had been eaten in quantity.

Juniperus virginiana L. Juniper

This and other species of juniper or cedar have the reputation in early Old World literature of being toxic to stock, but are eaten only under extreme duress. They are listed in some of the earliest American publications on poisonous plants [see review by Harshberger (644)], but instances of loss of animal life are not well presented. It is likely that these plants contain volatile principles causing digestive trouble if ingested by livestock in

Taxus cuspidata. Japanese yew. Detail of branch with fruits. Use of this illustration has been made possible by the Merck Sharp & Dohme Research Laboratories.

moderate amount. They may possibly cause abortion (1185). The plants are exceedingly distasteful.

Order Taxales

Taxaceae

Taxus spp. Yew, ground hemlock.

DESCRIPTION. Evergreen, gymnospermous trees or shrubs. Bark reddish-brown, thin, flaking in thin scales. Leaves linear, stiff, ½ to 1 in. long, two-ranked on twigs; upper surface dark green, lower yellow-green; midrib prominent. Flowers unisexual, axillary, inconspicuous. Fruit composed of a single stony seed mostly surrounded by a bright scarlet, thick, ovoid, fleshy cup, the whole ½ to ¾ in. long.

DISTRIBUTION AND HABITAT. *Taxus baccata* L. English yew. A spreading shrub or small tree in common use as an ornamental. Many horticultural varieties have been developed. Hardy as far north as New York.

Taxus cuspidata Sieb. & Zucc. Japanese yew. Similar to *T. baccata,* but hardier further north. Many horticultural varieties are in common use.

Taxus brevifolia Nutt. Western Yew. Native tree 15 to 75 ft tall with more or less drooping branches. Forests, wooded slopes and ravines, central California to Montana, British Columbia and Alaska.

Taxus canadensis Marsh. Ground hemlock. Spreading shrub, rarely more than 5 ft tall. Deep woods, Kentucky to north-central and northeastern states and Manitoba to Newfoundland.

POISONOUS PRINCIPLE. Most chemical investigations have been performed with the European species (*T. baccata*) (843). As early as 1856 an alkaloidal extract was obtained. It was named taxine in 1876, and has been reisolated several times in succeeding decades. Taxine has also been detected in *T. cuspidata* by Japanese workers. From either plant source taxine has been difficult to crystallize. Since the mid 1950's English and German investigators (81, 642) have separated crude taxine into two fractions, taxine A and taxine B (= taxine I) which have been crystallized and for which partial structural formulas have been suggested. Taxine B is present in greatest amount.

An analysis (843) of *T. brevifolia,* in which special pains were taken to detect the presence of alkaloids or glycosides, failed to reveal compounds of these types.

TOXICITY, SYMPTOMS, AND LESIONS. Foliage, bark, or seeds of *Taxus baccata* are toxic to men and all classes of livestock, green or dry. This plant is considered the most dangerous of all poisonous trees or shrubs in Britain (574). Numerous case reports occur in the literature of Britain and Europe. Reviews by Forsyth (574) and by Garner (607) may be consulted.

Symptoms, lesions, and toxicity are best known for *Taxus baccata,* but appear to be similar among the toxic species. Green foliage is toxic to horses and other monogastric animals at about 0.1 per cent of the animal's weight. For ruminants more is required, about 0.5 per cent. The alkaloid is depressant, causing the heart to be slowed, then stopped in diastole. Lesions of the nervous system have been described by Kohler and Grunberg and are assignable to results of circulatory failure (882).

Symptoms vary, depending on the severity of poisoning. It is usual for a large dose to be consumed. This results in sudden death without additional symptoms. Animals are found close to the offending plant and frequently have twigs or leaves still in the mouth. In such cases the cause of poisoning is indicated by the presence of recognizable material in the rumen or stomach. Significant lesions are absent. Less severely poisoned animals may display some nervous signs before succumbing. These typically include trembling, dyspnea, and collapse. The onset of symptoms is sudden and the course short, but a greater or lesser period of time intervenes between ingestion and appearance of symptoms during which the animal gives no evidence of poisoning.

A subacute condition has been recognized, particularly in cattle. Occasionally spontaneous recoveries occur; more frequently, the case is fatal. The time between ingestion and production of symptoms is as much as 2 days in subacute cases. In addition to the symptoms listed above, subacute cases display signs of gastroenteritis and diarrhea. The plant is known to contain a volatile oil which appears to be a slowly acting irritant. This conclusion has been supported by extraction of the oil and experiments with laboratory animals (882). Post mortem examination of subacutely poisoned livestock reveals moderate irritation in the upper digestive tract.

In this hemisphere yew poisoning has not been reported with as much frequency as in Europe. Three instances of multiple mortality in cattle have been described in Kentucky (182). In each, the animal died during the night and symptoms were not observed. These animals were poisoned by ornamental yew foliage (either *T. baccata* or *T. cuspidata*). In Rochester, New York, *Taxus cuspidata* (731) caused the death of four deer, one reindeer, and one burro (730) when yew branches were accidentally included with material placed in the pens with these animals. A goat poisoned at the same time was treated with atropine, to counter the depressant effect of taxine, with apparently clear-cut beneficial effect. Poisoning of cattle by *Taxus canadensis* has been reported (183) from British Columbia (where it had been planted about a farm as an ornamental). *Taxus brevifolia* has a reputation of toxicity (183, 1383), but conclusive cases do not appear to have been recorded.

CONDITIONS OF POISONING. *Taxus baccata,* and probably other species, is consumed readily by livestock. Cases may occur whenever animals have access to the plant. Accidental poisoning from trimmings or prunings are relatively common in Europe. The bright scarlet fruit is attractive to children. The pulp is not especially poisonous, but the seed may contain dangerous concentrations of the alkaloid.

Some English reports present conflicting evidence concerning the toxicity of *Taxus baccata*. It is possible that there is seasonal, geographic, or other variation in alkaloidal content of the plant.

Class Cycadopsida—Cycads
Order Cycadales

Cycadaceae

Zamia integrifolia Ait. Coonties, Florida arrowroots
The zamias are coarse, woody, fernlike plants with pinnately compound, palmlike leaves arising from a thickened, branched (in this species), underground stem. They bear separate cones of male and female organs. The latter are gymnospermous.

Zamia integrifolia is widespread in dry sandy soils of peninsular Florida.

This and other species of *Zamia* are known to produce a disease in cattle in South America (1347). The disorder is called wobbles and is characterized by atactic movements of the hind legs and peculiarities of stance. It appears several weeks after animals have had access to foliage of *Zamia* and injury is permanent. Species of the closely related genera *Macrozamia* and *Cycas,* sometimes cultivated as ornamentals in this hemisphere, produce a similar disease of cattle in Australia (605). Seeds may poison human beings. Animal poisoning from cycads has not yet been reported in the United States.

Additional reference: 810.

ANGIOSPERMS

Class Angiospermae—Angiosperms
Subclass Dicotyledoneae—Dicots
Order Ranales

Calycanthaceae

Calycanthus fertalis Walt. Carolina allspice
According to Chesnut (273) the seeds of this shrub, which grows in woodlands in the southeastern United States and is occasionally planted as an ornamental, are "strongly reputed to be poisonous to cattle in Tennessee." No specific cases are on record.

Annonaceae

Asimina triloba Dunal. Papaw
The fruits of this small tree native to, and cultivated in, the eastern and southern United States and southeastern Canada are commonly eaten by human beings. It is well established that a small fraction of the population is sensitive to this plant, reacting with contact dermatitis, but it is less well known that certain individuals may exhibit severe gastrointestinal symptoms after ingestion of the fruit even though insensitive to contact of the plant with the skin (64).

Lauraceae

Persea americana Mill. Avocado
Commercial production of the avocado is located primarily in southern California and Florida. Several commercial varieties are employed.
   Toxicity of the leaves, fruit, bark, and seeds has been reported. Cattle,

horses, goats, rabbits, canaries, and fish have been poisoned by ingestion of avocado under natural conditions (812) and toxicity studies with laboratory animals have had positive results (38, 1609). In cattle, goats, and horses (418), the primary symptom is that of a severe, noninfectious but sensitive mastitis accompanied by reduction in milk flow. With care, the mastitis may be controlled in about a week, but the milk flow never returns to its earlier level. Severe poisoning has resulted in death in goats. Canaries have been poisoned by being fed the ripe fruit. Several fish were lost in a backyard pool under circumstances which strongly incriminated avocado leaves that had fallen into the pool.

Some evidence indicates that not all commercial varieties of avocado are equally toxic (38). Rabbits fed on leaves of Fuerte and Nabal strains died within 24 hours. Those fed on Mexicola avocado developed no symptoms of poisoning.

Ranunculaceae

Aconitum spp. Aconite, monkshood
This botanically variable genus contains about a hundred species. Several are cultivated as garden perennials and several more occur wild in various parts of the United States. *Aconitum* is closely related to *Delphinium* which it resembles in color, habit and habitat, toxic principles, and syndrome produced, and with which it is often confused. The two may be told apart when in flower by the fact that the *Delphinium* flower possesses a prominent, backward-projecting spur which is absent in *Aconitum*. In *Aconitum* the leaves at the top of the plant have very short petioles; in *Delphinium* the upper petioles are longer and easily visible.

The species of *Aconitum* of the section *Napellus* which have been investigated have displayed marked uniformity in toxicity or alkaloid content (1557). Although few have been carefully investigated, all species should be held suspect. Some evidence (149) suggests that species with higher chromosome counts, or polyploids, are more toxic than others.

A. napellus L., cultivated aconite, monkshood, or wolfbane. In Europe this species has been long recognized as poisonous. It is commonly found in gardens in the United States and Canada.

A. columbianum Nutt., western monkshood. Perennial herb, 1 to 5 or more ft tall, growing from a perennating tuberous root. Leaves alternate, about 2 to 3 in. across, roundish in outline, but much divided and redivided into a number of narrow, palmately arranged segments with acute tips; venation corresponding. Leaves similar to those of a number of other plants in the Ranunculaceae (buttercup family). Inflorescence a terminal raceme, sometimes slightly compounded (paniculate) in its lower part. Flowers perfect, bilaterally symmetrical with prominent upper hood

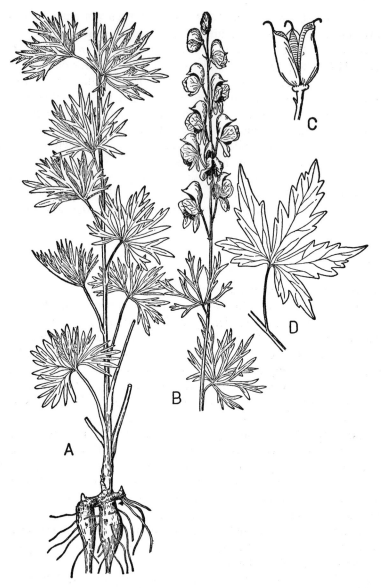

Fig. 7. A–C, *Aconitum napellus*. Monkshood. Flowering plant with detail of fruit. D, *Aconitum columbianum*. Western monkshood. Leaf. Courtesy of The Macmillan Company.

(whence the common name). Sepals and petals blue or rarely white. Carpels 3 (to 5), not united, ripening into a cluster of follicles bearing many seeds each. This species is native to the western United States in the mountains at elevations from 5000 to 10,000 ft along streams and wet meadows, from Arizona northward into Canada.

A. vaccarum Rydb. (= *A. reclinatum* Gray) of West Virginia was so named by Rydberg because it had been incriminated in several cases of loss of cattle (1379).

POISONOUS PRINCIPLE. A number of closely related monobasic alkaloids have been isolated from species of *Aconitum*. The literature has been reviewed by Stern (1523). They are similar to, and some are identical with, alkaloids isolated from *Delphinium*. The structure of one, aconitine, has been worked out (50, 1311, 1674, 1675). With the exception of three minor substitutions, it is identical with delphinine (p. 21). Both are polycyclic diterpenoid alkaloids.

TOXICITY, SYMPTOMS, AND LESIONS. Loss of life in livestock and in human beings has occurred from ingestion of *Aconitum* or extractions made from it. *Aconitum napellus* is considered (607) one of England's potentially most dangerous poisonous plants. Less than a pound of aconite root has been lethal in the horse, which represents toxicity of about 0.075 per cent of the animal's weight of fresh root. In the United States aconite poisoning of livestock has occurred but has been confused with larkspur poisoning. It is not safe to assume that cases ascribed to aconite poisoning are not actually larkspur poisoning (since the latter is much the more common plant) unless aconite has been identified without question.

Aconite poisoning in animals and the human being is intense. Death usually occurs within a few hours. Symptoms include restlessness, salivation, weakness and irregularity of heartbeat, and prostration. Bloating, belching, frothy salivation, and constant swallowing are common in livestock. Nausea, vertigo, paresthesias, impairment of speech and vision, anxiety, and oppressive pain in the chest are symptoms found in the human being. Post mortem lesions are neither marked nor specific.

CONDITIONS OF POISONING. Formerly, poisoning in the human being occurred occasionally from misuse of extracts of aconite. These are now only rarely employed in human or veterinary medicine. Aconite root may be mistaken for other, edible, fleshy roots. Aconite root with potent alkaloid content provokes a tingling sensation in the mouth when chewed raw (1557).

Poisoning by garden aconite is not common, either in Europe (1565) or in this hemisphere, but the possibility should not be overlooked. *Aconitum columbianum* and other native species do not appear to produce significant losses among livestock (86, 985). Most cases of poisoning ascribed to aconite on the range turn out on careful investigation to be cases of larkspur poisoning.

Additional references: 373, 466, 475.

Actaea spp. Baneberry, dolls-eyes

Several species of baneberries occur in the United States. Members of this genus, particularly the European baneberry, *A. spicata,* are considered

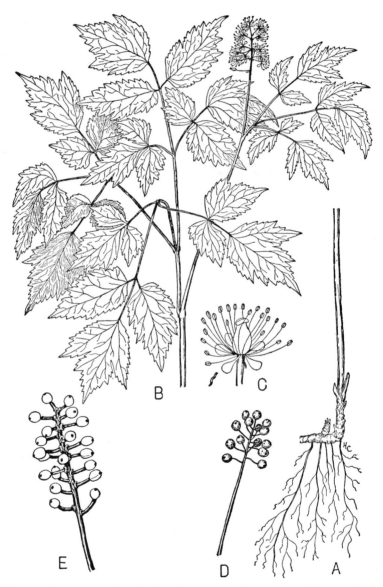

Fig. 8. *Actaea spp.* Baneberries. A–D, *A. rubra.* Red baneberry. Plant, with details of flower and fruit cluster. E, *A. alba.* White baneberry, Detail of fruit cluster. Courtesy of The Macmillan Company.

poisonous, and references may be found in European works concerning the death of children after eating the conspicuous berries. Toxic action is attributed to an essential oil which produces symptoms of severe gastroenteritis. Cases of loss of life, either human or of livestock, have not been recorded in the United States.

Reference: 53.

Adonis spp. Pheasants-eye

DESCRIPTION. Several species of this genus are sometimes cultivated in rock and flower gardens in the United States. Although no cases of poisoning are on record here, the plant is known to be toxic in other countries, and to have produced loss among animals when ingested in hay (892). In Australia several field cases in horses prompted experimental

Fig. 9. *Adonis vernalis.* Pheasant's–eye.

feedings (810) which showed *A. annua* lethal to sheep at about 1 per cent of the subject's weight of plant. *Adonis aestivalis* in hay has proved lethal to horses in Hungary (416). Species of *Adonis* contain phenanthrene glycosides (collectively called adonidin) with marked cardiac activity (1091, 1423). Symptoms in livestock are principally those of severe gastroenteritis.

Anemone spp. Anemone, windflower

The anemones are listed as poisonous in many of the world publications on poisonous plants, but without clear-cut substantiation (574). They have been suspected of having caused livestock loss in the United States, but without proof (277). Anemones contain ranunculin, which breaks down to yield toxic protoanemonin (574) (see *Ranunculus*). *Anemone patens* L. (syn. *Pulsatilla hirsutissima*), pasque flower, covers wide areas of the dry prairies of the Midwest and thus is potentially dangerous. It has been reported (1574) to have caused the formation of plant "hairballs" in the digestive tracts of sheep.

Fig. 10. *Anemone patens.* Pasque flower. Plant in flower and fruit. Courtesy of The Macmillan Company.

Caltha palustris L.   Marsh marigold, cowslip

This plant has worldwide distribution in the northern hemisphere and has been the subject of early European reports of toxicity in man, cattle, and horses (see 933). It has been shown (1290) to contain anemonin, whose precursor in the plant, protoanemonin, is known (1447) to be toxic. Symptoms and lesions are discussed under *Ranunculus*. With the exception of one unsubstantiated report (1335), no cases of livestock loss to this plant are recorded in the North American literature.

The yellow-flowered *Caltha palustris* is common in marshy areas throughout the northeastern and north-central United States and Canada, south to Tennessee and South Carolina. Several other species with yellow or white flowers are found in the western United States and Canada. Because of the widespread distribution of protoanemonin among other genera of the Ranunculaceae, these species of *Caltha* may also be expected to contain this substance.

Like buttercups, *Caltha* is acrid and distasteful to livestock. The young plant is apparently less poisonous or not poisonous at all (1335). Because the poisonous principle is volatile, marsh marigold in hay is harmless.

Clematis spp. Virgins-bower, traveller's joy

Many species of this plant are found in North America, particularly in the northeastern United States and southeastern Canada. None has definitely been recorded as toxic to livestock in this hemisphere and all are apparently distasteful. Yet the genus has a reputation for toxicity. Species not native to North America are strongly suspected of having caused live-

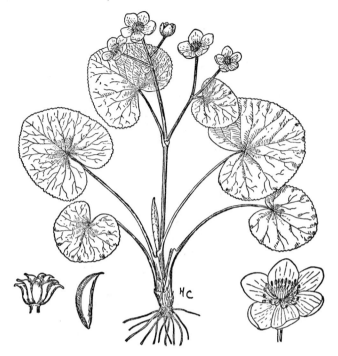

Fig. 11. *Caltha palustris.* Marsh marigold. Flowering plant, with detail of flower, fruit cluster, and single fruit. Courtesy of The Macmillan Company.

stock mortality in other countries (810). Early literature records extractions of alkaloidal, glycosidal, and saponic fractions from certain species. Because the sap is vesicant, and from the relationships of *Clematis* to others containing protoanemonin (see *Ranunculus*), it is likely that several or all species contain the same or a similar compound and may—rarely and under unusual circumstances—be dangerous to livestock.

Delphinium spp. Larkspur, delphinium

Larkspurs have been recognized as medicinal and poisonous plants from classical times, but only minor stock loss is attributed to them in countries other than the United States and Canada. In the United States, however, they contribute to losses in the West second only to those caused by the various locoweeds, and are the most important poisonous plant in terms of cattle poisoning in several states. Occasional loss is also experienced in the Midwest and the East. Mass mortality of livestock, attributed to larkspur poisoning, originally led to the establishment of the long-continued experi-

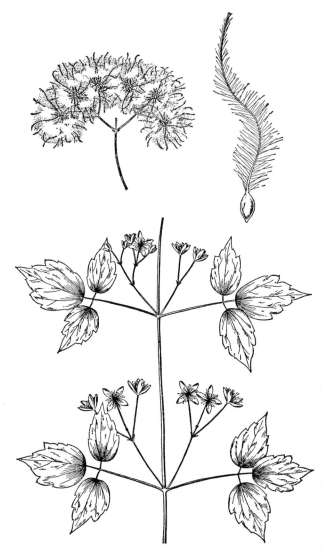

Fig. 12. *Clematis virginiana*. Virgins bower. Section of vine with leaves and flowers. Detail of fruiting clusters and a single seed. Courtesy of The Macmillan Company.

mental investigations of poisonous plants by the U.S. Department of Agriculture.

Information concerning the toxic nature and characteristics of larkspur has been derived from observations and experimental investigations of particular species. Species are not uniformly toxic (911, 1934), but considerable intergradation and hybridization occurs among the more than 80 wild species in North America and the larger number of named horticultural varieties. Accurate species identification is often difficult. Because of past confusion in identifications, all species of *Delphinium,* even the ones commonly cultivated in flower gardens, should be considered potentially toxic until proven otherwise.

The botanical description presented here is generalized to apply to all species of *Delphinium.* Distributions are given for the species most seriously concerned in livestock loss. In order that the literature may be more useful, synonymy between the usage adopted here and the names found in the major papers on larkspur toxicity is indicated. Much of this synonymy has been drawn from the comments of Ewan, and his monographic treatment of the genus *Delphinium* in North America (518) has served as the basis of taxonomic usage in this book.

DESCRIPTION. Perennial erect herbs (some cultivated larkspurs are annual), from a single tuberous, rhizomatous, or clustered tuberous rootstock. Leaves simple, alternate or clustered at ground level, petioled, palmately lobed to deeply divided (depending upon species) into 3 to 5 primary divisions; primary divisions slightly lobed to deeply and repeatedly redivided. Flowers bilaterally symmetrical, in erect terminal racemes or panicles, showy; sepals 5, blue, purple, white, red, or yellow, the upper prolonged backwards in a prominent spur; petals smaller and variable among species, usually 4 (sometimes 2), the upper pair projecting backwards inside the spur; carpels 1 to 5, sometimes fused, ripening into many-seeded follicles. Some cultivated forms are double-flowered and of more than one color.

In the West, where the larkspurs cause the most trouble, they may be divided on the basis of habit into two groups, the tall larkspurs and the low larkspurs. The former typically inhabit higher mountain elevations in open moist areas, canyons, and draws. They range from 3 to 6 ft or more in height, are usually distinctly stemmed throughout most of the season, flower in summer, and do not die back until fall. The low larkspurs typically are found at lower elevations in drier habitats, often covering extensive areas in the foothills and flats. They appear first as rosettelike clumps in early spring, soon producing an erect flowering stem, usually to not more than 3 ft in height, then die back in early summer. These characteristics, interacting with range husbandry practices, have greater influence in determining the severity of loss than relative toxicity of the species involved.

Examination of the flower of *Delphinium* permits ready recognition of this genus. The spur is distinctive and provides a means of distinguishing *Delphinium* from *Aconitum* (which see), the only other plant with which a

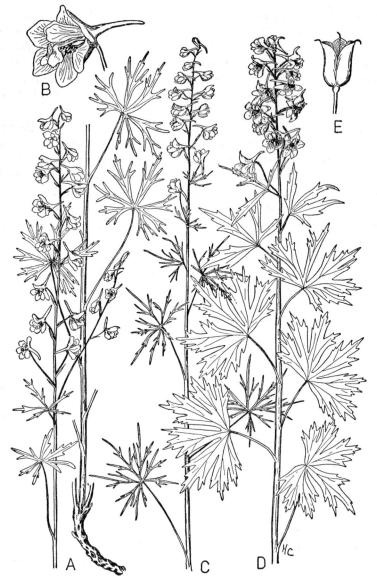

Fig. 13. Tall larkspurs. A,B,E, *Delphinium occidentale*. C, *D.
geyeri*. D, *D. scopalorum* var. *subalpinum*. Courtesy of The Macmillan Company.

flowering larkspur might be confused. Unfortunately, most cases of poisoning, especially by the low larkspurs, occur before the flowers have been
produced. At this stage of growth, larkspurs are easily confused with several

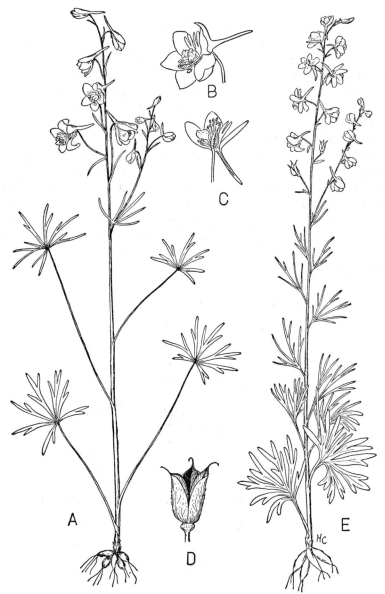

Fig. 14. Low larkspurs. A–D, *Delphinium menziesii*. E, *D. simplex*.
Courtesy of The Macmillan Company.

other plants of the Ranunculaceae. Chief among these are aconite and wild
geraniums. For a person in a given locality, the surest way to distinguish
among the species of these plants in his area is to learn the leaf characteris-

tics of the particular plants in question when they are in flower and can be recognized. Aconite and tall larkspurs often grow together in intermingled populations. Aconites have solid, pithy stems and their leaves are short-petioled, being borne almost against the stem. Tall larkspurs have hollow stems and their leaves are relatively long-petioled. Department Bulletin 365 of the U.S. Department of Agriculture (1009) presents descriptions and figures of the microscopic anatomy of larkspur stem sections which enable a person not only to distinguish between larkspur and other plants but also to identify larkspur in rumen contents of poisoned animals.

In the accompanying table an attempt has been made to include all major publications in which toxicity of identified species of *Delphinium* has been discussed on the basis of either experimental work or case evidence, and those publications concerned with the chemistry and identification of alkaloids where the investigations were prompted by the fact that the plants are toxic to livestock. Several additional species are listed as toxic in various publications (see especially 1014, 1934) without case or experimental substantiation.

PUBLICATIONS DISCUSSING TOXICITY OF IDENTIFIED SPECIES OF LARKSPUR

THE PLANT DISCUSSED HERE AS:	IS THE SAME AS:	IN:
D. andersonii Gray	*D. andersonii* Gray	1104
	D. Andersoni Gray	518
	D. andersoni	542
D. barbeyi Huth	*D. barbeyi* Huth	1006, 1014
	D. Barbeyi Huth	322
	D. barbeyi Huth.	83, 1009
	D. Barbeyi (Huth)	629
	D. Barbeyi H.	323
	D. Barbeyi (Huth) Huth	518
D. bicolor Nutt.	*D. bicolor* Nutt.	87, 277, 518, 1006
	D. menziesii DC.	274
	D. Menziesii	1678
D. geyeri Greene	*D. geyeri* Greene	83, 274
	D. Geyeri Greene	518
	D. Geyeri (Greene)	629
	D. Geyeri	87
D. glaucum Wats.	*D. glaucum* Wats.	518
	D. glaucum S. Wats.	1014, (1934)
D. nelsonii Greene	*D. nelsonii* Greene	629
	D. nelsoni Greene	1006
	D. Nelsoni Greene	518

	D. Nelsonii Greene	87
	D. nelsoni	109
	D. menziesii DC.	1009, 1014
D. occidentale Wats.	*D. Occidentale* S. Wats.	355
	D. cucullatum A. Nels.	1009
	D. cucullatum	87, 1006
	D. scopulorum	274, 1680
	D. glaucum S. Wats.	277, 1014
D. parryi Gray	*D. Parryi* Gray	518, 1383
	D. parryi	935
D. ramosum Rydb.	*D. elongatum* (Rydb.)	629
D. recurvatum Greene	*D. recurvatum* Greene	273
	D. hesperium var.	
	recurvatum Jepson	1383
D. robustum Rydb.	*D. robustum* Rydb.	1009
D. tricorne Michx.	*D. tricorne* Michx.	274, 518, 1009, 1014
D. trolliifolium Gray	*D. trolliifolium* Gray	274
D. virescens Nutt.	*D. virescens* Nutt.	1014
	D. camporum	1383

Note: *D. venenosum* A. Nels. was named in 1926 from specimens brought in during investigations of larkspurs as poisonous plants by the Wyoming Experiment Station. Toxicity is implied in its name and in the associations under which it is discussed (87, 97) but no definite statements as to its toxicity are made.

DISTRIBUTION OF PRINCIPAL SPECIES OF LARKSPUR

I. TALL LARKSPURS:

D. barbeyi. Colorado, Wyoming, Utah, Idaho. Violet-blue.

D. occidentale. Montana, Idaho, Wyoming, Utah. Blue-violet.

D. glaucum. Washington, Oregon, California, Nevada. Violet.

D. trolliifolium. California, Oregon. Dark blue.

II. LOW LARKSPURS:

D. nelsonii. Idaho, South Dakota, Wyoming, Colorado, Utah. Blue-purple to pale blue.

D. bicolor. Canada, North Dakota, Montana, Wyoming, Oregon, Washington. Dark purple.

D. virescens. Plains and Canada west of the Mississippi River, south to Texas. White.

D. tricorne. Pennsylvania to Minnesota and Nebraska, south to Oklahoma to Georgia. Blue or violet, or variegated with white.

D. andersonii. Oregon, California, Utah, Nevada, Idaho. Blue to purple.

III. CULTIVATED LARKSPURS:

D. ajacis L. Common annual larkspur.

D. cheilanthum Fisch., *D. elatum* L., and others. Common perennial larkspurs.

POISONOUS PRINCIPLE. Many species of *Delphinium,* not just the ones known toxic, have been investigated for the alkaloids that they contain. Several of these complex diterpenoid alkaloids have been named and characterized, and the structural formulas of some are now known (1523, 1675). The structural formula of delphinine is given on p. 21. The alkaloids in *Delphinium* are closely related to the alkaloids found in *Aconitum.* Both groups have been reviewed by Stern (1522).

TOXICITY, SYMPTOMS, AND LESIONS. Several factors influence the apparent toxicity of larkspur under field conditions: seasonal variation in toxicity, amount ingested and the length of time over which it was ingested, species of larkspur, species of animal, part of plant, and individual susceptibility (542) of animal. The unsuspected influence of some of these factors led to figures for toxicity in earlier publications that were too low (1009). It was believed that at least 3 per cent of an animal's weight of plant had to be consumed before poisoning would occur, and as a result, larkspur was viewed as only moderately toxic, to be feared in practice only under conditions in which animals would have access to large amounts. Later experimental work, however, showed (295) that *Delphinium barbeyi* in the early stages of growth can be fatal to cattle in amounts as small as 0.7 per cent, and toxic at 0.5 per cent of an animal's weight if ingested within an hour. Toxicity decreases with maturity of plant. At the time of flower-bud appearance, toxicity is reduced to about one-half, and to one-sixteenth when mature fruit appear (these ratios all dry-weight basis). The seeds, however, are highly toxic. Blighted plants whose development is arrested lose toxicity more slowly and may be a factor in late season poisonings.

For some unknown reason sheep are much less susceptible to larkspur poisoning than cattle. In experiments with *D. barbeyi* (295), it was found that about 6 times as much was needed on a percentage basis to produce poisoning and that toxicity of the plant to sheep did not decrease with maturity of the plant as sharply as did its toxicity to cattle. Horses have experimentally been poisoned (1009). Both sheep and horses show the same general symptoms as cattle.

The symptoms as manifested in cattle appear to be largely the result of general weakness brought about by the action of the alkaloids on the nervous system. In order of appearance they include uneasiness, stiffness of gait, and a characteristic straddled stance with the hind legs held far apart as though to prop up the animal. The animal collapses suddenly, usually fore legs first. The severity of poisoning often may be gauged by the position of the animal when prostrated. Slightly poisoned animals rest on the sternum with head erect. In more acute cases the head rests on the ground, and in severe poisoning the animal falls over on its side. Immediately after collapse, the animal may make violent attempts to regain its feet. These movements have been referred to as convulsions but appear voluntary in character. The poisoned animal then becomes quiescent. After a varying period of quiet the animal regains its feet. Usually signs of weakness return quickly and are often accompanied by involuntary muscular twitches, especially of muzzle, shoulder, flank, and hip. A stance with straddled legs and arched back is common, or the animal may move slowly backwards. Soon it goes down again. Periods of standing followed by falling may be repeated several times. If the animal is not fatally poisoned, each period of standing is longer than the one preceding and eventually the animal is fully recovered. Fatal poisoning terminates rapidly by one of two routes. Nausea and abdominal pain are commonly observed in larkspur poisoning. If nausea results in vomition, death occurs immediately in almost all cases by asphyxiation, and ingesta are found in the trachea and bronchi. Otherwise, in fatal cases, death results from respiratory paralysis. In all cases the pulse and respiration become rapid and weak during the periods of acute symptoms. The periods of recumbency may last only a very few minutes or as long as 24 hours. Constipation is universally observed in larkspur poisoning, and it has been found that if this condition can be relieved the animal may normally be expected to recover.

Bloating also is common in larkspur poisoning. On uneven ground animals tend to fall with their heads downhill. In this position they are unable effectively to relieve themselves of gas, and bloating may become the most significant aspect of the case.

Induced excitement in animals which have consumed a toxic amount of larkspur will bring on or intensify the severity of symptoms. The time-honored treatment (1014) of poisoned animals by subcutaneous injection of physostigmine salicylate, pilocarpine hydrochloride, and strychnine sulfate (1 grain, 2 grains, and ½ grain, respectively, per 500- to 600-lb animal) is usually effective in relieving constipation and stimulating respiration in experimentally confined and poisoned animals. However, its use on the range must be weighed against the excitement produced by giving the treatment.

Lesions are not specific in larkspur poisoning. They consist of widespread venous congestion and gastrointestinal inflammation of variable extent.

CONDITIONS OF POISONING. Cattle loss occurs throughout the West, especially on the summer mountain ranges. Horses under natural conditions eat larkspur but stop before consuming a lethal dose. Some of the first reports of larkspur toxicity referred to mass mortality of sheep (277, 1678). Doubt has been cast (1009) on larkspur as etiological in these cases, but sheep can be poisoned experimentally (295) and occasional range cases occur.

Larkspur is most toxic in its youngest growth. Therefore the most dangerous period in a given area will depend upon the factors determining growth. Generally, because of the nature of their typical habitat, low larkspurs produce poisoning in May and June, dying and disappearing shortly thereafter. Tall larkspurs are dangerous over the same period and into July at higher elevations where growth is initiated later. Late season losses may occur from tall larkspur which has set seed. In the East, larkspur losses occur in March, April, and May (1014).

Larkspur is not distasteful to stock. Cattle, particularly, seem to relish it under some conditions. The suggestion has been made (97) that "spring hunger" may be involved and that it is useful when ranging cattle in dangerous country to give supplemental high-protein feed. Sheep will graze most stands of larkspur with impunity and have widely been used in larkspur control.

Additional references: 190, 376, 891, 1588.

Helleborus niger L. Christmas rose

This common garden perennial has been considered poisonous by all the major authors from Dioscorides to the twentieth century, yet few documented cases of poisoning are on record, especially so in this century. Cornevin (335) is the source of the most frequently quoted figures on toxicity. It is evident that the plant contains purgative glycosidic principles which upon ingestion may produce gastric distress and other effects in animals and human beings. Secondly nervous effects also may be observed.

Additional references: 607, 1629.

Fig. 15. *Helleborus niger*. Christmas rose. Detail of leaf and flower.

Ranunculus spp. Buttercup, crowfoot

DESCRIPTION. A very large genus of perennial or annual herbs. Stem leaves alternate, palmately veined, entire, lobed, or dissected; basal leaves often present, numerous and distinctly different in shape. Flowers solitary, terminal, or in corymbose clusters; sepals green, usually 5; petals yellow, varying in number among flowers on the same plant, often 5; stamens numerous, varying in number. Fruit a small achene, ripening from each carpel, hence numerous, grouped on receptacle at maturity.

Buttercups are cosmopolitan weeds of worldwide distribution. Some species are among the commonest weeds of pastures or marshy fields. As far as has been determined they all contain the same toxic principle, although in varying amount, and produce an equivalent syndrome.

POISONOUS PRINCIPLE. The vesicant properties of buttercups have been known since ancient times. The juice of certain species may be used to produce ulceration of the skin. Steps leading to the chemical elucidation of the vesicant substance have been reviewed by Shearer (1447). Early in the nineteenth century it was known that a crystalline substance could be obtained from buttercups by steam distillation and that the remainder had lost its vesicant properties. This substance, named anemonin, was soon found to be innocuous. With slightly different distillation procedures, a highly irritant yellow oil could be obtained, from which crystals of anemonin precipitated spontaneously. The oil was named protoanemonin. Examination of buttercups for alkaloids and cyanogenetic glycosides showed these compounds absent or present in insignificant amount. This, together with a small amount of physiological work with laboratory animals, led Shearer to the conclusion that protoanemonin was the only toxicologically significant substance in buttercups. But protoanemonin is unstable, both as the pure oil and in aqueous solution. It spontaneously undergoes the polymerization reaction that yields innocuous anemonin. This relationship provides chemical substantiation for the well-documented observation that buttercup hay is harmless, but also requires in the growing plant a stable precursor to protoanemonin. Hill and van Heyningen (777) found the precursor, which they named ranunculin. It is a glycoside from which protoanemonin is split in an enzyme-mediated reaction.

ranunculin   protoanemonin   anemonin
(tentative)

TOXICITY, SYMPTOMS, AND LESIONS. Protoanemonin is not a highly toxic substance. Shearer found that the amount of protoanemonin in buttercups varied widely with stage of growth and with species of plant. The species he tested possessed highest protoanemonin content at flowering, the early growth stages possessing only about one-sixth as much on a percentage dry-weight basis. In the mature condition the following species contained amounts of protoanemonin ranging from 2.50 per cent (dry weight basis) to 1.45 per cent in the order named: *Ranunculus sceleratus, R. flammula,*

R. parviflorus, R. acris, and *R. bulbosus. Ranunculus repens* contained only 0.27 per cent. These species were grown under uniform conditions. The actual toxicity of buttercup under any particular circumstances depends, therefore, on a number of variables including amount ingested, stage of growth, species of buttercup, speed and degree of enzymatic release of protoanemonin, conditions under which the buttercup grew, and susceptibility of animal.

Symptoms derive from the irritant nature of protoanemonin and consist primarily of those associated with severe gastrointestinal irritation. Poisoning has been observed in all classes of livestock. In horses, goats, and pigs, oral tissues may be irritated and fiery red. In all animals salivation, diarrhea, and signs of abdominal pain are common. The animal may become depressed or excited. Blood-stained urine and blindness have occurred in some cases. In severe cases the animal dies following convulsions. Post mortem examination reveals irritant lesions throughout the digestive tract, especially in the small intestine. The presence of buttercup in the digestive tract is useful in establishing a positive diagnosis.

CONDITIONS OF POISONING. Despite the ubiquitous nature of many species of buttercup in pastures, buttercup poisoning is rare. Buttercups are strongly distasteful to grazing animals and will be rejected until all better forage is gone. But if started on buttercups, some livestock develop a persistent desire for this plant. Forsyth (574) has described the case of two heifers which were successfully treated for poisoning by *R. sceleratus,* but sought it out when returned to pasture even though better forage was amply available.

The following species have been found toxic or suspected of toxicity in the United States and Canada.

Ranunculus acris L., tall field buttercup. A common pasture weed of eastern and northwestern United States and southern Canada. This species has been considered responsible for producing symptoms of depression and paralysis of pigs in Illinois (1566).

Ranunculus bulbosus L., bulbous buttercup. A somewhat less common pasture weed of the northeastern states. It is similar to the common tall field buttercup in general aspect but may be distinguished by the presence of a distinct swelling or bulbous area of the stem just above the root system. This species is considered (1244) responsible for a case of poisoning in hogs in which the chief symptom was blindness. In England, Forsyth (574) has recorded the poisoning of children who ate the bulbous portion of several plants mistaking them for pignuts (*Conopodium majus*).

Ranunculus abortivus L., small-flowered buttercup. Another common buttercup of pastures and open woods, British Columbia, South Dakota, and Colorado eastward. This species may be distinguished by its flowers, the

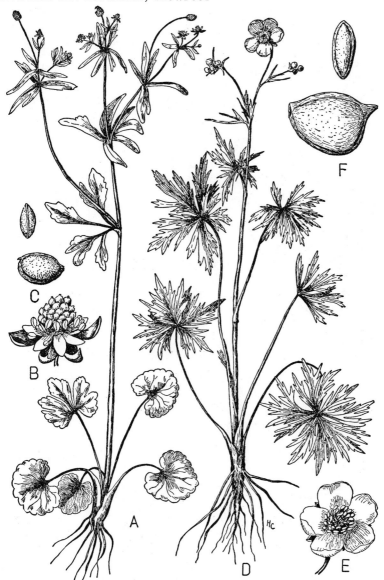

Fig. 16. Common buttercups. A–C, *Ranunculus abortivus,* including details of flower and fruit. D–F, *R. acris,* including details of flower and fruit. Courtesy of The Macmillan Company.

Fig. 17. Common buttercups. A–C, *Ranunculus sceleratus,* including details of flower and fruit. D,E, *R. bulbosus,* base of plant and fruit. F,G, *R. repens,* including detail of fruit. Courtesy of The Macmillan Company.

receptacle of which is globular, and the petals of which are equal to or smaller than the sepals, and inconspicuous. It has been suspected (1126) in a case of cattle mortality in Virginia, but feeding experiments performed with a sheep and a calf under somewhat less than ideal conditions were negative.

Ranunculus repens L., creeping buttercup. A plant of wet pastures, with scattered distribution in northern United States and southern Canada. It is especially common on the Pacific coast where it often forms extensive stands. Although partly erect, plants of this species may be distinguished by the common habit in which long stems grow horizontally over the surface of the ground. Frequent reports of poisoning incriminating this species have been received by the Oregon Agricultural Experiment Station (622).

Ranunculus cymbalaria Pursh (= *Halerpestis cymbalaria* Greene) has proven toxic experimentally to a yearling calf (538) but natural cases have not been reported.

Cases of buttercup poisoning have been reported with some frequency in Britain. Most of the species listed above have produced cases. The literature has been reviewed by Forsyth (538). In addition to these species, two which also occur in North America have been incriminated. These are *Ranunculus ficaria* L. (lesser celandine) and *R. sceleratus* L. (cursed crowfoot). The latter has high protoanemonin content and is considered especially dangerous. It is a common buttercup of marshy areas throughout the northern United States and southern Canada. It may be distinguished by its flowers, the receptacles of which are markedly elongate and the petals of which are small and inconspicuous.

In Australia (777) the following species of buttercup also found in the United States and Canada are considered poisonous: *Ranunculus parviflorus* L. (small-flowered buttercup) and *R. flammula* L. (spearwort).

Additional references: 767, 810.

Berberidaceae

Podophyllum peltatum L. Mayapple, mandrake

DESCRIPTION. One- or two-leafed herb, perennating from a horizontal, fleshy rootstock, ½ to 1½ ft tall. Leaves peltate, umbrella-shaped, irregularly 7- to 9-lobed, about 8 in. in diameter; single in flowerless plants, two in flowering plants. Flower single, axillary between the two leaves, nodding, white, about 2 in. across; petals 6 or 9, somewhat fleshy, stamens twice as many as petals; pistil consisting of a large, single, many-ovuled carpel. Fruit an ovoid, yellow, irregularly blotched, fleshy berry, 1 to 2 in. long.

DISTRIBUTION AND HABITAT. Wet meadows, open woods, roadsides throughout the United States and southern Canada.

Fig. 18. *Podophyllum peltatum*. May-apple. Flowering plant.

POISONOUS PRINCIPLE. May-apple was used by the American Indians for a variety of ailments. Its strong physiological activity recommended itself to the early settlers and preparations of the root, the most active part, soon entered the pharmacopoea and continued in use for many years. A crude resinous material having violent cathartic properties may be extracted from the root with alcohol and precipitated in water. This was given the name podophyllin. In 1942 it was shown that podophyllin had beneficial effect in treatment of condyloma acuminatum (a kind of venereal wart). This led to the recognition of compounds in podophyllin with marked cytotoxic effect. The possibility that one or another of these might have value in treating carcinomas prompted a continuing research interest in them. Podophyllin is a varying mixture of at least 16 physiologically active compounds divisible into two groups, the lignans and flavonols. The chemistry of these compounds has been reviewed by Hartwell and Schrecker (732).

TOXICITY, SYMPTOMS, AND LESIONS. Toxicity of mayapple to the human being is known primarily as the result of misuse of preparations made from it. The principal effect is one of severe, purging gastroenteritis accompanied with vomition. Persons handling the powdered rhizome in commercial operations often display severe conjunctivitis, keratitis, and ulcerative skin lesions. Millspaugh (1109) records the case of a person poisoned by ingestion of the young plant as a pot herb. The fruit is the least toxic part of the plant and is frequently eaten by children. Its taste is not markedly unpleasant. Occasionally catharsis may result. In earlier days it was generally believed that milk from a cow which had grazed mayapple was strongly cathartic.

Animals normally will not consume mayapple. Cases of poisoning are rare. McIntosh (1074) has reported a circumstantial, but apparently well-founded, case in a cow in Ontario. The animal exhibited salivation, anorexia, lacrimation, diarrhea, and excitement for about a day. The muzzle, inter-mandibular area, and eyes were swollen. All visible mucus membranes were congested. Hansen (713) records occasional poisoning of cattle, hogs, and sheep, particularly in the spring. Symptoms in cattle agree with those reported by McIntosh. In hogs, death resulted after few symptoms when the animals grazed on young mayapple shoots.

Menispermaceae

Menispermum canadense L. Moonseed

This woody vine is similar to wild grape in leaf, fruit, and general appearance. It may be distinguished from grape by the leaf, which, although of the same general shape, is broadly toothed in grape (20 or more blunt teeth) but lobed in moonseed (10 or fewer broad lobes), or by the seeds, which are numerous, ovoid in grape, but single, large, and crescent-shaped in moonseed. Moonseed usually twines on other vegetation and is found in woods, thickets, and fencerows. It is native to eastern North America.

Fig. 19. *Menispermum canadense*. Moonseed. Photograph of vine. Drawing of detail of leaf and seed. Drawing, courtesy of The Macmillan Company.

The plant is not common. Because of this and its habitat, it is unlikely to poison livestock. The fruit, however, look like small purple grapes, and may easily be mistaken for the latter by children. Loss of life in children has been reported but not described in Ohio (1399) and Pennsylvania (658).

Nymphaeaceae

Nymphaea tuberosa Paine. Waterlily

This is one of the common species of waterlily, native to North America in ponds of north-central states, south and east to Maryland, and in south-central Canada, east to Ontario. It may be distinguished from other wild species by its leaf which is orbicular, entire, 5 to 16 in. across, and its flower, which is white, odorless, 4 to 9 in. across.

According to Hansen, this species was grazed by hogs after a pond had been drained and produced severe illness followed by death (713).

Order Papaverales

Papaveraceae

Argemone mexicana L. Prickly poppy, Mexican poppy

DESCRIPTION. Coarse annual or in some places perennial herb, 1 to 4 ft tall, with spreading prickly branches and yellow sap. Leaves alternate, whitish, prickly, thistle-like, pinnately cut, 3 to 7 in. across. Flowers terminal on stems, showy, 1 to 3 in. across; sepals bearing a spiny appendage; petals delicate, pale yellow to orange. Fruit a capsule opening by reflexion of the walls only at the extreme tip.

DISTRIBUTION AND HABITAT. This species comes from tropical America and is now found in scattered distribution from Florida northward into Pennsylvania and more commonly westward to Texas and Arizona. Two closely related species have wider distribution in the West. Prickly poppy inhabits open waste areas and roadsides, and is an occasional weed of fields. It is well adapted to dry situations.

POISONOUS PRINCIPLE. The physiologically active isoquinoline alkaloids berberine and protopine are contained in the whole plant (1390); sanguinarine and dihydrosanguinarine in the seeds (1392).

TOXICITY, SYMPTOMS, AND LESIONS. *Argemone mexicana* and *A. intermedia* Sweet have been considered toxic, the former since before the turn of the twentieth century. They are obviously distasteful to animals and cases are rare or absent in the United States. However, the plant and its seeds contain alkaloidal principles which would prove toxic if ingested in sufficient amount. A number of suspected cases of stock poisoning from ingestion of *Argemone mexicana* have occurred in Australia (810). Feeding experiments for confirmation were inconclusive. Poisoning of fowl after ingestion of the seeds of this plant was also suspected and experimental feeding (729) gave positive results for toxicity. About an ounce of seed produced symptoms in a week and a half when fed in small amounts daily during that period. With exceptions, 2 oz. or less produced death within a month. The principal finding was widespread edema, observable before death as swelling of the wattles and darkening of the tips of the comb.

Ingestion of wheat contaminated with large amounts of prickly poppy seed has been held responsible for epidemic dropsy in human beings in India. The alkaloids contained in the seeds were identified (1392) and

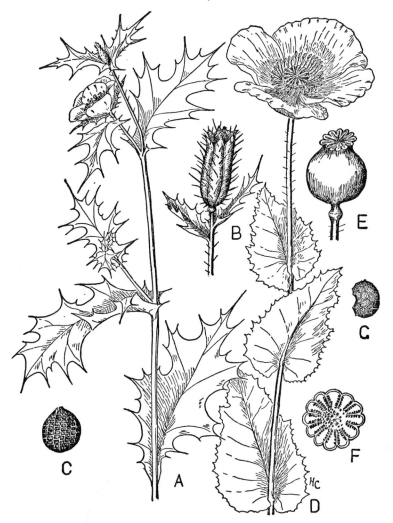

Fig. 20. A–C, *Argemone mexicana*. Prickly poppy, with details of fruit and seed. D–G, *Papaver somniferum*. Opium poppy, with details of fruit, fruit section, and seed. Courtesy of The Macmillan Company.

shown capable of producing dilation of the capillaries, leading to leakage of fluid. Epidemic dropsy from ingestion of *Argemone* oil has been reviewed by Chaudhuri (328) and Sanghri *et al.* (1389). Glaucoma, associated with dropsy, has been related experimentally with poppy alkaloids from *Argemone* and other members of the Papaveraceae and Fumariaceae (685). The alkaloid or a degradation product, may be transmitted in toxic amount through the milk of an animal not itself showing overt symptoms (686).

Chelidonium majus L. Celandine, celandine poppy

DESCRIPTION. Herbaceous biennial or perennial weed, much branched, to about 2 ft tall. Stems brittle; sap milky, bright orange-yellow. Leaves glaucous, alternate, deeply pinnatifid or twice pinnatifid. Flowers small, yellow, in terminal, few-flowered clusters; petals four, conspicuously displayed.

DISTRIBUTION AND HABITAT. Naturalized in gardens and rich soils, Quebec and Ontario to Georgia and Missouri.

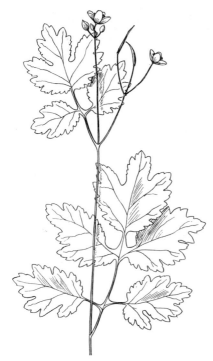

TOXICITY, SYMPTOMS, AND LE-SIONS. The conspicuous orange-yellow sap is extremely acrid. The plant has been used in homeopathic medicine from antiquity. Occasional poisonings in the human being and in livestock are described in European literature, but are uncommon. Animals normally refuse to eat celandine poppy.

The sap causes severe irritation and extreme stomatitis and gastroenteritis if ingested. A number of the poppy (*Papaver*) alkaloids have been detected in *Chelidonium*, including chelidonine, chelerythrine, sanguinarine, berberine, protopine, tetrahydrocoptisine, and others (62, 973). Loss of human life has been recorded (1628).

Additional references: 607, 1329.

Fig. 21. *Chelidonium majus.* Celandine poppy. Plant with mature flowers and fruits. Courtesy of The Macmillan Company.

Papaver spp. Poppies, wild and cultivated

This genus contains about 50 species worldwide, of which very few are native to North America. Somewhat less than a dozen, introduced from Europe, may be found in cultivation. A few of the more common escape cultivation and persist in a locality for many years, usually without spreading.

A large number of isoquinoline alkaloids have been found in various species of *Papaver* (972). By far the greatest number for a single species

22, have been isolated from *Papaver somniferum* L., the opium poppy. Among these are such medically useful alkaloids as morphine, codeine, and papaverine. The crude resin obtained by incising the unripe seed capsules is the narcotic drug opium. Misuse of opium and materials derived

Fig. 22. *Papaver somniferum.* Opium poppy. Mature fruit.

from it results in addiction in the human being and has prompted international, federal, and state legislation to control the growing of *Papaver somniferum* and the manufacture of drugs from it. Poppy seed, used as a condiment and as a source of an edible oil, is also obtained from this species. In the United States, by federal law, (1568) it is illegal for an unlicensed person to obtain, transport, or grow specimens of *Papaver somniferum,* or to permit this species to be grown on land under his control. Opium poppy, prior to control regulations, was a common garden plant, valued for its showy blooms. A number of cultivated varieties including double-flowered forms ("carnation poppy") exist. Not uncommonly, opium poppy still persists in old gardens or about abandoned houses.

The garden poppy most commonly cultivated at present is *Papaver orientale* L., oriental poppy. Alkaloids have been isolated from this species, including at least one found also in the opium poppy, but there is no record of toxicity under natural conditions for the oriental poppy.

Papaver rhoeas L. (corn poppy, red poppy) and *Papaver nudicaule* L. (Iceland poppy) are occasionally cultivated and infrequently found as garden escapes. Both species contain physiologically active principles and have been responsible for poisoning in livestock in other countries (810).

Poppies are distasteful to livestock, but most species contain a variety of potentially toxic alkaloids, sometimes in heavy concentration. Although poisoning of livestock is rare, all poppies should be considered potentially lethal until proven otherwise, particularly since as garden clippings they may be made available to livestock under conditions which promote poisonings.

The feeding of residues of opium poppy seed after oil extraction produced cattle deaths in Europe during World War II. Symptoms included excitement, ataxia, and gastroenteritis (574).

Poisoning or addiction in human beings from opium or its derivatives is not infrequent. Detailed discussions of the toxicological aspects of these drugs is beyond the scope of this volume. For such, the reader is referred to toxicological references, such as Bamford (61).

Sanguinaria canadensis L. Bloodroot, red puccoon

Bloodroot contains several poppy alkaloids of which sanguinarine is one of the more important. The physiological activity of sanguinarine has been investigated in connection with suspected poisoning by prickly poppy (*Argemone*) and is discussed under that heading.

Fig. 23. *Sanguinaria canadensis.* Bloodroot.

Bloodroot is a striking plant with unusual leaf and blood-red sap. It was once used medicinally. In moderate quantity bloodroot may be expected to prove poisonous, but in North America it does not seem to have caused poisoning in livestock or human beings under natural conditions.

Fumariaceae

Corydalis spp. Fitweed, corydalis, fumatory

DESCRIPTION, DISTRIBUTION, AND HABITAT. *Corydalis caseana* Gray (syn. *Capnoides caseana* Greene), of the several toxic species, has caused the greatest livestock loss. It is a biennial or weak perennial, succulent, bushy plant found in limited populations along watercourses in canyons of the Sierra Nevada Mountains at elevations between 5000 and 6300 feet. Numerous spreading branches grow to a height of 3 ft from a fleshy tap root and support many 2- to 3-times pinnately decompound leaves. The leaflets bear a distinct mucro. Conspicuous, very fragrant racemes, to 3 in. long, of creamy white, spurred flowers, each about ¾ in. long, are produced at the ends of the branches. The flowers may be tipped with purple.

Corydalis aurea Willd., a yellow-flowered species, more widely distributed at higher elevations in the Rocky Mountains from their southern limits to Alaska, and at lower elevations in the Southeast and Canada, has been suspected (1501) of having caused loss.

Corydalis flavula DC., another yellow-flowered species of rich woodlands in scattered areas of the eastern United States and Canada, has been suspected (1029) of causing livestock loss in Virginia.

POISONOUS PRINCIPLE. Various species of *Corydalis* have been shown (972) to be rich in the aporphine, protoberberine, protopine, and related groups of isoquinoline-structured alkaloids. This relationship with poppy alkaloids has prompted extensive chemical investigations in the genera *Corydalis* and *Dicentra* (which see). More than a half-dozen alkaloids have been isolated and identified from *C. caseana*. Several times this number have been obtained in total from the species of *Corydalis* that have been investigated. Which, or what combination, of these is responsible for the plant's toxicity is not known, but it has been shown (1105) that the toxicity resides in the alkaloidal fraction.

TOXICITY, SYMPTOMS, AND LESIONS. Feeding experiments with *C. caseana* and field investigations (545, 1105) performed by persons at the Nevada Agricultural Experiment Station after unexplained, repeated summer-range loss of sheep over several seasons, have established that this plant is toxic to sheep and cattle and that it is not distasteful to them. The amount of green plant necessary to produce death in sheep is variable, but on the average is somewhat less than 5 per cent of the animal's weight. As little as 2 per cent may provoke symptoms. The time between feeding and appearance of symptoms and the duration of symptoms also are variable. Symptoms from a lethal amount of plant often appear within minutes and usually within a very few hours. Death, if it occurs, usually takes place in less than 24 hours and often very rapidly.

Symptoms are like those found in *Dicentra* poisoning, and are similar in sheep and cattle. Obvious depression and uneasiness is followed by twitching, especially of the muscles of the face. Convulsive clonic spasms follow, lasting 5 to 15 minutes each, interspersed with irregularly spaced periods free of convulsions. Sharp stimulation during one of the seizures, as by a sudden noise, immediately results in muscular rigidity. Respiration is variable, sometimes increasing to panting. Animals may remain standing or may go down, staggering if up or making running motions of the legs if down. Scouring and bleating or bawling are common. Throughout the period of symptoms, characteristic biting movements are usually observed. Whether on its feet or recumbent, the animal snaps at nearby objects such as sticks, dirt, straw, and pebbles. Most of the activity is in the lips, and most objects are not actually taken into the mouth. In severely poisoned animals, death follows several successive convulsive periods and is immediately preceded by increasing weakness and quiescence. Animals not lethally poisoned make rapid, uneventful recovery. Lesions are not specific, consisting chiefly of variable congestion and some irritation of the gastrointestinal tract.

CONDITIONS OF POISONING. Typically, *C. caseana* is found in the shaded canyons of summer ranges where sheep take refuge from the sun or obtain water. The plant rarely is found in abundance, but since it is palatable it may be sought out and eaten freely. The plant has been shown dangerous throughout its life (545) and produces loss in sheep in July, August, and September, the months when the animals are on summer range. Cattle are susceptible, but are not usually grazed in areas where *C. caseana* grows. *C. flavula* is believed (1029) to have caused loss in horses.

Dicentra spp. (= *Bikukulla*). Staggerweeds, dutchman's breeches, squirrel-corn

DESCRIPTION. Delicate, herbaceous, early spring-flowering plants. Basal leaves broadly triangular, decompound and delicately dissected, giving the plant a lacy appearance; stem leaves absent in most species. Flowers pendant, bilaterally symmetrical, sepals reduced; petals 4, fused into 2 pairs, showy, prolonged backwards in two obvious spurs. Inflorescences racemose or paniculate.

About a dozen species occur in North America. The following have been investigated as possibly poisonous.

Dicentra cucullaria (L.) Bernh. Dutchman's breeches. Flowering plant 6 to 15 in. tall; growing from compact, compound bulbous base. Flowers white (sometimes with pink) with yellow tips; spurs long, widely divergent; inflorescence racemose. Woods, especially wooded slopes and woodland

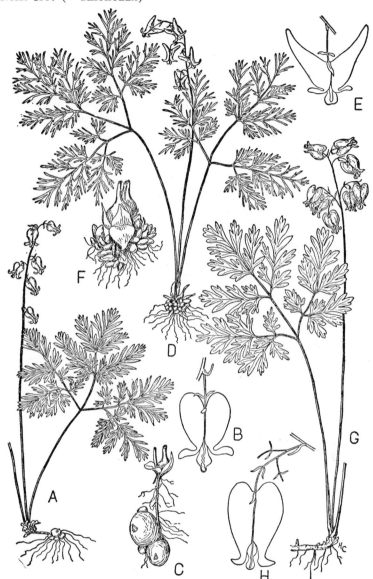

Fig. 24. A–C, *Dicentra canadensis*. Squirrel-corn. Plant, and details of flowers and tubers. D–F, *D. cucullaria*. Dutchman's-breeches. Plant, and details of flower and rootstock. G,H, *D. formosa*. Western bleed-ingheart. Plant and flower. Courtesy of The Macmillan Company.

pastures Nova Scotia to Minnesota, Nebraska and Missouri, south in the mountains to Alabama.

Dicentra canadensis (Goldie) Walp. Squirrel-corn. Flowering plant 6 to 12 in. tall; growing from a delicate, horizontal rootstock which bears a number of small, almost spherical tubers, each about the size of a grain of corn, near the base of the plant. Flowers greenish-white (sometimes with pink); spurs short, not divergent; inflorescence racemose. Habitat as above. Distribution much as preceding except south only to North Carolina and Tennessee.

Dicentra formosa (Andr.) DC. Western bleedingheart. Flowering plant 6 to 24 in. tall; growing from a fleshy, clustered, branching rootstock. Flowers rose-purple; spurs short, not divergent; inflorescence paniculate. Woods, fencerows and clearings, British Columbia to Oregon, less frequently to California.

Dicentra eximia (Ker.) Torr. Wild bleedingheart. Flowering plant 12 to 24 in. tall; growing from a branching, scaly rootstock. Flowers rose to pink; spurs short, not divergent; inflorescence paniculate in stronger individuals. Rocky woods and cliffs of the southern Appalachians.

Dicentra spectabilis Lem. is the common garden bleedingheart. Varieties of *D. eximia* also are cultivated.

POISONOUS PRINCIPLE. Various species of *Dicentra* have been shown (972) rich in the aporphine, protoberberine, protopine, and related groups of isoquinoline-structured alkaloids. Protopine is the only alkaloid yet characterized in *D. spectabilis* and has been found present in all other

protopine

species investigated (870). More than a score of these alkaloids have been extracted, characterized and named from various species of *Dicentra*. Interest in their chemistry derives from their structural relationships to the poppy alkaloids. Toxicity of the alkaloidal fraction has been demonstrated in *D. canadensis* (131), *D. cucullaria* (131), and *D. formosa* (130), but the degree of toxicity of the individual alkaloids is not clear ["cucullarine" of Black *et. al.* (131) has not been accepted (970)].

TOXICITY, SYMPTOMS, AND LESIONS. Only limited feeding experiments with livestock have been carried out with species of *Dicentra,* and *D. cucullaria* alone has experimentally been shown poisonous. In these experiments (131) 2 per cent of the animal's weight either of tops or of the fleshy underground portion of the plant produced equivalent symptoms, appearing within a day, in cattle. These amounts were not fatal, and as much as 4 per cent of an animal's weight failed even to provoke symptoms in another experiment.

Symptoms of *D. cucullaria* poisoning in cattle as determined by the experimental feedings are similar to those observed in the field. The first symptoms noted in the experimentally poisoned steers consisted of mild trembling and running back and forth with head held unusually high. Salivation was evident. Partially digested ingesta were forcibly ejected to a distance of several feet. Trembling became convulsive and the animals went down about 10 minutes after the onset of symptoms. A characteristic position was assumed with head thrown back and legs rigidly extended. There was evidence of pain and difficulty in breathing. In the experimental cases, symptoms gradually became less acute and the animals, although weak, were able to regain their feet about 20 minutes after falling. Complete recovery rapidly followed.

Although *D. canadensis* contains physiologically active alkaloids, the tops fed out in amounts equivalent to 2 or 3 per cent of an animals' weight failed to elicit symptoms (131). Other species have not been experimentally fed.

CONDITIONS OF POISONING. In practice, poisoning appears confined to cattle on early spring woodland pasture. Losses in cattle have been reported sporadically over many years in Virginia (131) and from Indiana (699). In Virginia the danger is usually past by mid-May but may last until late June at higher elevations. Cattle find the plants distasteful (131) but will consume them when other feed is scarce. *Delphinium* (which see) occurs in similar locations and produces poisoning with not markedly dissimilar symptoms. It is generally assumed by the farmers in the areas where poisoning occurs that rains predispose towards the occurrence of cases by softening the ground and allowing the fleshy underground portions to be pulled out and consumed.

Additional reference: 478.

Capparidaceae

Wislizenia refracta Engelm. Jackassclover

This annual herb of western Texas to southern California has trifoliolate leaves which look much like those of clover. Its numerous, small, yellow flowers form small, twisted, elongate fruits which cause the terminal, racemose inflorescences to appear to consist of masses of entangled, wiry stems.

Jackassclover is distinctly unpalatable, but preliminary feeding experiments, prompted by the suspicion that this plant had caused loss in livestock, indicate that it is toxic in amounts less than 1 per cent of an animal's weight (801).

Cruciferae

> *Amoracia lapathifolia* Gilib. (syn. *A. rusticana* Gaertn.; *Cochlearia amoracia* L.). Horseradish

Horseradish was introduced into this country as a condiment plant and is grown commercially in limited amount. It has escaped from cultivation and is now naturalized in moist ground throughout the East and Midwest to the extent of becoming a weed in some places. Horseradish is a coarse perennial plant growing from a large, woody, branching taproot, the source of the condiment. The leaves are simple, large, rough-surfaced, and somewhat variable in outline. The flowering stem, bearing a raceme of small white flowers, attains a height of 1½ to 4 ft.

Mustard oil (p. 28) is considered (574) the poisonous principle. It is composed of a mixture of allyl *iso*thiocyanate and beta phenyl *iso*thiocyanate; the former in larger amount (876).

Cases of loss of cattle, horses, and swine are on record (574, 675) in British literature. Poisoning has resulted from ingestion of the tops as well as the roots and has occurred both under pasture conditions and from horseradish roots thrown to swine in garbage.

The plant produces an acute inflammation of mucous membranes of the rumen or stomach. Excitement and pain are followed by collapse and death. An amount of raw horseradish root of the order of magnitude of 1 per cent of body weight has produced death in swine within three hours (574).

> *Barbarea vulgaris* R. Br. Yellow rocket, winter cress, etc.

This is one of the commonest weedy mustards. It is found throughout the northern United States and southern Canada as a biennial or perennial weed of hay fields and cultivated crops, and is especially abundant in the northeastern and north-central states, turning fields yellow in early spring.

One unusual case of poisoning in a horse has been described (713) which suggests that ingestion of relatively large quantities of this plant may produce gastroenteritis. The symptoms suggest mustard-oil poisoning (see p. 159).

> *Brassica spp.*

This genus in its species and botanical varieties includes many important weeds, truck crop plants, and forage plants, as, for example, the wild and cultivated mustards, charlock, kale, rape, Brussels sprouts, cabbage, cauliflower, broccoli, kohlrabi, rutabaga, and turnip. Many have proven troublesome under particular circumstances.

Taxonomically, the group has been treated variously in botanical and horticultural works; synonymy is considerable. The nomenclature here used follows that in the *Manual of Cultivated Plants* (54) for the cultivated members and Gray's *Manual of Botany,* 8th ed. (504), for the weeds.

Brassica hirta Moench. (syn. *B. alba* Rabenh. *Sinapis alba* L.). White mustard

A strong annual weed, 2 to 4 ft tall, occasionally cultivated for the seeds as a source of mustard or for the foliage for greens. Introduced from Eurasia and now naturalized in localities throughout the country in waste places and occasionally as a weed in grain crops. Leaves rough, petioled, ovate or obovate in outline, but deeply cut, forming 1 to 3 pairs of lobes. Flower with 4 sepals and 4 spreading petals, yellow and showy, about ½ in. across. Fruit "pod" a characteristic capsule, ¾ to 1½ in. long, densely hairy at base; base swollen, containing one or a few seeds; tip prolonged into a flat, curved beak equalling or exceeding the rest of the pod in length.

Cattle and sheep have been poisoned in Britain after ingestion of mustard seeds in meal (806), the podded plant (574), or mustard stubble (471). The poisonous principle is probably one or a mixture of *iso*thiocyanates (see mustard oils, p. 28). Symptoms and lesions are those of severe gastroenteritis. There is evidence of severe pain, salivation, diarrhea, and irritation of mouth and upper digestive tract. Symptoms appear soon after ingestion of a toxic amount and may terminate in death.

Brassica kaber Wheeler (syn. *B. arvensis* Rabenh.). Charlock, wild mustard

Annual weed, 2 to 3 or more ft tall. Introduced from Eurasia and now naturalized as a very common weed of grain crops throughout the United States, and as a weed in waste areas. Leaves simple, variable, obovate to ovate, variously lobed, with little or no petiole in the upper parts of the plant. Flowers in a raceme, yellow, fragrant, ¾ to 1 in. across, with 4 sepals and 4 spreading petals. Fruit "pod" a characteristic capsule, 1 to 1½ in. long, glabrous or sparsely hairy; swollen base containing several dark, slightly roughened seeds; tip prolonged into a 2-edged beak, somewhat shorter than the body of the pod.

Cattle (668) and swine (1574) have been poisoned in Canada; sheep in Britain (596). In all cases the seeds or podded plants were responsible. The poisonous principle is probably one or a mixture of *iso*thiocyanates (see mustard oils, p. 28) (1574).

Symptoms and lesions are those of severe gastroenteritis and are similar to those listed for *Brassica hirta.* Marked nephritis was observed in one instance (596). In the case involving swine, seeds were obtained in ground meal to which they had been added as an adulterant.

Fig. 25. *Brassica kaber*. Charlock, wild mustard. Plant, with details of seedling, flower, fruit, and seed. Courtesy of The Macmillan Company.

Brassica napobrassica Mill. Rutabaga, yellow turnip, swede turnip
Rutabaga has been found (654) to have a very high goitrogenic capacity. It contains the goitrogenic compound, L-5-vinyl-2-thiooxazolidone (see

goitrogenic substances, p. 26) (46). It is not known to have produced goiter in livestock under natural conditions. Development of puerperal hemoglobinuria of cattle in Scotland has been associated with feeding this plant.

Brassica napus L. Rape

Rape, an annual or winter annual in northern latitudes, is cultivated as a forage crop and for its seeds, from which an oil is obtained. It is widely grown as a late fall pasturage or forage crop in the northern United States, Canada and in other countries with similar climatic conditions. Large acreages were cultivated in Canada, Britain, Germany, and Scandinavian and other countries, especially during World War II, and the residue was used as a livestock feed. Wherever heavily used as livestock feed or forage, rape causes infrequent instances of difficulty. Occasionally, serious loss has occurred in this hemisphere. Rape has been incriminated in a variety of poisoning syndromes. Several have been reviewed by Coté (240), and his terminology will be followed.

RESPIRATORY SYNDROME OR PULMONARY EMPHYSEMA. Pulmonary emphysema associated with a toxic substance is unmistakable in its characteristics. It occurs in cattle on pasture and has been described and investigated in Canada (46, 1416), the United States (222), and other countries (1189, 1416). It appears most frequently when cattle are pastured on succulent rape forage but is also associated with succulent kale or turnip forage (see below) and has also been reported (1416) from alfalfa or other succulent pasturage. Factors such as species of plant or plants, succulence, climate, and soil have been suggested as influencing the development of the disease. Its occurrence is unpredictable.

Symptoms usually appear within 7 to 10 days after animals have been placed on rape forage. One or more animals will be noticed standing apart from the rest of the herd, with head extended, breathing with difficulty. Examination reveals increased heart rate, slight icterus, and paresis of stomach and intestines. Constipation is usual. Occasionally fetid diarrhea is found. Dyspnea, characterized by an expiratory grunt, increases in severity with exercise. If the disease continues for two or three days, subcutaneous emphysema in the cervical and lumbar area may develop. Temperature is rarely raised as much as a degree. Mortality ranges from 5 to 35 per cent.

The lesions of the lung are striking. The lung is heavy, distended, edematous throughout, congested, and permeated with numerous air pockets, the larger attaining the size of a small toy balloon. At the microscopic level the rupture of almost all alveoli is observed. The liver is pale and friable, showing variable areas of necrosis. The intestinal tract bears variable areas of inflammation.

The exact etiology of this syndrome has not been determined. It is conjectured (1416) that the emphysema is the result of a toxin. It has been shown (1416) that the bacterium *Clostridium welchii* forms a toxin capable of producing symptoms and lesions of emphysema. On the other hand, examination for this organism has been negative in several instances of the disease. Nevertheless, paresis of the gastrointestinal tract lends weight to the hypothesis of an enterotoxemia as responsible for development of the disease. It has also been suggested that the disease is an allergic reaction (222) or that it is related to lush forage of various kinds (968). Each instance of the disease may not have been produced in the same way.

DIGESTIVE SYNDROME. This manifestation of rape poisoning has been observed in cattle and sheep in Canada (240) and Britain (562, 1099). It is perhaps the most common type of rape poisoning and may be the result of simple engorgement (240).

Symptoms appear two or three days after animals have been placed on rape forage. The affected animal ceases feeding, stands apart from the rest, and appears uncomfortable. Examination shows complete paresis of the gastrointestinal tract, and constipation. In cattle, small quantities of sticky black manure may be found on rectal examination. The colon contains gas, but no excess is found in the rumen. Temperature remains about normal. Icterus of the mucous membranes may be observed. Mortality varies considerably but may run as high as 30 per cent (1099). In cattle, the rumen is found to be filled with a blackish mass of ingesta (240). Occasional inflammation of portions of the intestines may be observed. The liver occasionally displays necrotic areas and the kidney, degenerative changes.

Many of the symptoms and lesions of the digestive syndrome are found in other types of rape poisoning. Abrupt death may be the immediate result of enterotoxemia.

NERVOUS SYNDROME, RAPE BLINDNESS. This type of rape poisoning has been noted in cattle (340, 382, 395) and sheep (395, 1099) in Canada and Britain. The affected animal is first noticed standing alone or wandering aimlessly. Solid objects will not be avoided. The animal is obviously blinded. In many cases the disease arrests at this point. In others, the animal becomes aggressive. Steers may inflict considerable damage upon their surroundings and themselves before dropping of exhaustion. With the exception of lesions of the digestive system similar to those produced in other types of rape poisoning, lesions are absent.

Examination of the eye of blinded animals reveals no abnormality other than decreased or absent pupillary reflex. If the animals are stabled and given good feed and treatment, sight gradually returns. Recovery is usually completed in a month or month and a half (395). Occasionally permanent blindness results.

URINARY SYNDROME, HEMOGLOBINURIA, "REDWATER DISEASE." Hemoglobinuria in cattle (340, 504, 574, 799, 866) and sheep (1512) has been reported from the United States, Canada, Britain, and Ireland. Animals stand apart, not eating. The urine is dark, reddish or brown, and foams upon hitting the ground. Constipation may be evident. Visible mucous membranes are pale or icteric. The carcass is anemic or highly icteric. The liver is abnormal in appearance and shows moderately severe necrosis upon histologic examination. The kidney is dark in color, and congested but histologically not abnormal. The bladder is filled with dark-colored urine. The hemoglobin content of the blood is very low.

This disease is a hemolytic anemia associated with ingestion of rape, but the exact etiology is unknown. In symptoms and lesions it is almost indistinguishable from copper poisoning. Hemolytic anemia caused by certain plants indigenous to Australia and New Zealand has been shown to be mediated by copper in these plants. Such is not the case with rape (1512). If the urinary syndrome occurs in recently postparturient dairy cattle, it cannot be distinguished from the poorly understood puerperal hemoglobinuria. (See also *Beta,* sugar-beet residue.) There is some evidence that disturbances in blood ionic levels play a role in this disease (1512).

In the areas where rape forage has caused recurrent loss, farmers have developed practices they believe reduce the danger. Chief among these is the inclusion of hay or straw in the diet, or the provision for free access to old, unimproved pasturage along with the rape. Attempts to correlate potential toxicity of rape forage with features or conditions of soil, climate, weather, particular stage of growth, and the like have not been successful, although the belief persists that wet years or areas and early frosts are predisposing and that purple coloration of the plant may indicate potential danger.

In Michigan, rape pasturage has been incriminated (690) in the development of a condition in fowl in which the blood failed to clot and mortality resulted from uncontrollable hemorrhage. The fowl had been on rape pasturage for about two weeks and all deaths stopped within four days after they were removed from it. Supplemental grain and oyster shell had been provided. Rape pasturage has also been held responsible in various parts of the United States for provoking photosensitization in swine (260, 713) and other white-skinned animals (713). Case (260) lists it as a hepatogenic photosensitizer. In New Zealand mortality of a large number of ewes and lambs on second-growth rape was determined (187) to have been caused by nitrate poisoning. Methemoglobin was detected in the blood.

Oat-rape pasturage, in which the rape contained 5.25 per cent potassium nitrate, has been held responsible (259) in the United States for malformed fetuses and abortion in swine. The possibility of a casual relationship between abnormally low levels of vitamin A found in the blood and high nitrate in the forage was suggested.

Rape seed meal, available during World War II as a feed concentrate, produces goiter in animals if fed in more than small amounts. A goitrogenic substance, L-5-vinyl-2-thiooxazolidone, has been isolated (46, 250) from rape seed (see goitrogenic substances, p. 26). Several studies (19, 1181, 1603) have been undertaken to work out practical techniques for detoxication of rape seed meal and a rationale for its inclusion in poultry and swine diets. Hot-water extraction (19, 1181) or supplementation of the diet with iodine (19) can overcome most of the goitrogenic effect. The residual effect has been considered useful in provoking a lower metabolism and better use of feed in poultry (19, 1603). Rape seeds have also been found to contain volatile *iso*thiocyanates (503, 875, 1664) (see mustard oils, p. 28) which might prove troublesome if ingested in large quantity or concentration. Three *iso*thiocyanates have been isolated, of which 3-butenyl *iso*thiocyanate is predominant.

Brassica oleracea var. *acephala* D.C. Common kale

A nonheading cabbage, cultivated in a few areas for human consumption, but in larger acreages as a forage crop similar in culture and use to rape. Goiter, produced by continued ingestion of this plant, has been reported in Britain and New Zealand (1443, 1465). It is especially severe, causing heavy mortality, in lambs of ewes fed kale. The goitrogenic substance in kale is L-5-vinyl-2-thiooxazolidone (46) (see goitrogenic substances, p. 26).

Development of hemolytic anemia with hemoglobinuria similar to that seen in the urinary form of rape poisoning (see *Brassica napus*) has been reported (306, 504, 866, 1512) in cattle and sheep fed on kale in the United States, Britain, and other countries.

Brassica oleracea var. *capitata* L. Cabbage

Cabbage has been shown (271) to produce goiter in rabbits maintained on this ration in an experimental study of syphilis. This was the original demonstration of the goitrogenic capacity of plant materials. Since that time, many plants have been shown goitrogenic and in several the goitrogenic substances have been identified. The goitrogenic substance in cabbage is L-5-vinyl-2-thiooxazolidone (668) (see goitrogenic substances, p. 26). Development of hemolytic anemia with hemoglobinuria similar to that seen in rape (*B. napus*) poisoning has been reported (306) in Britain.

Brassica oleracea var. *botrytis* L. Broccoli

Ingestion of large quantities of broccoli by ruminants results in ruminal atony, inability to eat or drink, and, if unrelieved, death (801). This syndrome is similar, in part, to the digestive-syndrome type of rape poisoning.

Brassica oleracea var. *gemmifera* Zenker. Brussels sprouts

Cattle have displayed hemolytic anemia with hemoglobinuria similar to that seen in rape (*B. napus*) poisoning in Britain when foraging on Brussels sprouts (306).

Brassica rapa L. Turnip

The common cultivated turnip is occasionally used for sheep or cattle fodder. In New Zealand, turnips have caused congenital goiter in lambs (753) and have been demonstrated (46) to contain the goitrogenic substance L-5-vinyl-2-thiooxazolidone. Turnips also have been found (166, 1318) to contain dangerous levels of nitrate, and have been incriminated in the loss of cattle in the United States.

Other mustards

Mortality of sheep in Wyoming has been traced (97) to ingestion of an unidentified biennial wild mustard. Experimental feeding recreated the symptoms, which were those of "acute indigestion."

Brassica nigra Koch (black mustard) and *B. juncea* Coss. (Indian mustard) are common weeds and are also cultivated as mustard sources. The seeds of both have been shown (833) to contain allyl *iso*thiocyanate, and therefore may be considered potentially toxic. In Denmark, myrosinase-free mustard-seed cake from the latter plant caused mortality in several herds of milking cattle (1289). In this case the assumption was made that myrosinase obtained via ingestion of other *Cruciferae* at the same time as the press cake was sufficient to release allyl *iso*thiocyanate from the non-toxic glycoside in the cake. Feeding experiments with cake of known allyl *iso*thiocyanate content have established that a lethal dose of the oil for cattle is around 0.001 per cent of the animal's weight.

Brassica hirta, B. nigra, and *B. pekinensis* Rupr. (Chinese cabbage) are among those species which may be potentially goitrogenic (see goitrogenic substances, p. 26).

Additional references: 528, 965.

Cardaria draba (L.) Desv. (= *Lepidium draba* L.). White top, hoary cress

This weedy mustard has been suspected of slight toxicity in other countries. Feeding experiments at the Nevada Agricultural Experiment Station, briefly reported, demonstrate that it contains an irritant principle and may cause trouble under conditions of forage shortage (548).

Descurainia pinnata (Walt.) Britt. Tansy mustard

DESCRIPTION. Annual, to 2 ft tall. Stems and leaves covered with a fine pubescence giving the plant a whitish appearance. Leaves alternate, deeply pinnately dissected. Inflorescence an elongate raceme. Flowers small, with four spreading yellow to yellowish-green to white petals. Fruit ("pod") a capsule of two carpels, an inch or more long, bearing small waxy seeds in two rows.

DISTRIBUTION AND HABITAT. Widely distributed throughout the southern United States, forming heavy stands on dry sandy soils in arid areas. Much more abundant during summers following moderate winter rains than after dry winters in the arid Southwest.

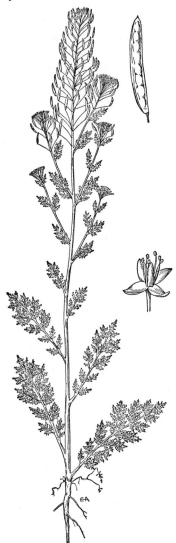

POISONOUS PRINCIPLE. Unknown. Despite similarity of the symptoms with those produced in one type of selenium poisoning, tansy mustard's selenium content is insufficient to produce the disease.

TOXICITY, SYMPTOMS, AND LESIONS. Continued ingestion of large quantities of this plant over a relatively long period of time is required before symptoms appear (754). In cattle on range the symptom first observed is partial or complete blindness. This is followed by, or accompanied with, inability to use the tongue or to swallow. The disease is popularly termed "paralyzed tongue." Because of blindness, animals may wander aimlessly until exhausted, or stand pushing against a solid object in their path for hours. Because of inability to swallow, animals may be observed standing at water unable to drink, or unsuccessfully cropping forage. Animals become thinner and weaker, and death will eventuate if treatment is not undertaken. Treatment is simple and effective. It consists of administering 2 to 3 gallons of water (with nourishment such as cotton seed meal in it if the animals are seriously weak) twice daily by stomach tube. This gets the digestive system functioning again and symptoms gradually disappear.

CONDITIONS OF POISONING. Cases occur in cattle on range in the Southwest. A diet consisting almost entirely of this plant is required. The appearance of stands of tansy mustard sufficiently thick to enable such a diet is erratic from year to year. If rainfall during the early winter months is adequate, the plant becomes well estab-

Fig. 26. *Descurainia pinnata.* Tansy mustard. Plant, with details of flower and fruit. Courtesy of The Macmillan Company.

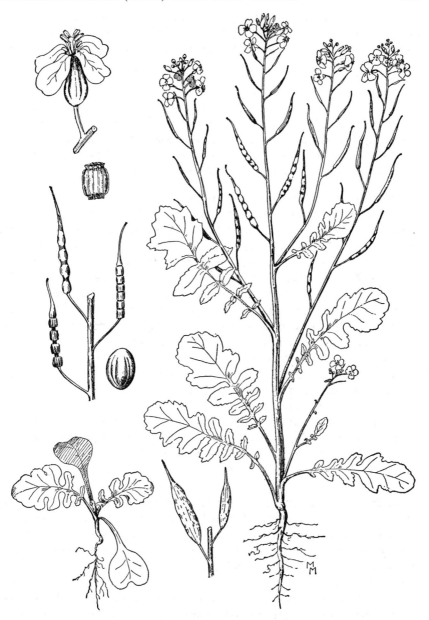

Fig. 27. *Raphanus raphanistrum*. Wild radish. Plant, with details of seedling, flower, young pod, dried (mature) pod, single-seeded pod fragment, and seed. Courtesy of The Macmillan Company.

lished and flowers during February, March, or April. It is dangerous during the period of bloom and until the pods have matured, when the plants become tough and fibrous. If other feed is scarce, tansy mustard is readily consumed in quantity.

Erysimum cheiranthoides L. Wormseed mustard

This plant is widely distributed in the United States as a weed of cultivation, roadsides, waste areas, and meadows. Its seeds contain allyl *iso*thiocyanate (876) (p. 28) and have been responsible for the loss of swine in Canada (1574). In the case reported, the shorts fed to the swine contained 1.7 per cent of the seed of this plant by weight.

Raphanus raphanistrum L. Wild radish

DESCRIPTION. Annual or winter annual, to 2½ ft tall. Stems much branched, growing from a strong tap root. Leaves alternate, pinnatifid, oblanceolate in outline. Inflorescence a raceme with flowers opening over an extended period of time; often, therefore, with maturing pods below and unopened flowers above. Flowers with 4 pale yellow or white, rarely light purple, petals with distinct purple veins. Fruit ("pod") a capsule of characteristic construction; long and narrow with 2 to 10 seeds, constricted between the seeds to give the appearance of a string of beads; indehiscent, instead breaking transversely into one-seeded fragments.

DISTRIBUTION AND HABITAT. A common weed of grain crops, other cultivated areas, and waste places in the northeastern quarter of the United States, into Canada, and in the Pacific northwest.

POISONOUS PRINCIPLE. Unknown.

TOXICITY. Wild radish has been considered dangerous to livestock both in the United States and in Europe. Reports of toxicity in the literature are, however, scant. Other species in this genus contain *iso*thiocyanates (876), especially in the seeds, which may produce gastroenteritis if enough are ingested (483, 1530).

A different syndrome was associated with loss of lambs in France occurring 2 days after the animals had been placed on a pasture with large numbers of flowering wild radish plants (1595). The flowering tops were eaten preferentially. Symptoms and lesions included rumen atony, icterus, friable liver, and blood-stained urine in the bladder. These symptoms and lesions are similar to those produced in the urinary form of rape poisoning (see *Brassica napus*). Wild radish also has been incriminated in the poisoning of dairy cattle in Australia with symptoms of hemoglobinuria (1249).

Stanleya pinnata (Pursh) Britt. Prince's plume

DESCRIPTION. Coarse herbaceous perennial, forming a clumped, erect plant, 1½ to 5 ft tall. Stems thick, coarse, woody towards base, mostly unbranched except distally. Leaves variable; lower usually pinnate or pinnately cut, 2 to 8 in. long, segments lanceolate; upper becoming smaller, ob-lanceolate, without petiole. Inflorescence a terminal, exserted, showy spike ½ to 1½ ft long; axis thick, more or less rigid; flowers numerous, yellow; sepals linear, green; petals 4, long, sharply expanded into an oval blade at tip, bright yellow; stamens exserted, anthers coiled. Fruit a silique.

DISTRIBUTION AND HABITAT. Desert soils, North Dakota to Texas, west to California.

Fig. 28. *Stanleya pinnata.* Prince's plume.

Prince's plume is a striking plant, easily noticed in a mass of desert vegetation when in bloom. It and other less common species of *Stanleya* are reliable indicators of seleniferous soil (1591) (see selenium, p. 44). *Stanleya pinnata* does not accumulate as high concentrations of selenium as do some species of *Astragalus,* but acute selenium poisoning has been induced with it in forced-feeding experiments (97). Whether it is ever toxic under range conditions remains an open question, since animals have never been observed to eat prince's plume, even under conditions approaching starvation.

Thlaspi arvense L. Fanweed, field penny-cress

A widely distributed annual weed of grain crops, waste areas, and gardens throughout most of the United States and Canada, but especially common in the prairie states and provinces.

The seeds of this plant contain allyl *iso*thiocyanate (876), which undoubtedly is responsible for reports (1574) of gastric distress in livestock upon ingestion of grain containing quantities of fanweed seed.

Fanweed has also been incriminated (736) in the development of hemo-

Fig. 29. *Thlaspi arvense.* Fanweed. Plant, with details of fruiting stem, winged fruit, opened fruit, attachment of seeds to fruit wall, and seed. Courtesy of The Macmillan Company.

globinuria in a herd of heifers in Washington state. The weed was obtained in hay, and examination of feces showed that they contained large quantities of fanweed seeds. Trouble ceased upon substitution of nonweedy hay.

Order Guttiferales

Hypericaceae

Hypericum perforatum L. St. Johnswort, Klamath weed, goatweed

DESCRIPTION. Erect perennial herb, 1 to 3 ft tall except to 5 ft in the Pacific coast states. Main stems usually clustered, woody below, bearing many lateral, opposite, sterile branches. Stems and branches 2-edged or winged. Leaves opposite, sessile, linear-oblong, ½ to 1 in. long, spotted with tiny dots which appear black except yellowish-translucent when held against the light; branch leaves usually subtending reduced, compressed branchlet systems. Inflorescence cymose; flowers numerous, ⅔ to 1 in. broad; petals 5, yellow; sepals 5, green; stamens numerous, in 3 to 5 clusters; ovary bearing 3 widely spreading styles.

DISTRIBUTION AND HABITAT. Aggressive weed in dry ground of roadsides, pastures, and ranges. Introduced many years ago into eastern states and now naturalized as a weed throughout most of the United States. There are some 200 species in the genus *Hypericum*. More than 25 may be found in the United States and Canada. In the world literature at least 6 species have been described as producing photosensitization. *Hypericum concinnum* Benth. has been suspected of producing photosensitization in California (1383). Otherwise, in the United States, reports of toxicity are thus far confined to *H. perforatum*. Since the photosensitizing pigment is contained in the characteristic glandular dots of the foliage and petals, it is not unreasonable to assume, until proven otherwise, that domestic species, such as *H. punctatum* Lam., which bear similar glands, may likewise be toxic. Many of the common species are glandless. Elsewhere livestock poisoning from one or another species of *Hypericum* has occurred in Australia, New Zealand, North Africa, and Europe.

POISONOUS PRINCIPLE. St. Johnswort is a primary photosensitizer (see photosensitization, p. 52). The photodynamic pigment has been the object of extractions and attempts at chemical identification since the latter half of the nineteenth century. A fluorescent pigment, isolated earlier by others, was given the name hypericin by Carny in 1911 (284). This pigment was red in acid or neutral media, green when alkaline. Ultimately it was identified (mostly by European work—see brief review in *Merck Index,* 7th ed.) as a dianthrone derivative (formula represented on page 173).

Hypericin of the plant remains chemically intact through ingestion, digestion, absorption into the bloodstream, and passage through the liver. It may

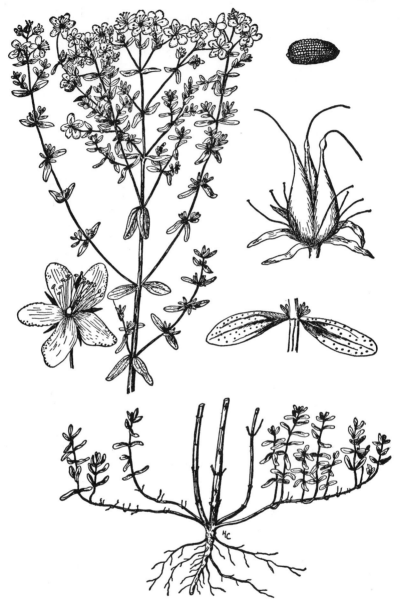

Fig. 30. *Hypericum perforatum*. St. Johnswort. Upper and basal parts of plant (latter with runners), and details of flower, fruit, seed, and leaves. Courtesy of The Macmillan Company.

be detected spectroscopically in the skin of rabbits fed St. Johnswort (1210). The liver is undamaged in *Hypericum* poisoning. It has also been shown using this plant that molecular oxygen is necessary for the reactions in the skin which result in the signs of photosensitization. Purified hypericin, given orally, can produce photosensitization in rats. The absorption spectrum of hypericin has been determined. It shows two major peaks, at about

hypericin

540 and 590 mμ. Although for various technical reasons it is difficult to obtain an action spectrum for the photosensitization process, responses which have been critically observed (138) indicate that the photodynamic reaction of *Hypericum* agrees with the observed absorption characteristics of hypericin. Ordinary window glass or a layer of water will not protect against this syndrome, thus absolutely differentiating it from sunburn—produced by invisible ultraviolet wavelengths of light which are absorbed by water or ordinary glass. The pigment is highly active. As little as 10-^{7} M sufficed to cause hemolysis of red blood cells on exposure to light of suitable wavelength in experiments of Pace and McKinney (1211).

TOXICITY, SYMPTOMS, AND LESIONS. The toxicity and photodynamic action of *Hypericum* have been reviewed extensively. The reviews of Hurst (810) and Clare (284) are general. Reference to the early literature may be found in the reviews of Marsh and Clawson (999), Rogers (1359), and Sampson and Parker (1384). Apparently the first report of *Hypericum* toxicity in the world literature appeared in 1787, and its recognition in the United States as a toxic plant dates from 1814. Thus it was the first plant recorded as a photosensitizer. Emphasis on the identity and action of the photodynamic pigment may be found in Blum's review (138).

Despite great interest in it and in the phenomenon of photosensitization, St. Johnswort has been the subject of very few feeding experiments. The most detailed are those of Marsh and Clawson (999). The results obtained in these experiments have been brought into question by some (284, 1384), partly because the methods employed to produce poisoning did not well reproduce conditions found in natural outbreaks, and the experimental cases were very mild compared with natural cases. Nevertheless, positive symptoms of photosensitization were produced in sheep and cattle. These experiments were performed at Salina, Utah, between 1925 and 1928 with material dried and shipped from California. It was found in sheep that about 5 per cent (calculated on a green-weight basis) of an animal's weight fed in one day would result in symptoms a day or two later. Protracted feeding of less than 4 per cent daily had no effect. Cattle were more susceptible. In this species, about 1 per cent was toxic, and death resulted in one instance when 5 per cent was fed at one time. In free-feeding experiments with hay, symptoms appeared after 2 to 16 days. On the range, symptoms of photosensitization usually appear 2 days to 3 weeks after animals have access to the plant.

Hypericum poisoning has been reported in sheep, cattle, horses (1359), and goats, although the latter are more resistant to its effects than the others. Classical symptoms of photosensitization are produced. The exact location and to some degree the nature of skin lesions depends largely upon the species or breed of animal. Black-skinned animals are rarely affected. In Holstein cattle, cases of *Hypericum* poisoning have been described (1359) in which the entire herd was found "with the white skin hanging in rags and the dark skin soft and supple as a glove." Animals suffering from an acute case of photosensitization develop intense itching and may rub affected areas raw. Often at the height of this reaction they act as though demented, charging about or casting themselves in water for relief. An intense reaction of this type may occur in sheep when sheared, since removal of the wool leaves the skin unprotected against sunlight. In severe attacks, death after convulsions occasionally occurs. More frequently, animals survive the acute stages of the syndrome but suffer more or less permanently from the aftereffects. Severe erythema of the conjunctiva and buccal mucous membranes often occurs, frequently resulting in complications such as blindness or refusal of the animal to eat. The great majority of deaths that may be laid to *Hypericum* poisoning are brought about by starvation.

Marsh and Clawson (999) noted additional symptoms including increase in rate of heartbeat and respiration, elevated temperature, and diarrhea. Hypersensitivity to contact with cold water has been observed in *Hypericum* photosensitization in New Zealand (284). Dipping or crossing streams with poisoned animals resulted in severe convulsions and often in drowning.

CONDITIONS OF POISONING. Hypericin is stable to drying and resistant to destruction by heat (810). Thus poisoning may be brought about by weedy hay. An instance of poisoning of 5 horses from hay containing about 50 per cent *Hypericum* has been reported in Maryland (1359). The young plant is almost equally as toxic as the mature plant (1432) and is more palatable to livestock. Sheep will readily graze the succulent stages if other forage is in short supply. Otherwise, livestock usually avoid *Hypericum*.

It was long supposed, probably from comparison with the effects of poison ivy, that *Hypericum* produced photosensitization by contact. Field trials, in which muzzled animals were run in a field heavily infested with *H. perforatum,* yet were not poisoned (284), serve to show that St. Johnswort is poisonous to animals only by ingestion.

Currently, economic loss from the effects of this plant is slight throughout the United States and Canada. This was not always the case. *Hypericum perforatum* was introduced into California around 1900 (1384) and spread throughout much of the drier ranges in that state. In 1951 it was estimated (800) to have infested some 2⅓ million acres in that state alone. In 1930 it was judged to be "the cause of the heaviest financial losses found on pasture and range lands of California" (1384). Loss was threefold. Occasional deaths occurred in poisoned stock. More important was loss represented by emaciated animals and poor wool crops from the aftereffects of nonlethal photosensitization. Most important, however, was the loss of useful grasses and other forage following infestation of ranges by this weed. The first attempts at eradication and control were not particularly successful (1327). Then, following observations and experiments in Australia, advantage was taken of the selective feeding habits of certain insects. The beetle *Chrysolina quadrigemina* Rossi had been found selective for *Hypericum perforatum* and not dangerous to desirable plants. The first beetles were imported in 1946, and after proper precautions, a large-scale control project was commenced in California in 1951. The literature concerning this project has been reviewed by Huffaker and Kennett (800) who state that control was more effective than the best hoped for and that a major improvement in California ranges resulted, reducing the incidence of *Hypericum* infestation to about 1 per cent of its former level.

Order Malvales

Malvaceae

Gossypium spp. Cotton

Toxicity of cottonseed meal depends upon a number of factors, one of which is the genetic constitution of the plant (142). Cotton has been grown for centuries, subject to selection and the genetic manipulation of man. It is difficult to determine the exact genetic complement of present commercial varieties. Two botanical species are the major sources of presently cultivated cotton varieties in the United States, although greater or lesser admixture of genetic material from additional species may have occurred (54). These are *Gossypium barbadense* L., sea-island cotton, and *G. hirsutum* L., upland cotton. Upland cotton constitutes more than 90 per cent of the American cotton crop. Sea-island cotton is grown principally in Texas, Arizona, and New Mexico.

POISONOUS PRINCIPLE. A pigment, gossypol, was isolated from cotton seeds by Longmore in 1886, more fully characterized by Marchlewski in 1899, investigated by many persons (252, 288, 1700), given a structural formula by Adams *et al.* in 1938 (5), and synthesized by Edwards in 1958 (477). It is a polyphenolic compound of empirical formula $C_{30}H_{32}O_9$, and does not fit into any of the usual classes of plant pigments. Gossypol is

gossypol, 2,2′-bi-8-formyl-1,6,7-trihydroxy-5-isopropl-3-methylnapthyl

accompanied in the seeds by a small number of other pigments in limited amount. Some of these may have toxicity greater than that of gossypol (947).

Gossypol is present in "glands" in the seed. These appear to the naked eye as tiny black dots in decorticated (hull removed) seeds. Pigment glands have been subjected to detailed investigation by Boatner and associates (141, 142, 1285). Each consists of a firm-walled sac filled with colloidal, amorphous material which contains gossypol in an amount approximating 50 per cent by weight. Pigment glands of this type are found only in the seeds of cotton and of a small number of closely related plants of the Malvaceae. In upland cotton they constitute from 2 to 3, sometimes to 5 per cent of the weight of the seed. The amount of gossypol in a given weight of seeds is proportional to the weight of pigment glands in the seed sample. Gossypol is not found outside the glands. Therefore the proportion of gossypol in each gland is relatively constant. In Russian work with several species of cotton [Smirnova, cited in (142)], it was shown that seeds of *Gossypium barbadense* regularly contained more pigment glands and gossypol than those of *G. hirsutum* and that these genetic differences were greater than differences in gossypol content resulting from difference in environment of the growing plant. On this observation have been based cotton breeding programs with the purpose of reducing gossypol in the raw seed.

The cellulose walls of the pigment glands are exceedingly tough. Although gossypol is soluble in a number of solvents, and reactive with a variety of compounds, it is not extracted from the seeds nor enabled to react with other compounds in most milling processes unless the glands are first ruptured. They are not ruptured by the rolling procedures in the course of milling. The gland wall, however, is very sensitive to the presence of water. It is composed of several plates which are joined along distinct seams. Addition of water immediately ruptures the seams and the contents of the gland are discharged. Certain polar, organic solvents bring about similar rupturing, but not as quickly. The speed of rupture depends in large measure on the amount of water present in the solvent.

In the traditional method of cottonseed-oil extraction, seed is heated to relatively high temperatures for relatively long periods of time before being mechanically pressed to expel the oil. During cooking the majority of pigment glands are ruptured and their contents released into the meal. Free gossypol is inactivated in time by reactions which occur spontaneously in the meal. The amount of toxic gossypol present in the meal at any time depends upon the degree to which the glands have been ruptured and the degree of subsequent destruction of gossypol by reaction with other compounds or otherwise. The term "bound gossypol" has been used to denote gossypol which has reacted during milling processes in such a way as to be converted into a nontoxic molecule (252, 288, 453, 917, 928, 946, 964, 1441, 1442).

TOXICITY, SYMPTOMS, AND LESIONS. Cottonseed contains about 20 per cent protein and 20 per cent oil. Meal made from it by the process described above contains about 40 per cent protein and 7 per cent oil. Meals resulting from newer processes employing solvent extraction contain less oil. Since it was first produced, cottonseed meal has been valued as a feed for livestock and widely used. Unfortunately, no commercial process for its production has been completely trustworthy in always producing a meal of low gossypol content. In earlier years, wherever cottonseed meal was used in large amounts, particularly with swine and poultry, difficulties ensued from time to time. A voluminous literature has resulted from numerous investigations, the purpose of which has been from one approach or another to find ways of taking full advantage in livestock feeds of the excellent potential protein values in cottonseed meal, without incurring the effects of its potential toxicity.

Instances of livestock loss were not uncommon before 1900 (591, 689). It was soon learned, more or less empirically, that toxicity could be reduced by proper heat processing during oil extraction, that cattle were relatively resistant to cottonseed poisoning, and that danger generally could be eliminated if certain precautions in feeding, such as controlling closely the amount fed, were observed. Nevertheless, experiments to identify precisely the source of toxicity, and others to make cottonseed meal a more generally satisfactory feed material were continued (380). Early experimental difficulties revolved mostly about two points—variability in toxicity of different samples of meal, and lack of knowledge about the requirements of a nutritionally adequate diet. With the statement of gossypol toxicity in 1915 (1700), an alternative explanation for cottonseed meal toxicity based on nutritional deficiency was put forth and supported by the experimentation of a number of persons (687, 694, 170). Cottonseed lacks adequate levels of vitamin A for use without supplementation. It is not necessary to review these apparently opposing views; the point of fact has turned out to lie somewhere between. Most mortality is the result of gossypol, but cattle loss with symptoms of blindness, ataxia, swelling of joints, and anorexia as described, for example, by Dinwiddie (427), has since been considered (687, 694) to have been caused by avitaminosis A.

Beginning around 1950 cottonseed meal received the coordinated attention of several score workers in federal, state, and private laboratories. Coordination was achieved mainly through periodic conventions. The proceedings of these conventions have been made available in mimeographed form by the Southern Utilization Research and Development Division, Agricultural Research Service of the U.S. Department of Agriculture. Nutritional work prior to 1948 has been reviewed by Hale and Lyman (687).

Conditions of extraction which increase the inactivation ("binding") of gossypol bring about an equivalent reduction in nutritive value of residue protein (140, 689, 761, 962, 1195). Principal among them is cooking at temperatures above 200°F. Experiments to locate the cause of reduction in protein value demonstrated that the amount of lysine is greatly reduced during cooking. It has been postulated that free gossypol reacts with the amino groups of lysine to form a physiologically inactive complex (946). This hypothesis is supported by parallel evidence. Free gossypol (as an isolated pure substance) loses most of its toxic activity within a few days when mixed in commercial feeds (765, 928). A similar reaction is probably involved. Furthermore, high protein level (providing amino groups) in the diet is protective against the effects of gossypol poisoning according to experiments at the Texas Agricultural Experiment Station (688) and elsewhere. Deaths in swine were produced at a free-gossypol level[*] of 0.02 per cent in the diet when the protein content of the diet was 15 per cent. No deaths resulted from gossypol at 0.03 per cent when the protein level was 30 per cent in the diet.

Milling procedures have been investigated to find commercially feasible methods to (a) insure meal of consistently low gossypol content and (b) retain the high protein value of the raw seed. Certain solvents may be used for extraction which do not require high-heat cooking in advance of extraction. However, the most useful of these in terms of cost and availability, hexane, does not extract or cause inactivation of much gossypol, and meals prepared by this process may be highly toxic. They contain typically as much as 0.6 per cent free gossypol. Successful laboratory procedures based upon breaking up the cottonseed flakes into very fine particles and subsequently removing pigment glands by flotation or differential sedimentation (1284, 1285) have not lent themselves to commercial adaptation. Meal made without cooking from material in which the glands were first removed in this way was essentially gossypol free, well colored, and highly nutritious (411). It has long been known that soluble iron salts added to the meal provide a protective effect, probably by reacting with free gossypol, but for other reasons their use has not met with favor. A combination of techniques may be used to insure meal of low free-gossypol content. The hydraulic-press and direct-solvent methods usually result in a product containing more than 0.04 per cent free gossypol. The screw-press, prepress-solvent, and direct-solvent methods followed by procedures for chemical inactivation of free gossypol result in meal containing less than 0.04 per cent active gossypol (688).

Useful toxicity figures for cottonseed meal are difficult to establish. Much research (687, 763, 764, 765, 917, 928, 1425, 1488) has well established that the toxicity (as opposed to nutritional effects) of cottonseed meal resides mainly or solely in its content of free gossypol. Some of the other pigments present in very small amount might be toxic, but their action would be negligibly small in comparison with that of gossypol. Toxicity follows the pigment glands in fractionation, and in most experiments it has been proportional to the amount of free gossypol detectable in the experimental material. Variation in toxicity from inheritance of gossypol-producing capacity in different species of cotton and from different techniques of extraction have been discussed. Further variation arises from geographical and ecological differences in the cotton-growing regions of the United States. Schwartze and Alsberg (1424) found a 300 per cent variation in gossypol content of seeds from different areas and a 200 per cent variation in seeds from the same area from one season to another. Their methods may be subject to some criticism, but the results agree with the widely held observation that meals from southwestern states are much less apt to be toxic than those from either southeastern states or California—differences which cannot be explained solely by methods of milling.

Variation also exists in species reaction to gossypol. Swine are much more sensitive to the toxic principle than are cattle or sheep. Rabbits and guinea pigs also are particularly sensitive. For swine, levels of gossypol in the diet must be less than 0.01 per cent to ensure harmlessness (689, 1442). Another general rule, based on the usual gossypol content of commercial meals, is that cottonseed meals may be added to swine feeds to a level of 9 per cent without danger (687, 689), but this level is insufficient to supply protein requirements when corn is used as the principal feed. With some attention to moisture content during cooking, commercial press-extraction meals can attain a constant free-gossypol average near 0.02 per cent. At this level these meals may safely be added to swine rations in amounts up to 25 per cent of the total.

Ruminants are resistant to the toxic principle and may consume relatively large amounts even of raw kernels without untoward effect (687).

The mechanism of gossypol detoxification by ruminants has been examined by Reiser and Fu (1331). They have shown that gossypol is bound to soluble proteins in the rumen to form a nontoxic molecule that is not broken in subsequent digestion. Experiments performed at the Texas Agricultural Station (917) with Holstein and Jersey calves fed cottonseed meal from birth had two interesting results. Cottonseed meals containing between 0.08 and 0.68 per cent free gossypol as 90 per cent of the diet were toxic to several of the Holstein calves but not to any of the Jerseys, although some of the latter consumed considerably more gossypol per unit body weight than the Holsteins. Deaths occurred in Holsteins on the 0.68 per cent diet in 60 to 70 days; on the 0.08 diet death occurred in one calf after 148 days. Symptoms and lesions were similar to those described below for swine poisoning.

Rats and poultry have intermediate sensitivity to gossypol. In poultry, amounts of free gossypol less than those required for producing death cause depression of growth rate and lowered hatchability, discolored yolks and whites, or whites of abnormal consistency. To avoid these effects, amounts of free gossypol in the diet should not be over 0.01 per cent (763, 764, 766, 928).

Pathological findings for swine have been reported by Binns (117), Wilde (1685), and Smith (689, 1486, 1488), and for the dog by West (1662). They are in close agreement. In swine, poisoning usually appears abruptly after animals have been on cottonseed meal for four weeks to as much as a year. In the typical case, death follows appearance of symptoms in 2 to 6 days. Occasionally symptoms persist for a month before death. The most prominent symptom is dyspnea with gasping or "thumping" breathing and occasionally the development of froth or bloody froth at the mouth. The rate of gain may have been somewhat reduced compared with animals on a complete diet, but poisoned animals often develop symptoms suddenly while gaining weight and while in apparently good condition. Emaciation and weakness appear with the other symptoms even though the appetite may be normal until shortly before death. Convulsions may accompany death, and cyanosis may be noted immediately before death.

Gross lesions consist of widespread congestion and edema, the result—at least in part—of progressive heart failure. Relatively large quantities of straw-colored or sanguineous fluid are usually found in the peritoneal, pericardial, and thoracic cavities. Lungs, kidneys, mesenteric lymph glands, and other organs may be swollen and congested. A variable amount of ulceration or irritation of the gastrointestinal tract may be observed. The liver appears congested and to the trained clinician presents some gross evidence of degenerative change, but the minor gross pathology contrasts markedly with the severity of damage observed in sections. In many instances most parenchymal cells have disappeared, leaving a thin zone of intact cells at the periphery of each lobule surrounding a blood-filled cavity. Areas of skeletal muscle appear white and may have undergone some pathological change. The heart is edematous, flabby, and on section shows areas of necrosis. In longer-standing cases, regenerative hypertrophy may be observed. Smith has compared (689, 1488) certain unusual features of these lesions with those produced in some dietary-deficiency diseases.

As early as 1922 experiments had been performed (1089) which showed that gossypol was much more rapidly toxic parenterally than when given orally. Using sheep erythrocytes it was found (1090) that gossypol prevented the release of oxygen from oxyhemoglobin, and that, *in vitro,* it caused lysis of erythrocytes. From these results it was postulated that gossypol produces death by reducing the oxygen-carrying capacity of the blood. Experiments with fowl (1342) support this conclusion. Rigdon *et al.* found that hemolytic anemia develops in fowl when the diet contains 0.03 per cent or more free gossypol. Necrotic lesions are absent in fowl, but a ceroidlike pigment is found in duodenal villi and sinusoids of liver and spleen. They postulated that the pigment came from the destruction of erythrocytes and that the beneficial effects of iron, found in studies by others, were the result of its value in hematopoiesis.

Additional references: 362, 1424, 1425, 1426.

Malva parviflora L. Mallow, cheeseweed

This species is a common annual weed throughout most of the United States and southern Canada. It is a relatively low-growing herb of varying habit, with long-petioled, palmately veined leaves that resemble those of the common greenhouse geranium, except smaller.

This species has experimentally been shown responsible for a disease known as "shivers" or "staggers" in livestock in Australia (810). The disease is also known in Africa, although it has not been experimentally confirmed there (1533). It affects horses, sheep, and cattle. Ingestion of a large amount of the fresh plant over the period of a few days results in a nervous syndrome characterized by severe muscular trembling. The syndrome is brought on or intensified by forced exercise and may result in prostration and death. Mild cases recover quickly if not excited. The appetite remains normal.

A syndrome like that described above was reported widespread in horses in California in 1906 (756) and circumstantially related to consumption of a plant identified as *Malva borealis* (now, *M. nicaeensis* All.), but from the description, the identification may have been at fault. Because of the demonstrated toxic nature of the plant in other countries, the difficulty with horses in California, and other reports incriminating the plant, Marsh *et al.* performed some feeding experiments with material collected in California at the USDA Salina (Utah) experiment station (1018). A sheep fed 154 per cent of its weight of the dry plant (this figure, however, expressed green-weight basis) over 26 days (= 5.9 per cent per day) was not poisoned, and other experiments were negative. Marsh *et al.* concluded that the plant probably was not toxic, but it should be noted that they used dried material, while most of the positive experiments performed elsewhere were done with fresh plant.

Seeds of *Malva parviflora* and other members of the Malvales, ingested by laying fowl, are responsible for yolk discoloration in stored eggs (934). Two fatty acids, malvalic and sterculic, are responsible (1450).

Modiola caroliniana (L.) G. Don. (= *M. multifida* Moench.)
Ground ivy
DESCRIPTION. Erect, spreading or prostrate, stiff-stemmed herb. Stems to 2 ft long. Leaves palmately lobed and veined; blades 1 to 3 in. across. Flowers axillary, about ¾ in. across, five-parted; petals scarlet or orange.

DISTRIBUTION AND HABITAT. Waste, low ground, Virginia to Florida, to Texas and California; Hawaii.

POISONOUS CHARACTERISTICS. King (864) reported circumstantial cases of incoordination and prostration in goats, sheep, and cattle. In goats, posterior paralysis was noted. Cattle and sheep displayed nervous disturbances with convulsions preceding death. This species has been suspected on two occasions in Australia of producing staggers in sheep (810).

Order Euphorbiales

Euphorbiaceae

Aleurites fordii Hemsl. Tung-oil tree
DESCRIPTION. A small cultivated tree; branches stout, often in whorls. Leaves simple, alternate, palmately veined, 5 to 10 in. long. Fruit pendant, nearly spherical, 2 to 3 in. in diameter, green, becoming brown, and containing 3 to 7 white-fleshed seeds.

DISTRIBUTION AND HABITAT. Introduced from China in 1905 and now widely planted in the Gulf Coast states as a source of tung oil and sometimes as a shade tree.

Aleurites montana (Lour.) Wils., *A. moluccana* Willd., and *A. trisperma* Blanco are closely related species sometimes cultivated for oil or occasionally as ornamentals. Experiments (491) in which poultry were fed foliage from these species have demonstrated their toxicity. They are increasingly less toxic in the order listed, the strongest being about half as toxic as *A. fordii*.

POISONOUS PRINCIPLE. Tung-oil meal is high in protein content. The residues after oil extraction are potentially valuable feedstuffs but cannot be so used because of their toxicity. Much experimental work has been performed to determine the nature of the toxic compound with a view to developing processes for detoxification and commercial utilization of the by-products in livestock feeds. Results are generally, but not completely, in agreement.

Residues yield two major fractions which are toxic. The toxic fractions may be separated by extraction with certain organic solvents. The toxic principle in the insoluble fraction is heat labile and has been termed (489) a saponin. The soluble fraction contains a toxic principle which is heat

Fig. 31. *Aleuritis fordii*. Tungtree. Photograph by W. C. Muenscher.

stable and has been shown (784) to be composed of two nitrogen-free compounds of close chemical and physical similarity. These compounds have been partially characterized. The heat-sensitive toxic principle has been called a phytotoxin by some (60) (cf. *Ricinus* of the same family).

TOXICITY, SYMPTOMS, AND LESIONS. Pathology is best known in cattle. Symptoms and lesions are comparable in other species. Ingestion of foliage or untreated tung meal by cattle (497) produces hemorrhagic diarrhea accompanied by anorexia, listlessness, and emaciation if prolonged. The primary lesion is hemorrhagic inflammation with necrotic erosions of the gastrointestinal tract. The abomasum, the first 3 to 6 ft of the duodenum, and the large intestines are most severely affected. Passive congestion of several organs may be marked. Symptoms appear 3 to 7 days after ingestion of a toxic dose, and death usually follows in 1 to 3 weeks. The histopathology is detailed by Emmel (497). In experimental feedings it was shown (497) that ingestion of 0.35 per cent of an animal's weight of macerated fresh leaves was sufficient to produce hemorrhagic diarrhea.

In the human being one seed can cause severe illness. Symptoms appear within a half hour after ingestion and consist of nausea, abdominal cramps, severe vomiting, diarrhea, weakness, and—after 3 to 5 hours— exhaustion. In more severe cases these symptoms are accompanied by signs of dehydration and shock, with cyanosis, respiratory depression, and diminished reflexes. Autopsy findings of gastroenteritis agree with post mortem findings in poisoned animals. Reported cases of poisoning in the human being have been reviewed by Balthrop *et al.* (60).

CONDITIONS OF POISONING. Poisoning is not uncommon in cattle. Cases of poisoning of horses, fowl, and the human being are on record. The first commercial harvest of domestic tung was made in 1932. Since that time the acreage planted to this crop has increased tremendously, and with it, the likelihood of poisoning.

Cattle pastured in tung groves rarely browse on the foliage, but prunings or clippings of tung trees are ingested readily by curious animals (497). The nuts are attractive to human beings, both in appearance and taste. The opened kernel may be mistaken for that of the Brazil nut. More than 40 cases of human poisoning have been reported in medical literature (60, 500, 1136, 1659).

Additional references: 406, 492, 912, 969, 1377, 1387, 1660.

Fig. 32. *Croton capitatus.* Hogwort. Flowering branch, with details of male and female flowers. Courtesy of The Macmillan Company.

Croton spp. Hogwort, croton

Croton texensis and *C. capitatus* are sometimes listed as poisonous (for example, 1270, 1566). Like others in the *Euphorbiaceae,* they are considered to contain acrid, irritant principles. *Croton tiglium* is the source of croton oil, formerly used in medicine as a purgative and one of the most drastic available. Only a few drops of the pure oil are lethal to animals (1628). Symptoms are those of intense gastroenteritis.

Croton is exceedingly distasteful and cases of livestock loss are rare. Care should be taken to avoid cutting it with hay, under which circumstances it may become less distasteful (1566).

Eremocarpus setigerus Benth. Turkey mullein

This common annual of dry ranges and waste places in the Pacific Coast states has caused illness in cattle, sheep, hogs, and turkeys (935, 1383) in California. Its fibrous nature promotes the formation of "hair balls" (phytobezoars or phytoconcretions) in the digestive tract. More than 20 of these have been removed from a single sheep. In cattle, symptoms include stiff gait, arched back, and diarrhea. In dairy animals there is an abrupt decrease in milk production.

Euphorbia spp. Spurges

More than fifty species of *Euphorbia* grow wild in the United States. Most are herbaceous plants with irritant milky sap; some southern species are woody bushes. A few are cultivated as ornamentals.

Euphorbias have long been used to produce blistering of the skin or purgation. Many species are discussed in the earliest works on poisonous plants. In 1775, for example, Gmelin (632) listed eleven. From these accounts and from the occasional case histories which have been reported since, it appears that many of the species of *Euphorbia* may infrequently cause poisoning of human beings or livestock. In most cases, poisoning is caused by an acrid principle which produces symptoms and lesions of severe irritation in the mouth and gastrointestinal tract and rarely death. However, Case has described (256, 260) photosensitization in lambs attributed to *E. maculata* in the southeastern United States, and some Australian species (particularly *E. drummondii* Boiss.) have been shown (605) to owe their toxicity to cyanogenetic potential.

The common spurges of the United States are mostly weedy annual or perennial herbs bearing simple, entire or dentate leaves oppositely or alternately along the stem. Flowering spurges may be recognized by the peculiar construction of the inflorescence. What is taken at first glance as the "flower" turns out to be a compound structure. It consists of a whorl of 4 to 5 petal-like members, usually yellow or yellow-green in color, surrounding a cluster of male flowers each consisting of a single stamen. In the center of the cluster of stamens is a single female flower. The female

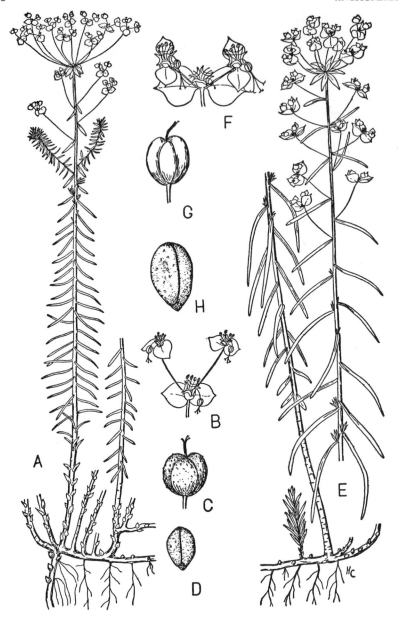

Fig. 33. *Euphorbia*. Spurges. A–D, *E. cyparissias*. Cypress spurge.
Plant, with details of flowers, fruit, and seed. E–H, *E. esula*. Leafy
spurge. Plant with details of flowers, fruit, and seed. Courtesy of The
Macmillan Company.

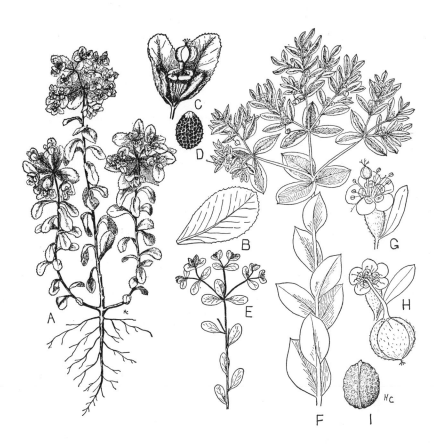

Fig. 34. *Euphorbia.* Spurges. A–D, *E. helioscopia.* Sun spurge. Plant, with details of leaf, flower, and seed. E, *E. peplus.* Petty spurge. Detail of branch. F–I, *E. marginata.* Snow-on-the-mountain. Branch, with details of male and female flowers, and seed. Courtesy of The Macmillan Company.

flower consists of a single pistil with three fused carpels, bearing three separate bifurcate styles. Nectiferous glands may be associated with the calyxlike whorl of leaves, and the leaves subtending the inflorescence may be variously modified or colored. The single central female flower may be exserted, either upright or pendant. It ripens into a 3-cavitied, usually 3-seeded capsule.

Many of the weedy species of *Euphorbia* are widely distributed throughout the United States. Descriptions, habitats, and distributions of eleven of the most common are given by Muenscher (1144). *Euphorbia marginata* (snow-on-the-mountain), *E. cyparissias* (cypress spurge), *E. milii* (crown-of-thorns), *E. pulcherrima* (poinsettia), *E. lactea* (candelabra tree), and *E. tirucalli* (pencil tree) are commonly cultivated species.

Poisoning by spurges has been reviewed by Long (933) in relation to species found in Britain, and by Hurst (722) in relation to those found in New South Wales. The following species of North America have appeared in the poisonous-plants literature.

Euphorbia corollata L. (flowering spurge) has caused poisoning of livestock in Indiana (713).

Euphorbia cyparissias L. (cypress spurge, graveyard weed). This species, shown poisonous to cattle when contaminating hay in large amounts, produces scours, collapse, and death (1142).

Euphorbia esula L. (leafy spurge). This spurge is reported (1142) from New York to have produced inflammation and loss of hair on the feet of horses from freshly mowed stubble during haying, and has caused mortality of sheep in Alberta (840).

Euphorbia helioscopia L. (sun spurge) has been held responsible for loss of human life and poisoning of cattle and lambs in Europe. A case of irritation and swelling of the mouth and tongue in lambs caused by this species growing as a weed in an unsuccessful stand of kale has been described by Forsyth (574). According to Hurst (810) 2½ lb. of partially dried sun spurge fed experimentally produced death in a 6-month-old calf.

Euphorbia lathyris L. (caper spurge) has poisoned children in California (274) and was responsible for the frequently cited case of the poisoning of five women who, mistaking this for capers, ingested pickles made of it, with severe but not fatal results (933).

Euphorbia maculata L. (eyebane, spotted spurge) has been considered the cause of photosensitization among lambs in the southeastern United States (256, 260). Instances have been described by Case, in which losses reached 30 per cent when flocks of Hampshire lambs were grazed on pastures in which this plant was the predominant weed. Feeding experiments showed the spurge highly toxic; 0.62 per cent of a lamb's weight of this plant produced death in a few hours. Photosensitization in animals not dying immediately consisted mainly of edematous enlargement of the head. Cases usually followed the drought-breaking rains of July and August.

Euphorbia marginata Pursh (snow-on-the-mountain) has been thought responsible for evil tasting, poisonous honey according to Chesnut (274). The juice of this plant has been used for branding cattle in preference to a hot iron. Experimental feedings of this plant made in Texas (1501) have shown that 100 oz. produces severe scours and emaciation in cattle, the latter persisting for several months.

Euphorbia milli Ch. des Moulins (crown-of-thorns), *E. lactea* Haw. (candelabra cactus), and *E. tirucalli* L. (pencil tree, spurge tree, Malabar tree, monkey fiddle, milk bush) are ornamentals which are attractive to children (1136). The juice is irritant but no cases of severe poisoning are on record.

Euphorbia peplus L. (petty spurge) has proven lethal to human beings in Europe (933). Feeding experiments described by Hurst (810) demonstrated that extracts of this species were capable of producing excess salivation and blood-stained feces in a calf. Its toxicity to fowl in moderate amount has been questioned (728).

Euphorbia prostrata Ait. has been shown experimentally (1501) to have a toxic effect on cattle similar to that of *E. marginata*. This spurge is a common weed from Louisiana to Texas.

Euphorbia pulcherrima Willd. (= *Poinsettia pulcherrima* R. Grah.) (poinsettia) has been responsible for the loss of human life (42). A two-year-old child died after eating a poinsettia leaf. Symptoms included intense emesis and catharsis, with delerium. This case occurred in Hawaii.

An unidentified species of *Euphorbia* is believed to have caused cattle and sheep losses in New Mexico with symptoms of scours and abdominal pain (1185).

None of the spurges are relished by livestock, but the tender young growth of some may be eaten more or less readily when other forage is not available. Toxicity is not lost upon drying, and at least in some instances hay seems more palatable to livestock than the fresh plant.

Hippomane mancinella L. Manchineel tree

DESCRIPTION. A small tree, 10 to 20 ft tall; trunk to ½ ft diameter; crown rounded; branches hanging. Bark brown or gray, forming small, thick plates in older trees. Leaves alternate, ovate, petioled, dark green, margin finely serrate, 2 to 4 in. long. Fruits round or slightly elongate, 1 to 1½ in. diameter; green or yellow-green, sometimes splashed with red at maturity, containing a single, irregular stone.

DISTRIBUTION AND HABITAT. Native to Central America and the West Indies. Common along sea beaches throughout that area. In the United States, restricted to peninsular Florida south of Palm Beach and Fort Myers. In Florida the early settlers, well aware of its poisonous nature, destroyed this tree wherever they found it. Thus it is now largely restricted to remote areas, chiefly in the Everglades.

Early literature dealing with the exploration and botanical characteristics of tropical America contains many references to the actual and supposed toxic characteristics of the manchineel tree (906). All parts of the plant contain a milky sap which is extremely caustic. Cases involving severe skin irritation and blindness (usually temporary) in human beings and animals were not unusual. Probably from the severity of reaction, the tree gained the unfounded reputation of being able to poison persons who merely came under its shade. The fruit is not offensive in odor or taste and has been the source of poisoning in human beings. At the time of the Spanish explorations, the Indians used the juice of the manchineel tree as an arrow poison. It also served as an ingredient in many native medicinal preparations. The wood was prized in furniture making, but it was found necessary to scarify and burn the surface of the trunk before cutting or handling.

Despite this long-standing reputation of toxicity, few investigations have been made to determine the source of toxicity or the exact nature of reaction to it. It is likely that more than one toxic principle is present (905, 1398) since reaction to contact with the plant is not exactly comparable with that resulting from ingestion of the fruit. Contact produces severe skin irritation (23, 610, 906, 1629) beginning as a simple erythema, followed by vesiculation and the formation of bullae in a day or so. Considerable danger of blindness exists from the ease with which severe conjunctivitis is produced when small amounts of the irritant principle enter the eyes via the fingers. Some individuals are more sensitive to the irritant principle than others (23).

Ingestion of the fruit may produce vomiting, abdominal pain, and bloody stools and occasionally results in death, although cases have been recorded (906) in which relatively large amounts were ingested without producing death in the human being.

Pharmacological investigation of the ripe fruit has led to the isolation (905) of an alkaloid which answers certain tests for physostigmine, an indole alkaloid. Other evidence suggests that the toxic principle is not a single substance. Extracts were more effective in poisoning laboratory animals than were whole plant administrations (251). Symptoms and lesions produced by extracts included drop in blood pressure, lacrymation and salivation, leukocytosis, and extensive hemorrhage.

Hura crepitans L. Sandbox tree

This striking, coarse tree is native to the American tropics but is occasionally planted in the extreme southern United States and Hawaii. It has long been recognized as a dangerous plant, but chemical analyses to determine the source of toxicity have not produced clear-cut results. It has been said to contain an emetic and cathartic principle, and also a phytotoxin. (Compare with the related genera *Ricinus* and *Hippomane.*)

Ingestion of two or three seeds produces severe emesis and purging. Contact with the plant produces severe irritation in some individuals. The woody fruit is occasionally made into jewelry.

Jatropha curcas L. Barbadosnut, physic nut, purge nut, curcas bean
DESCRIPTION. Coarse annual shrub or short-lived tree to 12 or 15 ft

tall. Stems thick, hairless, mostly herbaceous, green. Leaves alternate, long-petioled, cordate, about 6 in. wide, irregularly margined or more often 3- to 5-lobed, points acute or blunt, venation palmate. Flowers small, yellow, unisexual, in clusters in the leaf angles, mostly hidden in the foliage. Fruit an ovoid capsule, green and fleshy at first, becoming brownish or almost black and dry at maturity; containing three cavities and 2 to 3 black seeds; seeds ¾ in. long.

DISTRIBUTION AND HABITAT. Native to the American tropics, now widely distributed in tropical countries throughout the world. It is used horticulturally as an ornamental either singly or in hedges, being prized for its rapid growth. In Florida it is found chiefly south of Orlando. It is also a common plant in the Hawaiian Islands.

POISONOUS PRINCIPLE. This plant is closely related both to *Croton* and to castor bean (*Ricinus*). Like these, it contains relatively large amounts of a useful oil in its seeds. The oil is purgative, being between castor and croton oil in its potency. The seeds also contain at least one other toxic factor (879). Results of chemical investigations are somewhat at variance and in need of confirmation. It is commonly accepted that the seeds contain a phytotoxin, similar to ricin of *Ricinus,* and it has been stated (23) that they may be rendered nontoxic by roasting.

TOXICITY, SYMPTOMS, AND LESIONS. Reports of poisoning in human beings from overdoses of the oil or from ingestion of the seed may be found from England, Africa, the American tropics (23), Florida (1660), Hawaii (42), the Philippines (1321), and elsewhere. Details of symptoms and lesions in most reviews seem to come largely from the report of Kobert (879). In some instances as few as three seeds have produced toxic symptoms. In others, consumption of as many as 50 seeds has resulted in relatively mild symptoms. West, from cases in Florida, states (1660) that there are two strains of this species, one with toxic seeds and the other with seeds that are not poisonous. The two strains cannot be distinguished by sight. The seeds have a pleasant taste (42).

From the European literature, Völker (1628) cites cases of poisoning in cattle and swine.

Symptoms and lesions are similar to those in poisoning by castor bean and result primarily from severe gastroenteritis. A burning sensation in the throat, followed by vomition, diarrhea, abdominal pain, and associated symptoms have been reported.

Jatropha multifida L. Coral plant, physic nut

DESCRIPTION. Shrub, 3 to 7 ft tall. Leaves 4 to 8 in. wide; palmately 9- to 11-lobed; lobes narrow, entire or incised. Flowers small, unisexual. Fruits yellow, usually three-angled, not opening at maturity as in the preceding.

DISTRIBUTION AND HABITAT. This species is native to southern peninsular Florida and is cultivated occasionally outside its native range.

TOXICITY, SYMPTOMS, AND LESIONS. Cases of poisoning in human beings, particularly children, are not uncommon (1660). The yellow fruits
are attractive to children, especially after they have fallen on the ground,
and should be removed to avoid danger. Symptoms and lesions are similar
to the preceding. Another similar species, native to Key West, Florida, is
Jatropha gossypifolia L., bellyache bush (1660)

Jatropha spathulata Muell., a small shrub of the ravines and mountain
banks of western Texas and Mexico, has been the subject of feeding experiments by the Texas Agricultural Experiment Station. It was found (158)
toxic but not fatal to a sheep when the animal was fed 2 per cent of its
weight of green leaves. The seeds were fatal to a lamb at 3 per cent of its
weight in 3 doses over 12 days.

Jatropha stimulosa Michx. is the bull nettle or spurge nettle of the
Southeast. Its spiny hairs bear a caustic irritant which on contact produces
painful irritation in many persons and a severe reaction in some.

Manihot esculenta Crantz Cassava, tapioca

Cassava is widely cultivated in many varieties throughout the tropical
Americas as a food material. It is native to extreme southern Florida, and
may be cultivated in many of the Gulf States. Tubers, somewhat like
potatoes, are formed underground, and are used in several ways. Tapioca
is made from them by peeling, expressing the juice, grating and soaking the
pulp, and heating it. This causes the starch to form the small lumps characteristic of tapioca. The raw root is capable of forming lethal concentrations
of hydrocyanic acid. It was already known to the Indians that peeling the
roots and heating them rendered them innocuous. Such practices are now
well established; therefore there is little danger of poisoning from cassava.
Peelings, however, could prove lethal if fed raw to livestock.

Mercurialis annua L. Mercury, boys-and-girls

This annual weed found locally in waste areas throughout most of the
United States and Canada has a record of toxicity in Europe and elsewhere.
It has produced poisoning in most classes of livestock. Symptoms include
severe gastric irritation with diarrhea, and hematuria with profound anemia
developing. *Mercurialis* poisoning has been reviewed by Garner (607).

Phyllanthus abnormis Baill. Spurge

DESCRIPTION. Small, bushy annual or short-lived perennial herb,
branched from base; branches ascending, sparingly rebranched, to 10 in. tall.
Leaves crowded, alternate, oblong, about ¼ in. long, obtuse-tipped.
Flowers small, monoecious, axillary, in groups of 2 to 3.

Fig. 35. *Mercurialis annua*. Mercury. Plant, with details of male and female flowers, fruit, and seed. Courtesy of The Macmillan Company.

DISTRIBUTION AND HABITAT. Sand or sandy soil, western and southwestern Texas.

POISONOUS PRINCIPLE. Unknown. Not stable to drying.

TOXICITY, SYMPTOMS, AND LESIONS. Loss of a number of calves over several seasons prompted feeding experiments by Mathews at the Alpine substation of the Texas Agricultural Experiment Station (1055). It was not possible to duplicate exactly the pathology found in range cases, probably because of difficulties in obtaining sufficient fresh plant, but *Phyllanthus abnormis* was proven toxic to cattle, sheep, and goats under the conditions of the experiment. Great variation was found in amount of plant needed to produce symptoms. Variation in toxicity was attributed to geographic location of source of plant, loss of toxicity with drying, and variation of individual susceptibility of test animals. The least plant necessary to produce death was 1.5 per cent of the animal's weight in the case of a goat.

Symptoms in calves consisted of listlessness for several days, anorexia, then ceaseless walking, sometimes interspersed with periods of nonbelligerent charging about. Diarrhea and tenesmus with occasional rectal prolapse were observed in some animals. Exhaustion was followed by prostration and death. Lesions were found to consist mainly of albuminous degeneration of the kidney and cirrhosis of the liver, together with slight icterus, and petechiation, particularly in the axillae, subendocardium, and mesenteries. Gross pathology resembled that found in *Senecio* poisoning (*q.v.*). Microscopically, *Phyllanthus* poisoning in field cases could be distinguished from *Senecio* poisoning on the basis of extensive fibroblastic and bile-duct proliferation in the liver together with the absence of enlargement of the cytoplasm and nucleus of the parenchymatous cells, found in *Senecio* poisoning. Characteristic lipoid and yellow pigment deposits occurred in the reticuloendothelial cells of the hepatic lymph glands. It was not possible to reproduce some of these lesions in the experimental cases. A lesion found uniformly in all cases was the presence of extensive necrobiosis in the kidneys and plugging of tubules by cellular detritis.

CONDITIONS OF POISONING. Poisoning was associated with suckling calves on the range and occurred in the last three months of the year. It was shown that the poisonous principle was eliminated in the milk. Experimentally, symptoms could be produced in milking animals, but under range conditions poisonings were confined to calves, probably because they received a larger dose of the toxic principle, getting it both in the milk and also directly from the green plant, which was consumed by both cattle and calves in moderate amount. Sheep and goats are probably somewhat less susceptible to poisoning.

Reverchonia arenaria Gray. Reverchonia

This is a relatively uncommon annual, herbaceous spurge which is found on plains and hillsides, Texas to Arizona, southern Utah, and Mexico.

On the basis of limited feeding experiments prompted by cases in range animals, Huffman (802) found this species toxic to sheep at about 1 per cent of the animal's weight of freshly collected plant; slightly less toxic to cattle. Symptoms and lesions in the experimental cases were those of acute damage to liver and kidney, while range cases were characterized primarily by extensive fibrosis and more chronic symptoms.

In symptoms, lesions, toxicity, and general habit of plant, poisoning by *Reverchonia arenaria* is very similar to poisoning by the closely related spurge, *Phyllanthus abnormis*.

Ricinus communis L. Castor bean, palma christi

Large amounts of castor oil are employed as lubricants in industry; smaller amounts medicinally. Oil is obtained from the seeds, maturation of which requires a long frost-free growing season. Limited acreages of castor bean may be found in south-central states and in California. Elsewhere horticultural varieties are planted as fast-growing ornamentals for their bold, striking foliage.

The seed, press cake, and, to lesser degree, the foliage are poisonous. Castor oil is not toxic. The poisonous principle is insoluble in oil.

POISONOUS PRINCIPLE. The phytotoxin ricin (see phytotoxins, p. 37). This compound responds positively to certain tests for protein, is composed of a variety of amino acids, has many of the poisonous characteristics of a bacterial toxin, is antigenic, and is heat labile in solution. It produces agglutination of defibrinated blood and of red blood cells *in vitro*. Literature

Fig. 36. *Ricinus communis.* Castor bean. Plant apex, with details of male and female flowers, and mature fruit. Photograph of seeds. Drawing, courtesy of The Macmillan Company.

concerning the discovery and elucidation of the nature of ricin has been reviewed by Clarke (290, 292) and Steyn (1533).

TOXICITY, SYMPTOMS, AND LESIONS. Pure ricin is among the most toxic compounds known. It has excited much interest. The minimum lethal dose by injection is about 0.0001 mg per kg (0.00000001 per cent of the animal's weight). By oral administration ricin is several hundred times less toxic. Considerably greater variation is found in minimum lethal dose by oral route compared with parenteral administration of ricin. These facts suggest that ricin is not readily absorbed through the wall of the digestive tract, or that it may be partially destroyed during ingestion. In the case of whole seeds, the degree of mastication and digestion determines in part the amount of ricin available for intestinal absorption. Nevertheless ricin differs from many bacterial toxins and snake venoms in the relative ease with which it is absorbed through the intestinal wall.

Wide variation in susceptibility of individual animals to poisoning from whole seeds tends to obscure the fact that average species susceptibility varies with class of livestock. Horses are poisoned by about 0.01 per cent of their weight of seeds. Cattle, sheep, and hogs require about 0.2 per cent, while poultry must be fed about 1.4 per cent of their weight of seeds to produce poisoning (607).

Castor-bean poisoning in North America is infrequent. Symptoms and lesions are known largely through reports in the British literature. These have been reviewed by Garner (607).

Poisoning occurs most frequently when feed grains become contaminated with castor-bean seeds. (577). Animals usually refuse to eat more than a few mouthfuls of contaminated whole grain or mash, but only a few mouthfuls may prove fatal. Symptoms appear after a characteristic lag period which may vary from a few hours to several days, except occasionally in man, when a very large amount of castor bean has been consumed and symptoms appear almost immediately (1477). During the lag period the poisoned animal or person appears entirely normal. Symptoms consist of those associated with gastrointestinal irritation. Anorexia, cessation of rumination, evidence of abdominal pain, dullness, diarrhea, and weakness are common. In horses there may be initial trembling, sweating, and incoordination. Several investigators have described unusually vigorous heart contractions which shake the entire body in poisoned horses. The pulse is weak and its rate is greatly increased. Temperature may be moderately elevated at first. Diarrhea stained with blood is often found in castor-bean poisoning of cattle. Pigs vomit freely. This has been credited with preserving life in at least one instance (611). Poultry appear depressed, with ruffled feathers, drooping wings, and grayish wattles and comb. Egg production ceases, moulting begins, and emaciation occurs in birds that do not die immediately.

In the human being the seeds produce a burning sensation in the mouth and throat (1533). Otherwise symptoms are similar to those in animals. Man appears quite susceptible to the toxic principle. Two to four seeds may produce serious poisoning or occasionally a fatality, while eight seeds are usually lethal. A case has been reported (1236) from Cuba in which a single seed provoked symptoms in a particularly sensitive person. Severe reaction to a single seed (or less) may be allergenic in nature and anaphylactic in characteristics.

Lesions consist of inflammation and punctiform hemorrhage of the mucosal lining of the digestive tract. Liver and kidneys are swollen and edematous, and the lungs may contain fluid. Histological examination reveals irreversible cellular damage.

A high level of immunity may be built up in animals by administering increasing subclinical doses of seed. Serum from immunized animals is an effective treatment for poisoned animals if administered parenterally immediately or within a few hours after ingestion of a lethal dose of seeds (292).

CONDITIONS OF POISONING. In the United States castor-bean poisoning has occurred in all classes of livestock and in man. Seeds, obtained in grain or otherwise, have produced poisoning in horses (1227, 1318, 1485), pigs (1227, 1236, 1335), sheep (1335), cattle (1335), ducks (1318), and wild Canadian geese (1029). Leaves, stems, and unripe fruits have been fed experimentally at the Florida Experiment Station (1387). An amount equal to 1 per cent of the weight of a heifer produced purging. In California (1684) sheep were poisoned and some mortality resulted when a flock was put into an unharvested field of castor bean.

Ricin may be inactivated or destroyed by moderate heat. Castor-bean meal in which the ricin has been destroyed is not, however, useful as a poultry feed. It contains a second, heat-stable factor, which results in lowered growth rates (150).

In certain tropical countries some persons have been accustomed to chewing on a castor-bean seed when in need of a laxative. This practice may be effective but is dangerous. Two soldiers in Hawaii died as the result of trying it (42).

Stillingia treculeana (Muell. Arg). Johnst. (= *S. dentata*). Queen's delight

This is a perennial herb of western and central Texas. Although no cases of loss on pasture or range have been recorded, feeding experiments (158, 159) have shown that the plant may be highly toxic. As little as 0.5 per cent or less of an animal's weight of leaves and stems was quickly lethal to sheep. The poisonous principle is hydrocyanic acid.

Buxaceae

Buxus sempervirens L. Common box

DESCRIPTION. A cultivated ornamental plant obtainable in many varieties, some of which are used as hedge plants or for edgings, others of which may be used as individual shrubs or small trees. Plants shrubby, much branched. Leaves opposite, entire, leathery, lanceolate, ½ to 1½ in. long, dark glossy green on the upper surface, lighter green or whitish beneath.

DISTRIBUTION AND HABITAT. Native to Europe and Asia. Widely grown throughout the United States, except in the coldest areas where it is not hardy, usually as a hedge or edging plant.

POISONOUS PRINCIPLE. This species contains alkaloids and some other active principles (356).

TOXICITY, SYMPTOMS, AND LESIONS. Sheep mortality from box hedge clippings has been described from Maryland (1335). Horses, pigs, cattle, and camels have been killed by box in other countries (810). About 1½ lb. of leaves has proven lethal to horses (1628), for a toxicity of around 0.15 per cent, green-weight basis.

Symptoms and lesions are those of severe gastroenteritis, sometimes with bloody diarrhea. Death occurs within a short time through respiratory failure.

Fig. 37. *Buxus sempervirens.* Box.
Detail of leafy twig.

CONDITIONS OF POISONING. Wide use of this plant as a clipped ornamental, the natural curiosity of livestock concerning unfamiliar plant materials, and the high toxicity of the plant, all make possible occasional losses of livestock from clippings. *Buxus microphylla* Sieb. & Zucc. (Korean box) is also widely planted in the United States. Its toxicity has not been established.

Order Geraniales

Linaceae

Linum usitatissimum L. Flax, linseed

This species is grown in temperate regions for its fiber (flax) from which linen is made, or its seed from which an oil (linseed) is expressed. In the United States and Canada the latter is commercially more important than the former.

POISONOUS PRINCIPLE. The leaves and seed chaff contain the cyanogenetic glycoside, linamarin. The sugar moiety is glucose. An enzyme (linamarase) is present in the plant material which is capable of releasing cyanide from linamarin. Both the enzyme and the glycoside are considered identical with the enzyme and cyanogenetic glycoside (phaseolunatin) of lima bean (*Phaseolus lunatus*). The chemical investigations upon which this information rests were carried out mainly before the end of the first decade of the present century, and have been reviewed by Steyn (1533). In at least some oil-extraction processes, neither glycoside nor enzyme is destroyed or inactivated.

The production of cyanogenetic glycoside in the plant varies with genetic and ecological conditions under which the plants are produced. Flax grown in northern, temperate lands is much less apt to develop dangerous levels of cyanide than that grown at warmer latitudes.

TOXICITY, SYMPTOMS, AND LESIONS. In the world literature, cases of poisoning after ingestion of linseed press cake, press meal, or flaxseed chaff or screenings have been reported in all classes of livestock. Symptoms and lesions are those of cyanide poisoning (p. 26). Analyses of incriminated materials in these instances have shown them to contain cyanide levels well above the generally accepted minimum toxic amount.

CONDITIONS OF POISONING. A half-dozen cases involving the loss of a large number of cattle after ingestion of flax screenings were reported to the North Dakota Experiment Station within the period of a few weeks in 1911 (897). Cases were also reported in sheep. Flax screenings and chaff or meal were well known in the European literature at that time as potentially poisonous [see reviews by Steyn (1533) and Hurst (810)], but had not previously been reported toxic in the United States or Canada. Investigations at the North Dakota Station clearly demonstrated the cyanogenetic potential of domestic flaxseed screenings or chaff (818). Loss of cattle to flaxseed screenings with chemical identification of HCN as the toxic principle has also been reported from Canada (1574). In North Dakota the straw from immature growth is said (1524) to have produced numerous cases of loss.

Other species which have been suspected of having caused loss of life in livestock include *Linum rigidum* Pursh (yellow flax) and *Linum lewisii* Pursh. The former was associated with mortality in sheep in Kansas (609) and Colorado (465), while the latter, which has been shown to have cyanogenetic potential, has been incriminated in Colorado (465).

Ingestion of chopped flax straw resulted in mortality of 6 Hereford cattle (811) in which, from the symptoms, cyanide was not involved. This case was ascribed to the results of impaction.

The press cake remaining after commercial extraction of linseed oil may (but rarely does) contain dangerous levels of HCN. Knowledge of potential toxicity in this supplementary feed material comes largely from English literature (461, 1117, 1123). Cake made from immature seed is more likely to be toxic than that made from ripe seed. Toxic cake may be rendered safe by proper heat treatment, and press cake obtained from established commercial sources should be reliably nontoxic.

Under some circumstances, small quantities of HCN liberated in the animal after ingestion of flaxseed meal become chemically joined with sulfur in the liver, forming thiocyanates. Thiocyanates are compounds which may provoke thyroid enlargement and goiter in areas where there is low iodine intake in the diet, and loss of lambs with symptoms of goiter has been reported in New Zealand when the ewes had been fed flaxseed cake (240). (See discussion of goitrogenic compounds, p. 26.)

Linum neomexicanum Greene. Yellow pine flax

DESCRIPTION. Herbaceous annual or winter annual. Stems several, erect, straight, unbranched, 1 to 2 ft tall. Leaves opposite below, becoming alter-

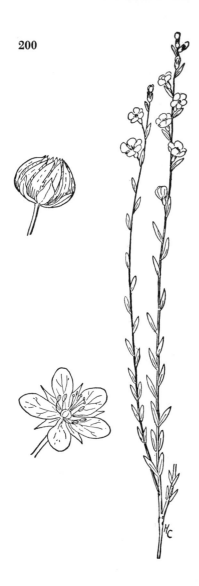

nate above, sessile, lanceolate below, becoming linear above, entire, about ½ in. long. Inflorescence a raceme, terminating each stem; flowers 5-parted, corolla yellow, about ½ in. across. Fruit an inflated, ovoid, incompletely 10-celled capsule, about ¼ in. in diameter.

DISTRIBUTION AND HABITAT. Range lands, especially where disturbed, at 5000 to 8000 ft elevation, New Mexico, Arizona, and south into Mexico.

POISONOUS PRINCIPLE. Eggleston *et al.* (479) isolated from this species and partially characterized a compound which proved uniformly toxic to laboratory animals. They gave it the name "linotoxin" but were unable to obtain it in crystalline form. It was easily extracted in alcohol, less so in water. It had the physical characteristics of a saponin when shaken in water, and answered certain chemical tests as a glycoside. Tests of this species for a cyanogenetic glycoside were negative.

TOXICITY, SYMPTOMS, AND LESIONS, AND CONDITIONS OF POISONING. The original impetus for the toxicological investigation of this species came from the fact that it is not common, but was found abundantly in two places where stock loss had occurred. Details of the latter were not given.

Fig. 38. *Linum neomexicanum.* Yellow pine flax. Plant, with details of flower and fruit. Courtesy of The Macmillan Company.

Oxalidaceae

Oxalis pes-caprae L. (= *O. cernua* Thunb.). Bermuda buttercup, Bermuda oxalis, soursob, sorrel

This species of *Oxalis* occurs in Florida and California as an introduced weed. It has caused loss of sheep in Australia (199). This and other species of *Oxalis* (especially *O. corniculata* L.) are known to form lethal concentrations of soluble oxalates under certain circumstances (1030). Symptoms and lesions are those of oxalate poisoning (see p. 33). Whether this occurs in North America or whether they are ever grazed sufficiently to be dangerous has not been determined. The common name "sorrel" is applied also to the unrelated genus *Rumex,* some species of which accumulate soluble oxalates. In the United States, losses ascribed to "sorrel" are probably referable to *Rumex (q.v.).*

Zygophyllaceae

Kallstroemia hirsutissima Vail. Carpet weed, hairy caltrop

DESCRIPTION. Much-branched, mostly prostrate annual weed, in large specimens forming a dense, carpetlike mat extending a foot or more about the central root. Leaves pinnately compound; leaflets 3 to 4 pairs, oblong-ovate, the majority about ½ in. long, entire, densely hairy. Flowers small,

Fig. 39. *Kallstroemia hirsutissima.* Carpet weed.

sepals 5, petals 5, equal to or hardly exceeding the sepals in length, about
¼ in. long, yellow fading to white.

DISTRIBUTION AND HABITAT. A weed of overgrazed pastures, neglected
cultivated fields and other disturbed soils, Kansas to Colorado, south to
Texas and northern Mexico.

POISONOUS PRINCIPLE. Unknown.

TOXICITY, SYMPTOMS, AND LESIONS. Knowledge of the toxic nature of
this species comes from the single description of natural and experimental
poisoning by F. P. Mathews (1053). He described an unusual instance in
which 5 head of cattle died and almost a score were poisoned in a herd of
48 which, on two occasions, was grazed on fields containing large stands of
carpet weed. From limited experimental evidence (one heifer, one sheep,
and one goat poisoned) it appears that symptoms are developed after an
animal has eaten one-third or more of its weight of the weed. Symptoms are
nervous in character and are brought on in mildly poisoned animals by
forced exercise. They consist of unusual flexure of the hind legs followed by
knuckling under. Severely poisoned animals display almost complete
posterior paralysis and are unable to stand. In the natural cases, cattle were
observed to move about by pulling themselves along with their forelegs. In
the first instance described, 3 animals died after about a week and a half on
badly infested land. In the second, 2 animals were lost after a similar period
of time. The exact cause of death in the fatal cases is not clear, but may have
been from secondary factors such as excess insolation. Animals not fatally
poisoned made complete recoveries after two and a half weeks or less on
fresh, uninfested pasturage. No lesions were found in one of the experimental animals that was examined grossly and histologically.

CONDITIONS OF POISONING. In the cases described, an unusual combination of circumstances led to the poisonings, and explains why this species had
not previously been suspected as toxic. The year in question was a year of severe dryness and the usual pasturage had been used up. Also large acreages of
land had been plowed but not seeded. It was on these lands that annual
carpet weed had made extensive stands, and it was these lands that were
employed when other pasturage gave out. In the feeding experiments the
heifer could not be forced to eat the plant voluntarily. The sheep would eat
it voluntarily after four days of forced feeding. In all cases of poisoning, both
natural and experimental, the appetite remained normal throughout.

Peganum harmala L. African rue

DESCRIPTION. Bright green, succulent, much-branched perennial herb,
bushy in habit, about 1 ft tall when fully grown. Leaves alternate, pinnate,
or twice pinnately divided; ultimate segments linear, fleshy, glabrous. Flowers single, white, conspicuous; petals 5. Fruit a 2- to 4-cavitied, many-
seeded leathery capsule, about ⅜ in. in diameter.

DISTRIBUTION AND HABITAT. This species is native to the deserts of Africa and southern Asia. It was first recognized in the United States on a section of land near Deeming, New Mexico, in 1935 and has since spread on dry range land into Arizona and western Texas (337).

Fig. 40. *Peganum harmala.* African rue.

POISONOUS PRINCIPLE. Alkaloids extracted from African rue have proven toxic to laboratory animals (1127), producing the same symptoms as observed when the whole seed was fed. The seeds of the plant have been shown to contain at least four alkaloids, of which three have the indole configuration (976).

TOXICITY, SYMPTOMS, AND LESIONS. Cattle loss on the range where this plant was first recognized prompted its investigation as a poisonous plant. Experimental studies have been performed at the Texas and New Mexico Agricultural Experiment Stations and by the United States Department of Agriculture. The ground seed is almost always lethal to guinea pigs at 0.15 per cent of the animal's weight (1127). Young leaves were toxic at 1 per cent, dry-weight basis, but older leaves seemed to lack toxicity. In guinea pigs the symptoms consisted of posterior paralysis and weakness of back muscles, appearing within an hour of feeding and lasting for several hours. No lesions of significance were found.

African rue is highly unpalatable to cattle (132), but if force-fed, it is lethal (1050). Sheep have been observed to eat the plant after it had dried under range conditions, but experimentally they could not be forced voluntarily to consume hay made from it (132).

Tribulus terrestris L. Puncture vine, caltrop

DESCRIPTION. Prostrate annual weed. Stems recumbent, pubescent, branching, to 1 yd in length. Leaves opposite, pinnately compound; leaflets

4 to 7 pairs, oblong to elliptical, about ½ in. long. Flowers single, axial; corolla of 5 yellow petals. Fruit a small bony capsule breaking apart into five spiny sections, each with two prominent, woody, sharp spines.

DISTRIBUTION AND HABITAT. Introduced from southern Europe. Now spread on dry soils of waste lands, roadsides, and deserts from Florida to California; less common north to New York and South Dakota.

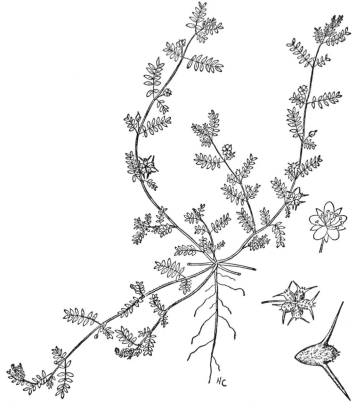

Fig. 41. *Tribulus terrestris.* Puncture vine. Plant, with details of fruit cluster and fruit. Courtesy of The Macmillan Company.

POISONOUS PRINCIPLE. A number of steroidal saponins have been isolated (154) from *Tribulus* in South Africa.

TOXICITY, SYMPTOMS, AND LESIONS. *Tribulus terrestris* produces hepatogenic photosensitivity in livestock (see photosensitization, p. 52). Its spiny burs are mechanically dangerous, producing lesions of the mouth or feet.

What appears to be the same species of plant as that found in the United States is one of the major causes of bighead in sheep in South Africa (geeldikkop) and Australia, resulting in much economic loss. The South

African literature describing experimental support has been reviewed by Steyn (1533) and Brown (180), and the Australian by Hurst (810). The syndrome is a hepatogenic photosensitization. In both countries the situation is sometimes complicated by the presence of high levels of nitrate in the plant and production of symptoms of nitrate poisoning in cattle and sheep.

In the United States *Tribulus* is much less troublesome. Photosensitization in sheep has been reported from Colorado (465) and New Mexico (754) under circumstances which incriminate puncture vine. Reported experimental feedings, however, seem to be limited to those performed at the Texas experiment station (315). No symptoms were produced in two goats fed puncture vine for almost a month, but post mortem examination revealed intensely yellow fat throughout the body. In the natural cases described by Hershey (754), typical lesions of severe photosensitization or bighead, including blindness, necrosis of skin, loss of lips and ears, and high mortality among young animals, were found.

In Africa, seleniferous soils correlate with areas of heavy geeldikkop incidence. It has been suggested (181) that subtoxic amounts of selenium in the diet predispose to photosensitization of animals by *Tribulus*.

Order Polygalales

Polygalaceae

Polygala spp. Snakeroot, milkwort
Polygala senega L. (snakeroot) of the eastern United States and southern Canada serves as the source of an irritant drug (senega). *Polygala sanguinea* L. (milkwort) of similar geographical distribution has been suspected of poisoning horses in Michigan (1245).

Order Rutales

Rutaceae

Citrus spp. Orange, grapefruit, etc.
Citrus paradisii Macf. is the grapefruit of commerce; *C. sinensis* Osbeck is the orange. Considerable tonnage of seed obtained as a by-product of the manufacture of citrus juice is pressure-extracted for its oil content. The residue has a protein level of about 35 per cent and a fat content greater than 5 per cent. These characteristics together with low fiber have suggested the use of press residue as a protein supplement in commercial livestock feed.

Experiments (627) have shown citrus seed residue, from commercial expeller processing, is palatable and equivalent to cottonseed meal when substituted for the latter in rations fed beef animals. When fed at the same or even greatly reduced levels to fowl or swine it has definite toxicity. Swine find it unpalatable at 10 per cent of the ration. At this level it results in decreased rate of gain despite increased feed consumption (627).

At the 20 per cent level in rations fed chicks it produces heavy mortality in the first three weeks (456). Lesions include enlarged gall bladder, mottled liver, ascites, and congestion of the intestinal tract.

The toxic factor can be removed from the residue by extraction with various organic solvents. It has tentatively been indentified (456) as limonin, a carbohydrate molecule responsible for the bitter characteristics of citrus.

Xanthoxylum americanum Mill. Prickly ash

Prickly ash is an aromatic, early-flowering shrub of woods and stream banks throughout most of the eastern and central United States and south-central Canada. It has been suspected of producing loss in cattle in Indiana (704), and considered responsible (713) for instances of sheep losses in the same state. The foliage is grazed when other forage is scarce.

Meliaceae

Melia azedarach L. Chinaberry tree, white cedar

DESCRIPTION. Small tree, 20 to 40 ft tall. Trunk often branched, relatively thick; bark gray or gray-brown, fine-furrowed. Leaves large, alternate, twice suboppositely compound; leaflets lanceolate, serrate or lobed, 1 to 2 in. long. Inflorescence axillary, paniculate. Flowers about 1 in. across; petals 5 or 6, narrow, purple. Fruit a smooth, ovoid drupe, green becoming yellow with maturity, about ½ in. in diameter; flesh thin, stone strongly ribbed lengthwise.

DISTRIBUTION AND HABITAT. Naturalized and locally common in the southern United States and Hawaii. Frequently planted as an ornamental, particularly in horticultural varieties, such as var. *umbraculiformis,* the Texas umbrella tree.

POISONOUS PRINCIPLE. Poisoning most often occurs from ingestion of the fruits. Toxicity of the fruits resides in a resinous fraction of the pulp, the chemistry of which remains inconclusively established (1132, 1533).

TOXICITY, SYMPTOMS, AND LESIONS. Chinaberry has caused repeated loss of life of livestock and man in Africa and Australia where, as a result, it has been extensively investigated [see reviews by Hurst (810) and Steyn (1533)]. In some cases feeding experiments had positive results; in others large amounts of the plant failed to evoke symptoms. It has been suggested not only that toxicity may vary with location or growing conditions but that it may be entirely absent (1132) in some botanical strains of this species.

Fig. 42. *Melia azedarach*. Chinaberry tree. Branch, with details of flower and fruit. Courtesy of The Macmillan Company.

Some experimental feedings of the fruit to pigs and sheep have established its toxicity to be in the neighborhood of 0.5 per cent of the animal's weight. Other classes of livestock and birds are more resistant, but cases have been reported in goats, cattle, fowl, and other animals. Loss of human life has followed ingestion of the berries, principally by children, or of decoctions of the leaves.

Symptoms are of two types. The plant is a severe irritant and produces nausea, vomition, constipation, or scouring, often with blood. In addition, nervous symptoms of excitement or depression, weakened heart action, and dyspnea are presented. Lesions are those consistent with gastroenteritis. Fatty degeneration in liver and kidney is found on histological examination if a day or two elapses before death. Symptoms may appear in less than an hour after ingestion of a toxic dose, or not for several hours. Death often occurs within 24 hours, but sometimes animals linger for several days before death occurs. Slow recovery may take place in animals less severely poisoned.

CONDITIONS OF POISONING. The leaves, bark, and flowers have been shown toxic, but the great majority of cases occur from ingestion of fruits. These have a peculiar odor and intense taste which is not usually attractive to animals. Pigs are most frequently poisoned and appear to be particularly susceptible to the poisonous principle. Occasional cases in pigs have been reported (273, 1234, 1483) in the United States, but in this hemisphere the plant does not seem to be as toxic as elsewhere.

Additional reference: 1661.

Order Sapindales

Celastraceae

Euonymus spp. Euonymus

A genus of many species and varieties of ornamental and wild bushes, vines, and ground covers. Two species, *E. atropurpureus* Jacq. (burning bush, wahoo) and *E. europaeus* L. (spindle tree) are frequently cited in lists of poisonous plants. Authority for their toxicity in the main traces back to Cornevin, 1887 (334), who stated (about *E. europaeus*) that the leaves, bark, and fruit act as violent purgatives and are dangerous to various livestock and children.

Cases of violent purgation in horses and poisoning in human beings have been described in Europe more recently (574, 1629). In the human being, ingestion of fruits of *E. europaeus* was responsible for vomiting, diarrhea, mental symptoms, and loss of consciousness. No cases have been described in North America.

The poisonous principle has not been completely identified. It may also be present in the common viny bittersweet (*Celastrus scandens* L.), which is listed as a suspected poisonous plant in several publications.

Anacardiaceae (contributed by Wm. Gillis)

Anacardium occidentale L. Cashew nut

The cashew has poison in the shell of the nut which causes a dermatitis indistinguishable from the poison-ivy syndrome (see *Toxicodendron*).

The shell is usually removed before reaching the American market, but the shell liquid has been used in electrical insulations in airplanes and has caused difficulties when repairs have been needed. The poisons, related to those in poison ivy, have been studied in great detail by Symes and Dawson (1558). They are known commercially as cardol, anacardic acid, and anacardol.

The "cashew apple," a large fleshy receptical beneath the nut, is harmless and a delicacy in areas where the cashew is grown.

There are a number of other genera in this family, native to Latin America and southeastern Asia, which produce similar poisons, some of whose chemistry is known.

Mangifera indica L. Mango

A poison has been found in the pedicel of this queen of all tropical fruits. The poison, presumably related to that in poison ivy (see *Toxicodendron*) (853), may adhere to the skin of the fruit after harvesting. For the sake of safety, the skin should be removed before eating the delicious fruit (874, 1455).

Metopium toxiferum (L.) Krug & Urban. Poison-wood

DESCRIPTION. Tall shrub or small tree. Leaves compound with five to seven broadly ovate to orbicular leaflets. The fruits are fleshy and about an inch in length.

DISTRIBUTION. Lime soil of the Everglades in Monroe and Dade Counties, Florida. where it presumably was introduced by hurricanes out of the Caribbean. Otherwise found in Cuba, Haiti, Puerto Rico, and the Dominican Republic. Related to *M. brownei* (Jacq.) Urban of British Honduras, Yucatan, Guatemala, and Caribbean Islands and to *M. venosum* (Griseb.) Engler of Eastern Cuba.

POISONOUS PRINCIPLE. It has never been identified, but presumably is closely related to those of poison ivy (see *Toxicodendron*). Like the latter, it blackens and hardens when exposed to air.

Toxicodendron radicans (L.) Kuntze (= *Rhus toxicodendron* L., *Rhus radicans* L.) Poison ivy, poison vine, markweed (erroneously called poison oak)

DESCRIPTION. Vigorous woody vine, shrub, or subshrub with trifoliolate, alternate leaves. In the eastern United States, it will be a vine or roadside shrub, reduced in size to subshrub abundant in forested, shady sites. East Coast form [var. *littorale* (Mearns) Barkl.] will have smooth-margined leaflets; central-states forms (var. *radicans*) will have obtuse notches or teeth on the leaflets. The variety from the Arbuckle Mountains of Oklahoma and the Edwards Plateau of Texas [var. *verrucosum* (Sheele) Barkl.] has a deep, acute lobe on either side of the terminal leaflet and on

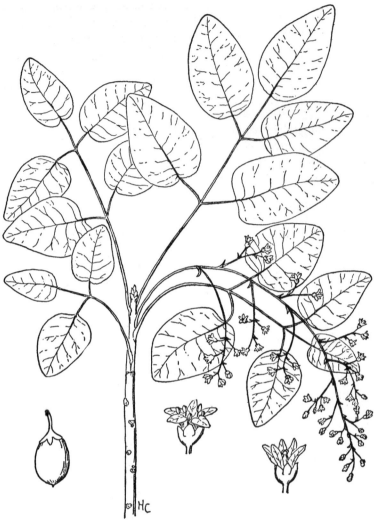

Fig. 43. *Metopium toxiferum*. Poisonwood. Fruiting branch, with details of male and female flowers, and fruit. Courtesy of The Macmillan Company.

the outer edge of each lateral leaflet. The variety from the Rio Grande basin [var. *eximium* (Greene) Barkl.] may have deeply round-lobed leaflets. Each leaflet will appear to be almost cut further into three leaflets, resembling the "club" on a deck of playing cards. Occasional clones of plants with leaves of more than three leaflets occur. The small flowers are greenish-white to cream, about a quarter of an inch across, and grow in the leaf axils after the leaves appear in spring. Males and females are on separate plants, the males conspicuous at flowering time by the five yellow anthers. The fruits, greenish when young, ripen into tan to yellowish drupes with a scaly outer coat and white, hard, waxy inner flesh with black striations. Populations from the East Coast north of Georgia, from northwestern Indiana, and from the Orient have hairs on the fruits.

Variety *rydbergii* (Small ex Rydb.) Erskine may be distinguished from all other forms by its nonclimbing habit, lack of aerial roots, larger fruits, longer petioles, shorter petiolules, broader leaflets, and a tendency for the leaflets to fold along the midrib so as to give a spoon shape to the leaflet. Poison ivy has been studied extensively by Barkley (66).

DISTRIBUTION AND HABITAT. The plant is usually thought to be ubiquitous, but actually prefers certain habitats and is absent from others. It is most common on flood plains, bottom lands, lake shores, and sand dunes. It is virtually absent from scrubby oak-pine savannahs of the Southeast and from oak-hickory woods. It is generally fond of the same kinds of habitats as willows but never grows with them. The species grows in all states of the United States east of the Cascade Mountains, the Great Basin, and the Mojave Desert (absent in Nevada). Variety *rydbergii* is the only form west of the 101st meridian of longitude (except for eastern Arizona and Texas) and north of the 44th parallel of latitude. Poison ivy is found in all states of Mexico except in the Yucatan Peninsula and northern Baja California, but is not at all common, except locally. It reaches its southern limit in Huehuetenango Department of Guatemala and its northern limit along an irregular line from the Gaspé Peninsula westward to British Columbia, approximating the 52nd parallel of latitude. It is found in Bermuda and several islands in the Bahamas. It occurs throughout Japan and the islands north of Japan. It occupies middle elevations in the mountains of Taiwan and of central and western China.

CONDITIONS OF POISONING. One may obtain a dermatitis upon contact with broken parts of the plant or with articles of clothing or implements which have touched broken parts of the plant. There is no evidence that unbroken leaves or stems give off any poisonous exudate. Chewings by insects may provide the exit of poison from the resin ducts of the phloem to the exterior, however. It is toxic all year; care should be taken in burning poison-ivy leaves, since the poison is present in *droplet* form on the particles of dust and ash in the smoke. Therefore, the woebegone sufferer who laughs with satisfaction as he watches poison ivy burn in a bonfire may not have the last laugh. Pulling up the plant after leaves have fallen is an equally precarious operation.

Animals, except for man and closely allied primates, are generally not sensitive, due chiefly to their coats of hair and fur. In spite of a protective coat, there are a few substantiated records of poisoning among animals (1084) other than human beings. Birds like the fruits for food during the

Fig. 44. *Toxicodendron radicans*. Poison ivy. Fruiting branch.
Courtesy of The Macmillan Company.

winter and are largely instrumental in the wide distribution of the plant,
especially near trees and fences.

POISONOUS PRINCIPLE. The toxin is a colorless or milky substance contained in resin canals throughout the plant except in the pollen. The chemistry of the toxic substance was worked out by Dawson (408, 409). It is 3-*n*-pentadecylcatechol:

There are actually four poisons, each with a differing degree of saturation in the side chain. The substance oxidizes (on the ring) and polymerizes readily, but the resulting products are still toxic to most people who are sensitive to the fresh product.

TOXICITY, SYMPTOMS, AND LESIONS. The syndrome recognized as poison ivy has been known since the days of Captain John Smith and is variously described in primitive Indian cultures. Natural immunity is originally present in all persons, but is reduced to one or another threshold of sensitivity by contact with the poison. A dermatitis is manifested by reddened and itchy skin in mild cases to blisters which exude serum in the most severe cases. Infection is a danger in the latter case. Mucous and alimentary canal membranes may be affected; serious gastric upset, even death, may result from ingestion of leaves or fruits of the plant. Eating a leaf, contrary to many old wives' tales, does *not* confer immunity. Infection or other complications may bring about death on occasion even when only the skin is affected.

Only about half of the population is sensitive to an "average" contact with the poison. Seemingly similar contacts resulting in different manifestations of poisoning have permitted fantastic tales to build up concerning poison ivy. Contrary to popular opinion, it is not possible to contact dermatitis "out of the air." Contact with the plant or a secondary carrier is essential to poisoning. The running sores will not spread the disease inasmuch as their content is solely body fluid. Reinfection from clothing, shoes, hunting or garden implements, or household pets is common and leads to the error of suspecting infection from the air or from broken blisters. It is possible by handling these implements repeatedly to reinfect oneself. The poison is not volatile. Differing degrees of contact also lead to misunderstood degrees of infection. Lack of recognition of the plant in all its forms is the chief cause of mishap, however.

Combination of the poison with skin proteins is believed to be *immediate* (877), and the now-famous washing with yellow soap will serve only to wash off excess poison which might be transmitted to other parts of the body or to other persons. Even by washing thoroughly with soap of any color it is difficult to remove all transmissible poison. Upon oxidizing, the poisons turn black and gummy like their relatives from the Oriental lacquer trees, whose poisons are collected to make the renowned lacquer ware of China and Japan.

Treatment is topical by a number of patent lotions and creams. This treatment is symptomatic only; there is no known cure. In severe cases, physicians will administer ACTH or a cortisone derivative under carefully controlled conditions. Prevention by use of pyridine-reacted and alum-precipitated toxin in water, taken orally several months in advance of the season, has had seemingly good results (594, 901, 1250), but is highly criticized by some (877) as performing no physiological reaction. Injections should generally be avoided since they produce sporadic results, often disastrous—especially when administered during an attack (877).

Toxicodendron diversilobum (T. &. G.) Greene (= *Rhus toxicodendron* L., *Rhus diversiloba* T. &. G.). Western poison oak

This species is closely related to poison ivy. It is found in western North America from southern British Columbia to northern Baja California. It grows between the coast ranges and the Cascades of Oregon and Washington (except for the Olympic Peninsula) and is ubiquitous west of the Sierra Nevada Mountains and Mojave Desert of California. It appears to have increased in abundance in historic times due to the activities of man. It interbreeds with poison ivy where the ranges of the two plants come into contact in the Columbia River gorge.

It is similar to poison ivy in that it has the familiar three leaflets (often five), grows as a shrub or vine, and produces a reaction in man that is *indistinguishable* from the dematitis of poison ivy. Its leaflets are larger and on longer pedicels than those of poison ivy, and autumn coloration generally is a deeper shade of red. Otherwise, information contained herein for poison ivy is applicable.

The poisons have never been studied, but are presumably closely related, if not identical, to those in poison ivy.

Toxicodendron quercifolium (Michx.) Greene (= *Rhus toxicodendron* L., *Rhus quercifolia* Steud.). Eastern poison oak

Eastern poison oak, though related to poison ivy, differs significantly from it. Poison oak inhabits the scrub oak-pine savannahs of the Atlantic and Gulf coastal plains on poor sandy soils in sand-hills forests where poison ivy generally does not grow. Its range, unlike that of western poison oak, overlaps the range of poison ivy, but the two seldom grow together due to differences in environmental requirements. Poison oak occurs from southern New Jersey to Marion County, Florida, west to eastern Texas and Cherokee County, Kansas. Where its range extends beyond the range of pine, it is found in scrub oak forests with a typical bunchgrass understory (Oklahoma, western Arkansas, and Missouri, for example). Eastern poison oak never climbs or produces aerial roots. Its leaves are densely pubescent;

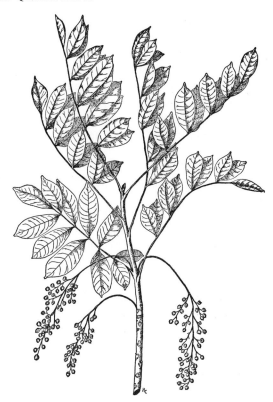

Fig. 45. *Toxicodendron vernix*. Poison-sumac. Fruiting branch. Photograph of branch. Drawing, courtesy of The Macmillan Company.

the fruits are pubescent and papillose, larger than those of the forms of poison ivy growing in the same range.

This plant rarely hybridizes with poison ivy and for all practical purposes is extremely distinct. It is fairly constant throughout its range, but the male plants will often have more deeply lobed leaflets than the females.

Its poisonous reaction is identical to that of poison ivy and Western poison oak. Its poisons may be the same as those in poison ivy or Western poison oak, but this, contrary to many literature references, has never been proven.

Toxicodendron vernix (L.) Kuntze (= *Rhus vernix* L.). Poison sumac, poison elder

DESCRIPTION. A tall, rangy shrub growing up to 15 ft in height. The leaves are compound with seven to eleven leaflets. The rachis is bright red, and the bright green leaflets have no teeth on their margins, differing thus from the nonpoisonous sumacs. The flowers are erect and axillary among the leaves and generally very abundant. They are smaller than poison-ivy flowers, but otherwise resemble them. The fruits are pendant when ripe and are glossy, pale yellow or cream with striations on the waxy mesocarp. Poison sumac is thus distinguished from the nontoxic sumacs which have red, erect fruits terminating the shrub axis in typical "stag-horn" fashion.

DISTRIBUTION. Poison sumac grows from southern Quebec to central Florida. It is predominately found east of the Mississippi River, but is known from some stations in the neighboring states west of the river. It is found only in bogs, swamps, and wet bottom lands, whereas benign sumacs never inhabit such wet places.

This plant is closely allied to *T. striatum* (L.) Ruiz & Pavon of southern Mexico, central and northern South America, and the various lacquer trees of eastern Asia. Its toxins have never been identified. Those of the Asiatic lacquer trees (*T. verniciferum* DC. Barkl.) were identified by Dawson *et al.* (408, 1554) and found to be similar (except for the triolefin) to the four toxic substances in poison ivy.

Aceraceae

Acer rubrum L. Red maple, swamp maple.

This is one of the common maples. It is widely distributed, usually in damp soils, throughout eastern North America. It forms a large tree at maturity, with 3- to 5-lobed leaves, each 2 to 4 in. long.

Two cases of death in livestock, involving cattle and horses, after eating maple leaves have been reported (332) from West Virginia. Further details are lacking.

Sapindaceae

Blighia sapida Kon. Akee

DESCRIPTION, DISTRIBUTION, AND HABITAT. This small tree, native to Africa, is cultivated in southern Florida and the tropics for its fruit which, when handled properly, is edible. Clusters of fruit are formed once, twice, or sometimes more often during the year. Each fruit is a leathery-skinned, fat capsule, about 3 to 4 in. long. At maturity the capsule wall dries and opens partially at the apex, exposing three compartments. Each compartment is occupied by a single, large, shiny black seed which is partially embedded in a very thick, squat stalk, the aril. The aril is whitish in color, light in texture, and heavily impregnated with oil. This is the part consumed. It is usually prepared by parboiling and then frying. It has a pleasant, slightly nutty flavor and is considered a delicacy.

POISONOUS PRINCIPLE. Two related compounds have been isolated from the seeds (734). They have both been shown to carry toxicity and to have marked hypoglycemic potency in experimental animals. They have been named hypoglycin A and hypoglycin B. Both are present in the seeds but only hypoglycin A, the more toxic of the two, was found in the aril and was in greater amount in the aril of unripe fruit.

TOXICITY, SYMPTOMS, AND LESIONS. A disease of undernourished human beings, especially children, in Jamaica and elsewhere, called "vomiting sickness," has been more or less conclusively linked with ingestion of akee. Vomiting sickness appears epidemically among children and sometimes adults in family groups during winter months. Its onset is sudden and consists of violent vomiting (771). One or more periods of vomiting and quiescence are followed by convulsions, coma, and death in a majority of instances. The attack usually lasts twelve hours or less. Principal finding is marked to severe hypoglycemia. Blood sugar is usually less than 20 mg per 100 cc, and fatty metamorphosis with gross depletion of glycogen is found on liver biopsy. Liver-function tests are normal.

CONDITIONS OF POISONING. It is generally believed that the fruit wall and seed of ripe akee fruits are toxic, that the aril of the unripe fruit (before it has opened naturally) is poisonous, and that the ripe aril associated with an undeveloped berry is toxic. Because of its high content of oil, the aril rapidly turns rancid in past-ripe fruit. It is generally believed that the rancid aril is toxic. Most of these beliefs have been substantiated by investigations into the toxicity of the fruit or its content of toxic principle (734, 771, 949, 1136). The belief that the ripe, cooked aril is nontoxic has been supported in some experiments (949) but is contradicted in part by the finding that even the ripe aril contains some hypoglycemic principle (734) and by the incidence of vomiting sickness in undernourished children.

Hippocastanaceae

Aesculus spp. Buckeyes, horsechestnut

DESCRIPTION. Trees or shrubs easily recognized by characteristics of leaves, inflorescences and fruits. Leaves opposite, palmately compound; leaflets 5 to 7, serrate. Inflorescences paniculate, large, erect, many-flowered, usually yellow. Fruit a 1- to 3-seeded leathery capsule bearing sharp spines when young; spines lost at maturity in some species, retained in others. Seeds large (about 1 in. in diameter), glossy brown when newly exposed, bearing a conspicuous scar (whence the name, buckeye).

DISTRIBUTION AND HABITAT. *Aesculus hippocastanum* L. is the horse-chestnut introduced from Europe and widely planted as an ornamental shade tree. Specific ranges and habitats of native species are listed below. This genus was considered toxic at an early time (1108, 1217). Various species have been listed in recent publications, some apparently on little additional evidence. The better-substantiated include the following.

Aesculus pavia L., red buckeye, is a red-flowered shrub or small tree of fertile valleys in the southeastern and south-central states. It has been administered experimentally to hogs, mules, horses, cattle, and fish (253). No deaths resulted, but symptoms of incoordination, twitching, sluggishness, or excitability were produced in cattle and horses. Results varied considerably, as did the methods of administration and part of plant employed. In some instances about 1 per cent of the animal's weight of plant in a single dose was sufficient to produce symptoms.

Aesculus glabra Willd. (including var. *arguta* Buckley), the Ohio buckeye, is a small tree with yellow flowers. It grows in rich woods and river banks in the area from western Pennsylvania to Nebraska, South to Texas and Alabama, and is occasionally cultivated as an ornamental. Several cases of cattle sickness after ingestion of sprouts from buckeye stumps on recently cleared land have been reported in Indiana (704). A prominent symptom mentioned was peculiarity of gait of the forelimbs as though the animals "were walking on a hot pavement." The variety has been reported toxic in Texas (1502).

Aesculus octandra Marsh, sweet buckeye, is a tree with greenish-yellow flowers. It is found on mountain riverbanks and in woodlands from Pennsylvania to Iowa and southward. This species is listed as among the ten most troublesome poisonous plants in the poisonous-plants bulletin of the North Carolina Experiment Station (127), but the basis for this estimation is not given.

Aesculus californica (Spach) Nutt., California buckeye, is a shrub or low tree of dry hillsides and canyons in the Pacific Coast Range and the foothills of the Sierra Nevada. This species is credited (935) with producing occasional poisoning in all classes of livestock. It is also reported (935) that the flowers of this species are poisonous to honey bees and that human beings have been poisoned by eating the honey produced from the nectar of this plant.

Aesculus hippocastanum L. is the common horsechestnut. Variously colored double-flowered and hybrid forms are commercially available. This

Fig. 46. *Aesculus hippocastanum*. Horsechestnut. Branch with leaves and inflorescence.

plant was used as a source of medicinal preparations in earlier days in Europe and it has been stated that ingestion of the nuts has killed children. In Maryland it has been reported (1335) that the leaves and dried fruits have caused cattle loss.

It thus appears that any of the 25 domestic species of *Aesculus* should be considered potentially toxic to stock, with some evidence that young growth, sprouts, and the mature nuts are especially dangerous. Alkaloids, glycosides, and saponins have all been held responsible for toxicity in this

$$C_6H_{11}O_4 \cdot O$$

aesculin

genus, but critical analysis (955) has resulted in the detection and characterization of a glycoside, aesculin. This molecule (6-β-glucosido-7-

hydroxycoumarin) shows a chemical relationship with the toxic principle produced in spoiled sweet-clover hay (see *Melilotus*).

Order Rhamnales

Rhamnaceae

Karwinskia humboldtiana Zucc. Coyotillo

DESCRIPTION. Woody shrub or small tree, 3 to 20 ft tall. Leaves mostly opposite, petioled, elliptical-ovate, entire or undulate, 1 to 3 in. long; veins pinnate, very distinct, ending at the slightly revolute margin. Flowers in axillary clusters, small, greenish. Fruit an ovoid drupe, brownish-black at maturity, about ½ in. in diameter.

DISTRIBUTION AND HABITAT. Gravelly hills, canyons, and river valleys along the southwestern border of Texas into Mexico and southern California.

POISONOUS PRINCIPLE. Unknown.

TOXICITY, SYMPTOMS, AND LESIONS. The "berries" from this plant were known by the Indians to produce paralysis, and accounts of their poisonous nature to human beings may be found in several of the early botanical writings concerning the area where this plant grows. Numerous requests for information concerning the poisonous nature of this plant to livestock and human beings prompted experiments by the United States Department of Agriculture which were carried out at the Salina station between 1921 and 1927 and were reported by Marsh *et al.* (1017).

Experimental evidence or reliable case reports have shown this species toxic to goats, cattle, sheep, hogs, fowl, and human beings. Two syndromes may be produced, only one of which, the paralytic, is recognized from natural cases. A striking fact about the paralytic syndrome is the lag period prior to the appearance of symptoms as compared with the sudden course of the latter. The lag period varies from a few days to several weeks. In experimental work at Salina one sheep did not show any signs of poisoning for 47 days after ingestion of a single toxic dose. In work at the Texas Agricultural Experiment Station (314), a lag of 125 days between consumption of a toxic dose and appearance of symptoms in an Angora buck was noted. A few reports of poisoning in human beings indicate that the subject is totally unaware of having been poisoned during the lag period.

Single-dose toxicity of whole fruit (including seed) varied from 0.05 to 0.3 per cent of the animal's weight, dry-weight basis, with cattle most susceptible, fowl least so. The first symptoms noted in experimental poisonings consisted of weakness and incoordination of the hind legs, or a dragging motion while walking. This was superceded by exaggerated high stepping or irregular action of the hind legs, later often involving the forelegs. In attempting to walk, severely poisoned animals might jump or move backward. Finally, complete prostration developed. Throughout this course of events the appetite remained normal. Animals could be kept alive if carefully cared for, but most severely paralyzed animals did not recover and would die from one cause or another under range conditions. In the experimental work, complete recovery in the few animals where it occurred required many weeks. No specific lesions, either gross or histological, were found on post mortem examination. With the exception of motor paralysis, the poisoned animals appeared normal in all respects.

It has been generally believed that only the seeds were toxic. Limited experiments were undertaken which showed that the fruit pulp also was toxic, though less so than the seeds. Experiments with the foilage showed that it, too, was toxic, but produced a syndrome different from the paralytic one produced by the seeds and fruit. Ingestion of 15 to 21 per cent of an animal's weight of green foliage by cattle and sheep over several days resulted, after only a few more, in loss of condition, wasting, nausea, progressive weakness, and death. Again cattle were found slightly more susceptible than sheep.

CONDITIONS OF POISONING. Coyotillo may be browsed when other forage is scarce. Losses in sheep, cattle, and goats are common in some areas of Texas. They are especially frequent in the winter season when the plants are heavily in fruit, but may occur at any time of year. Losses of 1,000 or more head have been reported by some goat raisers (1504). Children have been poisoned by eating the "berries."

Rhamnus spp. Buckthorn

Rhamnus cathartica L., the common buckthorn, is a shrub, introduced from Europe as an ornamental plant, often planted as a hedge, and now escaped from cultivation in eastern North America. *Rhamnus frangula* L., the alder buckthorn, is a shrub or small tree, also introduced, and now found as an escapee from cultivation in eastern North America. *Rhamnus purshiana* DC. is a small, deciduous tree, native to the Pacific Northwest. This species is the source of cascara sagrada, a commonly used laxative. All three species contain glycosides from which a purgative, anthraquinone, is obtained by hydrolysis. Poisoning is rare but has been described in Europe (see 607).

Vitaceae

Parthenocissus quinquefolia (L.) Planch. Virginia creeper, woodbine, American ivy

This very common vine of eastern and central North America occurs wild and in several cultivated varieties. It bears small, blue berries which are attractive to children. A very few cases are on record in which lethal poisoning of children has been traced circumstantially to ingestion of *Parthenocissus* berries, and one feeding experiment with the fresh berries has been reported in which a dozen were lethal within 36 hours to a guinea pig. *Parthenocissus* poisoning of human beings has been reviewed by Warren (1645), to which may be added another circumstantial case resulting in the death of one child and the serious poisoning of another, reported in the Albany, N.Y., press (13). Because of the confusion in identification of the plant through the variety of common and scientific names which have been applied to it, and the circumstantial nature of all cases cited, it is not possible definitely to list *Parthenocissus quinquefolia* as a proven poisonous plant, but the evidence is sufficient for suspicion to be attached to it.

Order Urticales

Moraceae

Maclura pomifera Schneid. Osage orange

Osage orange is native to Arkansas and Texas. It has been planted, particularly as a hedge, throughout much of the United States and has established itself in the wild in some sections. It has been suspected of having caused livestock loss here, but feeding experiments performed in Kansas, Kentucky, and Illinois with various classes of stock have universally been negative (839). However, some experiments have been reported from Australia (810) in which slight toxicity was demonstrated.

Osage orange gets its name from the fruits which are roughly spherical and about 4 to 5 inches in diameter. Fruit may cause death in ruminants by lodging in the esophagus and preventing eructation or release of ruminal gases.

Cannabinaceae

Cannabis sativa L. Hemp, marijuana, marihuana

DESCRIPTION. Coarse annual herb, 3 to 6 or more ft tall, reproducing by seeds. Leaves opposite below, alternate above, palmately compound with 3 to 7 linear to oblanceolate, coarsely dentate leaflets. Male and female plants separate. Male inflorescence a panicle of small green staminate flowers. Female inflorescence an axillary leafy spike or cluster of small green flowers each consisting of an inconspicuous perianth appressed to a long ovary, bearing 2 stigmas and ripening into a conspicuous achene

Fig. 47. *Maclura pomifera.* Osage orange. Ripe fruit.

("hemp seed"). Male inflorescences produced mostly at the tips of branches; female inflorescences along the length of a branch.

DISTRIBUTION AND HABITAT. Native to Asia, now widely spread throughout the world and throughout the United States. In the alluvial bottom lands of the Mississippi and Missouri Valleys it has formed populations covering several or many acres. Besides the narcotic principle which it contains, not legally produced for commerce in the United States, the plant is of economic importance for its fibers (hemp) and seeds which have been an important ingredient in birdseed mixtures and which are the source of a useful oil. In the United States the medicinal use of the narcotic principle, never large, was discontinued at the beginning of World War II, and other drugs were substituted. Cultivation for fiber ceased around 1955 when the remaining American processors closed down their decorticating plants and ceased contracting with farmers.

The species is highly variable. Varieties cultivated for fiber production are not the same as those cultivated for the narcotic principle. Even so, cultivation of all varieties for whatever purpose is under strict state and federal regulation and only by federal license (4).

POISONOUS PRINCIPLE. The narcotic principle is contained in the resinous fraction. Its chemical nature was difficult to elucidate, though not for lack of attempt. Early efforts at analysis produced from the crude resin a red oil which was further fractionated into two compounds, cannabinol and cannabidiol, whose chemical identity was established (4, 1585). However, neither of these compounds, although used as the basis of

Fig. 48. *Cannabis sativa*. Marijuana. Flowering branch with female inflorescences.

chemical tests for cannabis* (61, 116), possesses physiological activity. Physiological activity of the crude resin is derived from a group of chemically related tetrahydrocannabinols, which in turn are closely related to the compounds named above. The tetrahydrocannabinols are resins in physical properties and difficult to crystallize and separate. Synthetic manufacture of

tetrahydrocannabinol

a number of them together with clinical testing has established their individual degree of activity (1585). Gas chromatography has been reported by Lerner (921).

TOXICITY, SYMPTOMS, AND LESIONS. The effect of the narcotic principle on man has been known for more than 2000 years, and repeatedly

* The term "cannabis" is the name applied by the U.S. Pharmacopoeia to the drug obtained from *Cannabis sativa*. The name *Cannabis indica* is sometimes used for the variety of *Cannabis sativa* grown for the purpose of producing the narcotic resin.

described. Individual subjective reaction is extremely variable (61, 176). In general there is a period of euphoria and elation followed by heightened sensitivity to stimulation. Then hallucinations and mental confusion become evident. With heavy doses depression and comatose sleep terminate the immediate physiological reaction. Withdrawal symptoms experienced by long-time cannabis users are mild or absent. Moral degeneration and physical debility are said to accompany continued or heavy use. The drug is brought into the system by smoking resin-containing parts of the plant or by ingestion of the crude resin. Results are similar, though produced by more slowly by the latter route.

The plant is bitter and unpleasant tasting and is rarely consumed by animals. No clear-cut cases of livestock loss to this plant have been reported in the American literature. However, poisoning of farm animals may occur through ingestion of *Cannabis* seed press cake or the entire plant (1533). The loss of several horses and mules in Greece has been attributed to ingestion of *Cannabis* grown illicitly (239). The animals, belonging to a military party, were in rough country and left to their own devices for forage. Shortly after ingestion of *Cannabis* they showed excitation, difficulty in breathing, and muscular trembling. Although temperature was subnormal, the animals sweated and slobbered profusely. Death occurred in all cases within 15 to 30 minutes after onset of symptoms. Lesions observed on post mortem consisted mainly of congestion and ecchymotic hemorrhages of various organs, especially digestive. Positive identification of *Cannabis* in the stomach contents was made.

CONDITIONS OF POISONING. Seedlings contain little if any principle. Resin production in older plants varies within wide limits. Variation is dependent on variety of plant, geographical location, sex of plant, and nature of growing season (1349). The greatest resin content is developed in the female plant at time of flowering and is found concentrated in mature inflorescences. Its production is enhanced in warmer climates.

Control of cannabis is the object of federal and state legislation and regulation. Federal law (1191) prohibits (without license) the possession of living or dried *Cannabis* or parts of the plant.

Additional reference: 641.

Order Caryophyllales

Phytolaccaceae

Phytolacca americana L. (= *P. decandra* L.). Pokeweed, scoke, garget, pigeonberry

DESCRIPTION. Tall, distinctive, perennial herb, from a very large, fleshy taproot, much branched, to 9 ft tall. Stems stout, glabrous, purple

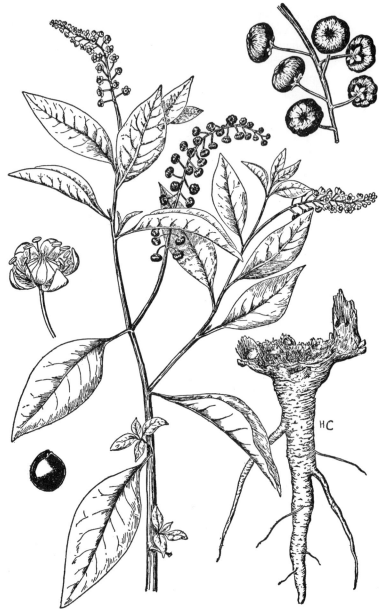

Fig. 49. *Phytolacca americana*. Pokeweed. Flowering branch, with details of root, flower, and fruit. Courtesy of The Macmillan Company.

or green. Leaves alternate, petiolate, entire, ovate; base and tip acute. Inflorescence racemose, terminal, drooping when in fruit; flowers numerous, small, white or greenish; sepals 5, petals absent, stamens 10, free, carpels 10. Fruit a 10-seeded, inky-juiced, shiny, purple berry.

DISTRIBUTION AND HABITAT. Disturbed, rich soils, especially of barnyards, low lands, eastern United States and southeastern Canada.

POISONOUS PRINCIPLE. The plant contains more than one physiologically active principle, the exact identities of which have not been determined. Before the turn of the present century pokeweed enjoyed considerable use in medicine (1393). Several active substances were named according to the methods of the times (1217). Some of these names appear in current publications, but all are in need of reexamination. Extracts of the root show saponic characteristics.

TOXICITY, SYMPTOMS, AND LESIONS. Pokeroot or decoctions of it was used by the American Indians and soon by the early settlers for a variety of illnesses. Occasionally, poisoning resulted from ill-advised treatments or accidental ingestion of pokeroot (590). In animals poisoning is rare, partly because the most toxic part of the plant is underground, and partly because the plant is not particularly palatable. The berries are the most attractive part and seem to be the least toxic, but may have been responsible for human fatality (275, 713). They are readily eaten without apparent toxic effect by wild birds, and feeding experiments have shown them harmless to domestic fowl (752). They are used by some persons in making pies. References to the poisoning of children by the berries are not conclusive. The young green shoots also are used as a boiled vegetable, a practice widely regarded as safe if the cooking water is discarded.

Pigs may be poisoned by rooting out and consuming the roots. Cases have been reported from Indiana (704) and Alabama (1251). Experimental feeding of a few small pieces of the root to a pig resulted in nausea, depression, and prostration the next day. The animal was sacrificed in moribund condition. The principal lesion consisted of severe local hemorrhagic gastritis of the mucosal membranes where they were in contact with pieces of pokeroot. Ulcerative gastritis and a swollen, dark-colored liver were observed in natural cases.

In the human being symptoms consist of a burning sensation in the mouth immediately upon consumption, followed in about two hours by gastrointestinal cramps, vomition, and diarrhea. Visual disturbance, salivation, perspiration, lassitude, prostration, and weakened respiration and pulse may be observed. Recovery occurs in about 24 hours, but some cases terminate fatally.

Additional reference: 1335.

Polygonaceae

Fagopyrum sagittatum Gilib. (= *F. esculentum* Moench, *Polygonum fagopyrum* L.). Buckwheat

Buckwheat is a small grain crop of minor importance. In the United States it is planted in northern areas as a ground cover, green manure, or occasionally for forage. Some acreage is harvested for the "grain," a small, pyramidal, hard, brown-black achene. Buckwheat flour has some commercial use in pancake mixes in the United States.

Buckwheat has long been recognized in Europe as a plant capable of producing photosensitivity (see photosensitization, p. 52) in animals and possibly in human beings. Although cases are not common, the disease has aroused interest and has been investigated in various ways, particularly in the late 1800's and early 1900's. Reviews by Blum (138), Clare (284), and Mathews (1042) are among those which may be consulted.

Under the proper combination of circumstances ingestion of moderate to large quantities of buckwheat forage green or dry, or the seed (1042, 1446), by cattle, horses, sheep, goats, swine, and fowl, followed by exposure to intense sunlight will result in photosensitization. In mild cases, symptoms may consist of no more than an erythema of white or unpigmented portions of the skin. In acute cases, nervous symptoms are observed. Erythema is followed by subdermal edematous swelling and eventual necrosis. Nervous symptoms include cerebral excitement, running about, grunting, squealing or bellowing, jumping, convulsions, and prostration.

Buckwheat appears to be a primary photosensitizer although liver damage has been mentioned in some discussions (574). Several persons have attempted to isolate, characterize, and identify the pigment contained in the plant which is responsible for sensitizing animals. Wender (1657, 1658) isolated and crystallized three fractions which he then showed capable of causing photosensitivity in experimental animals. The chief absorption band of each of these fell at or near 590 mμ, a figure in agreement with earlier approximations of action spectra. In other work a napthrodianthrone derivative, named fagopyrin, has been isolated (285).

In this hemisphere outbreaks of buckwheat photosensitization are rare. Bruce (184) in 1917 described an instance in British Columbia in which photosensitization of white Yorkshire pigs resulted from buckwheat pasturage. The pigs, aged from 3 months to old brood sows, developed symptoms 24 hours after being placed on a field of flowering buckwheat. Brief periods of quiescence were interspersed with longer periods of jumping, squealing, running about, and other signs of discomfort. A skin rash, characteristic of photosensitization, developed.

Fig. 50. Smartweeds. A–D, *Polygonum pennsylvanicum.* Plant, with details of flower, glandular flower stalk, and seed (achene). E–G, *P. hydropiper.* Flowering shoot, with details of flower and seed (achene). H–K, *P. hydropiperoides.* Flowering shoot, with details of flower and seed (achene). Courtesy of The Macmillan Company.

Most, if not all, cases of buckwheat poisoning in human beings are not photosensitizations, but are obvious allergic reactions to the plant (138, 139).

A situation in which five white-skinned cattle were poisoned in France has been described relatively recently (1299). The role of sunlight in poisoning was well demonstrated. These animals had been stabled out of the sun throughout their lives prior to poisoning. For three weeks before being pastured they had been fed flowering buckwheat exclusively, but no symptoms of photosensitization developed as long as they remained stabled. Within 2 hours of being put out—as it happened, on a bright sunny day— they were prostrated. The eyelids were swollen shut, the ears swollen to $3/4$ in. in thickness and pendant. A sixth animal was colored and less severely affected. In this and other cases treatment involves prompt removal from sunlight. Recovery is usual, although subsequent necrosis of skin from severely edematous areas often leaves permanent scars.

Polygonum spp. Smartweeds

Several species of *Polygonum* are common weeds of North America. They are closely related to buckwheat (*Fagopyrum*) and like the latter are characterized by alternate, entire leaves, sheathing stipules, and jointed stems.

The sap of these plants is acrid. In earlier literature on poisonous plants it was judged capable of producing skin irritation and gastrointestinal disturbance in farm animals [see review by Long (933)], but recent cases are not on record. Some suspect these plants of being photosensitizers by reason of circumstantial cases in cattle (184), an observation that gains weight from the proven photosensitizing capacity of buckwheat.

Rheum rhaponticum L. Rhubarb

The leaf petiole of rhubarb is a common item of human diet and the plant is found in many home gardens. The pleasant acidity of the petiole is derived largely from its malic acid content. Citric and oxalic acids are mainly responsible for the acidity of the leaf blade. The content of oxalic acid and soluble oxalates may be sufficiently great on occasion to cause relatively small amounts of the blade to be potentially lethal. Poisoning of all classes of domestic livestock from rhubarb leaf blades is recorded in the world literature, and outbreaks of human poisoning have occurred from time to time. During World War I, in an effort to conserve food materials, an official recommendation was publicized in England that persons should utilize the blades as well as the petioles of rhubarb. Several cases of severe poisoning and death resulted (30).

In the United States rhubarb poisoning seems infrequent. Hansen (713) has described a case of poisoning in hogs in which 9 died after being fed a wheelbarrow full of discarded rhubarb blades. Symptoms consisted of

blade

stalk

Fig. 51. *Rheum rhaponticum.* Rhubarb.

staggering, excessive salivation, and death in convulsions. Death occurred 3 to 5 hours after appearance of symptoms. A meal of fried rhubarb blades brought death to a Montana woman (1346). Severe intermittent abdominal pains, vomiting, and weakness were experienced. Death occurred about 36 hours later. It was also noted that the blood did not clot normally. (See oxalate poisoning, p. 33.)

Additional reference: 386.

Rumex acetosa L. ⎤
Rumex acetosella L. ⎬ Dock, sorrel
Rumex crispus L. ⎦

These are among the most common weeds of acid or sterile, gravelly soils of pastures and meadows throughout the United States and southern Canada. Members of this genus (there are more than 20 species in the United States) may be characterized as herbs (species named above are perennial) with alternate, mostly entire leaves, and petioles sheathing the stem. Flowers are small, numerous, greenish, crowded in terminal panicles. Fruit an achene with a papery, three-winged covering (almost lacking in *R. acetosella*).

These species of *Rumex* have been suspected for many years of producing occasional livestock loss in several countries. Few well-described cases of experimental feedings may be cited in support (none in North America), but two of them described below indicate that *Rumex* can, under certain circumstances, produce extensive loss of life.

Species of *Rumex* owe their toxicity to soluble oxalates (see p. 33). The degree to which oxalates are accumulated by plants depends upon a number of factors, and it appears that *Rumex* with a dangerous level of oxalate content is rare.

Several cases of poisoning in sheep have occurred in Australia in which species of *Rumex* were suspected (810). In New Zealand 10 per cent mortality was experienced in a band of ewes with lambs at side from *Rumex acetosa* (316, 1030). Oxalate level of 0.27 per cent was found in the plant, green-weight basis. The same species has been responsible for several deaths

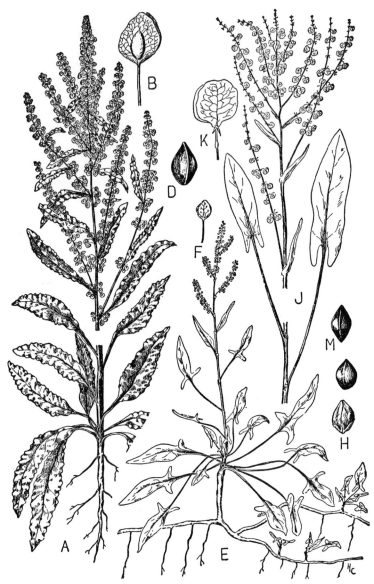

Fig. 52. *Rumex spp.* A–D, *R. crispus.* Curly dock. Fruiting plant, with details of winged fruit and seed. E–H, *R. acetosella.* Sheep sorrel. Fruiting plant, with details of winged fruit and seed. J–M, *R. acetosa.* Sour dock. Fruiting shoot, with details of basal leaves, winged fruit, and seed. Courtesy of The Macmillan Company.

in sheep in England (368). Symptoms appeared about 12 hours after the sheep were placed in a pasture where a seeding had failed and in which little else but *Rumex* had grown. They consisted of anorexia, severe ataxia, depression, prostration, and death. Specific gross lesions were absent.

Additional references: 372, 1233.

Atriplex spp. Saltbushes

The following species of *Atriplex* are secondary or facultative selenium absorbers (1591): *Atriplex canescens* (Pursh) James; *A. nuttallii* Wats. *Atriplex canescens* and *A. rosea* L. have been shown toxic by feeding experiment (538). (See selenium poisoning, p. 44.)

Beta vulgaris L. Beet, sugar beet, fodder beet, mangel, mangel-wurzel, mangold

Beets have long been cultivated and selection has established several types, not sufficiently different to be considered as separate species or even varieties by the botanist (with the exception of *B. vulgaris* var. *cicla,* Swiss chard). Nevertheless, these types, grown under commercial or trade names, vary in respects important to an understanding of their toxic potentialities. Sugar-beet tops are sometimes utilized as forage. Beet root crops grown for fodder (variously called fodder beets, mangolds, mangels, mangel-wurzels, etc.) vary in characteristics such as external color (red or yellow), internal color, and the degree to which they grow within or above ground. The factor in which they vary most significantly in relationship to their feeding value is dry-matter content. They may be classed in three groups (529); those with dry-matter content less than 15 per cent, those with dry-matter content between 15 and 20 per cent, and those with dry-matter content over 20 per cent (sugar beets).

In this hemisphere loss of livestock has occurred (1395) from ingestion of sugar-beet tops after the beet roots have been harvested. Symptoms led to the diagnosis of nitrate poisoning, which was later confirmed by analysis of the beet tops. Treatment of developing beet crops with small concentrations of 2,4-D for weed control causes metabolic derangements within the plant which result in the accumulation of highly toxic levels of nitrate in the foliage (1507). Levels as high as 8.8 per cent (as KNO_3, dry-weight basis) have been reported. In England, scouring and occassional loss of stock after ingestion of beet tops has been attributed (656) to their oxalate content. Beet forage may contain levels of total oxalate high enough (to 12 per cent) to be toxic (57), but the practice of wilting tops before feeding them, which seems to eliminate their toxicity, does not change the oxalate content. Poisoning from beet tops with symptoms excluding nitrate poisoning has been reported in the United States (1223).

Beet root grown for fodder in England and Scandinavian countries is toxic under certain circumstances. Cases in many instances are associated with a change from one type of fodder beet to another (82, 1707). Symptoms vary and appear to be associated with abnormal changes in rumen action. Hypocalcemia was found in a herd of Guernseys within a day after ingestion of large amounts of a new type of fodder beet substituted suddenly for the previous type (1707). In cannulated sheep, rumen ammonia level rises after ingestion of a large amount of fodder beet. In this respect, the hypocalcemia of fodder-beet poisoning may be similar to that in grass tetany (p. 504). The Guernseys were on lush grass pasturage at the time of poisoning.

Severe acid indigestion in sheep also has been reported in England (1397) after overeating on mangolds. Lactic-acid production greater than the normal neutralizing mechanisms of the rumen can handle results in lowering of ruminal pH, and is accompanied by cessation of rumen action. Both hypocalcemia and acid indigestion should be distinguished from "overeating" disease of bacterial (*Clostridium*) etiology.

Sugar-beet residue has been associated with, but not proven to be, the etiological factor in the widespread development of parturient hemoglobinemia in the United States (656) and elsewhere. (See also hemoglobinuria under *Brassica napus*.)

Swiss chard has been shown (654) potentially goitrogenic.

Additional references: 965, 1260.

Chenopodium spp. Goosefoots, pigweeds

Several of the more than 20 species of this genus, mostly annual weeds, found throughout the United States and the world have for various reasons been considered toxic or potentially toxic.

Chenopodium ambrosioides L., wormseed, is an annual weed introduced from tropical America and now found wild throughout much of eastern North America. It is also cultivated (as var. *antihelminticum*), especially in Maryland and South Dakota, for its antihelminthic oil. Overdoses of the oil have been fatal to animals and human beings (61, 607), evoking symptoms of gastroenteritis, but cases from the natural ingestion of the plant do not appear to have occurred except possibly in geese (1240). The active principle is the terpene, ascaridol, found in the oil expressed from the seeds.

Chenopodium album L., lamb's-quarters, and *C. glaucum* L., oak-leaved goosefoot, both widely distributed common weeds, have been found (261, 607, 620, 1200, 1668) frequently to contain potentially dangerous concentrations of nitrate. Loss of animals due solely to eating these species has not been reported, but their presence in toxic hay may have been a factor contributing to the toxicity of the hay. Other species, several of which are found in the United States, have been suspected of causing livestock loss in Australia (810). Some were shown weakly cyanogenetic.

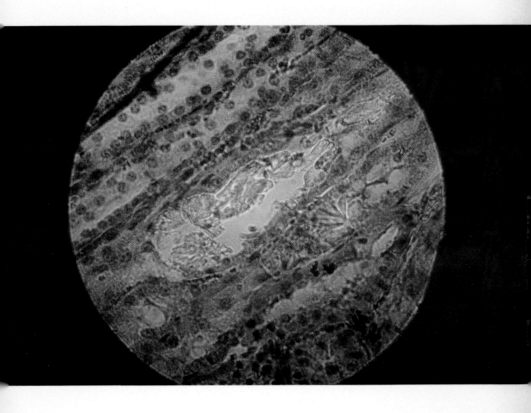

Section of kidney from sheep poisoned by *Halogeton glomeratus*. Use of this illustration has been made possible by the Merck Sharp & Dohme Research Laboratories.

Grayia spp. Hop sage
Grayia brandegei Gray has come under suspicion (1591) as a secondary or facultative selenium absorber. (See p. 44.)

Halogeton glomeratus (Bieb.) C. A. Mey. Halogeton, barilla

DESCRIPTION. Much-branched annual herb, major branches spreading, then upturned; plant 4 to 20 in. tall. Seedling prostrate with four main branches in cruciform arrangement. Seedling and mature plant bluish-green with reddish axes, later turning tan to straw-colored. Leaves in clumps along lateral axes, small, ¼ to ¾ in. long, fleshy, smooth, shiny, bluish-green, round in cross section, sausage-shaped, somewhat more inflated toward the blunt tip; tip bearing a terminal short solitary hair when green. Root a deeply penetrating [to 4 ft (318)] tap root. Flowers borne in leaf angles throughout plant, very tiny, almost invisible without magnification. Fruits bracted, conspicuous, usually mistaken for flowers; bracted fruit to ¼ in. across; bracts terminally expanded, petal-like, 5 in number, reddish to yellow-green to straw-colored; basally enclosing a single seed. Seeds about $\frac{1}{25}$ in. in diameter, of two types: black, winged, immediately germinating; brown, wingless, delayed-germinating.

DISTRIBUTION AND HABITAT. Halogeton is native to arid alkaline soils or saline clays of Russia from near the Caspian Sea eastward to the steppes of southwestern Siberia and northwestern China (410, 501). It was introduced into the United States, probably by means of a shipment of wool, animals, or agricultural seeds (105), an indeterminate number of years before 1934 when it was first collected in northeastern Nevada (410). At that time it occurred in stands in small, relatively widely separated areas (546). Since then it has spread throughout the alkaline desert soils of the Intermountain states and further. In 1960 it covered more than 10 million acres (1135) in all the eleven western states with the exception of Washington, Arizona, and New Mexico. Major infestations occur in Nevada, Utah, and Idaho. Wyoming and northeastern California also have relatively large areas of infestation.

POISONOUS PRINCIPLE. Soluble oxalates.

TOXICITY, SYMPTOMS, AND LESIONS. When first discovered in the mid-1930's, halogeton seemed to have great potential as a desirable range plant (1617). It was able to populate the most barren ground in the alkaline deserts and contained palpable moisture in its fleshy leaves. However, suspicious losses began to occur in sheep in the late 30's (319), and severe losses in 1942 near the town in Nevada where halogeton had originally been discovered prompted feeding experiments at the Nevada Agricultural Experiment Station which confirmed the potentially lethal nature of the plant. These experiments were first reported in 1943 (1106). During the 1940's the plant spread rapidly, yet was unfamiliar to most stockmen. As a re-

Fig. 53. *Halogeton glomeratus.* Halogeton. Photograph of a population of plants, and drawing of a single plant. Drawing, courtesy of The Macmillan Company.

sult some spectacular losses occurred. For example, in Idaho alone cases are on record in which 750 (1714) and 1620 (1135, 1545) sheep were lost in a single day. Sheepmen were put out of business (1545) and in 1949 scare headlines were appearing in the western press. These received national popular attention (e.g., *Life,* Jan. 15, 1951) and federal and state funds were forthcoming for experimentation and control projects. A number of state extension publications appeared at about the same time (41, 105, 464, 502, 527, 1544). The result was that stockmen in the states where halogeton grew and in neighboring states where it might later be found were alerted to the plant and its dangerous characteristics. Since that time few serious losses have occurred, even though the plant has continued its spread in grazing country.

Extensive experiments into halogeton poisoning have been carried out in the states where the loss has been greatest—Nevada, Utah and Idaho. They have been reported in the annual reports of the Nevada station and in station and other publications by investigators at the several stations.

The amount of oxalates found in halogeton varies with season, locality (82, 278), and part of plant. Oxalate in the plant is mostly in the form of the sodium salt, which is soluble. Small amounts of potassium oxalate (soluble) and calcium oxalate (insoluble) are also found. Insoluble oxalates are not absorbed into the animal's circulation, hence are nontoxic. Soluble oxalates are built up to very high concentrations during the growth of the plant, maxima having been observed from September to January or February. The green leaves and fruiting structures contain by far the greatest concentration. Reduction in concentration with maturity of the plant is brought about by three mechanisms: loss of leaves, leaching by rain or snow, and transformation of soluble to insoluble oxalates in the plant (278, 279, 1026). If snow buries the plants before leaf drop, the leaves are retained on the plant and leaching may be reduced. Under these and perhaps other circumstances it is possible for old halogeton plants to contain dangerous quantities of soluble oxalates into March, when losses are known to have occurred (1398), or April, when dangerous levels have still been detected (278). Levels of soluble oxalates as high as 34.5 per cent of the total plant composition, dry-weight basis, have been detected (278), but the majority of reported maxima fall within 18 to 28 per cent. Total oxalates are slightly higher.

Halogeton containing the higher levels of soluble oxalate is rapidly fatal to sheep in very small amounts. A fully fed sheep can be killed with about 0.11 per cent of its weight of oxalate, or as little as 0.3 per cent of its weight of halogeton containing 34.5 per cent soluble oxalates (120). The lethal dose for a fasted sheep is one-third or one-fourth as much (319). Toxicities representing between 0.3 and 0.5 per cent of the animal's weight have been reported by several investigators (410, 464, 1544, 1616) in poisonings of natural origin. Toxicity to cattle seems to be about the same, although figures are meager (26).

Presence of ingesta in the rumen markedly increases resistance to poisoning for the following reasons. Rate of absorption of oxalates is slowed by dilution, and some are precipitated with calcium before absorption. Fasting by itself reduces the calcium level of the blood serum significantly. In halogeton poisoning serum calcium has been depressed about 50 per cent by the time symptoms appear and to 20 per cent normal by the time of death (1616). Fasted animals before being fed halogeton or oxalates may exhibit reductions in serum calcium from normal of 5 to 10 per cent (1617). Experiments with calcium added to the diet in various forms have been only partially successful in pointing to useful control measures. Protection against poisoning is usually much less than expected. Of the sources of calcium employed, dicalcium phosphate has been most effective (120, 828). Good alfalfa hay has a marked protective effect.

Toxicity of halogeton seems to come entirely from soluble oxalates. It has been shown (319) that an equivalent amount of sodium oxalate will produce entirely equivalent symptoms and lesions and that (468) toxicity is entirely in the aqueous fraction when the plant is extracted with water, and is totally eliminated from the aqueous fraction by precipitation with calcium ion.

The symptoms and lesions of oxalate poisoning are discussed elsewhere (p. 34). At first it was thought that halogeton could cause chronic oxalate poisoning characterized primarily by abortion. Experimental feedings of sublethal amounts of halogeton over prolonged periods (319, 527) have disproved this concept.

CONDITIONS OF POISONING. Halogeton is normally distasteful to sheep and cattle. Under certain circumstances sheep may consume quantities of it even when other palatable forage is available. Losses have been confined almost exclusively to sheep, although rare loss of cattle has occurred (105, 1616). The circumstances under which sheep find the plant palatable have not been discovered. It was at first thought to be a reaction to salt hunger (546) and recommendations were made to provide ample salt for sheep when in dangerous country. This theory has been disproved (319, 1616). Fall rains soften the dry plant at a time when its oxalate content is at maximum. Most losses have occurred during late fall and early winter. Conditions predisposing to poisoning include driving hungry animals along walkways that are heavy with halogeton, unloading hungry animals into halogeton-infested locations, bedding down in dangerous country, and the like. Poisoning may be controlled by avoiding such practices and by providing supplemental hay when in particularly dangerous areas.

CONTROL OF THE PLANT. When, in 1949, national attention was called to this plant by a few spectacular instances of loss of sheep, the immediate reaction was to eliminate this introduced plant, or control its spread. Much effort that proved misdirected and unsuccessful was invested in eradicating the plant from large areas. Since we have in halogeton a well-documented example of learning the hard way how to cope with a particular poisonous-plants problem, it is worth review.

Halogeton is adapted to fertile or infertile acid or alkaline soils with annual rainfall between 3 and 20 in. below elevations of 7000 ft. It is particularly well adapted to the desert lands used as winter range. Because it is an annual plant, much effort was directed toward eradicating it from as much land as possible as quickly as possible. These efforts did not take into consideration the amount and viability of seed produced. It has been estimated (1135) that one plant can produce 50,000 seeds, and that an acre of halogeton produces some 500 lb of seed. In depressions or behind windbreaks seeds may accumulate by the handful. In eradication programs, leaving only 1 per cent of the plants alive provides ample seed to repopulate the same area the following season. Most seeds germinate the following season, but the seeds specialized for delayed germination remain in the ground from 1 to 5 years before forming plants (144, 1135). In laboratory studies, immediately germinating and delayed-germinating seeds together lose viability only slowly, retaining 60 per cent viability after 5 years in a cardboard box at room temperature (243). Fresh seed germinate between 90 and 100 per cent within 48 hours after being placed in moist paper (105, 243, 1617).

Halogeton seed is largely destroyed by passage through sheep or rabbit digestive systems, but enough remains viable so that these animals may accomplish dissemination of the seed into new areas (243). More effective in local areas is windborne dispersal, to which the fruiting bracts adapt the plant. Even more effective than these dispersal methods in introducing the plant into new areas far removed from the original are the actions of man. Seeds may be transported hundreds of miles in or on automobiles, trucks, trains, earth-moving equipment, in wool or other shipments, and in a myriad of other ways impossible to control.

Despite these formidable advantages, halogeton, as is true of most annuals, is unable to compete with established perennial vegetation. It will appear only on disturbed or barren soils. Thus injudicious mass eradication programs utilizing plowing or spraying with herbicides resulted in killing native perennial vegetation and in leaving the treated area bare for halogeton repopulation in greater abundance the next year. Control programs now concentrate on judicious use of selective sprays when relatively small areas can be treated thoroughly and often enough so that all plants of halogeton will be killed before forming seed, followed by a revegetation program. Crested wheatgrass has been found most valuable for replacing halogeton, and selective herbicides are available which may be used to discourage remaining halogeton while not harming the wheatgrass if properly used. Land should not be cleared for reseeding unless the chances are good that revegetation will be successful. Heavy stands of halogeton may influence the soil in some way so that germination of the seeds of other plants is markedly reduced (1482). The biology of the plant and control practices are discussed by Tisdale and Zappettini (1584), Fenley (527), and Morton et al. (1135).

It is obvious that halogeton will not be eradicated from the West, nor probably will efforts artificially to restrict its natural spread be successful. Yet in recent years, despite the spread and wide occurrence of this plant, losses have been slight. Reduction of losses has come about not by control of the plant, but by informed management practices. Halogeton will not invade ranges that are not grazed too heavily and are managed for the protection of the perennial plants. Proper management of animals in areas that are infested with halogeton reduces the risk of loss to a minimum, or eliminates it entirely.

Kochia scoparia (L.) Schrad. Summer cypress, burning bush, Mexican fireweed

This annual species is cultivated in gardens for its ornamental foliage and formal effect. It has escaped in localities throughout North America and become a weed on dry soils in some places. In Argentina it has been considered (1370) responsible for a large number of cases of photo-sensitization in cattle, sheep, and horses during the drought years of 1942 and 1943. Cases have not been reported in North America.

Salsola pestifer Nels. (= *S. kali* L. var. *tenuifolia* Tausch). Russian thistle

This weed of the United States and southern Canada, particularly common in the plains states, has been shown occasionally to contain toxic levels of nitrate (see nitrate, p. 38). A few cases of poisoning have been reported to the United States Department of Agriculture (804).

In Australia *Salsola* has been found to contain potentially lethal concentrations of soluble oxalates (1030). Several cases of poisoning in various classes of livestock have occurred in that country in which this plant was suspected.

Sarcobatus vermiculatus (Hook.) Torr. Greasewood

DESCRIPTION. Erect, woody, spiny, deciduous shrub, mostly 3 to 5 ft tall, sometimes more. Stems much branched, becoming gray with age. Leaves alternate, bright green, assuming a reddish cast with age, fleshy, almost round in cross section, $\frac{1}{4}$ to $1\frac{1}{4}$ in. long. Sexes separate; flowers reduced. Female flowers axillary, inconspicuous. Male flowers crowded in terminal spikes (catkins); spike about $\frac{3}{4}$ in. long.

DISTRIBUTION AND HABITAT. Confined to alkaline soils, often the dominant or exclusive vegetation of alkaline flats; Alberta to North Dakota, south to Texas, California and Mexico.

POISONOUS PRINCIPLE. Soluble oxalates (see p. 33).

TOXICITY, SYMPTOMS, AND LESIONS. Cattle are rarely poisoned under range conditions (754, 1383). Mass mortality has occurred in flocks of sheep in several states. Feeding experiments and chemical investigations of the plant have been performed by the U.S. Department of Agriculture (343, 1001), the Nevada Experiment Station (544), and the Montana Livestock Sanitary Board (1693). Findings are in agreement. Analyses indicate that the total oxalate content of greasewood leaves varies between 10 and 22 per cent, dry weight, mostly as soluble salts. Oxalate content is greatest in the leaves as compared with other parts of the plant and increases with maturity, reaching maximum in August and September. The amount of plant necessary to produce poisoning varies with soluble oxalate content,

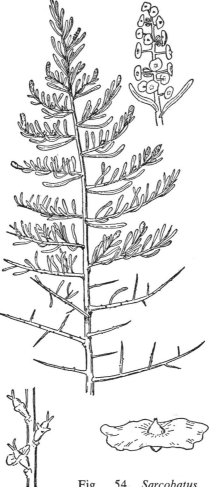

Fig. 54. *Sarcobatus vermiculatus.* Greasewood. Branch, cluster of male flowers, cluster of female flowers, and winged fruit. Courtesy of The Macmillan Company.

speed of ingestion, size of animal, and presence or absence of other material in the digestive system. Figures for toxicity vary from 1.5 per cent (1001) to 5 per cent (544) of an animal's weight in fasted animals.

Oxalates are readily excreted. Amounts of greasewood significantly larger than the lethal dose taken at one time after a short fast can be tolerated without harmful effect if spread out over the course of several hours or if taken with other food.

Symptoms and lesions are those of oxalate poisoning. Symptoms appear within 3 to 5 hours after ingestion of a toxic amount of greasewood, may occur abruptly after animals have been watered, and consist of listlessness, depression, weakness, prostration, coma, and death. Respiration and heart action grow progressively weaker and death occurs after 12 to 20 hours. No specific gross lesions are displayed, but kidney lesions (260) characteristic of oxalate poisoning are found on histological examination.

CONDITIONS OF POISONING. Greasewood is considered useful forage by most ranchers, and many large areas of range would be worthless for raising animals if it were absent. A moderate amount of other forage in the diet will prevent poisoning by greasewood. Other beneficial management practices include those which spread consumption of greasewood out over a period of time.

Instances of heavy mortality in sheep flocks have occurred in the past. In some instances over 1000 animals have been lost at a single time. Invariably heavy mortality has been associated with practices which put very hungry animals into almost pure stands of greasewood.

Suckleya suckleyana (Torr.) Rydb. Poison suckleya

DESCRIPTION. Annual, succulent, mostly prostrate herbs. Stems reddish, fleshy when alive, 4 in. to 1 ft long. Leaves alternate, long-petioled; blades broadly triangular, ½ to 1½ in. long; margins dentate. Flowers clustered in leaf axils, small, inconspicuous; plant monoecious; male flowers at branch tips, female flowers along remainder of branch. Fruit an indehiscent nutlet ("seed"), reddish brown, enclosed by two papery, ribbed, dark-colored scales which are joined except at tip, and about ¼ in. long.

DISTRIBUTION AND HABITAT. Rare, Montana to Colorado and New Mexico, except locally common, forming dense stands, in drying water holes, drying shallow ponds, on pond margins exposed as water recedes, or occasionally along stream banks.

POISONOUS PRINCIPLE. The plant is poisonous by reason of its hydrocyanic acid potential. The combined form of HCN in the plant is unknown, but probably it is glycosidal (72).

TOXICITY, SYMPTOMS, AND LESIONS. Losses in cattle and possibly sheep have been reported in Colorado and New Mexico (754, 1579). Symptoms and lesions are those of cyanide poisoning (see p. 26).

Analyses of the plant have been carried out at the experiment stations of both states, and feeding experiments with cattle and sheep have been performed at the Colorado station. Wide variation in cyanide potential has been found. Under some conditions plants have released only 0.01 per cent cyanide. Elsewhere they have been found to contain a potential as high as 0.24 per cent (72). With sheep it was possible to bring on transitory symp-

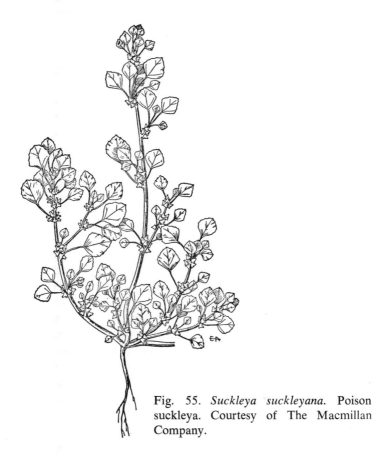

Fig. 55. *Suckleya suckleyana*. Poison suckleya. Courtesy of The Macmillan Company.

toms after fasting, with forced feedings of large amounts of plant containing 0.011 per cent cyanide potential. Plant material analyzing 0.036 per cent cyanide potential was uniformly lethal to cattle and sheep unless treatment for cyanide poisoning intervened.

CONDITIONS OF POISONING. Unexplained, and at times heavy, losses of cattle in Colorado and New Mexico over several years now seem undoubtedly caused by ingestion of poison suckleya. Losses are associated with heavy growths of the plant in the dry prairies or plains sections of these states. The appearance of symptoms may occur just after the animals have watered. At least sometimes poison suckleya is palatable and will be grazed preferentially to other forage.

Additional references: 1550, 1578.

Amaranthaceae

Amaranthus spp. Pigweed, carelessweed, redroot

Several species in this genus are common weeds of cultivation. Analyses (e.g., 583, 1200) have shown that pigweeds may accumulate dangerous levels of nitrate. *Amaranthus retroflexus* L. (166, 583, 1178) and *A.*

Fig. 56. *Amaranthus retroflexus.* Pigweed. Courtesy of The Macmillan Company.

palmeri S. Wats. (1281, 1575) have been incriminated in cases of live-stock loss (see nitrate poisoning, p. 38).

Portulacaceae

Portulaca oleracea L. Purslane, pusley

This is one of the commonest weeds of gardens throughout the United States and southern Canada. It may be recognized as a creeping, mat-forming, succulent annual herb, growing from a tap root. The fleshy, obovate, entire leaves are clustered or alternate along the much-branched, glabrous, often reddish stems.

Portulaca has not been reported toxic in North America, but has been the subject of investigations in Australia. There it was found occasionally to accumulate toxic levels of oxalates. Field cases of *Portulaca* poisoning in sheep with symptoms of acute oxalate poisoning (see p. 34) were observed. The plant in that instance was found to have 9.3 per cent oxalate content. Experimental feedings with *Portulaca* at 6.1 per cent oxalate content produced a chronic intoxication in one animal and eventual death (1030).

Caryophyllaceae

Agrostemma githago L. Corn cockle

DESCRIPTION. A conspicuous tall, silky, grayish winter annual (starting growth from seed in the fall, maturing and forming seed and dying the next summer), to 3 ft tall. Stem erect, branching above. Leaves opposite, 2 to 4 in. long, without petiole or stipules, linear to lanceolate; stems and leaves bearing a conspicuous covering of white hairs. Flowers showy, solitary, about 1 in. across, terminating long slender pedicels; calyx 5-parted, conspicuous; corolla of 5 pink to purple petals. Fruit a capsule, bearing numerous black seeds each about the weight of a wheat grain. Seeds covered with rows of small warts.

DISTRIBUTION AND HABITAT. Introduced from Europe and found throughout the United States as a serious weed of cultivation wherever winter wheat is grown. Occasionally found in winter rye and other crops and on roadsides. Selected strains are cultivated in flower gardens.

POISONOUS PRINCIPLE. The sapogenin githagenin is contained in the seeds and amounts to 5 to 7 per cent of their weight.

TOXICITY, SYMPTOMS, AND LESIONS. Information concerning the poisonous properties of *Agrostemma* seeds is largely European in origin and much goes all the way back to Cornevin's classic experimental work (334) which demonstrated that a lethal dose in cattle and hogs was about 0.1 to 0.25 per cent of the animal's weight of ground seed and about twice

Fig. 57. *Argostemma githago*. Corn cockle. Plant with detail of seed. Courtesy of The Macmillan Company.

that amount if ingested as whole seed. Presence of the seed coat reduces availability of the toxic principle. He also reported symptoms in various classes of animals and observed that acute poisoning of pigs was rare because of their ability to vomit freely. Symptoms are primarily those characteristic of severe gastroenteritis.

In this country poisoning has been observed in poultry. Experimental investigation in Maryland and New York (757, 1316) demonstrates that poultry find the seed unpalatable and will avoid feed containing them (but see also 112). Individual cockle seeds will be rejected in whole-grain mixtures, and mash containing even small quantities of cockle will not be consumed. From 0.2 to 0.5 per cent of body weight of seed is lethal to young birds; older birds are somewhat more resistant. Poisoned birds become listless and unkempt in appearance, develop a cheesy material in mouth and crop, and often show diarrhea.

Harshberger (726) described the death of several horses belonging to a Philadelphia brewery under circumstances incriminating *Agrostemma* seeds. Hansen (704) has described an unusual case in which hog mortality was attributed to ingestion of *Agrostemma* roots. The death of a cow occurred in New York following ingestion of grain heavily contaminated with *Agrostemma* seeds (1618).

CONDITIONS OF POISONING. Before the advent of machinery for cleaning wheat, *Agrostemma* seeds were often found as contaminants of wheat grain. Flour made from such a mixture has caused poisoning of human beings (1530). Similar grains or flours fed to animals also produce toxicity. With current methods, *Agrostemma* seeds are cleaned out of wheat, and the danger now lies in feeding wheat screenings containing quantities of these seeds.

Additional reference: 864.

Drymaria pachyphylla Woot. & Standl. Inkweed, drymary

DESCRIPTION. Tender, somewhat succulent, grayish-green, glabrous summer annual. Branches lying prostrate against the ground, radiating from a single root, and rebranching, forming a plant to 1 ft in diameter. Primary branches 10 to 20 in number, bearing in turn fan-shaped clusters of branches of the next order. Leaves paired, opposite, obovate to ovate, less than ½ in. long by ¼ in. wide, obtuse tipped. Flowers small, white, solitary, inconspicuous, borne singly in the leaf axils, with 5 sepals and five petals. Fruit a small capsule, bearing many very small seeds. A purplish juice may be squeezed from the immature capsules (hence the common name, inkweed).

DISTRIBUTION AND HABITAT. Alkaline clay soils, western Texas, southern New Mexico to southeast Arizona and northern and central Mexico. The

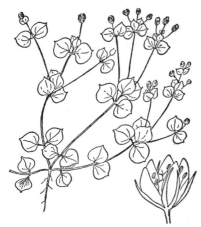

seeds germinate only when moist. On the ranges of the Southeast, germination usually does not take place until rainfall during the summer months. Drymary is killed by the first frost. Overgrazing has led to the establishment of heavy populations of drymary in some areas (930).

Fig. 58. *Drymaria pachyphylla.* Inkweed. Plant with detail of flower. Courtesy of The Macmillan Company.

TOXICITY, SYMPTOMS, AND LESIONS. Serious cattle losses in New Mexico prompted experimental feedings with this plant as early as 1923 (902). The original work was amplified and extended in further feeding experiments carried out in Texas (1034) some years later, after that state had experienced seasons with severe losses ascribed to drymary. While these feedings have not been extensive, they have established that drymary is highly toxic and highly unpalatable to all classes of livestock. About 0.5 per cent (green-weight basis) is uniformly lethal to cattle and sheep. Goats appear somewhat more resistant.

Symptoms appeared 18 to 24 hours after ingestion of a toxic dose in experimental feedings. The period between the onset of symptoms and death was unusually brief and is characteristic of drymary poisoning. It may be less than two hours. Because of this, symptoms are not usually observed under range conditions. In cattle, symptoms include loss of appetite, diarrhea, restlessness, arched back or "tucked up" appearance, depression, and frequently coma and death, usually without struggle. Otherwise recovery takes place in about two days.

Post mortem examination discloses petechial or larger hemorrhages of the heart and diaphragm. The liver, kidneys, and spleen are markedly congested. The wall of the gall bladder is edematous, a condition which often extends down the bile duct, and hemorrhage may be present. Mild gastritis and mild to severe enteritis is found in the abomasum and small intestine, and is most severe in the posterior third of the latter. Histopathological examination discloses congestion and hemorrhage around the central veins of the liver and gall bladder, together with some necrosis of liver cells and of the epithelial cells in the gall bladder. The kidney displays albuminous degenerative changes.

CONDITIONS OF POISONING. Drymary is exceedingly distasteful to stock. Animals in the feeding experiments would not touch the plant even after five days' starvation. However, in drought years when other forage is not available, sufficient amounts may be consumed to cause death. Severe mortality in cattle has been reported a number of times. The plant lies prostrate on the ground during the day and is relatively unavailable for grazing. During the night, however, it becomes turgid so that the branches are elevated a few inches, and is thus more easily consumed. Losses ascribed to this plant have occurred in every month of the year except January, February, and March (902) but are most common during the late summer months.

Drymaria arenarioides H.B.K. Alfombrilla

DESCRIPTION. Profusely branched short-lived perennial, forming dense clumps of vegetation to 1½ ft in diameter and 10 in. high. Leaves in clumps of 2 to 8 along the stems, linear-lanceolate, not much more than $\frac{1}{16}$ in. wide by less than ¾ in. long. Flowers white, conspicuous, about ½ in. in diameter; petals 5, each divided into 5 to 6 narrow lobes. Fruit a capsule, producing numerous very small seeds.

DISTRIBUTION AND HABITAT. Acid soils, northern and central Mexico. This plant is not yet known to occur in the United States, but reaches within 40 miles of the border (439).

TOXICITY, SYMPTOMS, AND LESIONS. High mortality in a shipment of Mexican cattle destined for the United States prompted investigation of this species of Drymaria, known as a poisonous plant in Mexico and suspected in this instance by authorities in Texas (431, 439). Feeding experiments were carried out with cattle, sheep, and goats which established this species to be toxic in amounts as small as 0.1 per cent of the animal's weight and uniformly lethal at 0.5 per cent. Symptoms and lesions generally corresponded to those produced by D. pachyphylla, described above. Trembling, muscular spasms, and salivation were noted.

CONDITIONS OF POISONING. In the instance cited, poisoning occurred when animals were held in a dangerous area during shipment. Cattle losses in Mexico to this plant have been estimated (635) at 3000 to 4000 animals during a three-year period. Horses do not appear to be affected.

Fig. 59. *Saponaria.* A–C, *S. vaccaria.* Cow cockle. Plant, with detail of pistil and seed. D, *S. officinalis.* Bouncing Bet. Courtesy of The Macmillan Company. D, courtesy Cornell Extension Bulletin #538.

Saponaria officinalis L. Bouncing bet, soapwort.
Saponaria vaccaria L. Cow cockle

Both species are weeds. The first is perennial, common in waste areas throughout much of North America. The second is an annual weed, particularly troublesome in grain crops of the northwestern United States and western Canada. Both are erect herbs with jointed stems and opposite, entire, simple, lanceolate leaves, without petioles. The leaves are palmately veined, sometimes appearing parallel-veined. The flowers are conspicuous in terminal cymose clusters, with calyx of 5 sepals, green, tubular; corolla of 5 petals, white, pink, or faint red; stamens 10, and styles 2. They are easily confused with certain other common weeds of the same family.

From the time of Dioscorides *Saponaria officinalis* has been employed as a soaplike material. The plant, and especially the seeds, contain relatively large amounts of a saponin, the sapogenin of which has been considered (884) the same as githagenin, the sapogenin of *Agrostemma githago* (*q.v.*). Both species of *Saponaria* have a generally accepted reputation for potential toxicity. Screenings of grain crops may contain large quantities of the seeds of *S. vaccaria*. Both species, however, are distasteful to animals, and no clear cases of poisoning have been recorded in North America.

Chesnut and Wilcox (277) produced definite signs of toxicity and death in rabbits with extracts from the seeds of *S. vaccaria*. Huffman (801) has performed feeding experiments with *S. officinalis*. He found the plant would kill sheep within four hours if fed in an amount equal to 3 per cent (dry-weight basis) of the animal's weight. Symptoms and lesions are similar to those produced by *Agrostemma*.

Order Primulales

Primulaceae

Anagallis arvensis L. Scarlet pimpernel

This species is a low-growing, orange-flowered annual herb of seacoasts and sandy soils throughout North America and is especially common in the Middle Atlantic and Pacific Coast states. It is commonly mentioned as poisonous in the world literature, but well-authenticated instances of poisoning are difficult to find. It has come under suspicion in recent years most strongly in Australia. Feeding tests with sheep (1312) established that under certain conditions, it could produce death in 2 days when fed at about 2 per cent of the animal's weight. At other times, later in the season, toxicity could not be demonstrated. Lesions included hemorrhage in kidney, heart, and rumen, congestion of lungs, and a very pale and friable liver. Symptoms were those of depression, anorexia, and diarrhea.

Reynard and Norton record the loss, based on a "reliable source," of 6 calves presumedly from ingestion of scarlet pimpernel. This loss

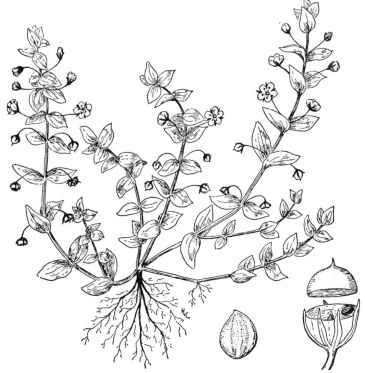

Fig. 60. *Anagallis arvensis*. Scarlet pimpernel. Plant, with details of fruit and seed. Courtesy of The Macmillan Company.

occurred in Pennsylvania in June when a number of calves were put out in a pasture in which scarlet pimpernel plants were later found to have been heavily grazed.

Additional reference: 1335.

Order Ericales

Ericaceae. Heath family

Those members of the heath family which are known to be toxic produce nearly or completely identical symptoms in poisoned animals and have been shown to contain the same toxic principle. Therefore it is most convenient to treat them together. The following species have produced livestock loss in the United States or Canada.

Kalmia angustifolia L. Lambkill, sheepkill, calfkill, dwarf laurel, wicky

DESCRIPTION. Open woody shrub, 1 to 4 ft tall, branches strongly ascending. Leaves mostly opposite or whorled in threes, oblong-lanceolate, 1 to 2½ in. long, coriacious, evergreen (persisting through the winter), entire; tips obtuse in most fully expanded leaves. Inflorescence corymbose, produced laterally on stems; flowers showy, rose or crimson, ¼ to ½ in. across; corolla widely campanulate, 5-pointed; stamens 10, anthers inserted, and held against tension, in 10 pockets in the corolla tube, springing forth when touched. Fruit a 5-cavitied, many-seeded capsule.

DISTRIBUTION AND HABITAT. Nonfertile soils of abandoned pastures and meadows throughout northeastern North America.

Kalmia latifolia L. Mountain laurel, calico bush, ivybush

DESCRIPTION. Dense, woody, round-topped shrub or small tree, to 10 ft tall. Leaves mostly alternate or whorled in threes, elliptical, 2 to 5 in. long, coriaceous, evergreen, entire; in most the ultimate tip is acute. Inflorescence corymbose, produced in groups at stem tips; flowers showy, rose to white with purple markings (other colors in some varieties); about ¾ in. across; otherwise as above. Fruits as above.

DISTRIBUTION AND HABITAT. Rocky wooded areas, sometimes in clearings, eastern United States.

Kalmia polifolia Wang. var. *microphylla* (Hook.) Rehd. Pale laurel, bog laurel

DESCRIPTION. Small woody bush, to 10 in. tall. Leaves mostly opposite, oblong, obtuse, coriaceous, whitish beneath, entire, ¼ to ¾ in. long. Inflorescence corymbose, terminal on stems, exserted; flowers showy, rose to purple, ½ in. or less across; otherwise as *K. angustifolia*.

DISTRIBUTION AND HABITAT. Wet meadows and bogs, Rocky Mountains from northern California to Alaska. The species itself is somewhat larger, with larger leaves, and is distributed throughout northern North America. Reports of toxicity are confined so far to var. *microphylla*.

Ledum glandulosum Nutt. Western Labrador tea

DESCRIPTION. Erect shrub with ascending branches, 1 to 2 ft tall. Stems pubescent, stiff, yellow-green. Leaves numerous, elliptic-oblong, entire, coriacious, ¾ to 1 in. long, persistent; lighter and resin-dotted beneath; tips mostly obtuse. Inflorescence corymbose, relatively few-flowered, mostly terminal; flowers white; petals 5, about ¼ in. long; stamens 10. Fruit a globose capsule.

DISTRIBUTION AND HABITAT. Boggy places or wet meadows above 4000 ft in the mountains of the western United States and Canada from California northward.

Ledum columbianum Piper. Pacific Labrador tea

DESCRIPTION. As *L. glandulosum* except to 3 ft tall; with larger, mostly acute-tipped revolute-margined leaves; stamens 6 to 7.

DISTRIBUTION AND HABITAT. Swamps and bogs below 2000 ft., California to Washington. Sometimes treated as a subspecies of *L. glandulosum*.

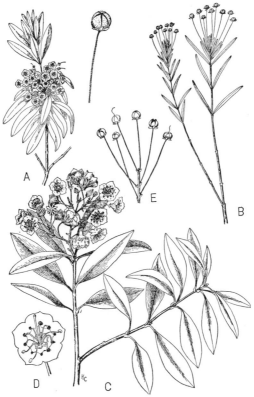

Fig. 61. Laurels. A, *Kalmia angustifolia*. Lambkill. Flowering branch. B, *K. polifolia*. Bog laurel. Flowering branch. C–E and photograph, *K. latifolia*. Mountain laurel. Flowering branch, with details of flower and cluster of fruits. Drawing, courtesy of The Macmillan Company.

Leucothoe davisiae Torr. Sierra laurel, black laurel.

DESCRIPTION. Woody shrub, 2 to 5 ft tall. Leaves oblong, stiff, entire or very slightly numerous-toothed, 1 to 2½ in. long, evergreen. Inflorescence racemose, erect, terminal; flowers whitish. Fruit a capsule.

DISTRIBUTION AND HABITAT. Wet ground in forests, 3000 to 8500 ft elevation, California and Oregon.

Menziesia ferruginea Sm. and *M. ferruginea* var. *glabella* (Gray) Pk. (= *M. glabella* Gray). Mock azalea, rustyleaf

DESCRIPTION. Open erect or straggling deciduous shrub, 3 to 12 ft tall. Leaves alternate, oblong, crenate or serrate, thin, mucronate, ¾ to 2½ in. long; upper surface sparsely covered with reddish pubescence. Flowers in small nodding terminal clusters; corolla yellow with red, bell-shaped, 4-pointed. Fruit a woody small capsule. The variety has less pubescence on twigs and leaves.

Fig. 62. *Menziesia ferruginea.* Mock azalea. Flowering branch, with details of flower and fruit.
Courtesy of The Macmillan Company.

DISTRIBUTION AND HABITAT. In woods along the coast from northern California to Alaska, eastward at lower elevations in mountains to Montana. The variety is found in the Cascade Mountains.

Pieris japonica D. Don. Japanese pieris

DESCRIPTION. Woody shrub or small tree, to 30 ft tall. Leaves alternate, obovate-lanceolate, 1½ to 3 in. long, evergreen; margins finely toothed.

Inflorescence paniculate, terminal on stems; flowers small, to ¼ in. across, white; stamens 10. Fruit a capsule.

DISTRIBUTION AND HABITAT. Native to Japan; used as an ornamental shrub. The closely related species, *P. floribunda* Benth. & Hook., is native from Virginia to Georgia.

Rhododendron albiflorum Hook. White-flowered rhododendron

DESCRIPTION. Erect woody deciduous shrub, 3 to 6 ft tall. Leaves thin, elliptical, 1½ to 3 in. long, tips mostly acute. Flowers in groups of 1 to 3, axillary; corolla about equally divided between tube and lobes, creamy white, to ¾ in. across; stamens 10. Fruit a capsule.

DISTRIBUTION AND HABITAT. Wet places in the higher elevations of mountains in Oregon, Washington, Montana, and British Columbia.

Rhododendron macrophyllum D. Don. (= *R. californicum* Hook.). California rose bay

DESCRIPTION. Coarse-branched evergreen shrub or small tree, 3 to 15 ft tall. Leaves coriaceous, glabrous above, finely pubescent beneath, alternate, elliptical, entire, 4 to 10 in. long. Inflorescence corymbose, terminal, densely flowered, showy; flowers rose to white, to 1½ in. across; corolla broadly campanulate, somewhat irregularly lobed, lobes about equal to tube; stamens 5. Fruit a subcylindric capsule about ½ in. long.

DISTRIBUTION AND HABITAT. In woods and thickets of the coast to middle elevations in mountains, California to Washington.

Rhododendron maximum L. Rhododendron, great laurel, rose bay

DESCRIPTION. Large evergreen shrub or open tree to 35 ft tall. Leaves alternate, extremely coriaceous, oblong, 4 to 10 in. long, acute at both ends. Flowers densely clustered, showy, rose to pink to white or mixed; corolla campanulate, deeply lobed, about 1½ in. across; stamens 10. This species has been hybridized with others to serve as the source of a number of horticultural rhododendrons.

DISTRIBUTION AND HABITAT. Native to moist ground in woods, Georgia and Alabama to Novia Scotia; common in the southern part of its range, less so northerly.

Rhododendron occidentale (T. & G.) Gray (= *Azalea occidentale* T. & G.). Western azalea

DESCRIPTION. Slender deciduous shrub, 3 to 9 ft tall. Leaves thin, alternate, elliptical, entire, 2 to 3½ in. long. Inflorescence corymbose, many-flowered; terminal; flowers white with yellow or pink markings; corolla campanulate, irregularly lobed, to 2 in. across; stamens 5. Capsule oblong, ¾ to 1 in. long.

DISTRIBUTION AND HABITAT. Moist soils, thickets, low and middle elevations toward coast in Oregon and California.

Fig. 63. Rhododendrons. A–C, *Rhododendron maximum*. Great Laurel. Flowering branch, with details of flower and fruit. D–E, *R. macrophyllum*. California rose bay. Flower and leaf. F–G, *R. albiflorum*. White flowered rhododendron. Flowering branch, with detail of flower. Courtesy of The Macmillan Company.

The list above includes only those species for which there are reliable reports of toxicity in North America. For almost all genera listed above additional species are commonly found. In *Rhododendron* alone, for example, there are about 250 species, and many horticultural varieties, often difficult of exact determination. It is likely that feeding experiments would show many if not most species in these genera toxic. This conclusion is based on the close botanical relationship among species in these genera, on analyses which have shown the same poisonous principle present in species tested, including species not yet known to have produced livestock loss, and on reports of toxicity from additional species in the world literature. Additional genera suspected of being toxic include *Lyonia* (maleberry, fetterbush, staggerbush) and *Andromeda*. All of these fall in the botanically related groups, Tribe *Rhododendreae* and Tribe *Andromedeae*.

REFERENCES FOR TOXICITY

Kalmia angustifolia	1000, 1301, 1335, 1651
Kalmia latifolia	274, 378, 561, 691, 726, 1000, 1335, 1375
Kalmia polifolia var. *microphylla*	296, 538, 1383
Ledum glandulosum	985, 1383
Ledum columbianum	470
Leucothoe davisiae	985
Menziesia ferruginea	981, 985, 1383
Pieris japonica	625
Rhododendron albiflorum	985, 1081
Rhododendron macrophyllum	621, 1383
Rhododendron maximum	561
Rhododendron occidentale	274, 1383

POISONOUS PRINCIPLE. An amorphous, physiologically active material was first isolated from *Andromeda* (= *Pieris*) *japonica* in 1882. Largely through the efforts of Plugge it was reisolated from that species and additional species in several other genera, partially characterized, and named andromedotoxin in work that was reported between 1883 and 1885. It is a white carbohydrate material, sometimes of amorphous structure and sometimes crystalline depending upon treatment, and is considered a resinoid. Plugge's work has been reviewed by Crawford (378) and Hardikar (718). Andromedotoxin has been pharmacologically investigated by Hardikar (718), Waud (1651) and others. The results are not in complete agreement, and it is unlikely that extracts employed represented pure andromedotoxin. Despite further analytical chemistry (1651), its structure remains unknown. Many of the effects of this substance in intact animals or on isolated tissues resemble certain effects produced by stimulation of the parasympathetic nervous system, but experiments of Waud led to the conclusion that the resemblances are superficial, and the effects are not produced via nervous stimulation by andromedotoxin. As early as 1886 de Zaayer (see 718) concluded that the characteristic vomition produced by andromedotoxin was mediated by direct stimulation of a vomition center.

Many of the Ericaceae contain arbutin, a glucoside of hydroquinone. Symptoms produced by hydroquinone alone (see *Xanthium*) resemble those produced by heath poisoning.

TOXICITY, SYMPTOMS, AND LESIONS. Symptoms produced by all of these species in a given class of livestock are remarkably similar. Toxicity to livestock, where it has been determined, falls within a single order of magnitude when expressed as percentage of animal's weight of plant necessary to produce toxic symptoms.

The following toxicities have been determined by experiment. They are converted where necessary and expressed as percentage of the animal's weight of green plant required to produce symptoms but not death.

ANIMAL	PLANT	AMOUNT (%)	AUTHORITY
sheep	*Kalmia latifolia*	0.6	378
	Kalmia latifolia	0.4	1000
	Kalmia angustifolia	0.15	1000
	K. polifolia var. *microphylla*	0.3	296
cattle	*Kalmia latifolia*	0.4	1000
	Kalmia angustifolia	0.2	1000
goats	*Kalmia latifolia*	0.4	1000
	Kalmia angustifolia	0.25	1000
	K. polifolia var. *microphylla*	0.5	296
deer	*Kalmia latifolia*	1.3	561

Toxic dosages in essential agreement with these, but which cannot accurately be expressed as percentages, include those for sheep and calves with *Kalmia polifolia* var. *microphylla* (538), for sheep with *Leucothoe davisiae* (985), and for sheep with *Kalmia angustifolia* (1301).

The Delaware Indians used laurel for suicide. An instance of poisoning in the human being is on record (1375) in which a decoction made from 2 oz of the leaves of *Kalmia latifolia* produced toxic symptoms but not death. Marsh, after preliminary feeding experiments with *Menziesia ferruginea* var. *glabella* and sheep concluded (981) that it was somewhat less toxic than other species tested by him. Elsewhere (985) he ranked *Rhododendron albiflorum* and *Leucothoe davisiae* increasingly more toxic in that order.

On the basis of experimental work, Chesnut (274) reported that fowl could be fed relatively large quantities of *Kalmia latifolia* without developing symptoms, but that their meat was thereby made toxic to cats.

Instances are on record (794) of human poisoning after ingestion of honey, in which several species in the *Ericaceae* have been suspected as supplying toxicity.

Descriptions of symptoms in various classes of livestock are in close agreement in all major particulars. Time from dosage to appearance of first symptoms is variable, depending largely on the amount fed, but averages around six hours. The duration of symptoms before death or recovery varies even more, from one or two hours to several days. Symptoms include, in order of appearance, anorexia, repeated swallowing or repeated eructation and swallowing of cud without mastication, copious salivation, dullness, depression, and nausea. Vomition is a characteristic symptom and may be accompanied by bloat, evidences of abdominal pain such as straining and grinding the teeth, and a mucous nasal discharge. Defecation is frequent and intestinal mobility may be detected by auscultation, yet post mortem examination usually reveals undigested leaves in the rumen or stomach. As the poisoning progresses animals become weak, atactic, and prostrated. Dyspnea is common. Some dyspnea and certain lung lesions may be the result of ingesta inhaled during vomition. The pupillary reflex is absent. In fatal cases coma usually precedes death.

Nonspecific gastrointestinal irritation and some hemorrhage is usually the sole post-mortem finding. Marsh and Clawson, however, describe (298, 1000) acute parenchymatous nephritis with some necrosis in the tubules; also some albuminous degeneration in the liver. It is interesting to observe, in connection with the nephritis, that Hardikar (718) found more than a third of the toxic principle was excreted unchanged in the urine when introduced into the experimental animal by injection.

CONDITIONS OF POISONING. Instances of relatively severe loss of life in livestock have been reported for most of the species of plants listed above. They have occurred primarily in the upland pastures of the East and the mountain ranges or coastal areas of the West. Sheep are usually involved, with cattle poisoning second in importance. The evergreen nature of the majority of these plants accounts in large part for the poisonings they produce. Several instances are recorded in which poisoning resulted when snow covered all other green forage, and several more occurred in late fall or early spring when the persistent foliage of these plants was all that was available. Except under such conditions these plants are avoided by livestock.

A number of unusual poisonings have occurred. Crawford (378) cites the case of a valuable monkey which was poisoned at the Washington zoo when it ate a few laurel flowers and leaves handed it by a visitor. Subsequent poisoning of angora goats there under similar circumstances resulted in a regulation that visitors could not bring laurel into the area. Several animals were poisoned and Barbary sheep killed in a Michigan zoo after being fed leaves of *Pieris* (625). During Christmas week in 1894 six trained goats on exhibition at the Philadelphia Dime Museum browsed upon laurel which had been used to decorate the stage. They later died at the University of Pennsylvania Veterinary Hospital (726). Halsted (691) has described a case in which several cattle in a pasture bordering a cemetery were poisoned when laurel wreaths used as decorations in the cemetery were discarded into the pasture.

Order Gentianales

Gentianaceae

Centaurium beyrichii Robins. Rock centaury, mountain pink.
Centaurium calycosum Fern. Buckley centaury; mountain pink.
DESCRIPTION. Erect, tufted annuals, mostly 6 in. to 1 ft tall. Leaves linear or nearly so, about 1 in. long, in the first species; lanceolate and somewhat larger in the second; inserted oppositely in pairs along the stems. Stems much branched. Flowers numerous, showy, bright pink, mostly at upper limit of plant, about as long as a leaf; calyx and corolla each five-membered with sharply pointed tips, tubular at first, then petals spreading.
DISTRIBUTION AND HABITAT. The first species inhabits range lands from western Texas to Arkansas; the second from southern California and western Texas to Mexico.
POISONOUS PRINCIPLE. Unknown.
TOXICITY, SYMPTOMS, AND LESIONS. Range losses, especially of sheep, have incriminated these plants in Texas and Mexico. Experimental feedings (437) with sheep and goats showed that the lethal dose was between 0.5 and 1.0 per cent of an animal's weight of *C. beyrichii* administered daily for several days. *Centaurium calycosum* was somewhat less toxic. Symptoms included anorexia, sluggishness, polyuria, diarrhea, and death. A principal finding on necropsy was severe gastroenteritis with occasional ulceration. Liver and kidneys were congested. Microscopic examination revealed hemosiderosis of spleen and mild toxic hepatitis and nephritis.
CONDITIONS OF POISONING. Plants are eaten only when other forage is scarce.

Loganiaceae

Gelsemium sempervirens (L.) Ait. f. Carolina jessamine, yellow jessamine, evening trumpetflower
DESCRIPTION. Woody perennial evergreen vine. Main stem gray, to 1 in. diameter and 20 ft long in older plants; younger stems much branched, tangled, shiny red-brown, wiry. Leaves opposite, short-petioled, entire, lanceolate, about 2 in. long. Flowers clear yellow, fragrant, tubular, 5-

lobed, about 1 in. long; formed in late winter or early spring, clustered, showy.

DISTRIBUTION AND HABITAT. In a variety of habitats in wild areas and fencerows, Coastal Plain and lower Piedmont from Virginia to Texas. Usually climbing on trees or other objects; occasionally trailing.

POISONOUS PRINCIPLE. This plant has long been used as the source of active principles in medicine. A great deal of analytic work has been done over the years to elucidate their chemistry, not yet with complete success. The plant contains a number of alkaloids of the indole configuration, related to strychnine (1396).

TOXICITY, SYMPTOMS, AND LESIONS. Carolina jessamine is generally considered poisonous to all classes of livestock in the southeastern states. It is ranked among the 10 worst poisonous plants in North Carolina (106). Children have been poisoned by sucking nectar from the flowers (1136). The symptoms are those of depression followed by death through respiratory failure. Experiments with steers at the Florida Experiment Station (1661) did not give positive results with feedings at about 1 per cent of the animal's weight. Experiments with fowl in which green leaves were fed over a period of two weeks resulted in death 5 to 11 days later with symptoms appearing 4 to 5 days before death. Under range conditions animals are usually found prostrated. Before they go down they exhibit muscular weakness, staggering, dilated pupils, and some convulsive movements preceding death. Death usually occurs 24 to 48 hours after the animals become prostrated.

Chesnut (274) has described a case occurring in 1885 in which circumstantial evidence pointed to the poisoning and death of three persons in South Carolina through the use of honey made from *Gelsemium* nectar. Gowanloch and Brown (641) have noted poisoning of young bees on the nectar of this plant.

CONDITIONS OF POISONING Loss of livestock usually occurs in the winter months when other forage is less available.

Order Oleales

Oleaceae

Ligustrum vulgare L. Common privet

DESCRIPTION. Deciduous shrub or small tree. Leaves opposite, simple, entire, petioled, lanceolate, 1 to 2½ in. long, dark green above, lighter beneath, glabrous. Flowers small, numerous, in small pyramidal panicles; ripening into a drooping cluster of black or blue, wax-coated berries.

DISTRIBUTION AND HABITAT. This and a few other closely related species are planted throughout the United States and Canada as one of the most common of hedge plants. It may also be grown in the form of indi-

Fig. 64. *Ligustrum vulgare*. Privet. Branch with leaves.

vidual ornamental specimens. The growth characteristics vary considerably, especially depending upon whether or not the plant is regularly clipped. If not clipped, it forms a relatively open bush. Hedges subjected to periodic clipping are much tighter in general aspect with more branches and leaves for a given area of plant.

POISONOUS PRINCIPLE. Unknown

TOXICITY, SYMPTOMS, AND LESIONS. Poisoning by privet is rare. Considering the world literature, cases have been reported in horses (574, 933), cattle (32), and children (810, 933). In the United States loss of life has been reported (1335) in a flock of sheep which had access to privet hedge trimmings.

Symptoms consist of severe gastric irritation, pain, vomition, and purging. Death may eventuate within a few hours or a day or so. Post mortem examinations in cattle and horses have failed to demonstrate lesions other than severe irritation in the gastrointestinal tract.

Order Apocynales

Apocynaceae

Allamanda cathartica L. Yellow allamanda

A vine or shrub with large yellow flowers, native to Brazil, introduced and now common in Florida south of Orlando, often grown as an ornamental.

This plant was once used as a cathartic. The fruit, especially, is considered dangerously poisonous, although recent conclusive circumstantial or experimental evidence in support is lacking.

Apocynum cannabinum L. Indian hemp, dogbane
Apocynum androsaemifolium L. Spreading dogbane

DESCRIPTION. Perennial erect herbs, growing from a spreading rootstalk; stems somewhat woody. Both species may be recognized by their milky juice, opposite-paired, smooth-margined leaves, and long, narrow, pencil-like pods hanging in pairs. Seeds are long and narrow, each with a tuft of long white hairs, and, as in milkweed, forming a cottony mass within the pod. *Apocynum cannabinum* is an erect plant, to 5 ft; *A. androsaemifolium* is smaller, more branched, and spreading.

DISTRIBUTION AND HABITAT. Both species are common weeds of open places, often in coarse soil and along streams. Both are widely distributed in the United States and Canada.

POISONOUS PRINCIPLE. Several resins and glycosides, some cardioactive, have been isolated from parts of these plants. The toxicity of some has been established in laboratory experimentation (356, 532, 1122). Interest in these compounds originated from use of preparations of *Apocynum* in medicine.

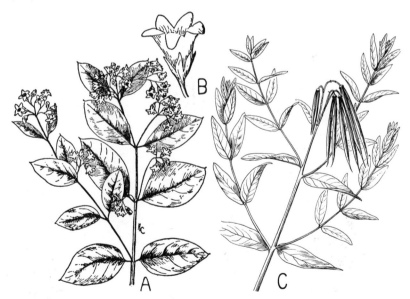

Fig. 65. A, B, *Apocynum androsaemifolium*. Spreading dogbane. Flowering shoot and detail of flower. C, *A. cannabinum*. Indian hemp. Fruiting shoot. A and B, courtesy of The Macmillan Company. C, courtesy Cornell Extension Bulletin #538.

TOXICITY, SYMPTOMS, AND LESIONS. Little is known concerning the action of these plants on stock. Much of what is in the literature is unreliable (870) having been drawn from a report (838) in which *Apocynum* was confused with *Nerium* (oleander). The toxic glycoside, apocynamarin, upon injection into a cat increased the blood pressure markedly. Certain resinoid fractions administered orally produced gastric disturbance and death in a dog (1122).

CONDITIONS OF POISONING. Animals find the dogbanes distasteful. Cases of poisoning are rare (277).

Ervatamia coronaria Stapf. Crape jasmine

An ornamental shrub, introduced from India, and grown in Florida gardens and as a landscaping shrub or hedge. Alkaloids and other physiologically active compounds have been isolated from this plant and from other Indian species. Some species are known to have caused loss of life. No cases have been reported in the United States.

Nerium oleander L. Oleander

Oleander is an ornamental evergreen shrub or bush, to 20 ft tall, which has been introduced from the Mediterranean region and is now

Fig. 66. *Nerium oleander.* Oleander.

cultivated widely throughout the southern United States and California. It produces large clusters of showy pink or white blossoms (other colors in some horticultural varieties). The leaves are leathery, entire, oblong-lanceolate, sharply pointed, with prominent midrib, 4 to 12 in. long. Oleander is occasionally found as a pot plant north of its hardy range.

Nerium indicum Mill. (= *N. odorum* Soland.), also called oleander, is similar in appearance. It is common in Hawaii.

POISONOUS PRINCIPLE. Glycosides have been extracted, partially characterized, and named in the case of *N. oleander*. The two major ones are oleandroside and nerioside. They are cardiac glycosides, similar to digitalis in physiological action. Steyn (1533) has reviewed the literature concerning them.

Nerium indicum has yielded similar glycosides. It has been shown (269) that one of them, odoroside, is chemically as well as physiologically similar to digitoxigenin, one of the components of *Digitalis*. Odoroside is a steroid glycoside.

TOXICITY, SYMPTOMS, AND LESIONS. Oleander (*N. oleander*) has been known as a poisonous plant since classical times. Mention of it may be found in Pliny, Dioscorides, Galen, and others. In the United States it has produced loss of life in various classes of livestock (575, 1318, 1488, 1660) and sickness in human beings (1695). Loss of human life has been severe in some countries. Both human and animal deaths from the effects of *N. indicum* have occurred in Hawaii (42).

Experimental feedings reported by Wilson, performed at the Arizona Agricultural Station (1695) with *N. oleander,* are the most detailed available. Others have been carried out in Australia (810) and South Africa (1533). Oleander is extremely toxic in all parts, green or dry, to all classes of livestock and to the human being. Leaves have been shown deadly at as little as 0.005 per cent of the animal's weight in horses and cattle. Sheep have been killed with 0.015 per cent of their weight. A single leaf is considered (1660) potentially lethal to the human being. Loss of human life, sometimes involving large numbers of persons during military operations, has repeatedly occurred when meat was roasted while skewered on oleander branches. West (1660) cites a case in which a number of persons were severely poisoned after eating frankfurters roasted on oleander stems. Horses may be lost when tethered very briefly to an oleander bush.

Symptoms in man and animal are those of severe gastroenteritis accompanied by the cardiac response to the glycosides. They include, in animals, increased pulse rate, cold extremities, mydriasis, discoloration of the mouth, sweating, anorexia, abdominal pain, nausea, vomition, weakness, and bloody feces. In the human being additional symptoms are dizziness and drowsiness. In terminal stages the heartbeat becomes weak and irregular and there may be dyspnea and coma.

Symptoms usually commence several hours after ingestion of a toxic dose. Death, if it occurs, usually follows within a day.

Lesions principally are those of gastroenteritis. Petechial hemorrhages may be found in various organs and membranes. Smith (1488) reported toxic hepatitis and toxic tubular nephritis in a case studied by him.

Nerium indicum as a poisonous plant has been reviewed by Chopra *et al.* (279). It is essentially similar in toxicity and symptomology.

CONDITIONS OF POISONING. Oleander grows rapidly, and, as an ornamental, is subject to frequent pruning. Clippings, therefore, are a prime potential source of trouble in livestock.

Additional reference: 1324.

Thevetia peruviana Schum. ($=$ *T. nereifolia* Juss.). Yellow oleander, be-still tree

DESCRIPTION. Large, rounded shrub or small, densely branched tree, to 30 ft tall. Leaves alternate, linear, sharply pointed at both ends, nearly without petiole, 3 to 6 in. long, about ¼ in. broad; margins revolute; upper surface dark green, lower surface lighter; venation pinnate, midrib very distinct. Flowers clustered at branch tips, bright yellow or orange, fragrant, showy, 2 to 3 in. long, corolla tubular with five spreading lobes. Fruit a drupe, broadly triangular in outline; outer portion fleshy, green becoming yellow, then black; inner portion stony, containing usually two kernels. The stone is sometimes used as a good-luck charm.

DISTRIBUTION AND HABITAT. A tropical plant, used as an ornamental in Florida (north to Orlando or slightly further) and Hawaii.

POISONOUS PRINCIPLE. Yellow oleander has been known since the nineteenth century to contain a compound with digitalislike activity. Extensive chemical and pharmacological investigations (266, 480) have shown this compound, named thevetin, to be a cardiac glycoside. Thevetin occurs in the kernels in an amount varying between 3.6 and 4 per cent of their weight. It is the principal physiologically active compound. The structural formula of thevetin has not been fully elucidated, but there are chemical as well as physiological relationships with the digitalis glycosides (480). It has had some use in medicine.

TOXICITY, SYMPTOMS, AND LESIONS. *Thevetia* has caused accidental poisoning and death in man and animal. All parts of the plant are dangerous. Early cases have been reviewed by Chen and Chen (266, 267). Most human fatality has occurred from misuse of the plant, or substances derived from it, as medicine by native peoples.

On Oahu, Hawaiian Islands, yellow oleander is considered (42) to be the most frequent cause of fatal or dangerous poisoning in man. Arnold has described (42, 43) two cases of mortality in children and another in fowl from eating the kernels. One child died 20 hours after ingestion of a fatal dose. Only one or a few "nuts" may be fatal.

Symptoms are similar to those of fatal digitalis poisoning. The pulse is slowed and becomes irregular. Severe vomition is common, together with other signs of digestive disturbances. Cardiac irregularities may be observed.

Asclepiadaceae

Asclepias spp. Milkweeds

DESCRIPTION. More than a score of milkweeds are found, often with wide distribution patterns, in the United States and Canada. They are perennial, summer- or autumn-flowering herbs with milky juice, erect, non-twining stems, and opposite or whorled leaf arrangement. The unusual flowers are clustered in terminal or axillary umbels and have a corolla of two five-parted whorls of petal parts—the outer strongly reflected back toward the pedicel, the inner much modified and horned, projecting forward about the massive stigma. The fruit, a follicle, is the familiar inflated milk-weed pod filled with numerous seeds, each bearing a tuft of long, silky hairs.

Milkweeds may be divided into two major groups. Narrow-leaved milkweeds have linear or narrowly lanceolate leaves. The leaves of broad-leaved milkweeds are usually more than 1½ in. wide throughout much of their length.

The following species have been found dangerous. All but the least toxic (all those with a toxicity of 2 per cent or greater) fall within three of the 17 groupings in the classificational scheme of Woodson (1704). Since few of the species have been explored for toxicity, this suggests that the remaining members of these three groups should be held in special suspicion as possibly highly toxic. It is likely that many or all species of *Asclepias* have some degree of toxicity.

Asclepias labriformis Jones (labriform milkweed). Narrow-leaved. Along old stream beds in sandy soils. Confined to Utah. Approximately 0.05 per cent of an animal's weight of green plant produces death (785, 804, 1546).

A. subverticillata Vail (= *A. verticillata,* = *A. galioides* of earlier references) (whorled milkweed). Narrow-leaved. Occurs on dry plains and foothills; capable of rapid spread along waterways and irrigation canals, and forming dense stands. Western Kansas and Oklahoma west and south to Utah, Arizona, Texas, and into Mexico. Approximately 0.2 per cent of an animal's weight of green plant produces death (630, 631, 1002, 1538).

A. eriocarpa Benth. (wooly-pod milkweed). Broad-leaved. Found on dry soils, California. Approximately 0.25 per cent of an animal's weight of green plant produces death (986).

A. latifolia Brit. (broadleaf milkweed). Occurs on dry plains, Kansas and Colorado to Texas and Arizona. Approximately 1 per cent of an animal's weight of green plant produces death (928, 1452).

A. pumila Vail (low whorled milkweed, plains whorled milkweed). Narrow-leaved. Distributed in small patches in draws east of the Rockies in Texas and New Mexico north to southeast Montana and southwest North Dakota. Approximately 1 to 2 per cent of an animal's weight of green plant produces death (992).

A. asperula Woodson [= *Asclepiadora decumbens* (Nutt.) Gray]. Occurs on open, dry soils Kansas and Arkansas to Nevada and Arizona, and south into Mexico. Approximately 1.2 per cent of an animal's weight of green plant produces death (804).

A. verticillata L. (eastern whorled milkweed). Narrow-leaved. Plant of dry, open areas, Texas to Michigan, east to Florida and Massachusetts,

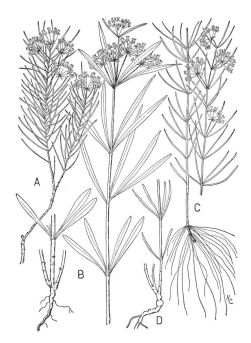

Fig. 67. Narrow leaved milkweeds. A, *Asclepias pumila*. Low whorled milkweed. B, *A. mexicana*. Mexican whorled milkweed. C, *A. verticillata*. Eastern whorled milkweed. D, *A. subverticillata*. Whorled milkweed. Base of plant. Courtesy of The Macmillan Company.

north into Canada. More than 2 per cent of an animal's weight of green plant is required to produce death (992).

A. mexicana Cav. (Mexican whorled milkweed). Narrow-leaved. This species has a spotty distribution along streams on the Pacific slope, southern Washington and Eastern Idaho south to California, western Nevada and Mexico. Two per cent or more of an animal's weight of green plant is required to produce death (232, 552, 993).

A. speciosa Torr. (showy milkweed). Broad-leaved. Plant of prairies and open areas. Minnesota south to Missouri and Texas, west to California. Large amounts experimentally given have produced symptoms (552).

A. syriaca L. (common milkweed). Widely distributed in open areas and along roadsides, eastern and central United States. This species is included here on the basis of a circumstantial report of toxicity (1335).

A. incarnata L. (swamp milkweed). Has been suspected of causing sheep mortality in Indiana (704).

Fig. 67a. Broad-leaved milkweeds. A–C, *Asclepias syriaca*. Milkweed. Flowering shoot, with details of flower and fruit. Photograph, *Asclepias latifolia*. Broad-leaved milkweed. Drawing, courtesy of The Macmillan Company.

POISONOUS PRINCIPLE. Species of *Asclepias* have been known as medicinally active plants from early times and have entered into various pharmacopoeias (349, 356, 552, 1002). Investigation of toxic species for the source of toxicity has led to the partial characterization (but not identification) of a resinoid, galitoxin, in *A. subverticillata* and *A. mexicana*. A similar resinoid is present in *A. eriocarpa*. These resinoids are considered responsible for the production of the spasms seen in *Asclepias* poisoning. In addition, several glycosides and a small amount of an alkaloid have been isolated. Although toxic, their effect is masked by the greater action of the resinoid.

TOXICITY, SYMPTOMS, AND LESIONS. Toxicities, determined experimentally with sheep, are given above with the species names. Sheep, cattle, goats, horses, and domestic fowl have been poisoned. Symptoms produced by various species of *Asclepias* differ only in degree. Profound depression and weakness accompanied by staggering appear first. After the animal goes down, tetanic seizures occurring repeatedly at short intervals are common. Labored respiration, elevated temperature, and dilation of the pupil have been noted. Death usually follows a comatose period of variable duration. Symptoms appear within a few hours of ingestion of a toxic dose, and death follows within one to a few days in most fatal cases. Lesions are not spectacular. There is a greater or lesser congestion of various organs including liver and kidneys with some degeneration of the latter observed in histological preparations. Irritation of intestinal mucosae may be mild or severe. In fowl, depression is accompanied by atonic crop and gizzard which, on necropsy, are packed with dry vegetable material.

CONDITIONS OF POISONING. All species of *Asclepias* are distasteful to livestock. Severe losses have occurred, especially in sheep, but only when the animals were forced to eat this plant by conditions of mismanagement or drought. The highest level of toxicity occurs prior to maturity in those species for which experimental data are available, dropping off somewhat as the plant dries. However, the more highly toxic species may retain enough toxicity to be dangerous in hay. Loss from *Asclepias* in hay has been reported for *A. eriocarpa* (80) and *A. subverticillata* (631). Sprouts have been poisonous to turkeys (1538).

Additional references: 984, 1061.

Cryptostegia grandiflora R. Br. Rubber-vine, pink allamanda

This thick-stemmed, leathery-leaved, woody vine is occasionally cultivated as an ornamental plant. It has become naturalized on roadsides and in waste soils in southern Florida.

This plant has not yet been reported toxic in the United States, but elsewhere it has caused loss of human life (279). It has also come under suspicion in poisoning of cattle and has killed a monkey (1653). The symptoms are those of severe gastroenteritis.

Additional reference: 1136.

Order Polemoniales

Convolvulaceae

Cuscuta spp. Dodder

This parasitic plant, when growing on clover, has been suspected of causing digestive upset in horses in Ohio and scours in cattle in Connecticut.

Ipomoea spp. Morning-glories, sweet potato

Ipomoea fistulosa Mart. is a South American vine which has become established in waste soils of the Coastal Plain from Texas to South Carolina, including peninsular Florida. Experiments performed in Brazil (1586) have shown that prolonged ingestion of this plant results in wasting, depression, and other ill-defined pathology in sheep, cattle, and goats. It has not been reported toxic in the United States.

Other species of *Ipomoea,* and of *Convolvulus* (common morning-glory and bindweed), may contain purgative principles which, according to Gates (609), have caused mild distress in hogs. A presumptive case of *Convolvulus* poisoning of hogs has been described in England (1196).

Ipomoea batatas Lam. is the sweet potato, cultivated in warmer areas of the United States. According to Hansen (708) the practice of feeding rotted sweet potatoes at one time resulted in rather frequent loss of life in cattle and other livestock. Principal symptoms are anorexia and dyspnea with death usually taking place within 2 to 5 days.

Boraginaceae

Amsinckia intermedia Fisch. and Mey. Tarweed, fiddleneck

DESCRIPTION. A variable, seed-reproducing annual, separated by some into several species. Stems erect, sparsely branching, 1 to 3 ft tall, covered with numerous white bristly hairs. Leaves similarly hairy, lanceolate, alternate. Inflorescence a raceme of small, perfect, five-parted orange to yellow flowers; racemes terminating stems, coiled, uncoiling from base to apex, as the flowers ripen; flowers all inserted on one side of axis (hence "fiddleneck"). Fruit at maturity separating into 2 to 4 gray to black nutlets, each about 0.1 in. long.

DISTRIBUTION AND HABITAT. Native to the Pacific Coast states, spreading eastward as a weed of dry open cultivated ground or waste areas. Troublesome as a poisonous plant when growing as a weed of wheat fields in clearly delineated semi-arid lands of California, Oregon, Washington, and Idaho.

POISONOUS PRINCIPLE. Unknown liver toxin; soluble in alcohol, insoluble in petroleum ether; apparently insoluble in water and possibly heat labile (1069). From the relationships of this plant with *Echium* and *Heliotropium,* and from the nature of liver lesions produced by it, the presence of pyrrolizidine (senecio) alkaloids may be inferred. Potentially lethal levels of nitrate have been detected (104) in two species of *Amsinckia* in California.

SYMPTOMS AND LESIONS. Lesions produced by the toxic action of this plant on the liver are relatively uniform among several species of animal, but symptoms, especially as developed under field conditions in livestock, show significant differences. Animals may be killed experimentally in relatively short periods with large amounts of *Amsinckia* seeds. Field cases usually develop slowly after long-continued ingestion of small amounts of seeds. For example, it has been observed that a diet containing about 5 per cent *Amsinckia* seeds produced death in a pig in about 2 months.

Horses, swine, and cattle have been poisoned experimentally and in the field. "Walking disease" of horses in the Pacific Northwest was first reported as of unknown etiology in 1925 (849), and had been recognized among farmers for at least 30 years prior to that date. "Hard liver disease" of cattle and particularly of swine had been earlier described but was not related to a poisonous plant until 1940. That year, McCulloch at the Washington Experiment Station published experiments (1068, 1069, 1070) demonstrating

Fig. 68. *Amsinckia intermedia.* Tarweed. Plant, with details of flower, fruit, and nutlets. Courtesy of The Macmillan Company.

that *Amsinckia* nutlets were the cause of these diseases. In the meantime, mechanization of farms had reduced the economic impact of "walking disease" in horses, but the use of wheat screenings for fattening swine had increased the incidence of *Amsinckia* poisoning in that class of livestock.

Horses, swine, and cattle show symptoms of unthriftiness and (sometimes weakly) icterus. Horses, in addition, exhibit nervous involvement which may take the form of sluggishness or sleepiness, furious delirium, or aimless walking. In the latter, present in about 80 per cent of cases, horses walk continuously in a straight line for miles if unimpeded or through fences and into obstructions. Small ulcers may develop on the mucosae of lips and gums and are often accompanied by an offensive odor. In prolonged chronic cases, emaciation may be marked. Icterus may disappear in the terminal stages of the disease as severe anemia develops.

Symptoms in swine are usually noticed first in the field as failure to gain weight. This may occur at any weight between 30 and 100 lb. The animal becomes long and narrow, and the head elongates. Cases are similar to those of acute parasitism, but parasites are absent or of minor importance upon necropsy. Cattle show little more than lack of condition and weak icterus. Diagnosis of *Amsinckia* poisoning in these animals is usually made at the abbatoir. From the lack of field cases and the results of experimental feedings of *Amsinckia* nutlets, sheep appear to be relatively resistant to the toxic principle. Mules also seem resistant. Fowl have been shown resistant to the action of the toxic principle, and even benefited from the vitamin D content of *Amsinckia* seed in one experiment as compared with the controls (1069).

The primary lesion of *Amsinckia* poisoning in all species of animal consists of necrosis of liver parenchyma and replacement with connective tissue. The liver becomes small, hard, and increasingly nonfunctional. Hemorrhage in subcutaneous tissues or in the gastrointestinal tract is sometimes observed (1159, 1705).

CONDITIONS OF POISONING. When horses were more plentiful, cases were common, appearing in early spring, after horses had been fed wheat straw or were pastured on wheat stubble through the winter months. Poisoning now occurs mostly when wheat screenings containing *Amsinckia* seeds are fed to cattle, horses, or swine. The plant is a common weed but is distasteful. It cannot compete in good stands of wheat, but is favored by drought conditions that limit the growth of the wheat. Thus, potential toxicity of screenings can be predicted in terms of bushels of wheat produced per acre. A harvest greater than 30 bu per acre can be expected to yield screenings of no significant toxicity (104).

Advantage may be taken of the fact that sheep are relatively resistant to *Amsinckia* poisoning. It has been shown (1159) that wheat screenings containing as much as 25 per cent *Amsinckia* nutlets may be fed as a fattening ration to feeder lambs for 4 months or perhaps longer without losing their palatability or producing demonstrable pathology.

Additional reference: 858.

Echium plantagineum L. Viper's bugloss

This species is recently adventive in a limited area of California. It is closely related to the poisonous plants, *Amsinckia intermedia* and *Heliotropium europeum,* which contain liver toxins. Like the latter, its liver toxin is a pyrrolizidine alkaloid (919). It has been found in Australia to produce poisoning in sheep similar to that produced by *Heliotropium.*

Additional reference: 204.

Heliotropium europaeum L. Heliotrope

This annual weed [not to be confused with garden heliotrope (= *Valeriana officinalis* L.)] occurs rather sparingly in the southeastern states from Florida to New Jersey and occasionally into New England. In Australia it has provoked extensive losses, particularly in sheep, and has been the object of considerable investigation. Losses are not known in the United States and are unlikely unless the plant increases in numbers, since disease results from ingestion of a large quantity consumed over an extended period of time.

Heliotrope contains two principal alkaloids of the senecio or pyrrolizidine type which produce liver damage. Similar alkaloids are found in the poisonous species of *Echium, Senecio,* and *Crotalaria* (see *Senecio* for a fuller discussion). The literature of Australian heliotrope poisoning has been reviewed through 1950 by Newsom (1176) and by Bull *et al.* (204), who present the results of extended studies into the pathological effects of heliotrope poisoning.

The two principal alkaloids are heliotrine and lassiocarpine (919). The N-oxide of each of these has also been found in the plant. The oxides are more soluble than the parent alkaloids. It has been suggested (204) that the content of oxides is more important in determining the severity of poisoning than that of the alkaloids because the latter suffer appreciable destruction in the rumen from contact with bacterial and plant enzymes. The more soluble oxides probably pass through the rumen much more quickly in the normal course of events, escaping destruction. The oxides may be reduced to the more toxic form in the tissues after absorption.

Heliotrope poisoning has several manifestations. All are related to decreased or changed metabolic activity in the liver. The liver toxin is slow-acting (203, 1410). With continued ingestion of heliotrope, liver cells increase in size, have an increased death rate, and lose regenerative powers. The characteristic changes, then, are those of atrophic hepatosis accompanied by only a small amount of fibrosis. In most cases, animals can consume large amounts of heliotrope over an entire growing season without developing clinical symptoms. However, liver-cell changes may be found, both on histological examination and by various metabolic tests. These changes persist and predispose the affected animal to serious poisoning in the second season.

On the other hand, a relatively acute situation may develop, particularly on young, vigorous stands of heliotrope, in which death occurs after the flock has been removed from the plant at the end of the season in apparent good condition. Bull *et al.* (204) suggest that this syndrome is the result of relatively severe liver damage which makes that organ unable to deal with increased nitrogen intake from lush pastures and is an acute ammonia intoxication.

The cumulative deleterious effect of continued heliotrope consumption in a second grazing season results in a syndrome characterized by progressive loss of condition and other changes in blood composition and metabolism characteristic of liver atrophy and regularly terminates in death. Symptoms and lesions of photosensitization also may be occasionally encountered.

A third clinical syndrome in sheep is characterized by sudden hematogenous jaundice. In this, the liver is found to have an abnormally high copper content, and it is clear that the observed pathological effects are the result of altered copper metabolism in the liver cells. This syndrome usually appears when animals that have been on heliotrope for a season are transferred to pasturage such as subterranean clover, that promotes a high copper intake.

Cattle have been poisoned only rarely. It appears, however, that cattle are more susceptible to the poisonous principle than sheep and that poisoning of cattle presents a more acute syndrome (206).

Gregory, on the basis of preliminary trials, suggests (657) that cobalt pellets be added to the diet of sheep and cattle subject to possible poisoning by pyrrolizidine alkaloids. Cobalt must be ample for the adequate formation of vitamin B_{12} in the rumen if maximum advantage is to be taken of a reaction there, dependant on the presence of B_{12}, in which pyrrolizidine alkaloids are detoxified.

Solanaceae

Atropa belladonna L. Belladonna, deadly nightshade
DESCRIPTION. Coarse herb with thick perennating root. Stems much branched, 2 to 5 ft tall. Leaves large, ovate, entire, alternately inserted, but axillary buds develop rapidly so that leaves appear to be inserted in pairs at

Fig. 69. *Atropa belladonna*. Belladonna. Leafy shoot, with details of floral construction, fruit, and seed. Courtesy of The Macmillan Company.

the same point, with one member of each pair larger than the other. Flowers solitary, nodding, 5-parted; calyx 5-pointed; corolla tubular, nearly 1 in. long, with 5 blunt points, dull purple. Fruit, a berry, purple to black (when ripe).

DISTRIBUTION AND HABITAT. This plant, native to Europe, has occasionally been cultivated in the United States. Except where it has escaped from cultivation, it is not found wild. As a garden escapee it is rarely persistent and never forms extensive growths.

POISONOUS PRINCIPLE. The solanaceous, tropane alkaloid, atropine (present in the plant as the isomeric and related alkaloid l-hysocyamine) (783). Alkaloid is present throughout the plant, increasing to a maximum at maturity (383).

TOXICITY, SYMPTOMS, AND LESIONS. Much confusion exists in toxicological literature concerning poisoning by ingestion of *Atropa* plants (869). Inadequately discriminating use of the common names "belladonna," "deadly nightshade," and others is the source. It must be concluded on botanical grounds that alleged cases of poisoning from ingestion of *Atropa* plants described in the literature of the United States and Canada most likely involve incorrect identification of the plant.

The physiology of the tropane alkaloids, the group to which atropine belongs, is well known from their use in medicine. These natural anticholinergic compounds remain pharmacologically useful despite the chemical synthesis of several tropanes. Pharmacodynamics and symptoms of poisoning after overdoses of the drug are well described in pharmacological texts and elsewhere (e.g., 819). Atropine blocks motor, secretary, and inhibitory effects of acetylcholine on smooth muscle tissue, thereby countering results normally associated with stimulation of the parasympathetic nervous system. Toxic effects of these alkaloids in natural cases are better known from poisoning by *Datura* and *Hyoscyamus*.

Verified poisoning by ingestion of *Atropa* is rare. A case is on record (1192) in which a British Toggenburg goat ate quantities of *Atropa* and *Sambucus* (elderberry) and subsequently died. Symptoms included trembling and excitement followed in about ten hours by prostration. The heartbeat was rapid, the pulse weak, and the eyes strongly dilated so that the animal appeared to be unable to see. Dyspnea and gastric atony were noted. Death followed a terminal comatose stage interrupted by occasional conclusive kicking. *Atropa* leaves were isolated from the forestomach on necropsy.

Forsyth (574) has observed instances of poisoning in calves from ingestion of *Atropa*. Symptoms cited are similar to the above. He found no significant lesions. Urine from the poisoned animals produced dilation of the pupil of a cat and of a cow. *Atropa* plants that showed signs of having been eaten were found in the vicinity.

CONDITIONS OF POISONING. Poisoning in animals is universally regarded as rare even where the plant is relatively common. In the United States, where the plant is not common, poisoning of stock probably never occurs under natural conditions.

Atropa is occasionally cultivated in garden collections of medicinal or useful plants. When encountered, it should be regarded as potentially dangerous, especially to children who may be attracted to its black berries. Ingestion of three of them has been known to be fatal to a child (574).

Cestrum spp. Jessamine, cestrum

The poisonous cestrums are large, handsome shrubs with alternate, simple, entire, mostly lanceolate or elliptical leaves and axillary clusters of fragrant, showy flowers. The flowers are trumpet-shaped, about 1 in. long, 5-parted. The fruit is a small berry.

Cestrum parqui L'Her. (green cestrum, willow-leaved jessamine) with greenish-white flowers is sometimes cultivated as an ornamental, and is found wild in woods, waste areas, and roadsides of the coastal plain from Florida to Texas. It has not been reported toxic in the United States but has been the subject of investigation in Australia. Experimental feedings (810) have demonstrated that the foliage is toxic to cattle in amounts greater than about 0.5 per cent of the animal's weight. The fruits are about ten times as toxic. Poisoning has been experienced in horses, sheep, cattle, hogs, and fowl (904). Symptoms include fever, gastroenteritis (including bloody feces), and occasionally excitement. Death usually follows within a few hours after onset of symptoms.

Cestrum nocturnum L. (night-blooming jessamine) and *C. diurnum* L. (day-blooming jessamine) are frequently used as ornamentals in southern states, and the latter may be found wild in waste areas in the Florida Keys and South Texas. In the latter the flowers are white and sweet-scented by day; in the former they are greenish-white and sweet-scented by night. Early references to the toxicity of these species have been reinforced by current experience. Cases of poisoning in pets and in the human being are on record (1136). Symptoms are largely nervous in character and resemble those produced by atropine, which is known to be present in several related genera (see *Atropa, Datura,* and *Hyoscyamus*). Included were hallucinations, muscular and nervous irritability, tachycardia, elevated temperature, salivation, dyspnea, and paralysis.

Datura spp. Datura, stramonium, thornapple, Jimsonweed, Jamestown weed, apple of Peru, tolguacha

More than a score of common names in English and many more in other languages are used for this cosmopolitan weed of worldwide distribution. Those cited above are in most general use in the United States.

DESCRIPTION. This genus contains more than a dozen species. Of these, several are found naturalized in the United States and several others are occasionally cultivated for their conspicuous flowers and fragrance. Most are large (mostly to 5 ft), coarse annual herbs, with large, alternate leaves and large, showy, tubular flowers; reproducing by seeds, inhabiting waste areas, particularly those with rich soils. The most common species are:

D. stramonium L. Three to 5 ft tall, glabrous or nearly so. Leaves ovate with irregular, acute lobes; 3 to 8 in. long. Flowers erect, 4 in. long; corolla 5-pointed, white (or purple in the variety *tatula* sometimes treated as a separate species). Fruit an erect, ovoid, spiny capsule, to about 2 in. long; opening by 4 regular valves (some capsules spineless in variety

Fig. 70. *Datura stramonium.* Thornapple, jimsonweed. Flowering shoot, with details of opened fruit and seed. Photograph of flowering plant in natural habitat. Drawing, courtesy of The Macmillan Company.

inermis). Widely distributed from Florida to Texas, north into Canada, and in the far western states, in waste areas and sometimes as a weed of cultivation. It is common on the rich soils of barnyards and heavily used portions of pastures.

D. metel L. Four to 5 ft tall, glabrous. Leaves ovate-lanceolate with dentate or undulate margins; 7 to 8 in. long. Flowers erect, 7 in. long; calyx purple; corolla 5-pointed, white to purple. Fruit a nodding, subglobose capsule with short spines; to about 2 in. long; opening irregularly. Common in waste areas along the Coastal Plain from Florida to Texas.

D. metaloides Dunal. One to 3 ft tall, grayish in color because of finely hairy surfaces. Leaves ovate with dentate to sinuate margin; 2 to 2¼ in. long. Flowers erect, to 9 in. long; corolla 10-pointed, white, often suffused with purple or rose. Fruit a nodding, subglobose capsule with long slender spines, to about 2 in. long; opening irregularly. Plains, dry hills and valleys from Texas to California and Colorado, locally eastward to Florida along roadsides.

D. suaveolens Humb. & Bonpl. Coarse, woody, treelike shrub, to 15 ft high, glabrous. Leaves ovate-oblong, entire, acute; 6 to 12 in. long. Flowers nodding, to 1 ft long; corolla white, with 5 weakly expressed points. Cultivated as an ornamental in the southeastern United States, where it does not form fruit.

POISONOUS PRINCIPLE. Species of *Datura* contain several solanaceous alkaloids (p. 18) of the tropane configuration. Principal among them are atropine, hyoscyamine, and hyoscine (scopolamine). The close chemical relationship of these molecules, their interconvertibility, especially in extraction procedures, and their presence in the plant in varying relative and absolute amounts engenders confusion which is reflected in the existence of a number of additional names in the literature of the past. Total alkaloid content is high, varying between 0.25 and 0.7 per cent. *Datura* alkaloids are useful in medicine and have been investigated both chemically and pharmacologically. Discussions from these points of view may be found in the appropriate texts and is not repeated here.

TOXICITY, SYMPTOMS, AND LESIONS. Poisoning may occur from an overdose of preparations of the plant (stramonium U.S.P.) or any of its alkaloids. Poisoning from ingestion of parts or decoctions of the plant by human beings is not uncommon (1112) and has been reviewed by several authors (807, 825, 826, 1046, 1112, 1537). It is usually impossible to determine or even approximate the amount of plant obtained, especially since in the case of seeds the degree of digestion is important. Small amounts will produce symptoms and larger amounts, death, if treatment is not swift and successful. It has been calculated (1112) on the basis of the toxicity of pure atropine that about 4 to 5 g of the crude leaf or seed of *Datura* approximates the fatal dose in a child.

Symptoms in the human being vary in time of onset with the form in which the plant was ingested. The exact picture presented during the sequence of symptoms varies somewhat with the relative concentration of the several alkaloids and also with individual idiosyncrasy. Symptoms may appear within a few minutes after ingestion of decoctions made from the plant or, in the case of ingestion of leaves or seeds, not for several hours (807, 832, 1112). Premonitory symptoms include intense thirst and disturbance of vision resulting from the strong mydriatic effect of the alkaloids. The skin becomes flushed and hyperirritability of the central nervous system is noted. Subjects become delerious, incoherent, and perform insensible motions, commonly picking at imaginary objects on themselves or in the air. Temperature may be elevated, and the heartbeat rapid and weak. Subjects may become violent and dangerous to themselves and others. If the poisoning progresses further, convulsions appear, followed by coma. Subjects usually drink large quantities of water in the first stages of poisoning. This, coupled with inhibition of parasympathetic function, usually results in distended bladder. In some individuals the comatose stage may be reached almost immediately upon onset of poisoning. If a less than lethal amount of the plant has been consumed, or if measures taken in treatment (such as gastric lavage) are successful, acute symptoms subside after 12 to 48 hours. The mydriatic effect may persist as long as two weeks.

Losses have been reported in the world literature in all classes of livestock, including ostriches. In the United States losses have been noted in horses, cattle, sheep, hogs, mules, and chickens (257, 274, 700, 704, 864, 865, 1335, 1661). The plant has been obtained fresh, in hay, or in ensilage. Chickens were poisoned by ingestion of seeds (1335). Figures are cited by Cary, Miller, and Johnstone (254) for toxicity of the tops of the plants (ranging from about 0.01 per cent) but the source of these figures, whether experimental or from the literature, is not given. Ten to 14 oz. (0.06 to 0.09 per cent of the animal's weight of plant) is lethal to cattle according to West and Emmel (1661). However, toxicity may vary with species and with climatic and seasonal factors [see especially the feeding experiments of Steyn (1533) in which only negative results were obtained]. Symptoms in livestock are similar to those produced in human beings. Lesions are not characteristic. It is possible to detect atropine in stomach contents and body tissues for some time after death (61), and small amounts of a mydriatic alkaloid may be detected in the urine of a poisoned subject by placing a drop of it in the eye of a laboratory animal.

CONDITIONS OF POISONING. *Datura* has been known as a poisonous plant from the ancient past. Decoctions of it were frequently employed to produce desired poisonings. Discussions of the plant and its activity are universally found in publications on materia medica from the earliest times and reference to it was made by Virgil, Shakespeare, and others (633).

This plant is unusual in that human poisonings are more commonly reported in recent literature than are animal poisonings. The large, showy flowers and spiny capsules especially intrigue children and lead to poisoning from sucking the nectar from the base of the corolla tube (1136), or from ingestion of the seeds (1282). A decoction or "tea" made from the leaves was used in an earlier time to relieve asthma. Such preparations are dangerous and account for many cases of poisoning. Poisoning has also occurred in other countries when datura seeds were ingested as impurities in bean mixtures. *Datura* occasionally is deliberately used for its hallucinogenic effects (825).

Of historic interest is the mass poisoning of soldiers sent to Jamestown,

Virginia, in 1676 to quell the Bacon rebellion. Beverly's contemporary account of the event has been quoted by several persons in recent sources more readily available (807, 832). It is from this widely publicized incident that the common names "Jamestown weed" and "Jimson weed" were derived.

Livestock find the evil-smelling daturas distasteful, and accounts of poisoning of livestock indicate that animals have been forced to eat the plant through shortage of more desirable forage. The plant is commonly found in hog lots and barnyards and thus is frequently available to livestock under conditions where other feeds may not be available. The plant may easily be controlled in such circumstances by cutting it before it goes to seed, since it is an annual.

Additional reference: 726.

Hyoscyamus niger L. Black henbane, henbane

DESCRIPTION. Annual or biennial, coarse, hairy, erect herb, 1 to 4 ft tall. Leaves oblong, coarsely few-toothed, alternate, mostly sessile below to clasping above, 3 to 8 in. long. Flowers produced singly on short pedicels or sessile in the leaf angles, becoming crowded near tip; corolla campanulate, 5-lobed, greenish-yellow or yellowish-white with purple veins, 1 to 2 in. across; calyx green, campanulate, 5-lobed, continuing growth during maturation of fruit, forming a ribbed, 5-pointed protective cover about the fruit. Fruit a globular capsule with circumsissile opening.

DISTRIBUTION AND HABITAT. Introduced to this hemisphere as a cultivated medicinal plant. Now escaped and naturalized in occasional, rather infrequent localities across southern Canada and northern United States. Locally common in some areas of the northern Rocky Mountain states. Found characteristically on somewhat dry soils of roadsides and waste areas. The biennial variety is more commonly found than the annual and is more suited for alkaloidal production in commercial gardens (780).

Henbane contains alkaloids of the tropane configuration, particularly hyoscyamine, but also hyoscine (scopolamine) and atropine. It has been used as a medicinally active material throughout history and is listed by all major authors on poisonous plants from Dioscorides to the twentieth century. In older times occasional poisoning in livestock and more frequent poisoning in human beings, particularly children, were recorded [see review by Long (933)]. Now because of the comparative rarity of the plant in the wild, its strong distastefulness to animals, and the stricter handling of commercial production, poisonings are rare. Chesnut has described (277) a case of loss of life in fowl following ingestion of the seed.

The action of the tropane alkaloids is well known from their use in medicine. Both symptoms and pharmacodynamics have been treated recently (974). Cornevin (335) appears to be the original source of the statement seen in some descriptions that poisoning by *Hyoscyamus* may be

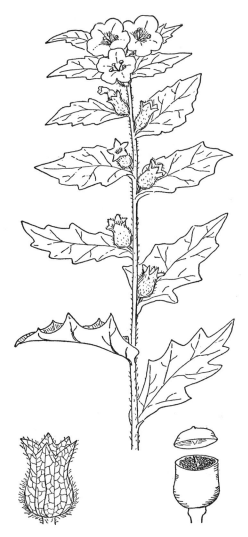

Fig. 71. *Hyoscyamus niger*. Henbane.
Flowering shoot, with details of flower and
fruit. Courtesy of The Macmillan Company.

distinguished from that by *Atropa* or *Datura* symptomatically from the
presence of copious salivation in the former compared with its absence in
the latter.

Lycium halimifolium Mill. Matrimony vine
DESCRIPTION. Woody upright shrub or vine with curving pendant
branches, to 10 ft tall. Branches numerous, occasionally bearing long woody

thorns. Leaves alternate, simple, lanceolate, tapering into petiole, mostly 1 to 1½ in. long. Flowers solitary or few in leaf axils; calyx green, bell-shaped, 5-pointed; corolla violet, 5-lobed; stamens 5. Fruit a small orange or red berry.

DISTRIBUTION AND HABITAT. Introduced as an ornamental shrub, common in older plantings, now escaped and naturalized locally in the northern United States and southern Canada.

POISONOUS PRINCIPLE. Unknown. Symptoms, lesions, and botanical relationship suggest the presence of solanaceous alkaloids (see *Solanum,* p. 287).

TOXICITY, SYMPTOMS, AND LESIONS. Cases of poisoning have been reported in calves and sheep (706). In both instances the animals had access to matrimony vines growing about abandoned houses. It was evident that a large amount had been consumed. Symptoms consisted of excitement and convulsions followed by death. Lesions of severe gastroenteritis were found.

Lycopersicon esculentum Mill. Tomato

Tomato is closely related to *Solanum,* having been considered a species of that genus by botanists at one time. The vines and suckers have proved toxic to livestock. Steroid alkaloids of the solanine type have been isolated from several members of this genus (1292).

Symptoms and lesions are those of solanine poisoning (see *Solanum,* p. 287).

Cattle have been poisoned when garden cleanings were thrown into the pasture (258), or when let into a garden of tomatoes which had not developed properly (257). Sows and feeder shoats have been killed by vines thrown to them (257). In England (574), pigs have been poisoned on the suckers removed from tomato vines in the usual horticultural practice.

Nicotiana spp. Wild and cultivated tobaccos, nicotiana

Probably all of the many species in this genus contain the highly toxic alkaloid nicotine. Several species are cultivated as "nicotiana" or "flowering tobacco" in flower gardens. *Nicotiana tabacum* L. is the tobacco of commerce. Poisoning in human beings and livestock is not infrequent from intentional or accidental misuse of nicotine or products containing it. The alkaloid is readily absorbed after either ingestion or inhalation or through scarified or intact skin and is rapidly fatal in small amounts. The discussion presented here, however, is confined to poisoning brought about by accidental ingestion of the plant. Livestock have been poisoned by the following species in the United States:

Nicotiana attenuata Torr. Wild tobacco, coyote tobacco (208, 1016, 1383)

DESCRIPTION. Erect, branching, herbaceous annual; stems hairy, sticky,

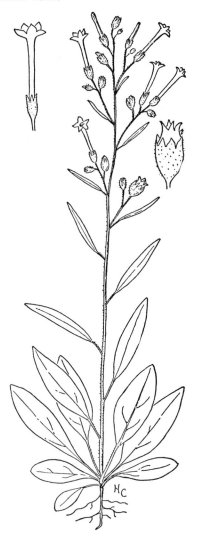

Fig. 72. *Nicotiana attenuata.* Wild
tobacco. Plant, with details of
flower and fruit. Courtesy of The
Macmillan Company.

1 to 4 ft tall. Leaves alternate, petioled, lanceolate, entire, 1½ to 4 in.
long. Inflorescence racemose; flowers long-tubular, night-opening, 5-parted,
white.

DISTRIBUTION AND HABITAT. Dry sandy stream beds and flats, Washington to Wyoming, south to Arizona and New Mexico.

Nicotiana glauca Graham. Tree tobacco (935, 1383)

DESCRIPTION. Evergreen, loose-branching shrub or small tree, glabrous, 6 to 18 ft tall. Stems pithy, leaves ovate, entire, glabrous. Inflorescence paniculate; flowers as preceding except yellow.

DISTRIBUTION AND HABITAT. Common in waste areas below 3000 ft, California. Common in Hawaii.

Nicotiana trigonophylla Dunal. Wild tobacco, desert tobacco (208, 1016, 1383)

DESCRIPTION. Slender, erect, herbaceous annual; stems hairy, sticky, 1 to 3 ft tall. Leaves alternate, sessile, or attached with clasping wings, ovate, 2 to 5 in. long below, smaller and lanceolate above. Inflorescence racemose or paniculate; flowers as *N. attenuata,* except day-opening, white or yellowish.

DISTRIBUTION AND HABITAT. Dry, desert soils, southern California, Nevada, Utah and Colorado, south to Texas and Mexico.

Nicotiana tabacum L. Cultivated tobacco (273, 574, 1335)

POISONOUS PRINCIPLE. The alkaloid nicotine has been demonstrated or assumed present in all these species and it is generally assumed that nicotine is responsible for the toxicity found.

TOXICITY, SYMPTOMS, AND LESIONS. All species produce equivalent effects. Poisoning has been reported in all classes of livestock from one or another of these species. Experimental feedings have been carried out at the USDA experiment station at Salina (Utah) using *N. attenuata* with sheep and *N. trigonophylla* with cattle, horses, and sheep (1016).

The minimum lethal dose of *N. trigonophylla* was found to be about 2 per cent of the animal's weight, green-weight basis. *Nicotiana attenuata* was less toxic. Symptoms appeared almost immediately (less than 15 minutes) or not for several hours. Larger doses produced symptoms more quickly. Symptoms are almost entirely nervous in origin and consist of shaking, shivering, or localized twitching of muscles, especially about the neck and shoulders, staggering, weakness, and eventual prostration. The heart action may be violent but the pulse becomes rapid and weak. Body temperature may be elevated while the extremities become cold. Vomition, diarrhea, and abdominal pain may be noted. Dyspnea is common. The only lesion of significance is the presence of ingesta in the trachea or lungs, which is found frequently as the result of inhaled vomitus. Staring or turned eyes or inability to see have been described in some cases. The duration of symptoms is variable and does not seem dependent on the dose. Some deaths occur after only a few minutes, while other animals linger for several days.

CONDITIONS OF POISONING. Tobaccos are relatively distasteful but may be consumed under certain circumstances. Horses have died from eating leaves of harvested tobacco when kept overnight in a tobacco barn (1335). Pigs have been killed when they got loose into a field of cultivated tobacco (574). Wild tobaccos may be consumed by range livestock under conditions that make more desirable forage unavailable (935).

According to the *Los Angeles Times* (June 10, 1962, B-8), a family that used wild tobacco as a boiled green was severely poisoned and one fatality resulted.

Additional reference: 549.

Physalis longifolia Nutt. Ground-cherry
Physalis peruviana L. Ground-cherry, poha
Physalis longifolia has been suspected of poisoning sheep in Iowa (1226). The fruit of *P. peruviana* is widely used for making preserves in Hawaii, but the unripe fruit is considered definitely poisonous (42). This species has also been suspected of toxicity in Australia (810).

Solandra spp. Trumpet flower, chalice vine
Several species in this genus are cultivated in greenhouses or outdoors in the warmest parts of the United States for the large, showy, white or yellow flowers. Alkaloids of the solanine type are contained in the plant and may produce poisoning of human beings if ingested (1136). Investigations of the toxicology of this plant have been reviewed by Hurst (810).

Solanum spp. Nightshades, bittersweet, potato, Jerusalem cherry, etc.
A genus of about 1500 species worldwide; those in the United States and Canada are annual and perennial herbs and shrubs with alternate, simple or compound leaves, axillary inflorescences, radially symmetrical flowers composed of 5 free sepals, 5 free petals, usually 5 stamens the anthers of which are grouped conically about the stigma; the fruit is a berry.

POISONOUS PRINCIPLE. It was known many years ago that species of *Solanum* contained a toxic alkaloid, to which the name solanine was applied. Further investigation showed that solanine was a glycoalkaloid. On hydrolysis it yields a sugar as well as an alkamine aglycone. The sugar was termed solanose and the alkamine solanidine. Since 1952 it has been learned that a number of sugars and at least six different alkamines are combined to form a variety of glycoalkaloids in species of *Solanum*. The sugars include di- and trisaccharides, some of which are branched chains. The alkamines are steroidal. The review by Prelog and Jeger (1293) may be consulted for the chemistry of these compounds.

TOXICITY, SYMPTOMS, AND LESIONS. Despite the ancient and general reputation of nightshades as poisonous plants, very few feeding experiments have been performed with any of the toxic species. It is generally believed that toxicity of a given species may vary over wide limits with factors of its environment, part of plant, and degree of maturity. Genetics may play a part.

Occasional cases and feeding experiments with *S. eleagnifolium* have shown that under some conditions this species can have relatively high toxicity. *Solanum eleagnifolium* has been found toxic to cattle at as little as 0.1 per cent of the animal's weight of plant.

Several different glycoalkaloids may be concerned in poisonings by various species of *Solanum,* yet symptoms and lesions are relatively uniform. The intact glycoalkaloid is irritant, but poorly absorbed through the intestinal wall. It is saponic in physical characteristics and causes red-blood-cell lysis *in vitro.* The steroid alkamine is probably more readily absorbed and responsible for the major nervous symptoms. If so, then the exact symptoms found in a given case will depend upon the balance between irritant effect of the intact glycoalkaloid and nervous effect of the released alkamine.

Nervous effects in poisoned animals include apathy, drowsiness, salivation, dyspnea, trembling, progressive weakness or paralysis, prostration, and unconsciousness. The pupils may or may not be dilated; if they are, it is not diagnostic of solanine poisoning. In human beings, symptoms include stupefaction and loss of sensations.

Effects of gastrointestinal irritation may be almost unnoticed or, at the other extreme, so severe as to overshadow the nervous effects. They include anorexia, nausea, abdominal pain, vomition, and constipation or diarrhea, the latter sometimes with blood.

Poisoning by *Solanum* species does not always terminate fatally. In the usual acute poisoning, nervous symptoms rapidly build to maximum, and death or recovery eventuates within a few hours to one or two days. Death is the result of paralysis.

Lesions are those of gastrointestinal irritation. They vary from minor inflammation of the mucosae to hemorrhage and ulceration. Specific lesions accounting for the nervous symptoms have not been found.

Symptoms and lesions are comparable in the human being (723) and various classes of livestock. Almost always acute poisoning is involved and follows the course described above. Occasionally chronic poisoning occurs. Symptoms in cattle associated with chronic poisoning by *S. carolinense* include emaciation, rough coat, anorexia, constipation, and ascites (257, 1566). Ascites likewise has been observed (168) in chronic poisoning by *S. nigrum.* Icterus has been associated with subacute poisoning by *S. carolinense* (257) and *S. eleagnifolium* (436). Dermatitis ("food rash") has been reported occasionally in animals fed potatoes (373).

Extracts from a number of species of *Solanum* have been shown (1207) to inhibit the action of cholinesterase *in vitro.* To associate this with the mechanism by which solanaceous alkaloids are toxic is an intriguing thought, begging experimental investigation.

CONDITIONS OF POISONING. Many species of *Solanum* have been found toxic in various countries. Furthermore, solanaceous alkaloids have been isolated from a large number of species. It is safest, therefore, to consider any species potentially poisonous until determined otherwise. Toxicity is not lost on drying. Any species toxic when fresh may be expected to prove toxic in hay.

The following species have been associated with cases of poisoning in the United States and Canada.

Solanum aculeatissimum Jacq. Devil's apple, soda apple
The fruits of this partly woody perennial of the Coastal Plain from Texas to North Carolina have a record of toxicity elsewhere (810) but seem harmless as commercially employed in florists' dried arrangements.

Solanum carolinense L. Horse nettle, bull nettle
Perennial, 6 in. to 2 ft tall. Stems and leaf veins bearing yellowish spines. Leaves simple, oblong, irregularly sinuate or lobed. Flowers pale violet or white. Berries yellow, about ½ in. in diameter. Common weed of cultivation and waste or neglected areas, Texas to the Atlantic Coast, less common northward to southern Canada.

Poisoning in cattle (257), sheep (256, 706), and possibly deer (257) has been reported. Acute and chronic syndromes have been differentiated (257, 1566). In sheep, berries produced severe intestinal lesions. In calves, inflammation of the mouth and esophagus were found. Solanine content of the plant was found to increase tenfold in the fall with maturity. The dried berries, clinging to the plant over winter in Missouri, killed cattle in March. They were sought out and eaten by preference.

The death of a 6 yr old boy in Delaware County, Pennsylvania in January of 1963 received considerable publicity in the local press. The plant materials involved, erroniously identified at first, appear to be the berries of *S. carolinense*.

Solanum dulcamara L. European bittersweet, climbing nightshade
Perennial; stems slender, woody, climbing or trailing, sometimes to 6 ft in length. Leaves simple, ovate to cordate, variable in outline, some with two opposite basal lobes. Flowers deep purple or blue. Berry red at maturity. Woods and thickets throughout North America, most common in northern United States.

Losses have been attributed (708) to this species in the United States. Better-documented cases in cattle, horses, and sheep have occurred in Europe (373). The berries may have been responsible for poisoning of children on Long Island (726).

Solanum eleagnifolium Cav. Silverleaf nightshade, white horsenettle, tropillo

Perennial, 1 to 3 ft tall, white-hairy leaves and stem. Leaves simple, thick, lanceolate to linear, entire to sinuate. Stems and leaf ribs usually bearing short stiff spines. Flowers violet or blue, berries yellow or orange. Serious weed of prairies, open woods, and disturbed soils, southwestern states and Mexico, north to Missouri, locally further north.

Considerable loss of life in range cattle prompted feeding experiments by the Texas Experiment Station (158, 191, 436). In cattle the ripe berries produced moderate to severe poisoning when fed at 0.1 to 0.3 per cent of the animal's weight. The green berries appeared slightly less toxic. The leaves were least toxic. Sheep were considerably more resistant than cattle to poisoning, and goats were not poisoned at all under the conditions of the experiment. Icterus was a characteristic of some subacute cases. In one instance fallen berries were ingested with feed spread on the ground.

Solanum gracile Link. Graceful nightshade

This species is closely related to *S. nigrum* and is similar but slightly larger in most of its structures. Sandy soils and dunes of the coast, Louisiana to North Carolina. This species has been listed as toxic to all species of livestock and fowl by the Florida Experiment Station (1661).

Solanum nigrum L. (= *S. americanum* Mill.). Black nightshade, deadly nightshade, common nightshade

Annual, 6 in. to 3 ft tall. Leaves simple, ovate to lanceolate, entire to sinuate-dentate. Flowers white. Berry black when ripe.

Recently it has been found that there are minor differences between native black nightshade and the form introduced from Europe, now widely naturalized. *Solanum nigrum* properly refers only to the latter, while the native form should be designated *S. americanum*. The introduced weed is more apt to be found on disturbed soils and waste areas, while the native species occurs usually in undisturbed habitats. It is impossible to tell which of these was involved in particular instances of poisoning previously ascribed in American literature to *Solanum nigrum*. Both *Solanum nigrum* and *S. americanum* are common throughout eastern United States, becoming less common westward.

The cultivated "garden huckleberry" or "wonderberry" is a species of *Solanum* closely related to *S. nigrum*. Bailey (54) considered it to belong in this species, but the cultivated and wild plants do not interbreed. The cultivated form is now designated *S. intrusum* Soria and appears to have dependably nontoxic fruit (1494, 1495).

Numerous cases of black-nightshade poisoning have been reported from various parts of the United States (168, 241, 264, 706, 708, 796, 1335).

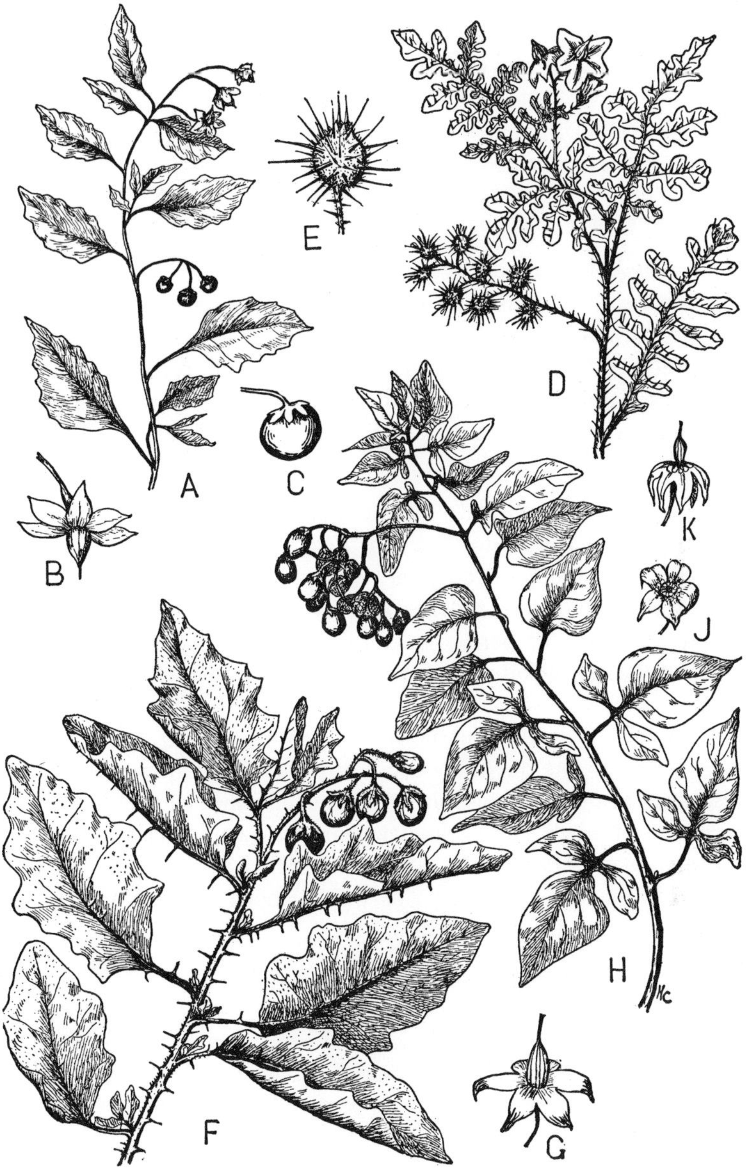

Fig. 73. Nightshades. A-C, *Solanum nigrum*. Black nightshade. Branch, with details of flower and fruit. D-E, *S. rostratum*. Buffalo bur. Flowering branch, with detail of fruit. F-G, *S. carolinense*. Horse nettle. Fruiting branch, with detail of flower. H-K, *S. dulcamara*. European bittersweet. Fruiting branch, with two detailed views of flower. Courtesy of The Macmillan Company.

Mortality or severe poisoning has been described for cattle, sheep, swine, horses, chickens, and ducks. Symptoms are relatively uniform and as described above for acute solanine poisoning. Poisoning has occurred both from berries (usually green) and from grazing the plant. As an annual weed, *Solanum nigrum* may invade forage crops which have not formed solid stands. Grazing of infested oat stubble has resulted in serious loss (168, 264). The green weed will be eaten in preference to the dry stubble.

Solanum pseudocapsicum L. Jerusalem cherry

This species is a common pot plant, much in evidence around Christmas and prized for its ornamental bright red berries. It has a long-established reputation for toxicity, but no clear cases are on record. Nevertheless solanaceous alkaloids have been isolated from it and it would be wise to caution children not to eat the berries. The review by Hurst may be consulted (810).

Solanum rostratum Dunal. Buffalo bur, Kansas or Texas thistle

Annual spiny weed, 1 to 2 ft tall. Leaves variable in size and shape, irregularly round-lobed, or once or twice pinnately deeply lobed, veins spiny. Flowers yellow; calyx densely covered with long spines, persistent, completely enclosing the berry, hence forming an oblong spiny bur. Native to the Great Plains, introduced and locally abundant eastward, and on the Pacific coast.

This species is considered normally unattractive to animals because of its spiny nature. The burs may produce mechanical injury. Simic (1454) has described a case of poisoning in hogs in which the animals readily ate this plant although other adequate feed was available. Hogs have also been poisoned after eating the roots which had been unearthed (257). In Simic's experience, severe enteritis with hemorrhage and ulceration was found on post mortem examination.

Solanum sodomeum L. Apple of Sodom, popolo

A shrubby, spiny, purple-flowered, yellow-fruited weed, native to the Mediterranean region, introduced and now common in Hawaii. This species has a general reputation of toxicity. Arnold (42) has recorded an instance of serious, but nonfatal, poisoning in a child in Hawaii.

Solanum torreyi Gray

Spiny perennial shrub. Leaves ovate, cordate; margins sinuate to lobed. Flowers violet. Berry yellow, about 1 in. in diameter. Prairies, Texas, and south-central states.

Experimental feedings with sheep have shown this species only mildly toxic (158). Symptoms were produced with green fruit at 3 per cent of the animal's weight, but were not produced with ripe fruit.

Fig. 74. Nightshades. Left, *Solanum rostratum*. Buffalo bur. Flowering branches. Right, *S. eleagnifolium*. Silverleaf nightshade. Plant in natural habitat.

Solanum triflorum Nutt. Three-flowered or cutleaf nightshade

Annual herb, stems often reclining, ½ to 1½ ft long. Leaves pinnately narrow-lobed. Flowers white. Berry green or yellowish, about ½ in. in diameter. Native to the prairies, now common as a weed of cultivation, disturbed soils, and waste areas, Minnesota to British Columbia, south to Oklahoma and California, locally elsewhere.

Horses and cattle have been poisoned by this species in the Middle West (1230). Experiments with laboratory animals (275) have proved its toxicity, and pharmacological investigations (1641) have demonstrated the presence and toxicity of solanaceous alkaloids. The berries of this plant are not easily separated from peas in commercial pea-canning operations. If present, the product is condemned for human consumption.

Solanum tuberosum L. Potato

Loss of life in livestock after ingestion of potato vines, sprouts, or peelings or of sunburned or spoiled potatoes has occurred with some frequency in North America (145, 257, 277, 705, 706, 708, 951), and human fatalities are not unknown here (705) and elsewhere (723). Solanine distribution in the plant has been investigated. Solanine concentration is greatest in green parts. The sprouts and sun-greened skin of the tuber are especially high. In the normal tuber, the peelings contain the major portion of solanine. Wholesome potato tubers contain about 0.009 per cent solanine. Those containing 0.04 per cent have been associated with outbreaks of poisoning (61). The symptoms and lesions are those of acute solanine poisoning. "Food rash" and other symptoms have been associated with potato poisoning in Europe (373). The toxicity of spoiled potatoes may be due in part to the activity of bacteria or fungi.

The great majority of cases of potato poisoning result from feeding sprouted, spoiled, or sun-greened potatoes, sprouts, or peelings to poultry or livestock in ignorance of the potential toxicity. Poisoning also has resulted from ingestion of vines or cull potatoes left in the field. Cooking in water tends to leach out, and perhaps destroy, the poisonous principle and may render safe what would have produced poisoning otherwise, but poisoning has occurred occasionally when cooked material was fed. Sprouts should never be fed or consumed under any circumstances, but potatoes from which they have been carefully removed should prove wholesome. Greened potatoes should be discarded or pared to remove all green tissue before use. It is common practice to cook potatoes to be used as animal feed.

Solanum villosum Mill. Hairy nightshade

Closely related to *S. nigrum,* differing in its densely hairy, smaller, foliage and yellow or red berry. Locally common in eastern states and Utah, occasional elsewhere, as an annual weed.

Pharmacological investigation of this species (667, 1641) has demonstrated the presence and toxicity of solanaceous alkaloids.

Solanum melongena L. Eggplant

Contains solanaceous alkaloids and has long had a reputation for toxicity, although supporting cases are absent. Nevertheless, eggplant vines should not be made available to livestock until proved nontoxic.

Order Lamiales

Verbenaceae

Aloysia lycioides Cham. (= *Lippia ligustrina* Britt.). Whitebrush
DESCRIPTION. Graceful, aromatic shrub, 3 to 10 ft tall. Leaves lanceolate, obtuse, pale beneath, $\frac{1}{4}$ to 1 in. long; small and entire on flowering branches, larger and toothed or incised on vigorous sterile stems. Inflorescence an open, leafy panicle; flowers very small, zygomorphic, white, sometimes with purple, fragrant.

DISTRIBUTION AND HABITAT. Common on rocky slopes in southern Arizona, Texas, and Mexico.

POISONOUS PRINCIPLE. Unknown. Water extracts possess toxicity to laboratory animals.

TOXICITY, SYMPTOMS, AND LESIONS, AND CONDITIONS OF POISONING. This plant had been suspected of being toxic to horses by ranchers in Texas. They attributed lack of stamina, emaciation, lameness or ataxia, and excessive sweating to browsing on this species. Feeding experiments were undertaken at the Texas Agricultural Experiment Station (1051) to substantiate or disprove these opinions. Horses, goats, a sheep, a calf, and an ass were confined in an area where whitebrush was the only available feed. Results were not clear-cut partly because of the small number of animals used. The sheep and goats not only evidenced no signs of toxicity, but thrived on a whitebrush diet over a period greater than 3 months. The calf was removed in an emaciated condition after about 3 months, but was somewhat emaciated at the start of the experiment. The ass became emaciated and died in 3½ months without having displayed any toxic symptoms.

Only the horses showed nervous symptoms in addition to emaciation. Symptoms of ataxia, weakness, paralysis, and prostration developed sequentially beginning about a month and a half after access to whitebrush, and terminated in death about a week after appearance of definite nervous symptoms.

On post mortem examination of the experimental horses, albuminous and fatty degenerative changes were found in liver and kidney. Edema between the pia mater and brain tissue was held responsible for the nervous symptoms; no other lesions were found in the nervous system.

Evidence from treatment of laboratory animals with plant extracts, from lack of certain characteristics in the horse lesions, and from the observed fact that whitebrush was extensively grazed supported the conclusion that emaciation was not simply the result of starvation.

The closely related South African species, *Lippia rehmanni* Pears., produces hepatogenic photosensitization. Two nearly identical polycyclic triterpenoids have been isolated and identified (76, 77, 1344). One, rehmannic acid, conveys toxicity (180) and is identical with the hepatogenic photosensitizing substance (lantadene A) in *Lantana*.

Duranta repens L. Golden dewdrop

This shrub or small tree of southern peninsular Florida contains a saponic poisonous principle. Its fruits are reputed to have caused illness and death among children, and the plant has been suspected in cases of livestock poisoning in Australia (1653).

Lantana camara L. Lantana

DESCRIPTION, DISTRIBUTION, AND HABITAT. Perennial shrub in central and southern Florida, herbaceous perennial further north, and a greenhouse plant, treated as a summer annual, in flower gardens of the northern United States and Canada. This species has been troublesome so far only in the South and in California where it has been planted widely as an ornamental and has escaped cultivation. It is particularly common south of Orlando, Florida, and may be found as a shrub persisting where no longer cultivated; also in fencerows, along ditch banks, and in fields. As a shrub it reaches 3 to 5 ft. Stem and branches square, bearing sparse and irregularly scattered weak spines. Leaves opposite or in whorls of threes, petioled, ovate, crenate-dentate, 1 to 5 in. long, aromatic when crushed. Inflorescences axillary, showy, long-stalked, flat-topped dense clusters, 1 to 2 in. across; flowers small, tubular, with four spreading lobes, yellow or pink when opening, changing to orange or bright red. Fruit a greenish-blue or black, fleshy, one-seeded drupe, about ¼ in. in diameter.

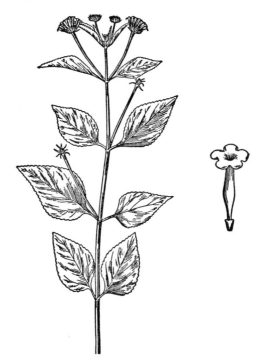

Fig. 75. *Lantana camara.* Lantana. Plant, with detail of flower. Courtesy of The Macmillan Company.

POISONOUS PRINCIPLE. A crystalline material, to which the name lantanin was given, was isolated by alcoholic extraction of the leaves of *Lantana* in South Africa (937). This substance produces characteristic symptoms when given orally to animals. It was renamed lantadene A (938) and chemically identified (78) as a polycyclic triterpenoid identical in structure with rehmannic acid, the active principle (180) in *Lippia.* Lantadene B, a closely related molecule (79, 938) also isolated from *Lantana,* is apparently physiologically inactive (938). The total amounts and relative proportions of lantadenes A and B in *Lantana* are subject to wide variation (78).

TOXICITY, SYMPTOMS, AND LESIONS. *Lantana camara* has been found toxic to sheep and cattle in Australia, South Africa, and the United States. Good circumstantial evidence leads to the belief that the berries have proven toxic and even lethal to children in the United States.

In livestock, it is a hepatogenic photosensitizer and also produces symptoms and lesions of severe gastroenteritis. Natural cases in cattle have been described from Florida (1385, 1386), Georgia (1071) and California (1318). Depending on the amount of plant consumed, and (under some circumstances) the intensity of light striking poisoned animals, the poisoning may take either an acute or chronic course. Experimental feedings (1385, 1386, 1536) have shown that *Lantana* is quite toxic. A dose of ¾ to 1 lb of the dry leaves was found sufficient to produce chronic poisoning in a 400-lb bovine, for a toxicity, green-weight basis, of about 1 per cent. In South Africa, Steyn and Van Der Walt (1536) produced the acute syndrome in a sheep, with death in five days, by feeding fresh *Lantana* at about 2 per cent of the animal's weight.

In either case, acute or chronic, symptoms appear in a day from ingestion of a toxic dose. In the acute syndrome they consist of severe gastroenteritis, bloody, watery feces, weakness, and death in 3 to 4 days. These may be accompanied by conjunctivitis and reddening of the muzzle, and by icterus in the later stages. In the more common chronic syndrome, less toxic principle is consumed, the animal lives longer, and signs of typical photosensitization develop if the animal is exposed to sunlight. These may vary from very mild to very severe. Signs and lesions of photosensitization have been discussed elsewhere (see photosensitization, p. 52). In mild cases lesions of photosensitization are confined to unpigmented or white areas of the animal. In severe cases pigmented areas also become involved. In relatively severe cases of *Lantana* poisoning in cattle, lesions extend from the muzzle into the mouth and nostrils, and consist of ulceration of cheeks, tongue, and gums and of swelling, hardening, and peeling of the mucous membranes and deeper tissues in the nostrils. The latter gives rise to dyspnea; the former impedes feeding. These lesions may be partially due to photosensitization and partially, perhaps, to the irritant nature of the plant. Secondary complications found in chronic cases include conjunctivitis, severe constipation, blow-fly and bacterial invasions of raw surfaces, matted eyelids, corneal opacity and blindness, and avoidance of light. Death often results after emaciation, or as the result of other secondary complications.

Post mortem examination reveals in all instances a highly pigmented liver which has undergone obvious degenerative changes. Lesions of gastroenteritis and evidences of stasis are also found. Icterus, subcutaneous and general edema, and hemorrhages in some organs usually occur in chronic cases, in addition to the obvious primary and secondary lesions of photosensitization.

Lantana poisoning of children has not yet been well documented. Cases in which *Lantana* berries have been recovered from the stools have been acute, characterized by extreme muscular weakness and circulatory collapse (1168, 1621). Children less severely poisoned have displayed mainly signs of gastrointestinal irritation. No characteristic lesions were found on post mortem examination of one fatal case.

CONDITIONS OF POISONING. *Lantana* growing inconspicuously in pastures has produced the majority of cases in beef and dairy cattle in the Southeast. In the case cited which occurred in California, clippings from a hedge of *Lantana* thrown into a pasture were the source of poisoning.

Additional species of *Lantana* have been found toxic, in Australia particularly (78, 1536). In Florida, the species *L. aculeata* L., *L. ovatifolia* Britton, and *L. sellowiana* Link & Otto are thought (1661) probably to have a toxicity equal to that of *L. camara*.

Additional references: 810.

Labiatae

Glechoma hederacea L. [= *Nepeta hederacea* (L.) Trev.]. Ground ivy, gill-over-the-ground, creeping Charlie

DESCRIPTION. Prostrate perennial herb forming a ground cover over greater or lesser areas, often to the almost complete exclusion of other vegetation. Stems prostrate, square, jointed, bearing leaves in pairs at the joints and rooted at the joints. Leaves opposite, orbicular, crenate, petioled, 1 to 2 in. across. Flowers small, blue, borne in leaf axils, inconspicuous; flowering from sping to early summer.

DISTRIBUTION AND HABITAT. A common weed of shaded moist areas. Introduced from Europe. Present throughout most of the United States and Canada, common in the northern states and Canada.

POISONOUS PRINCIPLE. The mints contain a variety of volatile oils which are physiologically active in moderate to large amounts. It has been

Fig. 76. *Glechoma hederacea.* Ground ivy. Plant
showing creeping habit, with detail of flower.
Courtesy of The Macmillan Company.

assumed that activity of this sort is responsible for the toxicity of ground
ivy.

TOXICITY, SYMPTOMS, AND LESIONS. Ground ivy, on various evidence,
has for many years been considered poisonous to horses in several European
countries (933). Some of the cases are well described and leave little
doubt that ground ivy has been responsible for mortality in the horse. A
single case has been reported from this side of the Atlantic (Prince Edward
Island) and resulted in the death of two horses (592).

Symptoms include salivation, sweating, dyspnea, panting, dilation of
the pupils, and sometimes signs of pulmonary edema. In the Prince Edward
Island case deaths occurred after five and eight days.

CONDITIONS OF POISONING. The plant is toxic if ingested in large
amounts either fresh or in hay. It has not been reported to have caused
trouble in animals other than horses.

Lamium amplexicaule L. Henbit, dead nettle

This very common weed of eastern North America and the Pacific
Coast has been incriminated in, and found experimentally responsible for,
cases of staggers in sheep, horses, and cattle in Queensland. No instances of
poisoning have been reported in North America (810).

Salvia reflexa Hornem. (= *S. laciniata* Willd.). Annual sage, mintweed

DESCRIPTION. Annual bushy weed, 6 in. to 2 ft tall. Stems angled;
branching pattern opposite. Leaves opposite, lanceolate to nearly linear,
short-petioled, to 2 in. long. Inflorescence an interrupted spike; flowers
opposite or 3 in an apparent whorl, blue, strongly zygomorphic, two-lipped;
lips of corolla spreading, the upper half as long as the lower.

DISTRIBUTION AND HABITAT. Relatively common weed of dry open
lands, Wisconsin to Montana, south to Texas and Mexico; less common
eastward to New Jersey.

Fig. 77. *Salvia lanciniata.* Annual sage. Courtesy of The Macmillan Company.

POISONOUS PRINCIPLE. This species has caused severe loss of life in Australian livestock (810, 836). Analyses of Australian material have shown it high in nitrate content, and symptoms agree with a diagnosis of nitrate poisoning. In the United States, this mint has caused loss of life in cattle. The symptoms do not agree well with those of nitrate poisoning.

TOXICITY, SYMPTOMS, AND LESIONS. Loss of life in cattle after ingestion of alfalfa hay containing a large amount of annual sage was definitely traced to the sage by feeding experiments with sheep performed at the Wyoming Agricultural Experiment Station (97). In affected cattle, symptoms appeared quickly and deaths occurred within a day. Symptoms consisted chiefly of muscular weakness. Intense inflammation of the gastrointestinal tract was found as the major lesion.

Stachys arvensis L. Fieldnettle
Stachys arvensis is a weed of local distribution in New England, New York, and Pennsylvania. Abundant field experience in Australia, supported by experimental feedings, has shown this species responsible for a nervous syndrome (intermittent staggering) in livestock, especially in sheep. Although the plant is widely distributed, its toxicity has not been reported in any other country (810).

Order Scrophulariales

Scrophulariaceae

Castilleja spp. Paint brushes
Various species of this genus are secondary or facultative selenium absorbers (1591). (See p. 45.)

Digitalis purpurea L. Foxglove
The common garden foxglove, introduced from Europe, is familiar to most persons. It is easily recognized by its raceme of pendant zygomorphic,

tubular, showy purple or white flowers, each conspicuously spotted on the inside bottom surface of the tube. Several species and several horticultural varieties of *D. purpurea* are found in cultivation. The purple-flowered variety of *D. purpurea* is naturalized and locally common in open rich lands, logged-off areas, and roadsides from British Columbia to northern California.

Digitalis purpurea has been known as the source of physiologically active materials from very early times. It contains a number (about a dozen, of which five are well known) of chemically and physiologically related cardiac or steroid glycosides. Chemically the aglycones are derivatives of cyclopentenophenanthrene and the sugars are unique methyl

digitoxigenin (6, 1103), the aglycone of digitoxin, considered the most important of the digitalis glycosides

pentoses. Physiologically they exert a twofold influence on the heart. They strengthen the force of contraction and, through stimulation of the vagus, slow it, prolonging the duration of diastole. The aglycone is the active substance, but in contradistinction to most glycosides, the sugar is physiologically important, primarily in imparting greatly increased solubility to the molecule. Because of its great value in human medicine, digitalis and the principles that it contains have been intensively studied. Reviews of the pertinent facts may be found in texts on pharmacology.

Poisoning in human beings results from overdoses of the drugs. Symptoms include nausea, diarrhea, and abdominal pain, gross disturbances in heartbeat and pulse, various mental irregularities or drowsiness, or tremors and even convulsions.

Poisoning in animals usually results from ingestion of the plant fresh or in hay. Poisoning is uncommon since the plant is not normally consumed. Foxglove was suspected in poisonings of Canadian pigs and cattle (183). Several cases are on record in Europe. The earlier literature has been reviewed by Long (933) and Craig and Kehoe (373). Recently, cases have been reported by Clec'h (304) and Parker (1248). Horses, cattle, pigs, and turkeys have been poisoned.

Cornevin's experiments, reported in 1887 (334), are usually cited for the toxicity of the fresh leaves. He found them to be highly toxic, only

Fig. 78. *Digitalis purpurea.* Foxglove. Flowering stalk, with details of a basal leaf, floral construction, and fruit. Courtesy of The Macmillan Company.

a few hundredths per cent of an animal's weight being lethal. Ruminants appear somewhat less succeptible than nonruminants.

Symptoms are variable but in general similar to those listed above for the human being. Commonly noticed are signs of gastric distress, including bloody stools; drowsiness, lack of appetite, frequent attempts at urination, abnormal urine, and symptoms associated with the cardiac effects of the glycosides.

Abrus precatorius. Precatory bean, photograph of seeds. Use of this illustration has been made possible by the Merck Sharp & Dohme Research Laboratories.

Post mortem examination shows congestion throughout the veinous circulation, greatly distended heart auricles, and a variable amount of gastrointestinal inflammation (373).

Toxicity of digitalis is not lost upon drying or boiling, and hay containing the plant has proven lethal.

Order Rosales

Leguminosae

Abrus precatorius L. Crabs-eye, precatory bean, rosary pea, jequirity bean

DESCRIPTION. Twining, perennial vine, climbing on other plants to a height of 10 to 20 ft. Stems green when young, gray-barked in older portions. Leaves alternate, compound, opposite-pinnate; leaflets 8 to 15 pairs, about ½ in. long, oblong. Inflorescences numerous, in leaf axils along stems, racemose, 1 to 3 in. long; flowers many, small, red to purple. Fruit a legume pod, 1½ in. long, or less, covered with fine, appressed hairs, containing many seeds. The seeds are a distinctive feature of the plant and are the most dangerous part. Each is ovoid, about ⅜ in. long, bright glossy scarlet with jet black. The black marking covers about a third of the seed, including the scar of attachment, and appears as though one tip of the seed had been dipped obliquely into black enamel.

DISTRIBUTION AND HABITAT. A common vine of tropical countries, where its toxic properties have long been known and put to use in legal and illegal ways; introduced into the United States, and now found as a weed of fencerows, citrus groves, and elsewhere in central and southern Florida. Occasionally cultivated as a screening vine or for the seeds, which are made into rosaries and necklaces or other decorations.

POISONOUS PRINCIPLE. The phytotoxin, abrin. The seeds also contain additional physiologically active principles.

TOXICITY, SYMPTOMS, AND LESIONS. Abrin, contained in the seeds, is one of the most potent toxic principles known. Less than one seed, if thoroughly masticated, is sufficient to kill an adult human being (toxicity, therefore, is about 0.00015 per cent of the subject's weight of seed by ingestion). The hard seed coat, if unbroken, retains most of the toxic principle. Abrin, once released from the seed, is not easily absorbed through the uninjured intestinal wall. If extracted and injected into the bloodstream it has a toxicity of the order of magnitude of a few millionths per cent (279, 1461). Few materials of any kind exceed this toxicity. Abrin is a severe irritant of mucous membrane, especially the conjunctiva, a fact sometimes used in tests separating it from ricin, the phytotoxin of castor bean (*Ricinus*). In the adult horse (1461), ½ oz. of powdered seed produces symptoms and 2 oz. (roughly 0.0062 per cent) is lethal. Cattle, goats, and dogs are relatively more resistant.

Symptoms are those of severe gastrointestinal irritation. In the horse, after a latent period, loss of appetite, violent purging, elevation followed by depression of temperature, and finally incoordination and paralysis are observed. Lesions include petechial hemorrhages throughout the body, inflammation and ulceration of the digestive tract, congestion of lungs, kidneys, liver, intestines, and bladder, swelling of mesenteric lymph nodes, and enlargement of the spleen. Histopathology has been detailed by Steyn (1533) and includes coagulation of erythrocytes with formation of small thrombi.

Specific immunity may be conferred by treatment with increasing small amounts of abrin (by injection or orally). By continued feeding of amounts increasing from ¼ oz. daily over 2½ months, Simpson and Benerjee (1461) were able to establish a degree of immunity in which 2 oz. of powdered seed could be fed to a horse without producing symptoms.

Additional references: 272, 473, 1136, 1322, 1660.

Acacia berlandieri Benth. Guajillo

DESCRIPTION. Perennial shrub or small tree, to 15 ft. Leaves alternate, twice pinnate, the first divisions of 3 to 9 pairs oppositely inserted, the second divisions (leaflets) 24 to 45 pairs oppositely inserted; leaflets about ¼ in. long. Flowers in dense groups, axillary, leguminous, white to yellow and sweet scented. Fruit a legume, flattened, 4 to 6 times as long as wide with somewhat thickened margins, obvious at maturity scattered amongst the foliage.

DISTRIBUTION AND HABITAT. Range land, southwestern Texas into Mexico. It may be the dominant plant in certain areas.

POISONOUS PRINCIPLE. The amine, N-methyl-β-phenylethylamine (227).

TOXICITY, SYMPTOMS, AND LESIONS. Feeding trials with sheep and goats have established (159, 228) that large amounts of leaves and fruits (around 15 times the animal's weight) consumed over a period of several months produce symptoms of ataxia ("limber leg" or "guajillo wobbles") and possibly death. Range experience is in agreement. Animals remain alert with normal appetite. Ataxia develops most commonly in the hind legs, but occasionally also in the front legs. Severe ataxia, especially marked when animals are excited, leads to prostration. If fed, prostrated animals may remain alive for several weeks. On the range, therefore, many deaths may be attributed to starvation or thirst. No significant lesions have been found.

Some of the toxicological effect of the poisonous principle may be, as in the case of the related ephedrine, the result of competition for and inactivation of monoamine oxidase, the normal function of which is oxidation of sympathomimetic amines such as epinephrine, preventing their excessive activity in the properly functioning body (226).

Poisoning by *Acacia georginae* F. M. Bail. has been reported (102) in

Australia, but the toxic principle is fluoroacetic acid (1190, 1671).

CONDITIONS OF POISONING. In areas where this plant is plentiful, it is readily grazed and may constitute the major portion of the diet, or even the entire diet. Over short periods of time it furnishes nutritionally adequate and desirable feed. However, cases appear in 6 to 9 months on such a diet. Mortality generally is low, but in drought years has reached 50 per cent. Uneventful recovery may be expected within a few months if affected animals are moved to better range.

A species of *Acacia* identified by the common name "catclaw" (probably *A. greggii* Gray) is considered (40) potentially lethal in the limestone area of Arizona. Cases occur in the fall at or near the time of first frost. Its high cyanide content is held responsible. Several foreign species of *Acacia* are known to contain dangerous amounts of a cyanogenetic glycoside (227). The toxic amine of *A. berlandieri* is chemically related to amygdalin, the cyanogenetic glycoside of the Rosaceae.

Additional references: 810, 1296.

Arachis hypogaea L. Peanut, groundnut.

About a year before the completion of this book much interest was generated in peanut meal as a potentially toxic feedstuff when it was shown in Britain that diets incorporating imported peanut meal from certain sources were responsible for "turkey X disease". A flurry of papers appearing during the year (see 17) has established that poisoning has occurred in turkey poults, chickens, ducklings, cattle, hogs, and experimentally in laboratory animals. Toxic meal has been identified in shipments from all the major geographical sources. Conversion of normally non-toxic meal to toxic has been ascribed to the activities of a fungus, *Aspergillus flavus* Link ex Fries. The toxic principle, which may also be produced by the fungus on substrates other than peanuts, has been named aflatoxin (1340).

Symptoms and lesions are those associated with severe liver damage similar in most respects to that produced by pyrrolizidine (senecio) alkaloids. Hill has discussed (773) the comparative pathology. Young animals are generally more susceptible to poisoning from a given exposure than are older animals.

The disease is currently under active investigation. Most cases have been reported from Britain, but poisoning of broiler chickens has occurred in eastern Canada from peanut meal of Brazilian origin (39), and some experimental work has been done with Canadian fowl (600).

Additional reference: 16.

Astragalus spp. Milk vetches, poisonvetches, locoweeds
Oxytropis spp. Point locoweeds, pointvetches

Some botanists estimate there are as many as 300 species of *Astragalus,* making this genus the largest of the legume family (Leguminosae) in North

America. Their taxonomy and identification are difficult. Even with a specimen in hand, it is often difficult for a trained botanist to identify an unknown *Astragalus* to species. *Oxytropis* is distinguished from *Astragalus* on the basis of characteristics that normally would hardly serve to separate species. Because of this, some botanists treat the species of *Oxytropis* as species of *Astragalus*. In any case, the taxonomy within that group of species which may be set off under the name *Oxytropis* also is uncertain. Some of the present confusion concerning the toxicity of species of *Astragalus* and *Oxytropis* can be eliminated if published reports dealing with any aspect of their toxicity are accompanied by reference to the botanist making the determination of the experimental or field material and the deposition of labeled representative specimens in an accessible herbarium.

DESCRIPTION. Species of *Astragalus* are mostly perennial stemmed or stemless herbs growing from woody underground parts. Leaves are alternate and pinnately compound (although in some the leaflets are reduced to 1). Flowers are leguminous, few to many, in axillary racemes. Fruit is a legume pod of various sizes, shapes, and surfaces among the species, containing one to many kidney-shaped seeds. *Oxytropis* may be distinguished from *Astragalus* by the fact that in the former the keel (lowermost petal) is prolonged into a long, distinct point (whence the common name, point vetch or point loco). The keel petal of *Astragalus* is blunt.

SYNDROMES OF ASTRAGALUS POISONING. Some species of *Astragalus* and *Oxytropis* are not toxic under any circumstances, and many of these are desirable forage or soil-building plants. Of those that are toxic, at least three groups may be recognized:

I. *Selenium.* Many closely related species of *Astragalus* (but none of *Oxytropis* as far as known) possess the ability to accumulate selenium. Because they grow only where selenium is present in the soil and always contain selenium at some stage in their growth, they are termed obligate selenophiles or selenium indicator plants. The common name, poisonvetch, has been suggested for seleniferous species of *Astragalus* to distinguish them from locoweeds. Twenty-one obligate selenium species are listed by Trelease and Beath. The names of these species and a discussion of toxicity, symptoms, and lesions of selenium poisoning will be found on p. 47, 48. It has not been established that selenium is the sole toxic compound in seleniferous species. Many obligate selenium plants are not toxic under range conditions because animals do not eat them. Among the most troublesome are *Astragalus bisulcatus, A. racemosus, A. pectinatus,* and *A. pattersonii.*

II. *Loco.* Long before 1873, when it first received formal attention by the Commissioner of Agriculture, a disease of stock termed loco had been recognized. Loco was not clearly characterized until the investigations of Marsh firmly established the symptoms and its etiology. It is now known to occur in the Rocky Mountain states westward, south into Texas and Mexico, and north into British Columbia. The name derives from the Spanish word for crazy and is applied because of the characteristic symptoms. Plants causing loco in horses, cattle, sheep, and goats on range constitute one of the more serious sources of domestic livestock loss. Their identity only slowly has emerged, and the exact nature of the toxic principle or principles they contain is still in large part obscure. Reasons for this do not include lack of investigation. The early history of loco poisoning has been reviewed by Crawford (377), Marsh (982), and Marshall (1025).

The following species of *Astragalus* and *Oxytropis* are true locoweeds— that is, they produce the symptoms characteristic of loco poisoning. It is unlikely that the list is complete.

Astragalus mollissimus Torr. (purple loco, wooly loco). Southwest South Dakota south to Texas and New Mexico (1005).

A. lentiginosus Dougl. (speckled loco). Washington to Idaho, Utah, and California (220, 1288).

A. diphysus Gray [= *A. lentiginosus* var. *diphysus* (Gray) Jones] (blue loco, rattleweed). New Mexico, Arizona, Nevada, and Utah (1005).

A. earlei Greene ex Rydb. (Earle loco). Big Bend area of Texas, New Mexico, and Mexico (1005, 1033).

A. wootonii Sheld. (Wooton loco) (annual). New Mexico, Arizona, and southwest Texas, into Mexico (1005, 1033).

A. nothoxys Gray (sheep loco). Southeast Arizona and New Mexico into Mexico (1005).

A. thurberi Gray (Thurber loco). Southeast Arizona and New Mexico into Mexico (1005).

A. argillophilus Cory (halfmoon loco). West Texas (336, 1005).

Oxytropis lambertii Pursh. (White loco, white point loco, stemless loco). Western Canada, Montana, North Dakota, and Western Minnesota south to Arizona, New Mexico, and Texas (1005).

O. sericea Nutt. ex Torr. & Gray [= *O. lambertii* var. *sericea* (Nutt. ex Torr. & Gray) A. Gray] (white loco, white point loco). Distribution similar to the above but including Idaho (1288).

Descriptions of each species may be found in the references cited.

A third species, *O. saximontana* A. Nels., has been cited as a locoweed. There is intergradation and probably hybridization (1288) among the locoweed species of *Oxytropis*. Some authorities (856) consider all three to be distinct species. Others (97, 1288) consider that *O. sericea* = *O. saximontana*. It is likely that in poisonous-plants literature, the names *O. saximontana* and *O. sericea* have been used synonymously (97, 585), the latter to be preferred. The white loco of Marsh (982), identified as *O. lambertii,* is probably (220) *O. sericea.* An older synonym from the genus *Oxytropis* that will be found in the earlier loco literature is *Aragallus.*

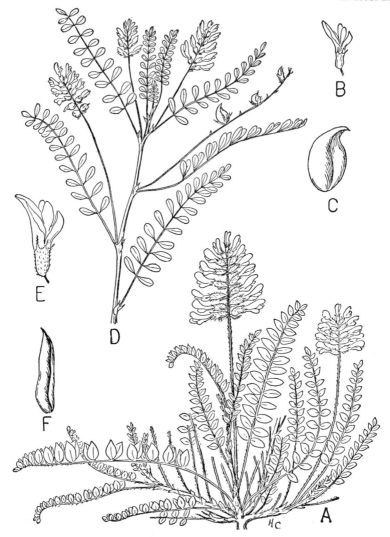

Fig. 79. *Astragalus spp.* Locoweeds. A-C, *A. mollissimus*. Purple loco. Plant, with details of flower and fruit. D-F, *A. diphysus*. Blue loco. Branch, with details of flower and fruit. Courtesy of The Macmillan Company.

Oxytropis besseyi Blank. and *O. condensata* A. Nels. are considered locos in Wyoming (97).

POISONOUS PRINCIPLE. Barium was proposed as the toxic principle in 1908; this has since been disproved. Other early attempts to isolate a poisonous principle were not successful. Some persons even denied its

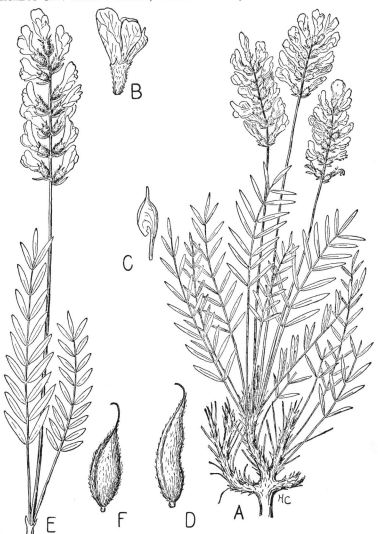

Fig. 80. *Oxytropis spp.* Locoweeds. A-D, *O. lambertii*. White loco. Plant, with detail of flower, characteristically pointed keel petal, and fruit. E-F, *O. sericea*. White loco. Details of leaves, inflorescence, and fruit. Courtesy of The Macmillan Company.

existence, ascribing the production of symptoms to a combination of starvation and parasitic infection. In 1929 Couch (348) isolated a nitrogen-containing but nonbasic fraction from *O. lambertii* but was unable to precipitate it. In 1936, a substance isolated from *A. earlei* was shown (584) to produce symptoms typical of loco. It gave a positive test with many of the standard alkaloidal reagents but did not meet all the characteristics of an alkaloid. The substance was named "locoine." Since that time, a number of investigations have been made (270, 524, 585) which more closely characterize but still do not identify the toxic principle.

TOXICITY, SYMPTOMS, AND LESIONS. A locoweed must be grazed for some time before symptoms are evident. The amount of locoweed necessary to produce symptoms or death varies with species of loco, species of animal, and among individual animals. The most numerous and recent experimental data concern *A. earlei* and *A. wootonii*. Within limits these data may be extrapolated to other locoweeds. It has been shown experimentally, and verified under natural range conditions, that symptoms appear in cattle and sheep after ingestion of about 90 per cent of the animal's weight of locoweed during a period of about two months. Death will result from ingestion of about 320 per cent of the animal's weight over three months. Horses are much more susceptible. Death follows ingestion of about 30 per cent of the animal's weight over a month and a half. In range terms, symptoms in sheep and cattle typically appear in 6 to 8 weeks, and death in an additional 4 to 6 weeks if the diet is not changed.

Symptoms develop from involvement of sensory and motor innervations. They differ somewhat among species of animals. In cattle, the head is carried a little lower than normal at first, later accompanied by a vacant stare, perhaps due to distorted vision. Locomotor ataxia appears and becomes pronounced as the disease progresses. Trembling of the head and difficulty or inability to eat and drink are observed. Abortion is common, especially in poisoning by southwestern locoweeds. Sheep display extreme cerebral depression, together with locomotor ataxia and inability to eat or drink in advanced cases. Goats develop an ascending paralysis which becomes increasingly severe, eventually involving the forelegs. Trembling of the head and terminal opisthotonus are frequently observed. In the horse the time between onset of symptoms and death is much shorter. The horse, listless in appearance, will not notice ordinary activities, but on being stimulated by some sudden event will become excessively excited and wild. Locomotor ataxia appears and increases in severity with time. This combination may result in an unsuccessful attempt to rear, the horse falling on its haunches instead. The final stages are characterized by inability to eat or drink and by locomotor paralysis. Horses in the early stages of loco poisoning are dangerous to ride or drive.

Lesions are not spectacular. About the only constant finding is ulceration of the abomasum, especially about the pyloric orifice. A generalized edematous condition, characteristic of emaciation, is often observed. In pregnant cattle, there is extensive edema of the fetal membranes with large quantities of amniotic fluid. "Water belly" is a symptom of locoed cattle sometimes reported by ranchers, and abortion is common. On microscopic examination, transitory edematous vacuolization of brain cells may be observed, followed later by the degeneration and eventual fragmentation of the cells of Golgi. This appears to be the most specific lesion in loco poisoning. In experimental work with cats it has been shown (524) that severance of the spinal cord of a severely locoed animal in the cervical region releases the limbs from their paralyzed, atactic condition, suggesting that the primary site of action of the toxin is in the cranial centers, probably of the cerebrum.

CONDITIONS OF POISONING. Locoweeds are unusual in that animals at first find them distasteful, but all classes of livestock may, if led to eating them by hunger, develop an eventual craving for them. Locoed animals seek out locoweeds from among other palatable forage. Considerable variation exists among animals in the ease with which craving may be developed. Sometimes recovered animals will retain an appetite for loco. Sometimes the appetite may be transferred from one loco species to another; sometimes it is not. Slow but uneventful recovery may be expected if locoed animals are removed to range where locoweeds are absent, if the symptoms have not progressed too far.

Bees have been poisoned after working the flowers of "spotted loco." Serious loss has been reported (1428) by the apiarists of Nevada.

III. A third group of species of *Astragalus* is definitely toxic, yet do not produce symptoms characteristic of loco poisoning and do not contain selenium in toxic amounts. The production of locoism requires the ingestion of a large amount of locoweed over an extended period of time. Species listed below, on the contrary, produce poisoning more quickly after ingestion of smaller amounts of plant. Respiratory involvement is absent in loco poisoning but is usually evident in poisonings by these species. While they share some characteristics, these plants have not been shown to contain the same toxic principle.

In 1927, Bruce (183) reported a disease of cattle, sheep, and horses in British Columbia, produced by ingestion of "timber milk vetch" identified as *Astragalus campestris* Gray. In 1932, Beath *et al.* (91) reported on the toxicity in Wyoming of "timber milk vetch" identified as *A. campestris* Gray. [= *A. hylophyllus* (Rydb.) A. Nels.]. In 1936, Newsom *et al.* (1177) reported on the toxicity in Colorado of "timber milk vetch" identified as *A. hylophyllus* (Rydb.). A. Nels. In 1952, MacDonald (961) reported on "timber milk vetch" poisoning in British Columbia naming the plant *A. serotinus* Gray and stating it to be identical with the plant called *A. campestris* Gray by Bruce. The name *A. campestris* Gray is untenable under botanical rules, having been published prior to Gray by Linnaeus for another plant. Other authors (856, 1143) have substituted in its place the name *A. convallarius* Greene. Marsh *et al.* (1005) refer to the *A. campestris* of Bruce as *A. palliseri* Gray and state that this plant is different from the Colorado and Wyoming species, which are considered to be a single plant. If the names here listed do not all refer to the same plant, they refer to two (or possibly three) closely related plants, all of which are locally called "timber milk vetch" and all of which produce similar symptoms in livestock. Descriptions may be found in the references cited.

TOXICITY, SYMPTOMS, AND LESIONS. Symptoms and lesions in cattle and sheep are described by all authors, and in horses by Bruce. They are centered in paralysis with respiratory involvement. In the majority of cases both are apparent, and thus poisoning by these *Astragali* is easily distinguished from loco on the basis of symptoms alone. In some instances it has been shown by chemical analysis that selenium is not involved. Symptoms usually appear in less than a week; in experimental work they have appeared in as little as two days. Range cases in cattle are characterized by poor condition, loss or huskiness of voice, dry or peeling muzzle, and coughing. There is no appetite. Upon being forced to exercise, cattle exhibit roaring or wheezing upon expiration. Incoordination, especially of the hind legs, is observed in cattle, together with a tendency for the hind feet to knock together. This has led to the common name, "cracker-heel disease," in Wyoming. Almost total paralysis may occur if the animal is driven, and sudden death is common.

The picture in sheep is similar but more acute. Symptoms may not be noticed until the animals are driven, whereupon rapid breathing, incoordination, and finally paralysis will develop. In horses, the symptoms are similar but even more acute. Upon being excited, an apparently normal animal quickly develops expiratory roaring, staggering, and salivation. Sudden death from asphyxia may occur.

There are no characteristic lesions. Strong dilation of the pupil has been noted in cattle, and occasionally transitory blindness may develop. Death is common but not certain. Animals recover slowly if taken from the plant soon enough. Incidence of death is spotty within an affected group of animals.

Beath *et al.* (91) report that the toxicity of *A. hylophyllus* correlates with specific geological formations. From the symptoms and this relationship, they suggest that a mineral element other than selenium is the toxic agent. Analyses have been made which show that toxic plants contain an unusually high tin content. They suggest, "It is probable that the presence of this element in organic combination causes the plant at first to exert effects characteristic of the organic compound in question, and that later upon dissociation the metallic ion produces the physiological effect more or less common to all metallic poisons."

Astragalus tetrapterus Gray was reported toxic by Marsh *et al.* (991) in 1920. Their report is not extensive, but serves to indicate that the plant causes loss among both cattle and sheep on the ranges of southern Utah and Western Nevada. Weakness, roughness of coat, staggering, and incoordination of the hind legs were noted in a typical range case in cattle. In preliminary experimental work a steer and a sheep were poisoned. Violent expirations were noted in the case of the steer.

Astragalus emoryanus (Rydb.) Cory has been the subject of extensive investigation in Texas (1048, 1506). It has been shown that this plant, when growing on limestone soils of the Trans-Pecos and on red sandy soils along the Llano River, may be toxic, yet is good forage elsewhere. Sheep, cattle, and goats may be poisoned. Symptoms appear within a few hours to several days after daily ingestion of from 1 to 2 per cent of the animal's weight of plant. Major symptoms include difficulty in breathing and locomotor ataxia, especially of the hind legs. In sheep, inspirations may be audible at distances greater than 100 yd. Goats display terminal opisthotonus. Fatalities are common, and animals that do not succumb tend to make a very slow recovery. Symptoms may persist for more than a year after the animal has ceased to have access to the plant. Characteristic gross or microscopic lesions are absent.

Astragalus sabulosus Jones has been reported (1005) acutely toxic to livestock only in a localized area in New Mexico, although it is found in wider distribution. Its toxicity to sheep has been confirmed experimentally. This plant may accumulate selenium.

Astragalus pubentissimus Torr. & Gray and *A. thompsonae* Wats. of the West, and *A. michauxii* (Kuntze) Hermann of the southeastern United States have experimentally been investigated for toxicity (193, 460) with positive results. In the case of the first two, elevation in serum transaminase activity was associated with development of symptoms and tissue necrosis of liver and kidney in experimental sheep and cattle.

Additional references: 980, 1057.

Baptisia spp. False indigo, baptisia

The older poisonous-plants literature credits *Baptisia* with having caused loss of livestock, especially horses, in hay and pasture. Hansen (713) cites a case of mortality of three cows after consuming hay contaminated with *B. leucantha* Torr. & Gray (wild indigo), a perennial herb of the central United States and Ontario. The plant causes severe diarrhea and anorexia. *Baptisia* is known to contain certain active principles (356, 1217) including quinolizidine alkaloids (1689) and appears in various early lists of medicinal plants.

Additional reference: 609.

Canavalia ensiformis DC. Jack bean

This relatively large bean, native to the West Indies, may occasionally be grown in the southern United States or be imported for livestock feed. It has a record of toxicity in Rhodesia that has been corroborated with experimental work (9, 1451). The seeds were lethal for cattle in amounts greater than about four per cent of the animal's weight. They produced severe diarrhea, weakness, inability to eat or drink, and stiffness. Lesions included dehydration, enteritis, nephritis, and pulmonary emphysema. Podded hay, forage, and bean meal produced poisoning in cattle under natural conditions. Poisoning from this source is not known to have occurred in the United States or Canada.

Cassia spp. Sennas

Senna of commerce (from the tropical species *Cassia fistula* L.) is used medicinally as a cathartic. A number of species found in the United States possess the same or similar active principle and if ingested in some quantity may cause distress and occasionally death in animals.

Cassia lindheimeriana Scheele, of Texas and Arizona, has proven toxic but not fatal to mature sheep when fed experimentally at 5 per cent of the animal's weight over three days (158).

Cassia fasiculata Michx. [= *Chamaecrista fasiculata* (Michx.) Greene] (partridge-pea), with several varieties in the southeastern United States as far north as Massachusetts and South Dakota, has been considered (609) toxic to animals, green, in hay, or by its seeds.

Cassia occidentalis L. (coffee-senna) of waste areas in the southeastern United States is considered (42, 279) weakly toxic.

Cassia tora L. (sicklepod) of the southeastern United States produces seeds which have been reported (641) fatal to quail. It has, however, not proven toxic to poultry in one feeding experiment (111).

Crotalaria spp. Rattlebox, crotalaria

Several species of *Crotalaria* have been proven toxic in the United States. Of the three most commonly mentioned, one is native and was believed toxic in the nineteenth century but has not been reported troublesome since, and two are introduced species which have become increasingly troublesome since 1931 as their agricultural use has grown.

Crotalaria sagittalis L.

DESCRIPTION. Annual (perennial in the southwestern portion of its range), 8 in. to 1½ ft tall, usually much branched. Stems and leaves bearing conspicuous, spreading, whitish hairs. Leaves simple, entire-margined, 1 to 2 in. long; lower leaves oval, upper leaves tending toward linear; hairy on both surfaces and especially along their margins; petioles conspicuously winged, wing tapering towards stem, prolonged into two sharp points at base of blade. Flowers yellow, inconspicuous, ¼ in. long, calyx longer than corolla. Fruits (typical legume pods) ¾ to 1 in. long, becoming black with maturity. Seeds kidney-shaped, flattish, brown, smooth, and shiny, ¹⁄₁₀ in. long. The seeds become detached in the dry, matured pods which rattle when shaken; hence the common name.

DISTRIBUTION AND HABITAT. Scattered populations in various habitats throughout the area bounded by Texas, Florida, southern New England, and South Dakota, but forming extensive stands in the bottom lands of the Missouri and other rivers.

POISONOUS PRINCIPLE. Unknown.

TOXICITY, SYMPTOMS, AND LESIONS. In 1884 Stalker (1509) reported on a disease of horses in the Missouri River Valley and associated it with ingestion of *Crotalaria sagittalis,* a native species, green or in hay. The disease, which had resulted in extensive mortality among horses, was generally known as "bottom disease" because of its localized occurrence on the bottom lands of the valley (108). Horses pastured on uplands seemed immune. Suspecting loco, Stalker made a survey of the pasturage, finding instead of locoweed (*Astragalus*) the related *Crotalaria.* He performed several feeding experiments in which he established that this species fed at 1 per cent of an animal's weight over two days brought death on the second, and that one quart of pods fed daily produced the characteristic stupor in five days and death on the thirteenth in an experimental animal.

Bottom disease of horses was characterized by slow emaciation, weakness, and stupor, and was uniformly fatal in several weeks or a few months after symptoms appeared. Lesions included congestion and hemorrhages in various parts of the body and degenerative changes in liver and spleen. The stomach often was abnormally filled with undigested food.

CONDITIONS OF POISONING. Loss was consistently noted (1692) in horses in pastures containing *C. sagittalis* and invariably in horses fed hay contaminated with this plant. Although Stalker (1509) mentioned that cattle occasionally were poisoned, Williams (1692) observed that cattle, fed hay producing death in horses, were not affected.

Bottom disease was never further defined. At present one cannot be sure that it was even a single disease entity. Even in the nineteenth century it was confused with loco, and some (1066) disbelieved that *Crotalaria sagittalis* was the real cause. One histological examination of livers from horses said to have died from bottom disease disclosed basic differences in the histological pathology among them (1492).

After 1900, bottom disease became less important (perhaps partly because horses were increasingly less used) and the term has been obsolete for many years. *Crotalaraia sagittalis* poisoning seems exclusively a disease of the nineteenth century.

Crotalaria spectabilis Roth (= *C. retzii* Hitchc.)

DESCRIPTION. Dense, erect annual (to perennial) plant, growing to 6 ft, never woody. Stems not hairy. Leaves simple, markedly obovate, the larger to 7 in. long, hairless above, finely hairy beneath; petioles not winged; stipules foliose. Flowers 1 in. long, yellow, tinged with purple or with purple veins; calyx half as long as corolla; inflorescence a showy terminal raceme of 30 to 40 flowers. Fruits (legume pods) about 2 in. long, inflated, hairless, becoming black with maturity, containing about 20 seeds. Seeds $\frac{1}{5}$ in. long, glossy black.

DISTRIBUTION AND HABITAT. Fields and roadsides of the southern states north to Virginia and Missouri. Cultivated as a soil-building green manure crop. Occasionally cultivated as an ornamental.

POISONOUS PRINCIPLE. Neal *et al.,* in 1935, isolated an alkaloid from the seeds, leaves, and stems of this plant, and named it monocrotaline (1170). Adams and coworkers in a series of papers (6, 7) furthered knowledge of the structure of monocrotaline. It is a diester of monocrotalic acid

monocrotaline

and the nitrogen-containing retronecine (919). Pyrrolizidine alkaloids are also found in the poisonous species of *Senecio, Heliotropium, Echium,* and *Trichodesma* (919). The latter does not occur in the United States. Physiological characteristics and lethal doses of the intact alkaloid and retronecine by itself have been investigated (919, 1325). Fundamental action of the pyrrolizidine alkaloids is discussed under *Senecio.* Retronecine has a lethal dose value (LD_{50}) of 634.0 $\pm$ 26.0 mg per kg by intravenous injection in mice. The comparable figure for the intact alkaloid monocrotaline is 261.3 $\pm$ 12.5 mg per kg. The alkaloid is present in greatest amount in seeds, the leaves and stems containing lesser amounts in that order (1273).

Isolation of monocrotaline from the liver of poisoned horses and its identification (by ultraviolet spectroscopy and color reaction with molybdic acid) has been suggested (369) as a method for conclusively differentiating crotalaria poisoning from others similar to it, such as *Senecio* and *Amsinckia* poisoning.

TOXICITY, SYMPTOMS, AND LESIONS. In 1921, the Bureau of Plant Industry began a program of introduction and experimentation with several species of *Crotalaria* as green manure crops for the sandy soils of the Coastal Plain in the Southeast (1077), and for their potentialities as forage and hay crops. Two of these species have proven toxic: *C. spectabilis* and *C. retusa.* The more important and more widely distributed species *C. spectabilis* was first determined toxic in 1931 (1572) and has been extensively investigated since. Toxicity of these species has been reviewed by Becker *et al.* (99).

Crotalaria spectabilis has caused severe loss in fowl, cattle, horses, and swine, and lesser loss in sheep, goats, and mules. Experiments have produced death in the usual laboratory animals including dogs. Depending upon amount ingested, degree of digestion (of seeds), period over which the plant is ingested, and species of animal, the symptoms and lesions vary. In most classes of livestock they have been separated into acute and chronic conditions, but these may intergrade.

In fowl, experimental feedings have shown (1273) that 80 to 160 seeds produce death, with symptoms and lesions of chronic poisoning appearing several weeks or a month or more after ingestion. Death in a few days results from ingestion of 320 seeds. Ingestion of seeds *ad libitum* from scratch feed produced death in just three days in one instance and indicates that the seeds are not always distasteful. In another (1273) the number of seeds ingested similarly *ad libitum* was observed to be 170 before inappetance appeared. Characteristic comb discoloration developed 29 hours later and death followed after 48 hours. Turkeys, however, could not be poisoned with 1000 seeds. Quail were easily poisoned, but refused the seeds under normal conditions. Quantities of *C. spectabilis* seeds as small as 0.2 lb per ton in poultry mash rations may interfere with growth; at 1 per cent they cause 100 per cent mortality, and at 0.1 per cent, 20 per cent mortality (1692).

In acute poisoning of fowl death occurs in 1 to 10 days. The comb becomes congested, dark in color, and scaly. Birds are depressed and display ruffled feathers. A severe greenish-yellow diarrhea may be observed. Post mortem examination reveals a full crop in which crotalaria seeds may be found. There is odor of crushed crotalaria leaves from the carcass. The most striking lesions include petechial hemorrhages of the serous membranes of the abdominal and thoracic cavities, petechiae and suffusions of the visceral fat and of the heart and musculature, and a dark, smaller-than-normal, "marbled" liver. Frequently the liver is ruptured. Massive hemorrhages and ascites may be observed (1601) in somewhat less acute cases.

Chronic poisoning in fowl presents similar symptoms except that as they are extended in time, the comb becomes pale and the birds severely anemic. Lesions observed in chronic poisoning include necrotic enteritis, ascites, partial atrophy of the spleen, and cirrhosis of the liver. The latter may have transudate coagulum adherent.

In cattle, Emmel (493) has recognized three syndromes: acute, chronic, and a third type intermediate in some characteristics. All three are known under natural conditions, but the chronic is by far the more common. In experiments duplicating natural chronic poisoning, it was found (1274) that 55 per cent of a steer's weight of crotalaria hay fed intermittently over a period of 67 days provoked characteristic symptoms which appeared on the

77th day (10 days after the last feeding of crotalaria hay). Death occurred on the 112th day without further crotalaria. On the other hand, 3.2 per cent of an animal's weight of hay fed over four days produced symptoms on the third and death on the fourth day in another experiment (100). A single feeding of 3 lb of seed in one instance was sufficient to produce symptoms of chronic poisoning in cattle (1388).

In the occasional natural acute poisoning, symptoms develop about a day after ingestion of crotalaria (493). Death follows in about four days. Profuse hemorrhages of the serous membranes of the abdominal and thoracic cavities constitute the prominent lesions.

Natural chronic poisoning has been reported by several investigators (100, 493, 1273, 1274, 1388). Symptoms develop within a few days of ingestion to as long as six months after animals have ceased to have access to crotalaria, and are followed by death in one and one-half to two weeks. Loss of appetite is followed by increasingly poor condition, and tenesmus. The animals may be nervous and excitable. Blood is usually noted in the feces three or four days before the animal becomes prostrated and death follows in another 48 hours. A bloody nasal discharge has been observed in some cases. Lesions include widespread hemorrhages, petechial or ecchymotic, in which nearly all tissues are involved. In long-standing cases the hemorrhages may be less evident. Ascites is common and edema of the mesenteries or intestinal wall may be observed. Sometimes icterus is observed. Degenerative changes occur in the parenchymatous organs. The liver characteristically is indurated, and bluish-gray in color.

In Emmel's third type, symptoms appear not more than two months after animals have been removed from crotalaria and last two to three months before death. Cattle become weak and emaciated, displaying incoordination and either constipation with hard dry feces, or diarrhea. Lesions on post mortem include atrophic cirrhosis of the liver, ascites, and petechiae on the intestinal serosa.

Mortality in horses has been reported in several instances (494, 618, 619, 1345). The chronic situation usually prevails. Death follows as much as six months after removal of the animals from access to crotalaria. Symptoms manifested include incoordination and aimless walking or pushing against objects for hours. Delirium, excitement, or apparent blindness may be noted. Death is preceded by weakness and stupor. Icterus is noticeable in many cases. Lesions are similar to those found in cattle.

Hogs may be poisoned by consuming green crotalaria forage. Experimental feedings with seeds have shown (495, 496) that they are highly toxic to swine. Chronic symptoms appeared in a week after daily feeding of seeds at about 0.05 per cent of the animal's weight (total dose) and in three weeks at 0.01 per cent. In natural cases, hogs begin to display symptoms several weeks after removal from crotalaria. Loss of hair and unthriftiness are common. Lesions include anemia, ascites, a firm, indurated liver, and hemorrhages, especially about the heart. Gastritis is observed with or without hemorrhages.

Studies (107, 725) with extracts of the alkaloid monocrotaline have shown that its fundamental action is to cause constriction of the lumen in the medium and small veins of the hepatic venous tree through subendothelial swelling. This is followed by sinusoidal congestion, hemorrhage, and later fibrosis and cirrhosis.

CONDITIONS OF POISONING. Cattle reject *C. spectabilis* in forage or hay when other forage is available. This species greens early and stays green during the dry summer months when much of the rest of available pasturage turns brown. Most cases occur when crotalaria has been ingested in early spring or late summer (494). Frosted plants and hay retain toxicity. Seeds may pass through cattle undigested and seedlings will be spread in the droppings (1274). Seeds apparently may remain dormant in the soil for many years, germinating when the soil is cultivated or disturbed (618). The plant is often sown in tung orchards as a soil builder and with corn and milo for the same purposes. Seeds have gotten into commercial feed mixtures with shelled corn and possibly with soybeans (1601), and have been particularly troublesome in home-ground feeds (114). They may easily be removed by screening. Swine find green crotalaria only moderately unpalatable under field conditions (495).

Crotalaria retusa L.

DESCRIPTION. Plant erect, not dense, to 2½ ft. Individual branches appearing very much like those of *C. spectabilis,* except that stipules are minute, stems bear a very fine hairiness, and the racemes of yellow or purple flowers tend to be lax.

DISTRIBUTION AND HABITAT. Waste places and roadsides in sandy soil in peninsular Florida. Occasionally planted as an ornamental.

POISONOUS PRINCIPLE. Monocrotaline has been isolated from the seeds and other parts of this species (7).

TOXICITY, SYMPTOMS, AND LESIONS. Major losses to the seeds of this plant have occurred in fowl. It has been shown experimentally (488) that 100 seeds force-fed as a single dose to a White Leghorn hen produced death in 1½ to 2 weeks, and that twice that amount fed 5 per day produced typical symptoms of chronic poisoning and death in one to five weeks. Seeds made available *ad libitum* produced death in two weeks to a month.

Symptoms and lesions are similar to those noted for *Crotalaria spectabilis* poisoning in fowl but are less acute and include less hemorrhaging.

CONDITIONS OF POISONING. Seeds may be obtained by fowl in various ways. Cattle find *C. retusa* distasteful and under ordinary circumstances will not eat it (1345).

OTHER POISONOUS SPECIES. Many additional species of *Crotalaria* have records of toxicity in other countries, including toxicity to human beings when the seeds have contaminated flour. Because of this record, potential introductions of *Crotalaria* have generally been subjected to toxicity trials before being planted in the United States and have not been introduced if toxic. *Crotalaria mucronata* Desv. (= *C. striata* DC.) and *C. incana* L., considered poisonous elsewhere, were found to lack toxicity under the conditions of one set of trials (100, 1345) but the former has shown moderate toxicity to fowl in other tests (114). At the level of one per cent of the diet, seeds of *C. mucronata* produced deleterious effects in chicks and laboratory animals in three weeks (855, 1484). At three and six per cent levels mortality was marked. This species is especially troublesome because it is used widely in the South as a green manure crop (under the name "giant striata") and commonly appears as a weed in cultivated crops. Its seeds frequently contaminate corn, pea, and soybean harvests. The seeds of *C. mucronata* are about one one-hundredth as toxic to fowl as those of *C. spectabilis*. *Crotalaria rotundifolia* (Walt.) Poir., a species of the coastal plain from Florida to Louisiana and Virginia, has been suspected of toxicity (1077).

Additional references: 20, 113, 487, 604, 1406, 1417, 1433, 1573, 1582, 1677, 1715.

Cytisus scoparius (L.) Link. Scotch broom

DESCRIPTION. Brushy, rigidly branched shrub, to 7 ft tall. Leaves small, trifoliolate. Flowers leguminous, bright yellow. Fruit a legume pod.

DISTRIBUTION AND HABITAT. This plant has been introduced and is well established on sandy soils along roadsides and near the shore along the East Coast south to Georgia.

POISONING. Loss of livestock to this plant is rare but has been recorded in Europe (607). It has been shown to contain small amounts of the toxic quinolizidine alkaloids sparteine and isosparteine (918).

Glycine max Merr. (= *G. soja* Sieb. & Zucc.). Cultivated soybean

Soybean itself is not toxic. In 1916, however, severe loss of life in cattle on several farms in Scotland was traced (1541) to toxicity in soybean-oil meal, the residue after commercial extraction of the soybean oil with the solvent trichloroethylene. Conclusions reached at that time—namely that cattle are extremely susceptible while other species are less sensitive, and that only trichloroethylene-extracted meal is dangerous—have since been supported in detailed studies, and lesions have become well characterized.

Residue after extraction of soybean oil by means other than with trichloroethylene does not support animal growth as well as the same material after being heated (98, 1309), but it cannot be said to be toxic.

Oil extracted by the trichloroethylene process is not toxic, nor is tri-chloroethylene itself in amounts equal to, or somewhat greater than, the amount remaining in toxic meal after extraction (1303). Toxicity, thus, appears to be associated with some reaction which occurs in the residue as the result of oil extraction with trichloroethylene.

Certain evidence that a derivative of cysteine was related to, or identical with, the toxic molecule (1078) has been followed by the experimental observation that soybeans and other materials treated with primary, second-ary, or tertiary amines become toxic. Such amines by themselves are highly toxic, and small amounts are sometimes added to commercial trichloro-ethylene to prevent certain spontaneous degradative processes (653). Auto-oxidation of trichloroethylene-extracted soybean-oil meal (TCESOM) does not seem to be involved.

Reactions of various classes of livestock and laboratory animals to TCESOM in their diets vary considerably. Only in horses and cattle have lesions characteristic of the disease recognized as TCESOM poisoning been produced. In sheep, a disease may be induced (1305), but lesions are variable and not consistent with the disease as known in cattle. In dogs and guinea pigs a wasting disease is produced (1309). Growth failure, decreased resistance to disease, aplastic anemia, and some death losses were found in chicks fed meal highly toxic to cattle (768), but on balance fowl are relatively resistant to the effects of the toxic principle.

As stated above, soybean is not poisonous. However, TCESOM poison-ing is discussed briefly below because of its association with soybean and because it is useful to compare this disease with bracken poisoning (*Pteri-dium*).

TCESOM poisoning has been investigated extensively by a group at the Minnesota Agricultural Experiment Station. Their papers (715, 1302–1309, 1394) may be consulted for a thorough discussion and historical re-view of the problem.

Serious outbreaks of TCESOM poisoning occurred in Germany and the Netherlands between 1923 and 1925, and in the United States and some other countries more recently. It was recognized between 1947 and 1952 in Colorado, Iowa, Kansas, Minnesota, Mississippi, Montana, North and South Dakota, and Hawaii.

Various batches of TCESOM vary in toxicity. The major factor upon which variation seems to depend is the length of time between harvest and processing. Beans which have been stored for a year or longer before extraction yield meals with greatly reduced toxicity.

In cattle, a disease indistinguishable in pathology from bracken poisoning is produced (1606). Symptoms appear after the animal has been on a diet containing TCESOM for from one to nine months, depending upon the amount consumed daily and the toxicity of the batch, and may appear many weeks or some months after the animal has ceased to have access to this feed. In most instances symptoms are acute and terminate in death after a few days; a chronic condition is found in a small number of cases. Symptoms are similar to those of bracken poisoning and include greatly elevated temperature, passage of blood clots with the feces, and bleeding from various body openings. Pathological changes, also, are similar to those in bracken poisoning. The disease is fundamentally the result of aplastic degeneration in the bone marrow. Blood studies show greatly diminished leucocyte and thrombocyte numbers and also reduction in erythrocyte count with concomitant signs of anemia. The bloodstream may be invaded terminally by bacteria, which may or may not account for the development of elevated temperature. Arterioles are damaged in places. Hemorrhages develop throughout body tissues. They are petechial at first, but because of the reduced thrombocyte complement can continue to develop, leading to ecchymoses and hematomas in the tissues or constant bleeding from the nostrils or into the intestines and elsewhere. In a chronic condition sometimes encountered with diets of threshold toxicity, anemia is accompanied by depression, ataxia, and sometimes icterus.

The horse can be poisoned with TCESOM, but relatively more is required. In successful laboratory poisonings of this species the symptoms and lesions are similar in all respects to those produced in cattle.

Other classes of livestock and laboratory animals whose reactions have been investigated do not develop symptoms and lesions identical with those in the bovine and equine species. Sheep may be poisoned, and losses in this species have apparently occurred under natural conditions in North Dakota (782). In laboratory feeding experiments it has been shown (1305) that sheep are less susceptible to poisoning. When poisoned, they develop a blood dyscrasia, but its characteristics are variable and not equivalent to those found in cattle; for example, in some cases normal or elevated counts have been found for leukocytes and thrombocytes. An elevated temperature, also, appears to be lacking. Attempts to poison swine with TCESOM of known high toxicity have not been successful (715). Swine are either completely resistant or only very slightly susceptible to TCESOM poisoning.

Soybean also possesses potential goitrogenic capacity (654).

Gymnocladus dioica (L.) K. Koch. Kentucky coffee tree

DESCRIPTION. Large, rough-barked forest tree, to 60 or 80 ft tall; trunk short, with many major branches. Leaves twice suboppositely pinnate, to a yard in length; leaflets ovate. Fruit a hard, brown, flat legume pod, 4 to 6 in. long, ¾ to 1¾ in. broad, containing 4 to 7 hard, flat, broad seeds.

DISTRIBUTION. Moist woods, in the area bounded by New York, South

Dakota, Oklahoma, Tennessee, and Virginia. Occasionally planted elsewhere.

POISONOUS PRINCIPLE. Unknown. Older analyses suggest the presence of alkaloids in this species.

TOXICITY, SYMPTOMS, AND LESIONS. Cases in sheep resulting in death have been described by Reynard and Norton (1335) and Hansen (704). Cattle and horses are said to be poisoned under some circumstances (1566) and experimental feedings by Marsh and Clawson (1335) have shown the plant toxic to cattle. Chesnut (274) describes the case of a woman who was poisoned after mistaking this tree for honey locust (*Gleditsia*) and eating some fruit pulp from it.

Precise observations have not been reported on the amount necessary to produce symptoms nor on the symptoms themselves, but the toxic effect appears to be relatively strong. The symptoms are those of intense gastrointestinal irritation accompanied with certain nervous manifestations which have been described as "narcotic." Death in the cases cited in sheep occurred in less than a day after appearance of symptoms.

CONDITIONS OF POISONING. Trees are not common but animals may have access to a toxic dose of foliage when a tree is felled or pruned. The sprouts from cutover lands have also proven dangerous.

Indigofera endecaphylla Jacq. Creeping indigo

DESCRIPTION. Annual or perennial herb. Stems trailing, 1 to 2 ft long. Stems and leaves almost hairless. Leaves nearly sessile, pinnate compound, 1 to 3 in. long; leaflets alternate, oblanceolate, ½ to ¾ in. long, 5 to 9 in number. Flowers purple, racemes 1 to 4 in. long. Fruits legume pods, straight, ¾ to 1 in. long.

DISTRIBUTION AND HABITAT. This species was introduced from the tropics of the Old World for experimentation by the Florida Experiment Station in 1925 (498), and more recently into the Hawaiian Islands. It was found to grow as a perennial as far north in Florida as Gainesville. Studies at the Florida station proved the toxicity of this species and it was not released for agricultural use. In Hawaii, it was found to have excellent characteristics as a soil builder and forage material and was in some use before its toxicity was discovered. Attempts are being made to find or breed less toxic or nontoxic varieties (324). In the meantime its general use has been curtailed.

POISONOUS PRINCIPLE. Beta-nitro-propionic acid has been identified in creeping indigo by infrared spectroscopy in comparison with a known material (324). That this is in reality the principle has been disputed (814). Analyses of the total nitrogen-containing fraction showed the plant to be unusually high in nitrite content. It has been postulated that some of the plant's toxicity may occasionally come from its nitrite complement.

TOXICITY, SYMPTOMS, AND LESIONS. Experimental feedings have been performed with rabbits (488, 1182), cattle (829, 1182, 1183), sheep (1182), fowl (1183, 1644), guinea pigs (1644), and pigs (1182), and mice (309, 814). All classes of stock except swine and fowl found the plant palatable, at least under experimental conditions. Swine would not eat creeping indigo; therefore, it was impossible to poison them. A relatively large amount was required to produce lesions. In fowl, depression of growth was detected with a diet containing 2.5 per cent of this plant and definite toxicity symptoms at 5 per cent. Cattle did not develop signs of toxicity in short-interval experiments (of a few weeks duration) until creeping indigo constituted 50 per cent of the diet or more. Sheep seem more susceptible to poisoning. Experimental feeding of amounts varying from 1 to 4 lb per day was sufficient to produce not only symptoms but also deaths. In experimental feedings of cattle only two deaths were produced, and these probably were caused by secondary complications attendant to reproductive difficulties rather than by the direct toxic effects of the plant. Abortions have also been reported (1710).

Pathognomonic lesions have not been observed in fowl. In other classes of livestock, liver and kidney damage has been found. In calves fed large amounts of the plant over short periods of time, Jeganathan (829) was able to produce lesions rapidly. He found that under these conditions kidney lesions seemed the more severe. In more slowly developing cases, some congestion and edema may be found in the kidneys, but degenerative changes in the liver are more significant. The exact nature of liver lesions varies with duration of disease. The toxin produces cloudy swelling of hepatic cells followed by fatty degeneration and necrosis, particularly about the central veins and in areas of congestion. Regenerative fibrosis follows, resulting, for longer-standing cases, in a cirrhotic liver. Beta-nitro-propionic acid by itself does not cause liver lesions and is absent in the seeds which, nevertheless, are toxic (814).

Symptoms vary somewhat with species of animal and level of *Indigofera* intake. Fowl display ruffled feathers, drooping or twisted head, muscular spasms, and often paralysis of wings and legs. Further work with fowl showed that the toxic principle was transmitted in the egg, and resulted in reduced hatchability of eggs, reduced livability of chicks, and depressed growth rate in chicks even in the absence of further *Indigofera*. Egg production also was lowered when laying birds were fed *Indigofera*. There is some evidence that the lowered growth rate observed in fowl on *Indigofera* diet is largely the result of reduced feed consumption. After avidly eating the plant, rabbits develop anorexia, emaciation, and weakness, sometimes accompanied by posterior paralysis. In rabbits poisoned by *ad libitum* pasture feeding, death occurs after 6 to 30 days.

In experimental work with cattle no similar acute toxicity was demonstrated although there was great variation in, or absence of, weight gain.

Toxicity was expressed primarily in reproductive difficulties. Dead or very weak calves were produced at term or usually prematurely (as much as 100 days) in animals pastured on *Indigofera* for 25 days or longer. In another instance, heifers aborted after being on *Indigofera* pasturage. Vulvar swelling was noted in some cases. Reproductive difficulties and abortion were found also in sheep and rabbits. Corneal opacity was found in some sheep. This was not associated with avitaminosis A. In guinea pigs, experimental feedings of *Indigofera* also produced reproductive difficulties and abortions, but the body weight was not affected.

CONDITIONS OF POISONING. Legumes completely suitable for use as forage crops or soil builders in tropical countries are difficult to find. In the early trials, before its toxicity was discovered, *Indigofera endecaphylla* seemed to offer the greatest promise among several hundred legumes with which experiments had been conducted in Hawaii (1715). Efforts are currently under way in Hawaii to select or breed a strain of this species with toxicity reduced or absent.

Several other species of *Indigofera* not found within the range of this book have been considered toxic in the world literature. One, *Indigofera enneaphylla* L., has been the subject of much recent investigation in Australia where it is responsible for the "Birdsville Disease" of horses. Although its toxic principle is unknown, dissimilarity in symptoms and the absence of lesions in Birdsville Disease compared with *Indigofera endecaphylla* poisoning indicate that the poisonings are not the same (605).

Additional references: 1362, 1363, 1364.

Laburnum anagyroides Medic. (= *Cytisus laburnum* L.). Golden-chain, laburnum

A large ornamental shrub or small tree commonly cultivated for its hanging racemes, about 1½ ft long, of golden-yellow flowers. Leaves trifoliolate, long-petioled. Fruit a legume pod containing up to 8 seeds. Widely planted in several varieties, some with yellow leaves.

This plant has not been the subject of reports of loss in this hemisphere, but it is considered (574) after yew (*Taxus*) the most poisonous tree in Britain. Recent cases in Britain are reviewed by Garner (607).

Laburnum contains the toxic quinolizidine alkaloid cytisine (918) which has an action similar to nicotine (820). Toxicity of the seeds orally for the horse is about 0.05 per cent of the animal's weight (1628). Loss of human life has occurred (574). Symptoms in general include excitement, incoordination, convulsions, coma, and death through asphyxiation. Vomition is common. Dilation of the pupils may be noted. Among other routes of excretion, cytisine is excreted in the milk. It is possible, therefore, to obtain poisonous milk from poisoned animals (933).

cytisine

Lathyrus spp. Vetchlings

INTRODUCTION. Poisoning of human beings and livestock after ingestion of large quantities of the seeds of *Lathyrus sativus* L. (grass pea,
Indian pea, green vetch), *L. cicera* L. (flatpod pea), and *L. clymenum* L.
(Spanish vetch) has been recognized from the time of Hippocrates and
has accounted for much disease and loss of life in Britain, Spain, France,
Italy, Russia, India, and northern Africa. It is associated in human beings
with conditions of poverty or drought which force upon people a diet
composed largely or entirely of seeds of these species, and is now primarily
of historical interest. Epidemics of lathyrism have been recorded, discussed,
"explained," and reviewed by many authors. Little purpose is served here,
therefore, to do more than outline the nature of the disease as it was
known in other countries and other times for comparison with the characteristics of livestock poisoning from several species of *Lathyrus* as it is now
known in the United States and Canada. Reviews, such as those by Steyn
(1533), Long (933), Stockman (1540), and Lewis *et al.* (926), may
be consulted for fuller descriptions.

Moderate amounts of the peas of these species in the diet do not produce poisoning. Large quantities, or an exclusive diet, either raw, cooked, or
in the form of flour, produce a paralytic syndrome in man and livestock.
In man, a diet composed almost exclusively of the peas of *L. sativus*
will bring on symptoms after 4 to 8 weeks. Amounts greater than one-third
or one-half the total dietary intake will result in symptoms after a proportionately longer period of time; smaller quantities appear innocuous. There
is a much higher incidence of disease among men in their early prime of
life than among women or older males. It is likely that the greater physical
demands upon this group result in a lowered nutritional reserve against
which the derangements caused by the toxic principle of *Lathyrus* (see
later) act more quickly and potently.

Symptoms in man consist of partial or total paralysis, usually confined
to the legs, but in severe cases, attacking also the arms. In contrast with
the long lag period, paralysis comes on rapidly. Prodromal symptoms of
pains, pricking sensation, hypothesia, or cramps may or may not be present.
Paralysis consists subjectively of a heaviness or weakness of limbs accompanied frequently with muscular tremors when the muscle is put under
load. Reflexes are markedly intensified and stimulation may result in

spasticity or rigidity of leg muscles. The characteristic posture is with the feet turned in, toes down. A variety of secondary symptoms may accompany the development of paralysis. These are lost if the diet is corrected, but the paralysis is permanent. It is not accompanied by muscular wasting or sensory disturbances. If the diet is not corrected, death ensues. Paralysis may be confined to the limbs or may include loss of bladder or bowel control.

Livestock show considerable variation in susceptibility with species of animal. The horse is particularly sensitive to the toxic principle and is the species most commonly poisoned. Large numbers of horses have been lost, in Britain especially, after being fed seeds of *L. sativus* imported for feeding purposes. A diet exclusively of *L. sativus* brings on symptoms in about 10 days. Symptoms develop only after two or three months when the animal is fed one or two quarts a day, and may appear a month or more after the peas have been withdrawn from the diet. The symptoms historically reported in livestock are mostly similar to those reported for the human being. In the horse paralysis of the hind legs is usually ac-companied by dyspnea and roaring, the latter laid to paralysis of the re-current laryngeal nerve. Paralysis of the lower or hind extremities in man and livestock is considered the result of degeneration in the motor tracts of the spinal cord.

The older literature is full of contradictory statements and confusion concerning many aspects of *Lathyrus* poisoning. It appears that factors such as misidentification of the seeds in question, geographical variation in toxicity, presence of contaminating toxic seeds of other species, variation in susceptibility of animal species, and poorly founded or improperly inter-preted experimental results, perhaps sometimes further complicated by deficiency syndromes, are largely to blame.

TOXIC SPECIES OF *Lathyrus* IN THE UNITED STATES AND CANADA. The genus contains some 100 species. The following species have been found toxic to livestock.

Lathyrus hirsutus L. Caley pea, wild winter pea, singletary pea

Annual, weak-stemmed forage legume, 1 to 3 ft tall. Stems prominently winged. Leaves compound, composed of 2 foliose leaflets and a terminal branching tendril; foliose leaflets 1 to 3 in. long, elliptical or lanceolate; major veins parallel. Flowers few, pealike, axillary, red to blue. Fruit a legume pod, 1 to 1¾ in. long by about ¼ in. broad, flat, many-seeded, hairy, splitting into two halves which become tightly twisted when dry. This species is used as an annual winter forage or cover legume in the southern third of the United States. It came into popularity around 1940 and may now be found naturalized throughout the area where it is grown, north to Virginia and also in California to Oregon.

Lameness in cattle has been reported from cases in Alabama (1551). Herds of animals placed on luxuriant growths of mature wild winter pea ate it ravenously almost to the exclusion of all else. Symptoms of lameness appeared between the third and fifth days. The plants were found to bear large quantities of immature and maturing seeds. Experimental feedings and pasture studies with wild winter pea corroborated observations from natural cases. Only occasionally was lameness severe. In most cases symptoms of lameness gradually disappeared even when animals were not removed from wild pea forage. It is possible that the amount of seeds consumed by these animals decreased as the pods matured, opened, and the seeds dropped out. Experimental feeding of hay cut at the time of maximum observed toxicity proved negative for toxicity, perhaps again because of loss of seeds during curing and handling. In pasture experiments no animals developed lameness until the plant had reached the stage of seed production.

Experimental feedings to chicks, pigs, and laboratory animals performed by the Alabama Agricultural Experiment Station (1604, 1605) produced reproductive difficulties in chicks on a 10 per cent wild winter pea diet, lameness in pigs on a diet in which wild winter pea was used as the sole protein supplement, and lameness with moderate to severe skeletal deformity in chicks, pigs, and rats on diets containing 25 to 50 per cent wild winter pea. Toxicity was shown to be retained after cooking.

Lathyrus incanus (Smith & Rydb.) Rydb. [= *L. polymorphus* ssp. *incanus* (Smith & Rydb.) Hitchc.]. Wild pea

Like the foregoing except 4 in. to 1 ft tall; leaves compound with 3 to 4 pairs of leaflets; leaflets linear, ½ to 1½ in. long, densely hairy; pods 1 to 1½ in. long. This species is native to the dry sandy plains of Nebraska, Colorado, and Wyoming. In Wyoming it has been suspected (97) of producing lameness in horses on the range.

Lathyrus pusillus Ell. Singletary pea

Similar to *L. hirsutus* except smaller, more recumbent; stems winged, to 2 ft long; leaflets linear or narrow-lanceolate, ¾ to 2½ in. long by about ¼ in. wide; flowers purple; pods narrow, 1 to 2 in. long, glabrous. This species has come into favor in the Gulf States as a winter cover crop. It is also found naturalized from Texas and Kansas to Florida and North Carolina.

This species is reported (910) to have been responsible for livestock poisoning in the southeastern states. Experimental work with chicks and rats has shown it to produce lameness in chicks and lameness with bone deformities in rats.

Lathyrus sylvestris L. Everlasting pea, flat pea

Similar to *L. hirsutus* except coarser, persistent perennial; recumbent stems heavily winged, 3 to 6 ft long; leaflets lanceolate, about 4 in. long by ⅝ in. wide, petioles winged; flowers rose and purple, in axillary racemes of 4 to 10; pod 2½ in. long, ½ in. wide. Found naturalized in northern United States and southern Canada. This species was tested as forage by the Washington Agricultural Experiment Station many years ago, but for certain reasons was not considered satisfactory. Seedings made at the time of the original trials persisted, however, with great tenacity. For this reason renewed interest was taken in this species as a possible cover or forage crop for use under adverse conditions in western Washington, to which it was particularly suited. Field grazing trials have resulted in the death of sheep one to two weeks after being placed on this forage (391). Symptoms were not reported; no pathognomonic lesions were found.

TOXIC PRINCIPLE AND NATURE OF POISONING. In 1933 experiments designed to clarify the role, if any, of avitaminosis A in lathyrism were undertaken (612) using the common garden sweet pea (*Lathyrus odoratus* L.), a species which had not previously been reported toxic. In this work Geiger *et al.* found that diets containing 25, 50, and 80 per cent of the seed of *L. odoratus* retarded growth and produced lameness, hernias, and, particularly, skeletal deformity in rats. This work was repeated and extended about a decade later by a group at the University of Michigan in the first (925) of a series of experiments into the toxicity of a number of species of *Lathyrus* to laboratory animals (926, 927, 1419). Several unexpected and curious aspects of *Lathyrus* toxicity were discovered, and a great deal of experimental and biochemical work has been forthcoming from a number of laboratories.

Species of *Lathyrus* which have been shown toxic in experiments using laboratory animals are listed in the accompanying table. These species

TOXIC SPECIES OF LATHYRUS

SPECIES	AUTHORITY
Lathyrus hirsutus L.	926, 1604, 1605
Lathyrus latifolius L.	927
Lathyrus odoratus L.	926, 1286
Lathyrus pusillus Ell.	463, 911
Lathyrus sphaericus Retz. (?)	926
Lathyrus splendens Kellogg	1419
Lathyrus strictus Nutt. (?)	1419
Lathyrus sylvestris L.	795, 926
Lathyrus tingitanus L.	926

have been divided into two groups on the basis of symptoms produced in rats (463, 910, 1076, 1419). The seeds of one group (species *sylvestris, splendens,* and *latifolius;* decreasing toxicity in the order named) are highly toxic. In *sylvestris* and *latifolius,* they produce characteristic nervous symptoms of hyperexcitability, convulsions, and death without skeletal lesions. The seeds of the remaining species (*tingitanus, strictus, odoratus, hirsutus,* and *pusillus;* decreasing toxicity in the order named, except for the last) are less toxic and produce lameness, paralysis, and skeletal deformity. It was postulated (1419) that death supervened before skeletal deformity could appear in the case of the high toxicity of the first group, but it now appears that two different toxic compounds are involved (1076, 1332, 1333).

The compound producing paralysis and skeletal lesions upon ingestion of the seeds of *L. odoratus* and *L. pusillus* has been identified as beta-(gamma-L-glutamyl)-aminopropionitrile (463, 1076, 1403). Further investigation (52, 398, 1287) has shown that the nitrile group together with a reactive amine group is necessary for toxicity. Synthetic aminopropionitrile, aminoacetonitrile, and some other compounds are capable of producing symptoms and lesions comparable with those produced by seeds.

The symptoms of poisoning in rats by *Lathyrus pusillus* have been separated into two major effects named above; (a) skeletal deformity with growth suppression, and (b) paralysis (appearing suddenly) by Lee *et al.* (911), who further showed variation in response of these effects with nutritional level in poisoned animals (see also 399). They found that casein and some other nutrients, when added to the diet, protected against the paralytic effect. Casein has been found (51) partially effective also against aneurysms (see later). Lee *et al.* (911) suggest that skeletal deformity with growth suppression results from toxic interference with amino-acid metabolism and that sudden paralysis is the effect of a second toxic mechanism which produces a more intense reaction when the growth-depressing reaction is partially frustrated by dietary supplementation, and growth is more nearly normal.

Skeletal deformity in the rat after *Lathyrus* poisoning is like idiopathic scoliosis in the human being. The nature of the changes that take place in the bones of laboratory animals have been described in detail (603, 1286, 1652). The normal construction and resorption processes are disturbed in such a way that cartilage proliferates and proper calcification and resorption do not take place. Gardner (603) has suggested from the presence of abnormal amounts of soluble collagen that bone lesions may result from a failure of polymerization, perhaps equivalent to the depolymerization of premature aging. Levene suggests (923) that lathyrogenic compounds block carbonyl groups and thus prevent cross-linkage of collagen.

The substance in *Lathyrus sylvestris* and *L. latifolius* which produces nervous symptoms of hyperexcitability, convulsions, and death without skeletal lesions is L-alpha, gamma-diaminobutyric acid (1332, 1333). It has been proposed (1333) that L-alpha, gamma-diaminobutyric acid and beta-aminopropionitrile, the skeleton-deforming principle in other species, are biosynthetically related to the same precursor, beta-cyano-L-alanine, itself a dehydration product of L-asparagine. Beta-cyano-L-alanine has been detected in physiologically significant amounts in the seeds of two species of another closely related legume (*Vicia sativa* L. and *V. angustifolia* L.) (1333). This compound also is toxic, producing symptoms similar to the hyperexcitability syndrome of *Lathyrus* poisoning.

Many instances in older literature of poisoning of man by *Lathyrus sativus* remain unexplained. It has repeatedly been impossible to produce symptoms in experimental animals with this species. In at least some instances of poisoning attributed to *L. sativus,* and in one instance when it was attributed to wheat, seeds of *Vicia sativa* were present as contaminants. Ressler has suggested (1333) that the latter were the actual source of toxicity and that beta-cyano-L-alanine was the compound involved.

Several additional characteristics of lathyrus poisoning have turned up in laboratory studies. It has been shown that the developing embryo is particularly sensitive to the toxic principle of *Lathyrus odoratus* and that random resorption of the fetus occurs in poisoned pregnant rats (1637). It was further found (1638) that estrogenic hormones, particularly in combination, are protective against this effect. Further work (1434, 1435) has shown that additional hormones can influence other characteristics of poisoning. Somatotrophic hormone increases the skeleton-deforming effect of amino-acetonitrile, while cortisol acetate inhibits this effect. Dissecting aortal aneurysms have been produced in rats by seeds of *Lathyrus odoratus* under some experimental conditions (852, 1286) and can be produced also with beta-amino-propionitrile. It has been found (1434) that aneurysms can be produced with greater-than-normal frequency using certain experimental techniques involving desoxycorticosterone acetate. Aneurysms produced in these ways are similar to some found under natural conditions in turkeys but the etiology of the natural cases remains undetermined (70, 899, 1372).

Lespedeza stipulacea Maxim. Lespedeza, Korean lespedeza

Several instances of a hemorrhagic syndrome similar to sweetclover (*Melilotus*) poisoning have been reported (1145) in Missouri livestock in which sweetclover was not involved. All cases had molded lespedeza hay as a dietary factor in common. One case in cattle was investigated in detail and supplemented with experimental feedings to rabbits.

The principal abnormality in advanced cases was decreased prothrombin activity. Fibrinogen levels were normal. Prothrombin reduction was severe enough in some natural cases to result in death after uncontrollable hemorrhage following dehorning or parturition. The syndrome was reproduced in rabbits with symptoms appearing after about three weeks. Bright, properly cured lespedeza hay did not produce the disease.

Leucaena glauca (L.) Benth. Koa haole, lead tree

DESCRIPTION. Deep-rooted perennial shrub or tree to 30 ft tall. Leaves bipinnate, 6 to 10 in. long; pinnae 4 to 8 pairs; leaflets 10 to 15 pairs, blades narrow-oblong, $\frac{1}{4}$ to $\frac{3}{4}$ in. long. Inflorescence an axillary, long-pedicelled, spherical head, about an inch in diameter; flowers numerous, tightly grouped, white or pink. Fruit a many-seeded legume pod, 4 to 6 in. long.

DISTRIBUTION AND HABITAT. Local in waste lands, Coastal Plain from Florida to Texas. Widespread on arid lands in the Hawaiian Islands and under cultivation there as a soil builder or forage crop.

POISONOUS PRINCIPLE. Mimosine, an alpha-amino acid. The literature

mimosine (Beta-[N-(3-hydroxy-4-pyridone)]-alpha-propionic acid)

pertaining to the isolation, determination, and synthesis of this compound has been reviewed by Matsumoto and Sherman (1059).

TOXICITY, SYMPTOMS, AND LESIONS. Experiments at the Hawaii Agricultural Experiment Station and elsewhere have shown that this species has high value as a source of forage protein for livestock (1560). Experience in the Islands and in other tropical countries where the plant is established, however, made it clear that ingestion of large quantities of this species result in poor rates of gain, general poor condition, and as the most conspicuous symptom, loss of hair. This phenomenon has been observed in horses, mules, donkeys, swine, and rabbits in Hawaii. Experimental work with rats produced similar symptoms followed by death. Under natural conditions hair is again grown when livestock are removed from this plant. It has been generally assumed that toxicity was limited to nonruminants. Experimental feedings, however, have been reported from the Belgian Congo, in which sheep (396) and cattle (313) were affected with loss of hair. The sheep in these experiments found the plant distasteful but, as in Hawaii, it was relished by cattle. These results contrast with apparent nontoxicity of the plant to cattle under Hawaiian conditions (1560) in the Bahama Islands (1146), and elsewhere. Fowl also thrive on the plant.

From comparison of symptoms, it was first thought that the toxic principle was selenium. This has been disproved, at least in Hawaii. Because of the high potential usefulness of koa haole if it could be made nontoxic, much attention has been paid to methods for determining mimosine content (1059), and for inactivating or destroying it (1060), the latter with partial success.

Additional reference: 1711.

Lotus corniculatus L. Birdsfoot trefoil

This popular forage crop has been shown occasionally to produce potentially toxic amounts of a cyanogenetic substance in Europe, Britain, Australia (810), and the United States (448, 449). Cases of livestock loss have not been reported except possibly in Australia.

Lupinus spp. Lupine, bluebonnet

GENERAL DESCRIPTION. Range species are mostly low perennial shrubs. Leaves alternate, palmately compound; leaflets 5 to 17, mostly oblanceolate (from almost linear to obovate). Inflorescence terminal, racemose, often showy. Flowers papilionaceous, blue, white, red, or yellow; stamens 10, filaments united in a single tubular structure; anthers free, alternating long and short. Fruit a several-seeded, flattened legume pod.

About 100 species of lupine occur in the United States and Canada. Most of theses are native to the states and provinces from the Rocky Mountains westward. California alone, for example, has more than 80 native species. Species and varieties are taxonomically difficult, and it is unwise to place absolute dependence upon names used in the poisonous-plants literature. This is particularly unfortunate since it has been shown (a) that different lupines produce different symptoms in a given class of livestock (356, 1010), (b) that susceptibility of different classes of livestock to particular lupines varies under range conditions (97, 294), (c) that species of lupine vary seasonally in toxicity in different ways (28, 1176), and (d) that some species of lupine, perhaps the majority, are acceptable or desirable forage under usual range conditions (356, 804). Recent taxonomic treatments covering the majority of western species of *Lupinus* are those of Munz (1149) and Smith (1481).

POISONOUS PRINCIPLE. More than a score of alkaloids have been isolated from species of *Lupinus*. Most are quinolizidine alkaloids, but some piperidine and other types of alkaloids have been found. The nitrogen oxides of some of these bases have also been detected in the plants. The extensive chemical investigations of J. F. Couch (345, 356) into the alkaloids of lupines were prompted by the investigations of the United

CH_2OH

lupinine

States Department of Agriculture into their toxicity to livestock, but now are mainly of historical interest. The voluminous literature dealing with lupine alkaloids from a chemical point of view has been reviewed by Leonard (920). It appears that lupine alkaloids are quite reactive, and minor changes in structure may be responsible for major changes in toxicity (804). Some of the alkaloids which have been isolated do not possess significant physiological activity.

TOXICITY, SYMPTOMS, AND LESIONS. Because of the large number of species which have produced loss under natural conditions, and the variability in characteristics of poisoning with species of plant, species of animal, and age of plant, it is difficult to present lupine poisoning as a single entity. The gross clinical picture may be one of depression or of excitation. Sheep are most commonly affected under range conditions but cattle and horses have been poisoned. Marsh *et al.* (1010) state that goats, swine, and deer also have been poisoned.

Principal toxic species

Lupinus leucophyllus Dougl. Wooly-leaved lupine
Leaves and stems densely hairy; flowers white, pink, blue, or purple. Eastern Washington and western Montana to central Utah and northern California on dry soils.

Lupinus leucopsis Agardh. Big Bend lupine
Leaves and stems silky-haired; flowers violet-blue or pale purple. Open lands, Oregon and Washington.

Lupinus argenteus Pursh. Silvery lupine
Stems hairy, leaves mostly glabrous above, hairy beneath; flowers blue or purple. Dry flats and slopes in woods, 4000 to 5000 ft, Montana to California and New Mexico.

Lupinus sericeus Pursh. Silky lupine
Leaves and stems silky-haired; flowers purple, blue, rose, creamy or white. Dry hillsides and valleys, Utah and Wyoming to Montana and British Columbia.

The four species listed above have served as the basis of most of the investigations of lupine poisoning (28, 88, 97, 277, 1010, 1081, 1383, 1682). As far as evidence is available they produce similar poisonings and are responsible for the syndrome recognized as typical American

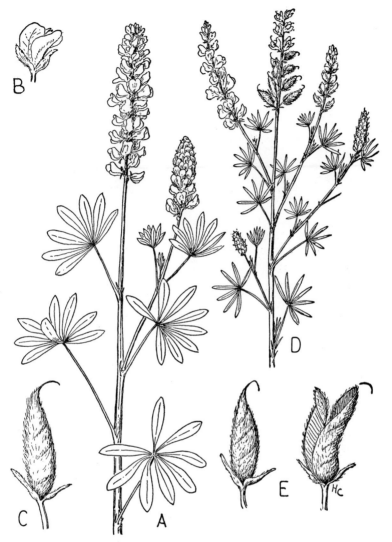

Fig. 81. A-C, *Lupinus leucophyllus*. Wooly-leaved lupine. Flowering shoot, with details of fruit and flower. D-E, *L. argenteus*. Silvery lupine. Flowering shoot, with detail of fruit. Courtesy of The Macmillan Company.

lupine poisoning in sheep. The identity of *L. leucopsis* is open to question. The material so identified was collected at Greycliff, Montana, which is outside the range of that species as currently conceived. The most probable identity of the species collected there is *L. sericeus*.

Ingestion of a relatively large quantity of lupine over a brief period of time is generally required for the production of lupine poisoning. It seems that the poisonous principle is readily excreted. Amounts which should prove fatal if ingested at one feeding were found harmless (1010) if ingested over the course of a single day. Although alkaloids may be

Fig. 82. *Lupinus sp.* Range lupines under natural conditions.

isolated from the foliage, the greatest concentration is in the seeds. Plants in preflowering stages of maturity are unlikely to be dangerous under normal range conditions (1010). Nevertheless there is strong evidence that lupine poisoning has occasionally occurred from young lupine [probably *L. leucophyllus* (801, 1176)].

The alkaloids are not lost or detoxified on drying of the plant. Range hay made from lupines may be highly toxic if the seeds are retained. This usually occurs when the hay is cut while the majority of pods are immature. Mature pods open on drying, releasing the seeds, which drop from the hay as it is handled. For many lupines the time and degree of seeding is quite variable from year to year.

Marsh *et al.* (1010) found *L. leucopsis, L. leucophyllus,* and *L. argenteus* about equally toxic. Beath *et al.* (88, 97) found *L. argenteus* only about three-fourths as toxic as *L. leucophyllus.* The seeds alone have a toxicity to sheep between 0.25 and 0.5 per cent of the animal's weight. Fully developed pods with seeds were found toxic at about 1½ per cent.

Symptoms have been variously described for typical lupine poisoning in sheep. The nature of breathing is most characteristic. In many cases breathing becomes heavy and labored, the animal is depressed, becomes comatose, often with snoring, and after a greater or lesser period of time, dies without struggle. In other cases severe dyspnea develops rapidly and the animal throws itself about violently. It may butt other animals or stand with its head lowered, pressing against a fence or other solid object. Trembling and convulsions may occur. Death results from respiratory paralysis after periods of convulsions with increasingly brief remissions, or after a comatose stage.

Symptoms may appear within an hour after a toxic dose has been consumed, and death may follow within a day, or symptoms may not be developed in other instances until as much as 24 hours after the toxic dose has been consumed and death, if it occurs, several days later. In cases where death does not come quickly, the pulse is markedly weak and respiration slow. Lesions are those characteristic of death by respiratory paralysis and are not specific for lupine poisoning.

Several cases involving the loss of more than 1000 head of sheep are on record (277). Lupines are probably responsible for greater loss among sheep than any other single plant in Montana, Idaho, and Utah. Cases of poisoning among cattle and horses are rare (85), perhaps because these animals do not readily eat the pods. Sheep neglect lupines for other forage, if available. Almost all cases of loss occur under circumstances which cause the animals to consume large quantities of podded lupine over a brief period of time. These include driving hungry animals quickly through areas heavy with lupine, so that they have little chance to be selective in their grazing; unloading or bedding down hungry animals where lupine is the major vegetation; and trailing animals where snow has covered the grasses, leaving lupines as the only green vegetation available. Poisoning also occurs from feeding podded hay, which is not distasteful. Most cases of serious loss occur in the fall when the conditions cited above are met. Lupines remain green and somewhat succulent after most other forage has dried.

In addition to the above, evidence exists for the toxicity of the following species:

Lupinus cyaneus Rydb.
Similar to *L. leucophyllus,* except greener. Flowers smaller, light blue. Montana. Chesnut and Wilcox (277) consider this species toxic with those discussed above. Extracts were shown to be toxic to laboratory animals (1010).

Lupinus onustus L. Wats. Plumas lupine
Flowers deep blue. Open pine woods, California. Considered (1383) a typical toxic lupine in California.

Lupinus laxiflorus Dougl. Douglas spurred lupine
Flowers blue, rose, or pale yellow. Hillsides, dry soils, Washington, Oregon, and Idaho. This species and a variety have been tested for toxicity

by the United States Department of Agriculture at the Salina (Utah) experiment station (294) and at the University of California (1631). The nearly mature fruit were found especially toxic to cattle, being only one-tenth as toxic to sheep. About 0.2 per cent of an animal's weight of green seed pods brought on symptoms within a day. Symptoms in cattle were very much like those from larkspur poisoning, with which it had been confused in the field. They consisted of weakness, muscular trembling, ataxia, and prostration. Horses appeared as though contending with severe colic. Sheep became nervous and excitable.

Lupinus alpestris A. Nels.
Flowers light blue. Dry, rocky soils, California to Montana, Colorado, and Arizona. This species is considered among the typical lupine poisoners by Beath *et al.* (97), whose experiments have shown it somewhat more than half as toxic as *L. leucophyllus.*

Lupinus caudatus Kell. Kellogg's spurred lupine
Flowers violet-blue or white. Exposed hillsides, Oregon, Idaho to Utah, Nevada, and California. This species is considered (28, 801) responsible for cattle loss in Utah and Nevada.

Lupinus greenei A. Nels.
Flowers purple or blue. Plains and hills, Wyoming, Nevada, Colorado, and Arizona. Recorded (465) as toxic in Colorado.

Lupinus pusillus Pursh. Low lupine
Flowers blue or white. Dry plains, Saskatchewan to Kansas, New Mexico, and Arizona. Recorded (1383) as poisonous in California.
Alkaloidal extracts of *L. polyphyllus* Lindl. (large-leaved lupine) and *L. spathulatus* Rydb. have proven toxic to laboratory animals (345). Likewise, leaves of *L. cumulicola* Small, a species of the Southeast, have been shown toxic to fowl (460), but natural instances of poisoning by either have not been observed. *Lupinus perennis* L., the common eastern lupine, has frequently been considered poisonous (28). Several alkaloids have been found in it, but no cases of poisoning under natural conditions are on record in the United States or Canada, and some feeding experiments (460) have had negative results. However a case of poisoning in a 2 yr old boy, reported to a New Hampshire poison control center as resulting from ingestion of garden lupine seeds, may have been caused by this or another common species.
Prior to the discovery of the toxicity of American species of lupine, European species had been investigated extensively as poisonous plants (674, 1679). References to lupines may be found in Dioscorides, Cato, Pliny, Theophrastus, and other classical authors. In the decade following 1870 widespread severe cases resulting in loss of life in livestock were

Fig. 83. *Lupinus perennis*. Eastern lupine.
Plant, with details of flower and fruit.
Courtesy of The Macmillan Company.

traced to ingestion of native European species of lupine. These cases divided
into two distinct types, acute and chronic. The acute was similar to American lupine poisoning described above, with the exception that icterus was
often a prominent symptom. In the chronic syndrome icterus was always

pronounced and symptoms were largely those associated with liver damage. The factor in the lupines responsible for liver damage was found to be distinct and different from the physiologically active alkaloids that were extracted and shown responsible for the majority of symptoms in the acute syndrome. The "ictrogen," however, resisted all efforts at elucidation and was only partially characterized. The commonly accepted theory of the time was that molds were responsible for the formation of "ictrogen" in the lupines.

The numerous investigations of lupine poisoning in Europe received wide contemporary publicity in the United States through reviews in veterinary journals and elsewhere. Unfortunately, information in these reviews was transferred into the American literature dealing with native lupine toxicity, and has been carried along to the present time. Specifically, the statement that one of the chief characteristics of lupine poisoning in the United States is icterus may be found in occasional American publications, even of recent date. With the exception of the secondhand mention of icterus in an experiment involving lupines fed to horses (1010) there is no record of icterus associated with American lupine poisoning.

It is interesting, in the context of the above, to note that several species of *Lupinus,* which had been used for years as minor forage in western Australia, recently have been producing cases of poisoning in sheep and cattle in which icterus is a major symptom (601, 605). Investigations (106) have shown that this syndrome, termed lupinosis, is unrelated to alkaloidal content of the plant, and is cumulative in nature. The mechanism of toxicity has not yet been elucidated. Actual liver damage has been traced (601) to abnormal uptake by the liver of iron. The prime cause appears to be a biochemical lesion in the liver cell, but conditions which yield anemia reinforce the severity of iron accumulation.

Lupinus serecius (35, 119, 469) and *L. laxiflorus* (1631) have been implicated in a syndrome the characteristics of which are markedly different from typical lupine poisoning described above. This syndrome, called "crooked calf disease," has been reported in the area from South Dakota and Nebraska to the Pacific, south to Utah, and north to adjacent Canada. Malformed calves are born, usually alive, at full term. Lesions appear to be confined to the skeletal system. They consist of misaligned joints and twisted bones. In mild cases deformity is confined to mild bowing of the forelegs. In severe cases the forelegs are twisted and cannot be fully extended. The neck ("wry neck") and back may be involved, and rarely the hind legs. Sometimes a cleft palate is found.

Incidence is spotty both geographically and from year to year within a given herd, varying from less than 1 up to 100 per cent of the calf crop. It does not follow patterns of heredity nor is it associated statistically more with one breed of beef or dairy cattle than with another. In some areas it is always associated with early calves and may be controlled by delaying breeding. The dangerous period of pregnancy appears to be one to three months after conception. Vitamin A levels are normal in the livers of poisoned animals (1214). Attempts to determine the cause of the disease have focused upon plants and mineral characteristics of soils associated with it. *Lupinus serecius* and *L. laxiflorus* have been incriminated in separate studies, but separate feeding experiments with either failed to elicit symptoms characteristic of the disease. Abundance of lead and deficiency of manganese likewise have separately been associated with production of the disease. Feeding of physiological amounts of lead alone has not produced the disease. However, acutely deformed calves have been produced in experiments (35, 119) in which both lead (as lead acetate, 5 mg per kg per day) and *L. serecius* (about 1½ lb per day per animal) were fed during the breeding period.

Additional reference: 727.

Medicago sativa L. Alfalfa, lucerne
Medicago hispida Gaertn. ($=$ *M. denticulata* Willd.). Bur clover, trefoil

It is not surprising when, occasionally, difficulties are traced to a plant in such general use for forage and hay as alfalfa. Bloat may occur when large quantities of alfalfa are consumed by cattle, and the saponin content of the plant may in part be at fault (1643), but alfalfa is not generally considered a poisonous plant on this account. Moderate amounts of alfalfa in the diet of chicks result in lowered growth rate. The saponic content of alfalfa seems responsible for this effect also (762). Two saponic fractions have been isolated. One has been partially characterized (1643) as a monounsaturated dihydroxy dicarboxylic acid (probably a triterpenoid) of formula $C_{30}H_{46}O_6$.

Other undesirable effects may result from ingestion of large amounts of alfalfa by livestock. As with several other agricultural legumes, occasional cases of photosensitization (see photosensitization, p. 52) have been reported in several countries and attributed to ingestion of alfalfa (574). In Canada, a Holstein cow kept in a poorly lighted barn for three weeks during inclement weather and fed alfalfa hay, developed well-marked symptoms of photosensitization on the white areas of the skin when taken into the pasture on a subsequent sunny day (958). Photosensitization has been experimentally produced in guinea pigs (430) by dosing with the closely related *M. hispida*. This investigation was prompted by widespread photosensitization in Australia among just-sheared sheep pastured on this species in lush condition. In another case, also in Australia, alfalfa and trefoil growing together produced photosensitization of white-skinned pigs (224). In general, *Medicago* photosensitizations are mild. In most instances no signs of liver damage have been observed and it has been assumed that the photosensitivity was of the primary type. In a few cases, however, icterus has been observed (574).

Schofield (1415) observed a case of acute pulmonary emphysema in Canadian cattle which had been pastured for five days on lush, second-growth alfalfa. Two deaths resulted. Blood phosphorus was low and icterus was noted in these animals. Alfalfa is low in phosphorus content. Madsen and Nielsen (966) experimentally produced parturient hemoglobinemia in a diary cow by feeding a low-phosphorus diet of alfalfa and beet pulp. Erythrocyte destruction was correlated with low phosphorus levels.

Melilotus alba Desr. White sweetclover

Melilotus officinalis Lam. Yellow sweetclover

These are the principal species of biennial sweetclovers that are found as roadside weeds throughout much of the United States and southern Canada. They have been used widely as a forage crop and as soil builders since about 1920.

Chronological treatment serves best to present sweetclover poisoning. It was first recognized as a severe hemorrhagic disease of cattle in the United States and Canada in 1921. Subsequent investigation (929) culminated in the development of the medically valuable anticoagulant dicoumarin and the agriculturally useful rodenticide Warfarin.

Prior to 1921, the suggestion had been made in the literature (1239) that a bitter principle, coumarin, found in sweetclover was responsible for a paralytic syndrome occasionally associated with feeding sweetclover seed. Feeding experiments with seed were negative. The bleeding disease of cattle, now generally called sweetclover poisoning, first was recognized in 1921. The next year a report from Ontario (1412) describing it as a new disease and associating it with ingestion of molded or spoiled sweetclover hay brought it to wide attention, and within the next year or two it had been recognized in many states. Probably the sudden apparent outburst of sweet-clover poisoning in 1921–1922 is attributable to a combination of factors including new widespread use of sweetclovers as hay and silage, a partic-ularly moist harvest season, and the recognition that previous diagnoses of sweetclover poisoning as blackleg or hemorrhagic septicemia were incorrect. Loss of cattle has been reported from Ontario (586, 1412, 1413), Manitoba (179), Washington (1253), North Dakota (1356, 1400), Nebraska (1400), Minnesota (535), Wisconsin (229), Illinois (1065), Indiana (710), Ohio (175), and elsewhere. Principal research efforts have been carried out in Canada (1412, 1413), North Dakota (1354–1356, 1400), and Wisconsin (229–231, 798, 867, 929, 1508).

CHARACTERISTICS OF SWEETCLOVER POISONING. Sweetclover poisoning is restricted almost exclusively to cattle. Only very minor loss in sheep and horses (1253) has occurred, and it has been shown (1356) that sheep fed experimentally with the same hay producing severe illness in cattle are much more resistant to the toxic principle and are poisoned only with difficulty. Poisoning is contracted from molded hay or molded silage. A large amount is required. In experiments (1356) designed to duplicate conditions of feeding on the average farm, moderately toxic sweetclover hay produced clinical symptoms in cattle in from 3 to 8 weeks, the average being about a month. Young animals are more susceptible than older (175, 1356), and instances are recorded of typical symptoms and lesions in newborn calves when they were not detectable in the dam (586, 1413). Susceptibility of newborn animals may be due in part to inadequate synthesis and reserves of vitamin K (see later) at birth.

Severe loss has been sustained. Before owners were alerted to the possible toxicity of sweetclover hay, losses of 8 to 15 animals per farm were regular. The death rate in sweetclover poisoning is high, because in the majority of instances the disease has progressed beyond the point where removal of sweetclover will help when the first symptoms are noted.

Sweetclover poisoning is a hemorrhagic disease in which the animal bleeds to death either internally or externally. In a typical case not associated with surgery or wounds, the course is abrupt, death following within one to a few days after appearance of symptoms. The majority of deaths occur at 3 days. In acute cases of this type the first symptom noted is the sudden appearance of a subcutaneous swelling, which may be located on any part of the body but commonly occurs on either side of the vertebral column, on the thighs, or about the shoulders in stanchioned cattle. The swellings are large and obvious. Some have been described which were several feet in circumference, protruding as much as 10 to 12 inches (1253). If the swelling forms rapidly, its contents may fluctuate when manipulated. More slowly developing swellings may be pitted by pressure of the finger. No gas is present in them. Additional symptoms include blanching or pallor of the visible mucous membranes, weakness, and death without struggle. The heartbeat increases in strength, undoubtedly in compensation for the reduced volume of blood in the circulatory system, and the pulse becomes fast and weak just before death. Sweetclover poisoning may be distinguished from infectious diseases which it resembles on the basis of normal or subnormal temperature throughout, signs of anemia, and the absence of inflammation or great pain about the swellings along with the clinical history and diet.

The obvious subcutaneous swellings are caused by subdermal hemorrhage. These are usually accompanied by internal hemorrhaging in the muscles and membranes throughout the body. Occasionally less acute cases are found in which hemorrhage is confined to the internal tissues, and the only clinically observed symptoms are pallor and weakness. Death is likely to occur, but a few days later than usual with the acute type. A variety of complications may arise from hemorrhages into particular tissues. For example, hemorrhage into the eye may produce blindness. Hemorrhage into nervous tissue may produce paralysis. Blood in the milk may be found in a few cases. Post partum hemorrhage is common.

For some time before massive observable hemorrhages occur, cattle on molded sweetclover hay have blood with reduced capacity to coagulate. Simple operative procedures such as dehorning, castration, and the like or small wounds result in uncontrolled hemorrhage and death. Schofield (1413) described a case in which 21 of 22 animals which were dehorned died as the result. The amount of blood lost in these instances may appear small in most cases, but the animal is already anemic as the result of internal hemorrhage.

On post mortem examination the carcass appears as though extensively bruised. The large, subcutaneous swellings are found to consist of fluid or coagulated blood. In many cases serum has separated from the coagulum, forming an edematous or gelatinous mass associated with the swelling. Hemorrhages are principally subcutaneous and intermuscular and vary in size from small petechiae to ecchymoses or hematomas of the size indicated above. Gross hemorrhages may also be found in almost all tissues with the exception of some parenchymatous organs. A layer of coagulated blood an inch or two thick may be found beneath the scapula. The diaphragm is frequently hemorrhagic. Hemorrhages into the marrow of the long bones, into the brain, and elsewhere have been described. The heart almost always bears subendocardial hemorrhage, particularly in the left ventricle. Histopathology has been detailed by Roderick (1354). Lesions of note include fatty degenerative changes in the liver, and nephritis. The liver bears gross hemorrhages that look like buckshot on the surface.

The primary lesion is the reduction of prothrombin level in the blood. No other blood abnormalities have been found (1356) to explain the failure to coagulate. Sweetclover poisoning anemia is not due to blood-cell destruction but results entirely from hemorrhage. It has been shown that blood prothrombin level drops regularly in animals on a toxic sweetclover diet, and that this reduction is parallel (inversely) to the hemorrhagic tendency (1315). Death is solely the result of hemorrhage. Examinations to discover lesions in the blood vessels permitting hemorrhages to occur have been unsuccessful (1354). Blood specimens taken regularly from cattle on toxic sweetclover hay display reduced prothrombin levels after 10 days to 3 weeks, average about 2 weeks (1356). The poisonous principle of sweetclover does not operate to reduce prothrombin in vitro (229). According to Quick (1314), plasma with reduced prothrombin values clots as readily as normal plasma, when tested with dilutions of thrombin, thus demonstrating the absence of an antithrombin.

POISONOUS PRINCIPLE. From the first, sweetclover poisoning was associated with moldy sweetclover hay or silage. However, it was soon learned that not all molded sweetclover was poisonous, and some was highly toxic that had no obvious external manifestation of mold. In the latter it was found that the coarser stalks, when broken open, had fungus growths in the cavity, and an experiment in which stalks with fungus were separated from those without fungus in the same stack, followed by feeding experiments with rabbits, showed that only those with mold growths in them were toxic (1413). Schofield as early as 1924 (1413) reported that isolations of fungi from molded sweetclover, grown on other substrata, had not proved toxic. Later experiments amply confirmed this observation. In limited experiments designed to produce toxic sweetclover hay at will (1356) it was found that hay stacked with a moisture content of 50 per cent readily molded and became toxic. Sweetclover hay retains its toxicity 3 to 4 years or more (1356).

A series of investigations in Wisconsin (229, 231, 798, 1508) resulting in the elucidation and synthesis of the poisonous principle was triggered by the observation (172, 1493) that a species of sweetclover (*M. dentata*) lacking bitterness to the taste (bitterness had caused some palatability trouble with the usual species of sweetclover) also lacked coumarin, and did not produce toxicity when molded. It was demonstrated next that chemically pure coumarin added to alfalfa hay would result in toxicity if the hay were handled so as to mold. But coumarin, itself, was not toxic nor was molded alfalfa without coumarin. After much extraction work, a procedure was developed which allowed the isolation and identification of the toxic product synthesized from coumarin in molded sweetclover hay and silage. It turned out to be 3,3'-methylenebis(4-hydroxycoumarin) (1365)—since termed dicoumarin. A mass of information which cannot be

coumarin

dicoumarin

reviewed here has developed from use of dicoumarin in human medicine as an anticoagulant. Nevertheless, the fundamental reaction whereby prothrombin synthesis is prevented is not yet known. Observations of a partially protective effect of alfalfa in the diet of animals (867, 1315) led to linking vitamin K with dicoumarin action. It has been shown (310) that vitamin

K and dicoumarin act mutually in opposition. Dicoumarin is prevented from producing lowered prothrombin in the presence of vitamin K, while lowered vitamin K levels in the animal will not be restored if dicoumarin is present when vitamin K is given. It is suggested (310) that both have an affinity for the apoenzyme essential to prothrombin synthesis. Other experiments (867), however, tend to indicate that not all the effects found in sweetclover poisoning can be explained on the basis of a simple hypoprothrombinemia alone.

Administration of vitamin K has proven effective in human medicine for counteracting the effects of dicoumarin (929). Oxalic and malonic acids may be very effective in controlling hemorrhage in dogs poisoned by Warfarin (125).

A similar bleeding syndrome has been observed in cattle fed molded lespedeza (*Lespedeza*) hay.

Phaseolus lunatus L. (= *P. limensis* Macf. in part). Lima bean, Java bean, Burma bean, Sieva bean, etc.

This legume comprises a group of related, named horticultural varieties. The species embraces also a variety of wild forms in tropical countries throughout the world. All varieties which have been tested have been found to contain a cyanogenetic glycoside (1623). The cyanogenetic potential in lima beans grown in the United States has never been found to exceed 0.01 per cent, a level considered nondangerous for human consumption, and usually is much less. The hydrocyanic-acid content of beans from tropical countries, however, is generally greater than 0.01 per cent, and frequently much greater.

The large, flat, almost white beans grown for human consumption in the United States are easily recognized. Some of the smaller, plumper, colored forms of this species that occur in other countries and occasionally are imported as livestock feed are more likely to be confused with other kinds of beans (other species of *Phaseolus*). *Phaseolus lunatus* is the only species of bean known to be cyanogenetic. Mistaken identification of a tropical form of lima bean for "navy bean" has resulted in human poisoning. Lima beans of all types may be distinguished from almost all other beans with which they might be confused (such as navy beans, soybeans, etc.) by the presence of distinct lines radiating over the entire surface of the seed from the scar of attachment, and by the fact that the scar of attachment is located in the center of the inner curved surface. Other morphological and chemical criteria for positively distinguishing seeds of *Phaseolus lunatus* from those of other species are given by Viehoever (1623).

The cyanogenetic glycoside present in lima beans is phaseolunatin, identical with that in flax (linamarin, see *Linum*). An enzyme capable of releasing HCN from the glycoside is also present in the seed. Usually in plant tissues cyanogenetic glycosides are readily broken down and HCN, a volatile molecule, is quickly lost under conditions brought about by cooking in water. Cooked lima beans have less cyanogenetic potential than raw, but tropical lima beans of very high original cyanogenetic potential may not be rendered completely safe by cooking in the usual fashion. The beans are thick and dense and resist physically the release of cyanogenetic glycoside at the center.

Some tropical forms of lima beans have been found to contain as much as 0.3 per cent hydrocyanic acid (= 300 mg per 100 g) (1623). Plants containing 0.02 per cent HCN or more generally are considered potentially dangerous to livestock (see cyanogenetic glycosides, p. 23). Tropical varieties of *Phaseolus lunatus* usually may be distinguished from other varieties by beans that are small, plump, and solidly colored or with colored spots.

In the years immediately following the turn of the twentieth century and again during World War I beans imported into European countries, primarily as livestock feedstuffs, were occasionally responsible for loss of life in livestock. At least one such shipment caused trouble in the United States (1221). As a result, regulations were forthcoming which required analysis of such beans before importation and set forth maximum permissible cyanogenetic content. The United States rejects beans containing more than 0.01 per cent HCN, while Canada stops imports with more than 0.02 per cent (1623). Most of the beans that have caused trouble have originated in Java or India. The small, black lima bean of Puerto Rico has been found (1623) to contain as much as 0.3 per cent HCN and to have caused loss of human life on that island.

The cyanogenetic glycoside phaseolunatin is present in all parts of the plant. In the human diet lima beans are rarely consumed as a meal in themselves, hence the HCN they may contain is diluted by other items in the diet ingested at the same time. Animals, on the other hand, may consume relatively larger quantities of bean vines. Cattle mortality has been produced under such circumstances in several instances on farms in Maryland (1335) and South Carolina (1232). Some of these cases were associated with vines that had been frosted. The symptoms were typical of cyanide poisoning. Further, one or two cases of supposed cyanide poisoning in cattle have been reported to the United States Department of Agriculture (804) in which lima-bean ensilage was involved.

Phaseolus coccineus L. (= *P. multiflorus* Lam.), widely planted as an ornamental vine under the common name scarlet runner bean, has a record of toxicity in Europe (1629).

Pisum sativum L. Garden pea

Ensilage made from the vines and pods from canning peas has been responsible for the production of nervous symptoms in sheep and cattle. In Alberta (1670) ewes fed such ensilage as a part of their diet remained in excellent flesh and general health but gave birth to lambs which developed nervous symptoms within one to three days. These consisted of periodic tenseness, running about, or backing up, or a stance with depressed back and lowered head. Attacks were interspersed with periods of quiescence during which animals appeared normal. Forced exercise precipitated and intensified further attacks. Affected lambs grew normally and eventually ceased to display symptoms if carefully handled. Otherwise, deaths were frequent in lambs which became separated from their dams.

Lesions were carefully investigated. The only pathological changes found were confined to the central nervous system and consisted of degeneration of the Purkinje cells in the cerebellum and vacuolar degeneration of certain neurons in the cerebrum. Marked swelling of a few neurons was also found in the more distal sections made of the spinal cord. Experiments to determine whether a vitamin or mineral deficiency was involved were negative.

Shaw and Muth (1444) observed atactic behavior in cattle being trailed to summer range in Oregon. If hurried they would fall and go into convulsions. These animals had been wintered on pea-vine ensilage, but a factor complicating the conclusion that *Pisum sativum* was responsible in this instance was the presence of nightshade (*Solanum nigrum, q.v.*) berries in the ensilage.

Pisum sativum L. var. *arvense* Poir. Field pea, Austrian pea

Lameness in hogs has been experimentally traced by the Alabama Agricultural Experiment Station (1382) to field-pea pasturage. Field cases had been reported from various sections of the state. A group of experimental animals was placed on field-pea pasturage. Symptoms of mild incoordination of the hind legs were noted in a few animals in the fifth week. By the end of the sixth week all animals were affected. Paralysis or incoordination, beginning at the hind feet, involved more of the leg as it increased in severity. Knuckling under of the hind feet while walking was followed by reeling and eventual prostration in the most severely affected animals. A control group of hogs on oat pasturage not only failed to develop nervous symptoms but also made better gains.

Field-pea vines after threshing have been used extensively as winter roughage for horses in the Palouse River Valley of Washington and Idaho. Heavy mortality has resulted from this practice (860). Field-pea vines bring about intestinal impaction, particularly in the pelvic flexure, cecum, and small colon in horses. The impaction is extremely firm and often impossible to treat successfully.

Poinciana gilliesii Hook. (syn. *Caesalpinia gilliesii* Wall.; non *Strelitzia*). Poinciana, bird of paradise

Poinciana is a showy shrub (sometimes slightly climbing) or small tree which is cultivated as an outdoor perennial in the Gulf Coast states westward, and elsewhere as a large pot plant. The terminal, racemose inflorescences are composed of large, light yellow leguminous flowers with exserted red stamens. The fruit, a legume pod, is up to ¾ in. wide and to 4 in. long.

The green seed pods are severely irritant in the digestive tract (235). Two boys who each consumed approximately five pods developed, within 30 minutes, symptoms of nausea, vomiting, and profuse diarrhea. Recovery occurred after about 24 hours. Experiments with animals have confirmed the irritant nature of the pods.

Prosopis juliflora (Sw.) DC. Mesquite, kiawe bean

DESCRIPTION. Deciduous shrub or tree with several trunks, 9 to 23 ft tall. Branches arching, irregularly bent; ultimate branches bearing paired large woody spines at leaf axils. Leaves bipinnate; pinnae 2 to 4; pinnules (leaflets) 7 to 17 pairs; leaflets linear, about 1 in. long. Inflorescence a catkinlike spike, 1½ to 2½ in. long; flowers small, numerous, leguminous. Fruit a leathery legume pod, 2 to 6 in. long, more or less constricted between the beans; seeds brown or reddish brown.

DISTRIBUTION AND HABITAT. Common on dry ranges, washes, and draws at low elevations, especially along streams and where the water table is high; California to Texas, Kansas, and Mexico.

Fig. 84. *Prosopis juliflora*. Mesquite.

POISONOUS NATURE. Ingestion of large amounts of mesquite by cattle over an extended period of time results in rumen stasis and impaction with associated symptoms, and eventually in death. The biochemical pathology is only partially understood. In some ways the syndrome produced by a diet of mesquite is best considered a nutritional problem.

Mesquite-bean poisoning has been described in Hawaii (8, 749) and in Texas (438). Experimental feedings at the Marfa substation of the Texas Agricultural Experiment Station have reproduced the disease as known under range conditions. It was found that animals given mesquite beans and foliage without other feed would consume about 2.5 per cent of their weight daily. The amount consumed initially was less, but increased during the course of the experiment. All experimental animals died after a terminal period characterized by decreased consumption of mesquite, and emaciation, the deaths occurring between 8 and 12 months after commencement of the experiment. Deaths also were induced in another experiment in which animals were allowed oat hay with the mesquite diet. In this instance they occurred after a somewhat longer period.

Symptoms appear only after several months on mesquite diet, during which the animal may gain weight. As described in Texas, they consisted of profuse, foamy salivation, continuous chewing, eventual rumen stasis, and emaciation. The disease is characterized in many animals by abnormalities in use of jaw and tongue and stance with tongue protruding between the lips at rest. Transitory edematous submaxillary swelling is frequently observed. On post mortem examination the masseter and sublingual muscles are flabby, off-color, and often spotted with petechial hemorrhages. As animals become increasingly poisoned, frequency of eructation is decreased and eventually it ceases. Sometimes it is accompanied by forceful expulsion of mesquite beans from the mouth. Terminal stages may be characterized by nervousness and muscular tremors, especially about the head.

On post mortem examination the rumen is found to be full of mesquite pods and seeds. Instances have been observed in which pods and seeds were still present in the rumen as much as 9 months after the animals no longer had access to mesquite. In the Texas cases, gross abnormality was observed in the kidney and liver. Hawaiian cases were characterized by atrophic cirrhosis of the liver (as opposed to the diffuse toxic necrosis of ketosis in postparturient dairy cattle). A severe anemia was characteristic of the Texas animals, while a high ketone level (mainly beta-hydroxybutyric acid) in blood and urine and lowered blood sugar were the only significant biochemical findings in Hawaiian cattle.

It has been postulated (8) that the primary lesions are those of indigestion and acetonemia resulting from an unbalanced diet. It is held that mesquite is high in sugars, which, together with inadequacy in other dietary factors, depresses microfloral activity in the rumen (detected in Hawaiian cases). Cellulose is not broken down into metabolically available sugars, protein synthesis is reduced, and symptoms of starvation appear. Ketosis, which then follows, also involves degenerative changes in liver and kidney.

Some Texas findings tend to support this hypothesis. Chopped hay passes through the digestive tract of affected animals unchanged. On the other hand, lush pasturage promotes improved condition and weight gains in affected animals. Such animals should then be marketed, since ability to digest cellulose seems permanently impaired.

CONDITIONS OF POISONING. In Hawaii, losses are associated with management practices which make use of kiawe bean as the exclusive forage during a large part of the year. Likewise in Texas and New Mexico, losses occur in areas where several bean crops are produced each year, allowing ingestion of relatively large amounts over a period of many months. Elsewhere in the United States, even though the plant may be common, cases have not been reported.

Psoralea argophylla Pursh. Scurf pea
This white, silky-haired, perennial, herbaceous legume of dry prairies from Saskatchewan to Wisconsin, Missouri, and New Mexico has been suspected (1217) of causing severe poisoning in a child who ate a quantity of the seeds.

Psoralea tenuiflora Pursh. Scurf pea, Indian turnip
This species is an open, bushy (to 3 ft), blue-flowered, perennial herb with palmately 3 to 5 foliate, glandular dotted leaves. It is a common legume of dry prairies and open woods, Indiana, and Montana to Missouri and Arizona. The United States Department of Agriculture has received many reports of the toxicity of this species to horses and cattle (985), but with the exception of a single experiment (277) in which toxic effects were noted in a rabbit dosed with an aqueous extract of this plant, no experimental or clear circumstantial evidence is available in support.

Robinia pseudoacacia L. Black locust
DESCRIPTION. Small, coarse-barked tree to 75 ft tall. Trunk straight, long, slender in relation to length. Spines unbranched, resembling large rose thorns, scattered on younger branches, persisting several years. Leaves alternate, pinnately compound; leaflets entire, elliptical, opposite in 3 to 10 pairs. Inflorescence racemose, drooping, 4 to 8 in. long; flowers leguminous, white, showy. Fruit a straight, flat, many-seeded legume.

DISTRIBUTION AND HABITAT. Gregarious, forming woods and thickets, eastern and central United States and southern Canada. This species is native to the central eastern states. Following the chestnut blight, black locust was widely recommended as a source of fence posts resistent to decay. It is also valuable for timber and has been planted in some areas as an ornamental.

POISONOUS PRINCIPLE. Several investigators isolated, partially characterized, and named compounds from black locust which they held to be

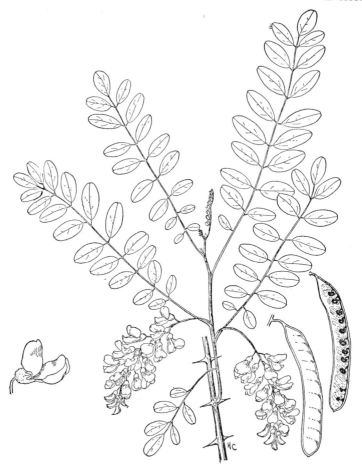

Fig. 85. *Robinia pseudoacacia*. Black locust. Leafy flowering branch, with details of flower and fruit. Courtesy of The Macmillan Company.

responsible for its toxicity. Results are not in agreement, and additional confusion has arisen from inaccuracies in translation of names. Most commonly cited are results of Power (1291), who characterized the toxic substances as a heat-labile phytotoxin ("robin"), and Tasaki and Tanaka (1563), who have extracted a glycoside ("robitin") from the bark.

TOXICITY, SYMPTOMS, AND LESIONS. Feeding experiments have been limited. In Alabama, (254) a horse displayed symptoms one hour after an aqueous extract of bark representing about 0.1 per cent of the horse's weight had been administered. In Japan, a horse was poisoned with 0.04 per cent of its weight of powdered bark (1563). Symptoms appeared in about 1½ hour. The poisonous principle appears to be about one-tenth as toxic to cattle (1563).

Symptoms are similar in various classes of livestock and in the human being but vary somewhat with severity of poisoning. They appear within a few hours after ingestion of a toxic dose. Especially noted are anorexia, lassitude, weakness (posterior paralysis in horses and cattle), nausea (vomition in human beings), coldness of extremities, and marked dilation of pupils. The pulse is weak and irregular. In severe cases marked dyspnea is present. Diarrhea may occur and blood may be present in the feces. Several persons have described a thumping noise in severely poisoned horses which was ascribed by some to spasmodic contraction of the diaphragm, but more frequently to increased force of heart contractions (1241). In fatal cases, death occurs within two or three days. Lesions consist mainly of irritation and edema of the mucous membranes of the digestive tract. In poultry, degenerative changes in liver and kidney have been reported (68).

CONDITIONS OF POISONING. Fatal cases are rare. Recovery usually requires several days or weeks. Horses, cattle, sheep, and poultry have been poisoned. Poisoning most commonly occurs when horses strip and eat the bark of black locust trees to which they have been tied (602, 695, 1636). Cattle and horses have been poisoned from grazing sprouts on cut-over lands (254, 695, 1335), poultry by leaves (68), sheep by pods (cited in 704), and horses by trimmings (1335).

Some evidence suggests (68) that toxicity, at least of leaves, is seasonal. Experimental feeding of poultry with old leaves failed to produce any signs of toxicity.

Several cases of human poisoning are on record. Millspaugh (1109) cites a case in which children were poisoned by seeds. Especially noteworthy is a case of poisoning in 32 boys at the Brooklyn Orphan Asylum which occurred in 1887 (485). For some reason they ate the inner bark of black locust fence posts which were being stripped in the orphanage yard. Two were severely poisoned and became stuporous, but all eventually recovered.

Sesbania spp. Coffeeweed, coffeebean, bagpod, rattlebrush, rattlebox, sesbane, poison bean

Three species of closely related legumes of the Gulf Coastal Plain have been found toxic to livestock. Confusion has prevailed not only among common names but also among a half-dozen or more Latin names used by various authors to identify these species. The symptoms and lesions elicited by all three are similar. A conservative taxonomic treatment emphasizes the similarity and will prove easiest for the veterinarian and rancher to use. Therefore, the three plants in question are here treated as species of the genus *Sesbania*. Synonymy as it appears in the veterinary literature and in Small's *Manual of the Southeastern Flora* is as follows:

THE PLANT TREATED HERE AS:	IS THE SAME AS:	IN:
Sesbania vesicaria (Jacq.) Ell.	*Sesbania vesicaria* (Jacq.) Ell.	157
	Sesbania vesicaria Ell.	273
	Sesbania platycarpa Pers.	1224
	Glottidium vesicarium (Jacq.) Harper	460, 486, 490, 526, 560, 1175, 1186, 1661
		1460, 1477,
Sesbania drummondii (Rydb.) Cory	*Sesbania drummondii* Rydb.	1477
	Sesbania drummondii	1501
	Daubentonia longifolia DC.	983, 990
	Daubentonia drummondii	986
Sesbania punicea (Cav.) DC.	*Daubentonia punicea* (Cav.) DC.	460, 1661
	Daubentonia longifolia DC.	1445

Sesbania vesicaria (Jacq.) Ell. Bagpod, bladderpod, coffeebean, etc.

DESCRIPTION. Vigorous erect annual with a bright green, straight, erect, slender, somewhat woody stem; branching variable. Plants often in dense clumps. Leaves alternate, pinnate-compound; leaflets 20 to 52, narrowly oblong or elliptical, mucronate, ¾ to 1½ in. long by about ¼ in. broad, green, waxy. Flowers in long-peduncled axillary racemes of 2 to 5; yellow (or bright red in var. *atrorubrum*), about ½ in. across. Fruits 2-seeded, pendant, elliptical, somewhat compressed legume pods, acuminate at both ends, wingless; valves peeling back lengthwise with maturity so that the seeds remain encased in a thin, white, papery membrane (whence "bladderpod" and "bagpod"). The woody stem remains erect after the leaves have fallen and bears the persistent pods.

DISTRIBUTION AND HABITAT. Rich soils, old fields no longer cultivated, especially in damp soils or along streams; the Coastal Plain from North Carolina and Florida to Texas.

POISONOUS PRINCIPLE. Saponins have been detected (560) but not yet chemically characterized (1186).

TOXICITY, SYMPTOMS, AND LESIONS. Experimental feedings have been made to chicks (460), fowl (486), sheep (157), cattle (490, 526, 1175, 1460), and the cat (560). Hogs and goats have also been reported poisoned (1661).

In fowl, Emmel (486) found 100 seeds toxic; 150 seeds lethal. Death occurred in about a week after ingestion of 200 seeds and after from 2 to 7 weeks when the seeds were fed at rates between 5 and 20 seeds per day, with considerable variation shown. Duncan *et al.* (460) fed amounts of seeds representing 1.13 and 2.00 per cent body weight to chicks and found these amounts rapidly lethal; leaflets at 2 per cent, however, showed no toxicity. Symptoms in fowl included diarrhea, prostration, and dark, congested comb when large amounts were fed; emaciation, diarrhea, and light, scaly comb with smaller amounts. Post mortem examination showed necrotic enteritis and inflammation and necrosis in the gizzard. Fatty degeneration was observed in the liver and degenerative changes in most parenchymatous organs.

In sheep, Boughton and Hardy (157) found the minimum lethal dose of seeds to lie near 0.05 per cent of the animal's weight, an amount which produced symptoms in 24 hours and death in 56 hours. Larger amounts reduced the time intervals (0.25 per cent brought symptoms in 8½ hr and death in 22 hr). Less than lethal amounts elicited symptoms that lasted up to two weeks before recovery was complete. Poisoned sheep displayed uneasiness, depression, arched back, anorexia, diarrhea, shallow and rapid respiration, and fast, irregular pulse. They became comatose in the final period before death. Post mortem findings which were reported included dark, tarry blood, degenerative changes in the gastric and mesenteric lymph glands, some hemorrhaging, and gastroenteritis posterior to the rumen. Liver and kidneys were congested and friable.

Cattle have been poisoned experimentally by several investigators (490, 526, 1175, 1460). Figures for toxicity of seeds range from 0.15 per cent, which produced chronic poisoning and death after 14 days (1460) to 2 per cent, which produced symptoms in 24 hr and death in 2 days (490). Considerable variability was found and is perhaps explained by the fact that not all seeds are digested (1460). Cattle display symptoms and lesions similar to those found in sheep, although constipation has been reported (526) in some instances. Hemorrhagic diarrhea has also been reported (1460). Post mortem examination reveals a severe or hemorrhagic inflammation of the abomasum and small intestine. Histologically, generalized albuminous degeneration was found (490) in kidneys and liver, with some necrosis in the latter. Rumen stasis appears complete, and sprouted seeds may be found in the rumen during post mortem examination (1175, 1460).

CONDITIONS OF POISONING. Loss of cattle has been known from the late 1800's (273, 1224). Cases occur in fall and winter when the pods, still carried on the erect dead stems, are available to livestock after other forage has become scarce. Cases in cattle are common when animals are moved into a new pasture containing the plants (526). Generally the plant seems distasteful. It was found that semistarved fowl would not consume a lethal dose (486), but cattle have been observed to develop a craving for the seeds even when ample forage was present (1460).

Sesbania drummondii (Rybd.) Cory. Coffeebean, rattlebrush, rattlebox, etc.

DESCRIPTION. Perennial shrub or small tree. Leaves alternate, pinnate-compound; leaflets 12 to 60, narrowly oblong or elliptical, mucronate, ½ to 1 in. long. Flowers in showy, slender, loosely flowered racemes which do not exceed the leaves in length, yellow, about ½ in. across. Fruits several-seeded, oblong, compressed, longitudinally 4-winged legume pods, 2½ to 3½ in. long, on a stalk ½ to ¾ in. long. Seeds separated by transverse partitions.

DISTRIBUTION AND HABITAT. Sandy soils, especially in seasonally wet areas of waste places and previously cultivated fields; Coastal Plain from Florida to Texas.

POISONOUS PRINCIPLE. Undetermined.

TOXICITY, SYMPTOMS AND LESIONS. Sheep and goats have been poisoned under natural conditions. Experimental feedings have been performed with sheep (983, 990). Cattle may also be poisoned (983, 1501) but no cases are described in the literature. In sheep, 0.07 per cent of the animal's weight provoked symptoms, while about 0.1 per cent was the minimum lethal amount. Symptoms appeared in 8 to 30 hours, commonly after about 24, and were similar to those described above for *S. vesicaria* poisoning of sheep. Post mortem observations (990) included degenerative changes in the lymph system and smooth musculature, and small thrombi of clumped degenerated red blood cells in the circulatory system, together with a characteristic gastroenteritis. The leaves were found less toxic, and the pods had no demonstrated toxicity.

CONDITIONS OF POISONING. As for *S. vesicaria*.

Sesbania punicea (Cav.) DC. Purple sesbane, purple rattlebox, etc.

DESCRIPTION. Perennial shrub or small tree, to 12 ft tall. Leaves alternate, pinnate-compound; leaflets 12 to 40, oblong or elliptical, mucronate, ¾ to 1 in. long. Flowers in showy, dense racemes, projecting outwards or pendant, red, orange or scarlet, ¾ to 1 in. across. Fruits several-seeded, oblong, compressed, longitudinally 4-winged legume pods, 2 to 3 in. long, on a stalk ½ in. long or shorter.

DISTRIBUTION AND HABITAT. Introduced into Florida from Mexico as an ornamental. Cultivated. Also escaped and naturalized on ditch banks, fencerows, and waste places, northern Florida to Louisiana.

POISONOUS PRINCIPLE. Undetermined; probably a saponin (1661).

TOXICITY, SYMPTOMS, AND LESIONS. Experimental feedings have been made to fowl (460, 1445); the plant is also considered toxic to sheep and

Fig. 86. *Sesbania punicea.* Coffeeweed. Flowering stem, with detail of fruit. Courtesy of The Macmillan Company.

pigeons (1661). Shealy found (1445) that 9 seeds per bird were lethal to three out of five hens, but as many as 36 seeds could be fed without provoking death in another instance. Duncan *et al.* made feedings of seed at 0.63 to 0.86 per cent and 1.46 to 1.47 per cent to chicks, with resultant death of all birds in each group. West and Emmel (1661) report, without describing the experiment, that as few as 6 to 18 seeds may prove lethal in fowl. They also state that 50 grams per hundredweight will produce fatalities in sheep ($= 0.1$ per cent).

Symptoms and lesions agree with those described for other species of *Sesbania,* and consist mainly of depression, diarrhea, and evidences of gastric and enteric irritation. Duncan *et al.* found death to occur after 5 to 18 hr in the group of chicks fed the lesser amount; in 3 to 9 hr in the group fed the larger amount.

CONDITIONS OF POISONING. Fowl appear to be poisoned most frequently under field conditions. The seeds did not appear distasteful in one experiment (1445), and death followed in 24 to 72 hours when birds were given free access to them. Poisoning can be prevented by removing and destroying the developing pods from ornamental bushes before the seeds are released.

Sophora secundiflora (Ort.) Lag. Mescalbean, frijolito

DESCRIPTION. Woody, evergreen shrub less than 10 ft tall or, in limited areas, a tree to 35 ft tall. Leaves alternate, pinnate, oppositely once compound, with terminal leaflet; leaflets 7 to 13, leathery, entire, oblong, narrowing gradually to attachment; leaflet tip obtuse or sometimes retuse. Inflorescence a many-flowered, one-sided terminal raceme, to 4 in. long; flowers leguminous, purple, strongly fragrant. Fruit a large, hard, woody, jointed, 1- to 8-seeded legume pod, cylindrical, 1 to 7 in. long, ½ in. or more in diameter. Seeds bright red, very hard-surfaced, about ½ in. long.

DISTRIBUTION AND HABITAT. Limestone range lands, hills and canyons, southwestern Texas into Mexico.

POISONOUS PRINCIPLE. Alkaloids of quinolizidine (lupine) structure have been isolated from this and other species of *Sophora* (918).

TOXICITY, SYMPTOMS, AND LESIONS. A disease of range sheep has been traced to this plant. The syndrome is nervous in character and rarely fatal. Affected animals, on being forced to exercise, begin to tremble violently, walk with stiffened gait, finally fall, and after one or two unsuccessful attempts to stand, become somnolent for about five minutes. Then alertness returns, the animals regain their feet and immediately return to grazing. The syndrome may be repeated by forced exercise throughout the time (usually several days) that the animal is under the effects of the poisonous principle.

Feeding experiments (154) proved the toxicity of seeds and foliage to sheep, goats, and cattle. Symptoms comparable to those of range cases were produced in sheep and goats. Considerable variation was found in susceptibility of individual animal. Single feeding of toxic doses in the neighborhood of 1 per cent of the animal's weight of mature foliage produced a period of susceptibility to attack lasting up to 12 days. Limited experiments with goats showed them about equally affected. The whole seeds pass through the digestive system intact and are harmless. Ground seeds have a toxicity equal to or somewhat greater than that of mature foliage. Immature or young foliage is considerably less toxic than older.

Cattle are probably never poisoned under range conditions, but were shown highly susceptible to the toxic principle in feeding experiments. Death occurred in a calf less than 2 hours after it had been dosed with 1 per cent of its weight of foliage. One-quarter per cent produced death in another after 45 hours.

No specific lesions were found in either sheep or cattle.

Mescalbeans once had the reputation (1514) of being highly toxic to human beings. They were used to produce an intoxication characterized by excitement and delirium, followed by a period of deep sleep lasting two or three days. Children were said to have been fatally poisoned, and one seed, masticated, was considered a lethal dose for the human being.

Sophora sericea Nutt. Silky sophora
This small, hairy-leaved, brushy plant of the Great Plains has had the reputation (273) of being toxic to horses. Feeding experiments have been reported (465) in which large amounts failed to provoke symptoms.

Sophora alopecuroides L.
This species, considered for introduction by the U.S. Soil Conservation Service as a soil builder, was shown to be toxic at 1 per cent and lethal at 2 per cent of an animal's weight (801). It was withdrawn, and test plantings destroyed.

Stizolobium deeringianum Bort. Velvet bean
Velvet bean is an introduced, viny, long-stemmed legume, with three leaflets. It is grown in peninsular Florida where it was first used as an

ornamental vine and later widely employed as a soil builder. Reports of the toxicity of this plant to livestock under natural conditions are lacking. The beans attracted experimental investigation to determine whether they would prove acceptable food for man. Even boiled for an extended time, the beans were found (1102) unpalatable and produced, an hour or more after ingestion, symptoms of nausea and discomfort. While cooking, the beans gave off a volatile substance which produced a smarting sensation in the eyes and a pronounced headache among those experimenting with them. Experiments with poultry indicate the presence in velvet bean seeds of some factors which interfere with the normal processes of growth and egg production (722).

Thermopsis rhombifolia Nutt. ex Rich. False lupine, yellow bean, golden banner

This prairie legume is a common herbaceous perennial of dry plains or slopes from Alberta and North Dakota to Nebraska and Colorado. It produces a raceme of bright yellow leguminous flowers, curved pods, and palmately trifoliolate leaves with large stipules.

False lupine has been suspected of causing loss of life in cattle (277) and horses (1524). The seeds have been reputed to be poisonous to children in western Canada. In all instances the plant has been incriminated on rather tenuous circumstantial grounds. It contains a number of quinolizidine alkaloids (1689).

Trifolium spp. Clovers

It would be surprising if plants used in agriculture as extensively as the clovers did not occasionally cause trouble. In all instances where trouble has occurred, commercial strains of clovers cultivated in pastures or for hay have been involved. Below, several clovers are listed in order of decreasing importance from the point of view of contributing to animal disease.

Trifolium hybridum L. Alsike clover

A relationship between ingestion of alsike clover and the production of photosensitivity in horses was established in England as early as the late nineteenth century. In the United States it was first described from Tennessee in 1905 (1128). Since then, according to published reports, alsike poisoning has occurred sporadically in widely scattered parts of the United States and Canada and has been recognized in hogs, sheep, and cattle, but is most prevalent in horses (530, 712, 1228, 1335, 1414). It usually occurs among animals on alsike pasturage in bright, sunny weather, but some of the characteristic symptoms and lesions have been experimentally reproduced in animals fed alsike hay (1414).

The exact nature of the syndrome produced in horses varies. In each instance, photosensitization or liver injury, or both, have been found. In addition, symptoms of nervous and digestive disorders occasionally have been described. The symptoms and lesions of alsike poisoning in livestock other than horses are not well known.

Alsike-induced photosensitization has been called trifoliosis. It is usually characterized in horses by reddening of the skin under the influence of sunlight, followed by either superficial or deep dry necrosis of the skin or by edematous swelling and serous discharge from the affected area. It has been noted repeatedly in horses that the areas of skin most likely to show lesions are those which contact moisture when the animals are at pasture—namely the feet and muzzle. For this reason, the disease has become generally known as "dew poisoning" in some areas. Inflammation about the muzzle commonly extends into the mouth and involves painful irritation or shallow ulceration of oral mucous membranes and the tongue. Since these parts are not exposed to sunlight, these lesions may be produced directly by the plant during ingestion. Colic, diarrhea, and other signs of digestive disturbances have been noted in some instances. Poisoned animals may be markedly depressed or excited. If stomatitis is severe, horses will not eat and become emaciated.

Lesions of photosensitization provoked by alsike in horses are characteristic (see photosensitization, p. 52). Whether alsike photosensitivity is primary or hepatogenic is not clear. In the majority of instances icterus or other signs of liver dysfunction have not been recorded. At the other extreme, poisoning of horses in Ontario was characterized (1414) solely by liver lesions and directly associated symptoms. Signs of photosensitization were absent. The syndrome was designated "big liver disease" from the appearance of the liver on necropsy. Livers may weigh as much as 50 to 60 pounds. They are pale in color and rubbery in texture. Symptoms commonly appear in horses pastured on rank, lush alsike, usually after several weeks. Not all animals are affected. Symptoms consist of recurring attacks of severe icterus accompanied with increasingly severe emaciation, sluggishness, anorexia, unsteadiness, depression, and eventual stupor, or continuous, manic walking about. Urine is commonly dark-colored. The syndrome is fatal unless reversed in its early stages.

Stomatitis has occasionally been absent in instances of alsike poisoning in horses. On the other hand, Pammel has described a case of alsike poisoning in which stomatitis was the sole symptom (1228).

Cases in which photosensitization is the chief finding usually make a prompt recovery on being removed to alsike-free pasturage.

Trifolium pratense L. Red clover

Hay containing large or moderate amounts of second-cutting or late-season red clover produces a syndrome characterized by slobbering in cattle, horses, and sheep (1187). The disease has been recognized in

Missouri, Illinois, Indiana, and Ohio. It has been experimentally reproduced in cattle at the Missouri Experiment Station. Ten pounds of toxic hay per day provoked slobbering after three days. Symptoms continued with increasing severity as long as the hay was fed. In certain instances, bloating, stiffness of gait, depression of milk flow, diarrhea, emaciation, or abortion have been reported. Toxicity is not related to the saponin content of the hay, and the toxic factor is water- and alcohol-soluble.

Burnside (213) has described a case of severe photosensitization in a herd of Georgia cattle pastured on red clover in which symptoms typical of photosensitization appeared after three days on pasture. Impairment of vision or blindness developed in some animals after edematous swelling and necrosis of tissues about the eye. The nictitating membrane was entirely lost in some instances. Icterus and dark-colored urine were observed, but no post mortem examination was made to determine the degree of liver involvement, if any. Although the pasture contained a number of kinds of weeds, red clover seemed the plant most likely to have caused the photosensitivity.

In New Zealand, *T. pratense* is associated with a disease displaying symptoms similar to those of "stiff lamb disease" (caused by a deficiency of vitamin E), and also may contain an estrogenic factor (607).

Trifolium incarnatum L. Crimson clover

Crimson clover is used as a winter annual, particularly in the central eastern states. It provides useful cover during winter months and may be used for pasturage or hay in the following season. Short, barbed hairs are produced especially about the pedicel and calyx of the flowering plant. As the flowers set seed, the hairs become stiff and wiry. Hay made from overripe crimson clover may be dangerous to horses. Death from impaction has followed its use in Delaware, Virginia, North Carolina (367), and elsewhere. Dense, feltlike balls with a diameter of 3 to 4½ in. composed almost entirely of crimson-clover hairs have been recovered from the intestines.

Trifolium repens L. White clover

Certain strains of white clover have a moderate cyanogenetic capacity. These strains originated, at least in part, from natural collections in Europe. Breeding work with white clover in New Zealand has shown that the desirable characteristics are often accompanied by increased cyanogenetic capacity in selections. Such selections grown in the United States have retained their cyanogenetic capacity (1357). On the other hand, no actual cases of loss of life have been attributed to this species, either in the United States or elsewhere (333).

Several other syndromes have been associated with white clover in other countries. They include an ergotlike syndrome, bloat, and paresis in newborn pigs from demyelination of the spinal chord. The literature on these syndromes has been reviewed by Garner (607).

Trifolium subterraneum L. Subclover, subterranean clover

This species was introduced into the United States some years ago and has found use as a pasture crop in the Pacific Northwest. In Australia subterranean clover has caused considerable economic loss to sheep farmers. A number of investigations have culminated in the discovery of an estrogen (genistein) in the green growing plant. Symptoms observed in sheep include changes in the sex organs, abnormal lactation, infertility, and, in the ewe, dystocia and prolapse of the uterus. The literature has been reviewed by Gardner and Bennetts (605).

Additional reference: 1129.

Vicia spp. Vetches, fava bean

Species of vetch, many cultivated, have occasionally been recorded as producing disease or loss of life in livestock and human beings. The literature has been reviewed by Hurst (810) and Steyn (1533). *Vicia sativa* L., common vetch, figures most prominently in other parts of the world. It has been shown on occasion to contain lethal concentrations of a cyanogenetic glycoside in the seed (1350, 1373), to have produced liver lesions in horses similar to those of European lupine poisoning (1533), and to have produced photosensitization (574). *Vicia sativa* and *V. angustifolia* L. contain beta-cyano-L-alanine, a physiologically active compound related to the toxic principle in some species of *Lathyrus*. (See *Lathyrus* for a fuller discussion.) The former is common in North America but has been responsible for no recorded losses except rarely through its cyanogenetic potential. Several other species of *Vicia,* some of which occur also in the Western hemisphere, have been reported toxic in other parts of the world, but not here.

The following species have records of toxicity in North America.

Vicia faba L. Fava bean, broad bean, horse bean.

Native to the Mediterranean region, widely cultivated there and elsewhere, throughout history, as a food for man and animals. Limited amounts are grown in scattered areas of the United States and the beans also are imported.

Ingestion of the beans, especially raw or partially cooked, or inhalation of pollen produces acute toxic hepatitis in human beings, commonly called "favism." Only certain individuals are susceptible. The disease is frequent among residents of the Italian island of Sardinia and is present in much of the Mediterranean area. It seems to show differential incidence with race, family, and sex. Occasional cases have occurred in the United States among persons of Italian or Jewish descent. When cases are properly diagnosed, a history of the disease is often determinable among other members of the subject's family. Males are more commonly affected than females. Mortality has been estimated by one investigator (943) at somewhat less than 10 per cent; it is almost entirely confined to children.

Various theories have been advanced to explain the apparent toxicity of the fava bean. It once was generally believed (943) that symptoms are produced in sensitized persons by an allergic reaction. Evidence is at hand (1713), however, which suggests that persons susceptible to poisoning suffer from a genetically determined biochemical deficiency in the red blood cells. The defect is characterized by unusually low levels of whole-blood glutathione (which can be reduced still further by incubation with acetylphenylhydrazine) and a deficiency of glucose-6-phosphate dehydrogenase activity, and seems to be transmitted as a sex-linked factor of intermediate dominance.

Symptoms may appear within minutes after inhalation of pollen, or after 5 to 24 hours by ingestion of the bean. They include, in order of appearance, headache, dizziness, nausea, yawning, vomiting, abdominal pain, and marked elevation of temperature. In mild cases (symptoms no more severe than those listed above) subsidence may follow spontaneously. In more serious cases there is a sudden onset of hemolytic anemia with hemoglobinuria and icterus, becoming intense. These symptoms are the most characteristic of the disease. Collapse may occur. The typical case lasts 2 to 6 days with symptoms of icterus and anemia persisting, the latter for as long as a month.

Specific blood dyscrasias and diagnostic test results may be found in the review of Luisada (943).

Vicia villosa Roth. Hairy or winter vetch

At least one instance is on record (1533) in which this plant caused loss of life in cattle in Europe. In the United States the seed has been held responsible for the loss of five cows in Alabama (303). Symptoms appeared about a day after the animals had ingested relatively small quantities of vetch seed from a bag left in the barnyard. The authors felt that "possibly one handful of hairy vetch seed would kill a cow." Symptoms were almost identical with those of rabies and consisted of extensive pain, bellowing, sexual excitement, and convulsions, the latter initiated or intensified by excitement in treating the animals. These symptoms are not identical with those reported in the European literature.

An unidentified wild vetch has been considered (456) responsible for provoking photosensitivity in pinto horses in Colorado. Other vetches have been generally believed responsible for occasional cases of hepatogenic photosensitivity elsewhere (574). It might prove fruitful to search for relationships between vetches and other legumes in which liver lesions or hepatogenic photosensitivity are produced, as for example, *Medicago, Trifolium,* and European *Lupinus* poisoning.

Additional references: 815, 1361, 1587.

Wisteria spp. Wisteria

Nearly a half-dozen species of this woody vine are cultivated for the pendant, showy, fragrant racemes of flowers. *Wisteria floribunda* DC. (Japanese wisteria) and *W. sinensis* Sweet (Chinese wisteria) are the most important. Flowers are blue, white, pink, or purple depending on variety, in Japanese wisteria; blue-violet in Chinese wisteria.

Wisteria was considered toxic in Europe before the turn of the twentieth century but, probably as the result of negative experiments by Cornevin (335), has generally been omitted from more recent publications. Recently, however, several cases have been reported in which children have been poisoned by consumption of seeds or pods. The National Clearinghouse for Poison Control Centers has collected six cases (1167) while the author has received reports of seven (890, 1703), and two others have been reported by Jacobziner and Raybin (827). In all cases, symptoms consisted of mild to severe gastroenteritis with repeated vomiting, abdominal pain, and diarrhea. In the more severe cases, clinical dehydration occurred and some patients were put on the critical list. Nevertheless, signs abated and recovery was essentially complete within 24 hours.

The amount of plant ingested is not known, although there is some evidence that amounts as small as one or two seeds may have been involved in some instances. Neither is the toxic principle known, although some crudely characterized physiologically active principles were isolated in the 1880's.

Rosaceae

Cercocarpus spp. Mountain mahogany

Of the several species of this genus, two have been incriminated in the loss of livestock by means of their cyanogenetic potential. *Cercocarpus montanus* Raf. of Kansas to Arizona, South Dakota, and Montana and *C. breviflorus* Gray of the area from Texas to Arizona are shrubs affording excellent browse when not containing dangerous amounts of cyanogenetic glycoside. Analyses of *C. breviflorus* (754) have shown it to contain concentrations of cyanogenetic glycoside that are usually, but not always, below the dangerous level. Both species have been more or less definitely considered responsible for occasional scattered cases of loss of livestock (208, 609, 754, 1185). (See cyanogenetic glycosides, p. 23.)

Malus sylvestris Mill. Apple

Apple poisoning, particularly of cattle, but also in horses (1092) and mules (709), has occurred sporadically. Animals, either accidentally or otherwise, are allowed access to an orchard after the apples have fallen in the autumn, and may eat large quantities. Apple poisoning as used here refers to development of symptoms of anorexia, dullness, weakness, staggering, and occasionally death upon ingestion of rather large quantities of apples under circumstances that rule out spray residues as the toxic factor.

The toxic principle is unknown. Farmers, because of the staggering, often believe the animals drunk. It is more likely that rapid ingestion of apples causes an abnormal reaction in the rumen or stomach similar to that produced by overfeeding on grain, beets, or other substances. In some cases poisoning may have been the result of cyanogenetic foliage (709).

Apple seeds are cyanogenetic. A man, who found apple seeds a delicacy, saved a cupful of them. Eating them at one time, he was killed by cyanide poisoning (1335).

Prunus spp. Wild cherries

Nearly fifty species of *Prunus* occur in North America. Several have been shown to produce dangerous levels of a cyanogenetic glycoside in leaves and fruit stones. Poisonous species include apricot, bitter almond, peach, and several wild cherries.

Together, they have been responsible for much loss of life in livestock and human beings. The cyanogenetic glycoside in several is amygdalin. The structure of this compound, and the toxicity, symptoms, and lesions of cyanogenetic glycosides, are discussed on p. 24. Prulaurasin and prunasin, cyanogenetic glycosides closely related to amygdalin, have been detected in *P. laurocerasus* and *P. serotina* respectively.

GENERAL DESCRIPTION. Trees and shrubs. Leaves simple, alternate. Flowers radially symmetrical, white or pink, usually grouped in showy racemes or umbel-shaped clusters; sepals 5, partly joined; petals 5, separate, white or pink, spreading; stamens numerous; pistil single, superior, containing usually one, sometimes two ovules. Fruit a drupe, in most with fleshy outer layer enclosing a single, hard stone; in some, such as almond, outer portion is leathery.

(A) Wild species of *Prunus*

Prunus serotina Ehrh. Wild black cherry (275, 709, 1133, 1335)

Tree, becoming large with age (to 90 ft tall, 4 ft diameter); bark rough, dark; inner bark aromatic; twigs reddish. Leaves oblong-lanceolate, serrate, with incurving teeth, undersurface lighter in color than upper.

Inflorescence racemose, appearing when the leaves are half developed or later; flowers less than ½ in. across. Fruit black, less than ½ in. in diameter. Woods and fencerows, eastern North America.

This species is the most dangerous of the eastern wild cherries. Cases reported to the New Hampshire Experiment Station prompted an investigation of wild-cherry poisoning as early as 1898 in that state (1133). Fresh leaves contained on the average 212 mg HCN per 100 g of leaves, or more than 10 times the minimum amount considered dangerous. At this level, less than ¼ lb of fresh leaves would prove toxic to a 100-lb animal (toxicity about 0.2 per cent). It was widely believed that only wilted wild cherry leaves were dangerous. Therefore, a further experiment was performed at the New Hampshire station to determine the change in HCN content as leaves wilted. These experiments, carried out with other wild cherries as well, and repeated later by others, indicate that the potential cyanide content of fresh leaves is increased but little in absolute amount as leaves wilt, but as water is lost from the leaves, remaining cyanide is concentrated, so that wilted leaves may contain a somewhat larger amount of cyanide on a final-weight basis. Cyanide is volatile and is released and lost as the leaves continue to dry. Greatest cyanide concentration occurs at about 75 per cent original moisture content (when the leaves begin to appear limp and lose their gloss). Only when the original material contained unusually large levels of cyanide did dried leaves retain enough to be potentially dangerous. All classes of livestock have been killed by ingestion of black-cherry leaves. Chesnut (275) states that children have died after ingestion of the kernels. It is one of the most dangerous plants to livestock in the East. The larger, tenderer, more succulent leaves (those on vigorous shoots or sprouts) contain the largest amount of cyanide. Those on old, dry, woody growth contain much less.

Prunus virginiana L. Choke cherry (97, 540, 543, 754, 1133, 1276)
Coarse shrub or small tree; bark gray, nonaromatic. Leaves ovate to obovate, sharply serrate, thin. Inflorescence racemose, appearing after the leaves have begun to appear; flowers less than ½ in. across. Fruit red or red-purple, astringent. Thickets, fencerows, edges of woods, eastern North America.

Fresh samples of the leaves of this species averaged 143 mg HCN per 100 g in experiments at the New Hampshire station. Concentrations in wilted leaves reached a recorded maximum of 243 mg per 100 g of wilted leaves.

Var. *demissa* (Nutt.) Sarg. (= *P. demissa* Walp.). Western chokecherry
Characteristics as preceding. Habitat—damp woods, slopes, and flats, among scrub growth, mostly in mountains below 8200 ft; distribution Washington to Idaho and California.

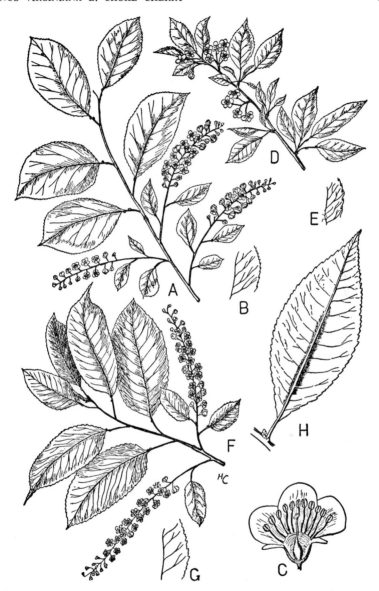

Fig. 87. Wild cherries. A-C, *Prunus virginiana.* Choke cherry. Flowering branch, with details of flower structure, and leaf margin and venation. D-E, *P. pensylvanica.* Pin cherry. Flowering branch, with detail of leaf margin and venation. F-H, *P. serotina.* Wild black cherry. Flowering branch, with details of leaf showing lower surface with hairy fringe along midrib, and leaf margin and venation. Courtesy of The Macmillan Company.

Var. *melanocarpa* (A. Nels.) Sarg. (= *P. melanocarpa* Rydb.). Western chokecherry

Characteristics as preceding except fruit dark purple, becoming almost black when ripe. Habitat generally as preceding, distribution British Columbia and Alberta to California and New Mexico.

Both varieties of western chokecherry are cited in various publications as poisonous. The most extensive investigations of western chokecherry are those of Fleming *et al.* at the Nevada Experiment Station (540, 543). In these publications, the species is given as *P. demissa,* but from the description and distribution it is most likely that the plant experimented with was what is now recognized as *P. virginiana* var. *melanocarpa.* Both varieties and the species proper (eastern chokecherry) are closely related, and it is likely that the toxic properties are similar among all three.

Fleming *et al.* performed extensive analyses and feeding experiments with cattle. In one specimen of fresh leaves, 368 mg HCN per 100 g was detected. Toxicity in cattle paralleled HCN content. They concluded that 0.25 per cent of an animal's weight of leaves represented an amount normally lethal. Seasonal studies indicated that HCN content was greatest in the young leaves, decreasing as they matured and dried. Other studies showed no diminution in sensitivity of experimental animals after administration of repeated sublethal amounts. The high speed of elimination of cyanide in the animal body was shown by studies in which an amount of chokecherry leaves that could be given repeatedly at hourly intervals without effect, when given at half-hourly intervals provoked symptoms with each administration.

The berries of this variety may be eaten by campers or used in making preserves and are attractive to children. The flesh is not toxic, but poisoning and death have occurred in children who consumed large amounts of the berries without removing the stones (1276).

Prunus caroliniana Ait. American cherrylaurel, southern mock orange

This evergreen tree, native to the southeastern states and planted as an ornamental there and in California, is considered toxic in Louisiana (641).

Prunus pensylvanica L. Pin cherry, wild red cherry, bird cherry, fire cherry (1133)

Large shrub or tree to 35 ft in height; bark smooth, reddish. Leaves oblong-lanceolate, doubly serrate, rough beneath. Inflorescence umbellate, appearing before the leaves; flowers about ½ in. across, fruit red, about ¼ in. in diameter. Dry open woods and openings, especially after fire, Labrador to British Columbia, south to Colorado and Tennessee.

This species was found less toxic than the preceding in the New

Hampshire studies. The fresh leaves averaged 91 mg per 100 g, and as much as 143 mg per 100 g was found in wilted leaves. Both levels are potentially lethal to livestock.

CONDITIONS OF POISONING. Eastern wild cherries are responsible for much loss of life in livestock under conditions which make foliage available to pastured animals. Although wild cherries commonly occur in fencerows where animals have ready access to them, they are usually left alone. In more than 100 cases of eastern wild-cherry poisoning which he investigated, Hansen (709) found that the four principal causes were trees or limbs blown down, trimmings from fencerow cleanouts or electric-company line pruning, sprouts in cut-over areas, and—least important—standing scrub cherry growths.

Western chokecherry poisoning is frequent in cattle and sheep. Cases commence when more desirable vegetation becomes scarce. The sooner range grasses disappear, the more likely cherry poisoning becomes, since the leaves have their greatest danger early in the season. By the end of the summer, cherry leaves have lost most of their cyanide content and provide useful range forage. They are also apparently more palatable at that time and are grazed freely. Another factor to be considered in western wild-cherry poisoning is the fact that cherries often grow near water. Animals, especially sheep, may "shade up" among wild cherries.

The release of cyanide from the leaves requires a certain amount of moisture. On the western range, under particularly dry conditions, it has been observed repeatedly that mass mortality may occur suddenly, within minutes after animals have been watered. Frequently this has prompted an investigation of the water source when the trouble actually was cyanide poisoning. Drinking prompted quick release of cyanide from previously ingested dry cherry leaves.

(B) Cultivated species of *Prunus*

Prunus persica Batsch. Peach

Of the various cultivated species of *Prunus,* the peach seems the only one to have caused much trouble in North America. All parts of the plant contain cyanide, but the stone kernels are particularly rich. Morse and Howard (1133), for example, cite a figure of 164 mg per 100 g. Peach pits have caused mortality in hogs in Maryland and Indiana, with symptoms of cyanide poisoning (709, 1335). Lethal amounts of peach seeds may accumulate from home peach-canning projects. Hansen records a case resulting in the death of a cow after ingestion of frozen fallen leaves from a peach tree. In Australia (810) peach leaves were found to have cyanide content of 66 mg per 100 g.

Prunus armeniaca L. Apricot

Apricot kernels have caused the death of children in Australia (810). On analysis they were found to contain 275 mg cyanide per 100 g.

Prunus amygdalus Batsch. Almond (279)

Almonds may be divided into bitter and sweet varieties. Those cultivated for human consumption are of the sweet variety. Bitter almonds are grown for an oil which may be obtained from the kernels. Its characteristic odor comes from one of the products of amygdalin breakdown (benzaldehyde). Only the bitter variety contains amygdalin in quantity, and hence only the bitter variety is dangerous. Unfortunately no stable botanical characteristics exist by which the two varieties may be distinguished. Commercial almond production in the United States is confined to the sweet, nontoxic varieties.

Prunus laurocerasus L. Cherrylaurel (810, 1133)

This variable evergreen shrub, native to southeastern Europe, has been used widely as an ornamental in the warmer parts of the United States. It has long been known in Europe and elsewhere as a cyanogenetic plant. Loss of life in livestock may occur when trimmings are thrown into a pasture (623).

Other species of cherry have been found to contain cyanide. For safety the foliage and fruit of all species of *Prunus* should be treated as potentially dangerous.

Additional reference: 933.

Rubus laciniatus Willd.
Rubus macropetalus Dougl. } Blackberry

These species of creeping wild or naturalized blackberries have been responsible for mechanical injury in cattle in western Washington where they grow abundantly in pastures and woodlands (1252). Injured cattle often have bloodstained nasal discharge. Examination reveals one or more blackberry stems in the nasal passage. Blackberry stems enter the nasal passages from the pharynx, forming bundles lodged in the upper rear portion of the passages or sometimes further forward. The recurved spines on the stems prevent their expulsion.

Saxifragaceae

Hydrangea spp. Hydrangea

Various authors include several species of hydrangea in lists of poisonous plants. *Hydrangea macrophylla* Ser. (= *H. hortensis*) is the common greenhouse hydrangea, sometimes also planted outdoors. Wild hydrangeas *H. quercifolia* Bartr. and *H. arborescens* L., the former restricted to the southeastern states, the latter more widely distributed from New York to

Florida west to Iowa, are also commercially available and treated as garden subjects within and outside their natural ranges.

Phytochemical investigations at Kew Gardens, in the first decade of this century, disclosed that hydrangeas on occasion contained quantities of a cyanogenetic glycoside. The few reported cases of hydrangea poisoning in livestock, however, present symptoms and lesions that are not equivalent to cyanide poisoning. Cases have been reported in Vancouver, British Columbia (186), and in Florida (1660). In the former, a horse had been observed to consume the major portion of a single potted hydrangea. Symptoms of a painful gastroenteritis and diarrhea accompanied with blood developed within a few hours, but the animal made an uneventful recovery the following day. Experimental feedings of guinea pigs with alcoholic extracts of hydrangea performed on this occasion produced similar symptoms and lesions of well-marked gastrointestinal irritation. In Florida, a family was poisoned when the children added hydrangea buds to a tossed salad. Symptoms were those of gastroenteritis and nausea.

Order Myrtales

Myrtaceae

Eucalyptus spp. Eucalyptus

More than a dozen species of this tree have been introduced from Australia into California where they are now widely planted. Several species are suspected of toxicity in Australia, and one, *E. cladocalyx* F. Muell., has caused serious loss of sheep by reason of its high HCN content (810). No cases have been reported in the United States or Canada.

Order Umbellales

Araliaceae

Aralia spinosa L. Hercules-club, devils-walking-stick, angelica tree

This is a striking shrub or small tree, conspicuous because of its thick, clublike, spiny branches each tipped with a cluster of very large, twice pinnately compound leaves. It occurs wild from Pennsylvania to Florida and west to Illinois and Iowa, and is sometimes cultivated as an oddity.

This species was suspected (1335) of poisoning livestock in Maryland. Feeding experiments with seeds have shown them lethal to guinea pigs.

Hedera helix L. English ivy

This common cultivated vine, hardy throughout most of the United States, has been considered poisonous since the time of Pliny. A few cases of poisoning in children after ingestion of the berries are reported in the older European literature. The plant is said to be purgative and also if ingested in quantity, to produce symptoms of excitement, labored respiration, and eventual coma in the human being. Forsyth (574) has described similar symptoms in cattle after ingestion of a "very considerable"

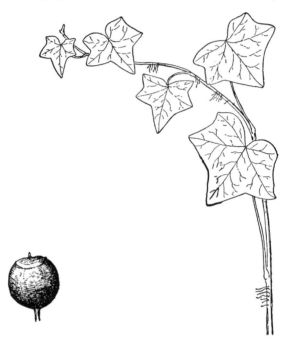

Fig. 88. *Hedera helix*. English ivy. Leafy branch and growing tip, with detail of fruit. Courtesy of The Macmillan Company.

quantity of ivy vine. Uneventful recovery occurred after three days. He also cites poisoning in the human being from ingestion of ivy leaves. No cases of poisoning are known to have occurred in the United States. The toxicity of ivy is probably the result of the presence in this species of a saponic glycoside (hederagenin).

Umbelliferae

Aethusa cynapium L. Fool's parsley

An annual weed of waste places and gardens, belonging to the carrot family; introduced and naturalized in the northeastern United States and southeastern Canada. The reputation for human toxicity possessed by this species (574, 1628) may be traced to early European literature. It is stated to have poisoned human beings who mistook it for parsley.

Swine have been killed by it in Britain (71). The chief symptom was ataxia, especially of the posterior, which, together with the botanical relationship of the plant, suggests the presence in it of an alkaloidal poisonous principle.

Ammi visnaga (L.) Lam. Bishop's weed

This carrotlike weed has been introduced and now has a spotty distribution in waste areas, principally in states of the seacoasts of the southern half of the United States.

It has been of particular interest as the source of three important pharmacologically active principles, one of which is the smooth-muscle relaxant khellin. No cases of toxicity of the plant itself have been reported from North America but its seeds, ingested as contaminants in wheat, have been shown (1593) to produce photosensitivity of fowl in Uruguay.

Apium graveolens L. Celery

Celery tops containing dangerous levels of nitrates have caused loss of dairy cattle in California. The tops were found (1318) to contain between 3.24 and 8.67 per cent nitrate, dry-weight basis.

Berula pusilla (Nutt.) Fern. (= *B. erecta* Coville). Water parsnip

This plant is distributed along waterways and in wet habitats from Ontario to British Columbia south to Michigan in the East, further south to Oklahoma and New Mexico and westward to California. It is listed here on the basis of reported loss of cattle in the Fraser Valley, British Columbia, Canada (183), in which it was circumstantially incriminated.

Cicuta spp. Water hemlock

The most useful common name of this genus is water hemlock. In appearance the plant is not easily distinguished from several other members of the family Umbelliferae. A profusion of common names, locally applied, has resulted. Among such names are: cowbane, poison parsnip, wild parsnip, snakeroot, snakeweed, beaver poison, muskrat weed, spotted hemlock, spotted cowbane, musquash root, false parsley, poison hemlock, wild carrot, fever root, mock-eel root, and spotted parsley, and carotte à moreau in French Canada.

This genus is considered by many authorities (356, 1011) to be the most violently poisonous plant of the North Temperate Zone.

DESCRIPTION AND HABITAT. Members of the family Umbelliferae (parsley or carrot family) tend to have many characteristics in common and to bear close resemblance to each other. Casual examination even by a trained botanist is often not enough to distinguish species within a genus nor occasionally to distinguish between genera. Characteristics of the fruit (a small two-carpellate capsule) are of basic taxonomic significance among members of the Umbelliferae, and small differences are used as indices of species separation. Many authorities recognize several types of water hemlock and have given them separate species names. A few of these entities are distinctive and easily determined by characteristics of morphology, habitat, or geographic distribution. Others require detailed examination of the fruiting structure. Unfortunately for persons interested in *Cicuta* as a poisonous plant, the fruiting structure is not present during the period when the plant is most dangerous.

Surprisingly few feeding experiments have been carried out with *Cicuta*. The few that have, suggest that the various species develop roughly equivalent toxicity at a given stage of growth. It has been generally assumed, perhaps unjustly, from this and from field cases that the species all have similar toxicity. The description which follows is intended to characterize only the genus *Cicuta* and distinguish it from other Umbelliferae of similar appearance. If it is necessary to separate species, a botanical manual or a botanist should be consulted.

Cicuta is spread primarily by seeds, which are produced in large numbers. Under proper conditions the seed germinates and develops into a small plant the first season. Flowering is delayed until sufficient food reserves have been set aside by the plant in its thickened root system to permit growth of the characteristic flowering stem. This may take place the second year or not until later. Flowering occurs in spring or early summer and exhausts the stored reserves. Before the thickened root system disappears, however, it produces a lateral shoot which overwinters and initiates a new plant the following spring. A given stand of *Cicuta,* therefore, tends to persist from year to year in the same spot, even though the plant is, strictly speaking, not a perennial.

The thickened storage portion of the plant is very characteristic and is the most useful single feature in distinguishing *Cicuta* from its relatives. It is composed of stem and root. The lowest inch or more of the stem is much thickened. To this are attached several (occasionally only one) roots which also are greatly thickened in their upper portions. The bundle of roots is like that of a dahlia but smaller in size. The thickened underground portion of the stem, when cut open lengthwise, displays two additional important features. (1) It is composed of a region of greatly compressed nodes and internodes. As in the mature stem, the internodes are hollow and a diaphragm of pith tissue is formed horizontally across the cavity at each node. Thus the storage portion of the stem gives the appearance of a series of squat air chambers separated by thin diaphragms of pith. Very young stems may be solid, but their layered nature is demonstrated by horizontal yellow lines in a white matrix. (2) The cut surface of the stem exudes drops of a yellowish oily liquid with the characteristic pungent odor of raw parsnip.

Fig. 89. *Cicuta maculata.* Water hemlock. Lower and upper portions of flowering stem, with details of chambered pith at rootstock, flower, and fruit. Courtesy of The Macmillan Company.

Taken together, these features—fascicled, tuberous roots; chambered, swollen rootstock; yellowish, oily drops; and characteristic smell—serve to distinguished *Cicuta* in almost all stages of growth from other umbelliferous plants (which may show some but not all of these features).

The first foliage is developed early in the spring from food stored over-winter in the structure described above. A cluster of leaves appears at ground level. As the leaves mature they reach a length of 1 to 3 ft and are pinnately two or three times compound. The leaflets in all but *C. bulbifera* are lanceolate, serrate, and 2 to 5 in. long. Leaflet venation is pinnate. A feature useful in separating members of this genus from relatives of similar appearance is the disposition of the major vein branches from the midvein of the leaflet in relation to the serrations of its margin. In all species of *Cicuta* except *C. bulbifera* and *C. californica* the majority of primary vein branches are directed toward the notches of the serrations rather than the points. In some cases they split just before reaching the notch and do not actually make contact with it as they do in other cases, but in all instances their course is towards the notch as opposed to the tip. In umbellifers in general the equivalent veins approach the tip or end at the tip of the serration (147).

The primary stem of the plant is produced just before flowering. It is distinctly jointed, hollow except at the joints where the leaves are inserted, attains a height of 5 to 10 ft, and terminates in several globose clusters of small umbellate inflorescences of tiny white or greenish flowers.

Cicuta bulbifera is distinctly different from other species in having very narrow, almost linear leaflets and in producing small bulbils in the angles of the upper leaflets of each leaf.

Cicuta was not distinguished from *Conium* (*q.v.*) before 1500, although one or both plants had been used as sources of poison for many centuries. The first mention of the genus in the United States did not occur until the eighteenth century. Linnaeus in 1753 (the starting point of botanical nomenclature) recognized three species of *Cicuta: C. virosa, C. maculata,* and *C. bulbifera.* The first is the common European water hemlock; the latter two are found in the United States. *C. virosa* and *C. maculata* appear similar to the untrained eye.

The following species are found in the poisonous-plants literature of the United States and Canada.

Cicuta bolanderi Wats. Found only in a very small area about Suisun Bay in central western California.

Cicuta bulbifera L. Distributed across southern Canada and the northern United States, south in the East to Virginia.

Cicuta californica Gray. Localized in coastal California from Mendocino to Monterey counties.

Cicuta curtissii Coult. and Rose. Southeastern United States on the Coastal Plain from Virginia to Louisiana.

Cicuta douglasii (DC.) Coult. and Rose. Found at higher elevations in California and Arizona northward into Alaska.

Cicuta mackenziana Raup. Southeastern Alaska north to the Brooks Range.

Cicuta maculata L. Eastern United States and Canada south to Missouri and west to Texas.

Cicuta occidentalis Greene. Rocky Mountain area from the Black Hills and Washington to Nevada and New Mexico.

Cicuta vagans Greene. Northwestern United States and British Columbia.

All species of *Cicuta* occupy similar habitats. They are found *only* in swampy or wet habitats, as along streams and in marshes or areas that are swampy at least part of the year.

TOXIC PRINCIPLE. The toxicity of the plant has long been associated with the yellowish, oily liquid found in the thickened root and rootstock and to a lesser extent in the lower portions of the aboveground stem. Those attempting to extract a poisonous compound of definite characteristics from this material encountered difficulty. Jacobson (824) in 1915 partially purified, but was unable to crystallize, a compound which he considered a resinoid. More recently the toxic principle (from extracts of *C. virosa*) has been crystallized and characterized (27) as a highly unsaturated higher alcohol with the following structure:

$$HOCH_2(CH_2)_2(C\text{=}C)_2(CH\text{=}CH)_3CHOHCH_2CH_2CH_3$$
(*trans*) heptadeca-8:10:12-triene-4:6-diyne-1:4-diol

The toxic principle of *Cicuta* has been known as cicutoxin ever since the earliest crude attempts at its extraction and characterization. With the structure indicated above it is isomeric with oenanthotoxin obtained from the related genus *Oenanthe,* which has proven poisonous in England and elsewhere.

TOXICITY, SYMPTOMS, AND LESIONS. Despite the toxicity of this plant, it has been the subject of only very limited feeding experiments. The data presented in the accompanying table are derived in each case from experiments with only one or a few animals and can serve only as a general indication of degree of toxicity. The figures represent amounts that produced death.

Cicuta has been shown toxic to all classes of stock and to human beings. Field observations or feeding experiments have established the toxicity of the following species: *C. bolanderi* (1383), *C. bulbifera* (704, 1007), *C. californica* (1007, 1383), *C. curtissii* (1007), *C. douglasii* (14, 1383),

C. maculata (658, 896, 1216, 1335, 1474), *C. occidentalis* (277, 555, 1007) and *C. vagans* (174, 743).

TOXICITY OF CICUTA

SPECIES	PART	ANIMAL	TOXICITY	REF.
C. occidentalis	"old tubers"	sheep	0.2%	555
	"young tubers"	sheep	0.5%	555
	"old tubers"	cattle	0.1%	555
	"old tubers"	horse	0.5%	555
	"roots"	sheep	0.5%	1007
C. maculata	"roots"	hog	0.3%	1474
C. vagans	"one bulb"	heifer	—	743

Symptoms in human beings and various classes of livestock are similar. They were well described several centuries ago, and are generally well known. They are specific and distinctive. Cicutoxin, acting directly on the central nervous system, is a violent convulsant. Symptoms appear within 15 minutes to more than an hour, but usually within about a half-hour after ingestion of a lethal dose. Excessive salivation is first noted. This is quickly followed by tremors and then by spasmodic convulsions interspersed intermittently with periods of relaxation. The convulsions are extremely violent; head and neck are thrown rigidly back, legs may flex as though running, and clamping or chewing motions of the jaw and grinding of the teeth occur. Abdominal pain is evident. In some cases the tongue is chewed to shreds; in others, teeth have been broken in an unsuccessful attempt to pry the mouth open to administer treatment. The pupils of the eyes are dilated and temperature may be elevated several degrees. Delirium is encountered in human beings. Nausea is common, although vomition may not be accomplished because of the nature of the animal or, in human beings, because of convulsive closure of the mouth. If vomition can be obtained when the symptoms first appear, prognosis is good. Because of this, in cases of human poisoning, fatalities are somewhat reduced. If the poisoning terminates fatally, the periods of relaxation between convulsive seizures become shorter and death through respiratory failure follows after a period of complete paralysis. Death may occur as quickly as 15 minutes after ingestion of a lethal amount or not until after 8 hours. Bloat is common. Post mortem examination shows no specific lesions, although irritation of the mucous membranes lining the stomach or rumen has occasionally been noted.

CONDITIONS OF POISONING. Scores of cases of the loss of human life to this plant are on record in the United States (684). The tuberous roots are attractive to children, and they may be mistaken for edible roots such as wild parsnip (*Pastinaca sativa*) or wild artichoke (*Helianthus annuus*). Wild parsnip and *Cicuta,* both members of the carrot family, have somewhat the same appearance and characteristic odor. Both plants have thick fleshy roots, but in wild parsnip there is but a single long tap root, contrasted with the bundle of fleshy roots in *Cicuta*. One often encounters the belief among rural people that cultivated parsnip escaped from the garden and "run wild" becomes toxic. Wild parsnip (*Pastinaca*) or parsnip escaped from cultivation never develops toxicity.

It has been shown (555) that the roots of *Cicuta* are toxic at all stages of growth except the very youngest, and that even the old dead roots and rootstocks which have given rise to new offshoots may retain a high degree of toxicity. The early spring growth (the shoots before the leaflets have fully opened out) also has been shown (555) to be highly toxic. On the other hand the foliage of matured plants has been shown (1007) to be nontoxic, although poisoning associated with ingestion of mature foliage has been reported (259, 896). Toxicity of roots is not lost upon drying (555).

Most loss of livestock occurs in early spring. At that time the toxic new growth appears before other palatable forage has become available. Also at that time of year the ground is soft, permitting the roots to be pulled up by grazing animals and ingested along with the tops. Roots exposed by plowing can also be the source of livestock loss. At one time the seeds were thought toxic, but this has not been borne out experimentally. Poisoning resulting from ingestion of *Cicuta* is particularly difficult for the veterinarian to deal with. Its rapidity of action is one contributing factor. Another results from the fact that *Cicuta* often grows in a relatively solitary manner. Since one root can easily kill a cow (743), the entire evidence may be ingested and may not be detected in the rumen.

References 555, 824 and 1007 contain useful reviews. Additional references are: 707, 746, 1235, 1574.

Conium maculatum L. Poison hemlock, hemlock, spotted hemlock, California or Nebraska fern

This genus is often confused, especially in common name, with its relative, *Cicuta maculata* (*q.v.*).

DESCRIPTION. Plant coarse, erect, 4 to 8 (to 10) ft tall. Stems stout, rigid, glabrous, hollow except at nodes, ridged, and usually spotted with purple especially in the lower portions. Leaves large, much dissected, triangular in outline, glabrous, pinnately to 4 (or 5) times oppositely decompound, ultimate segments pinnatifid; borne as a rosette from the tap root, or alternately on the erect stem. Flowers small, white, in umbellate clusters. Fruits grayish-brown with conspicuous wavy, somewhat knotted ridges. Root a fleshy, usually unbranched, white tap root.

This plant resembles wild carrot (*Daucus carota*) to which it is related. The two may readily be distinguished by the fact that the stem and leaves of wild carrot are distinctly hairy. The dissected leaf of *Conium* gives it a lacy, fernlike appearance and it has been planted for this effect in flower gardens.

DISTRIBUTION AND HABITAT. Poison hemlock was introduced from Eur-

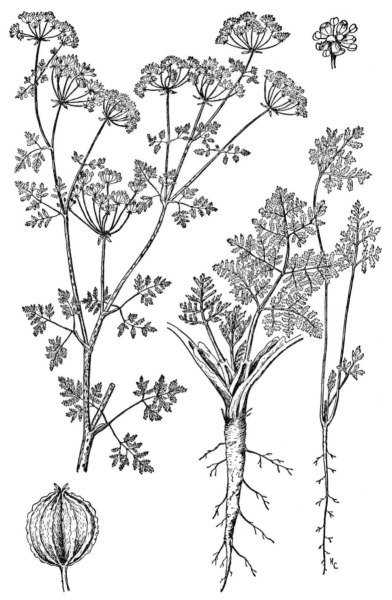

Fig. 90. *Conium maculatum*. Poison hemlock. Flowering stem, with details of tap root, seedling, flower, and fruit. Courtesy of The Macmillan Company.

ope many years ago and now is found throughout the United States and southern Canada, especially in the northeastern, north-central, and Pacific northwestern states and adjacent Canada, as a luxuriant weed of roadsides, ditches, edges of cultivated fields, waste areas, and the like. The plant is a biennial, sometimes perennial in favorable locations, reproducing by seeds. It may readily be controlled with herbicides.

POISONOUS PRINCIPLE. *Conuim* contains at least five distinct yet closely related alkaloids: coniine, N-methyl coniine, conhydrine, lambda-coniceine, and pseudoconhydrine. Of these, lambda-coniceine predominates in the plant during its vegetative growth while coniine and N-methyl coniine increase and become predominant in the fruits with maturity (384, 519, 520, 778). Coniine, synthesized by Ladenburg in 1886, was the first alkaloid to be synthesized (778, 975). Its structure is based on a pyridine nucleus:

coniine

Coniine is a colorless, volatile, strongly alkaline oil.

TOXICITY, SYMPTOMS, AND LESIONS. *Conium* has been known as a poisonous plant from very ancient times. On the basis of symptoms[1] this is the hemlock, an extraction of which was used to put Socrates to death, and not the water hemlock (*Cicuta*) with which it was then confused.

Despite the known toxicity of the plant, little experimental work has been reported to establish the degree of toxicity. Figures given by Cornevin in 1887 (334), repeatedly cited since, give the toxicity for the horse (green-weight basis) at about 0.25 per cent of the animal's weight; for the cow, about half that (0.5 per cent). On the other hand, it has been shown that the predominant alkaloid in the plant changes with stage of development, and even from hour to hour (384, 519, 520), that the total amount of alkaloid varies with the stage of growth and part of plant (975) and with geographic area, the plants from southern latitudes being held more poisonous on the average than northern-grown ones (334). Variability in toxicity of this kind may explain the fact that in experimental feedings of a cow in Texas, *Conium* was found to produce symptoms but not death at about 2 per cent of the animal's weight and did not produce death even at almost 4 per cent (1405). Coniine is volatile and is lost slowly from *Conium* while drying. The hemlock alkaloids are present in least amount in

[1] An account of the death of Socrates, translated from the *Phaedo,* is given in J. W. Harshberger, *Pastoral and Agricultural Botany* (New York: McGraw-Hill Book Company, Inc., 1920).

the root. As the plant grows, they accumulate in the stem, leaves, and fruits, being greater in amount in these organs in the order listed and in each reaching a maximum just prior to maturation of the seeds (975). Concentrations of total alkaloids as high as 1.6 per cent have been measured in the green seed.

It appears that all classes of livestock and the human being are susceptible to poisoning by this plant, despite statements to the contrary in the older literature. Toxicity to cattle (574, 1259, 1405), sheep (1405), horses (957), swine (34, 194), goats (327), and fowl (609, 935) has been reported in relatively recent times. With continued repetition from Greek and Roman times, the symptoms usually listed are truly classical. They include, in order of appearance, nervousness, trembling, ataxia, especially involving the lower or hind limbs, dilation of the pupils, weakened and slowed heartbeat, coldness of the extremities or the entire body, coma, and eventual death through respiratory failure (373).

In the few recent reports that are available, we find some differences from the classical picture. Bloody feces and gastrointestinal irritation have been reported in cattle (1259) and goats (327). Nausea, vomition, and convulsions have been reported from the human being. The corneal reflex was found present in comatose horses (957). Convulsive attacks have been suggested (327) more than once in animals but have not been emphasized, perhaps because they run contrary to the classical picture. Temperature has been reported from subnormal (194) to normal (957) to elevated (34) in particular instances and animals. Respiratory involvement is common. Widespread congestion is found on post mortem examination, but characteristic lesions are absent.

Symptoms usually appear soon after ingestion of hemlock. When *Conium* seeds were fed with grain in an experimental feeding of swine, symptoms were observed as soon as 12 minutes following their ingestion (34); in general they occur within an hour or so. The plant is not always lethal. Stimulants may be used to advantage. Recovery when it occurs is uneventful and complete within a few days. Abortion may occur in pregnant animals that recover (574).

Conium alkaloids structurally are related to nicotine (see *Nicotiana*) and function somewhat similarly. They produce a transitory stimulation followed by severe depression of the central nervous system resulting in symptoms of paralysis, coma, and slowing of heart. Death occurs when the respiratory muscles become paralyzed.

CONDITIONS OF POISONING. The plant is a common weed. Poisoning in human beings usually takes place as a result of its being mistaken for an edible plant such as parsley, or the seeds for anise. The root looks something like a wild carrot, but both the root and the remainder of the plant have a distinctive odor, usually described as "mousey," which makes the plant unpleasant to human beings and perhaps accounts for its usual distastefulness to stock. This characteristic odor may be detected in the breath and urine of a poisoned animal (574). Most animals will not touch hemlock unless forced to do so by conditions of improper management, but occasionally a particular animal may take a liking to it (1259). Extensive mortality of hogs has been reported (34) in California following the use of home-grown barley contaminated with *Conium* seeds. Otherwise there have been few recorded cases of livestock loss to this plant in the United States.

Additional reference: 1225.

Daucus carota L. Wild carrot, Queen Anne's lace

This is one of the commonest weeds in North America. According to European sources, it may possess mild toxicity for horses and cattle, giving rise to nervous symptoms, but despite its commonness no record of toxicity has been established on this side of the Atlantic (1628).

Sium suave Walt. (= *S. cicutaefolium* Schrank). Water parsnip

A large, coarse, erect, perennial herb, 2 to 6 ft tall, which somewhat resembles species of water hemlock. Like *Cicuta,* it is found on marshy lands and wet soils throughout most of North America. Its white-flowered umbelliferous inflorescence resembles that of *Cicuta* and other members of the same family. *Sium* may be distinguished from *Cicuta* by its stem, which is strongly ribbed or corrugated, and its leaves, which are once pinnate. The leaflets, from 5 to 17 in number, are linear or lanceolate with serrate margins.

This species of *Sium* has been suspected of poisoning hogs and cattle in Indiana (713), cattle in Ontario and Saskatchewan (592), and cattle in California (1706). The cases are not entirely convincing, and the symptoms vary widely. In the Indiana case there was trembling, rapid respiration, decreased heartbeat, and bloating preceding death. The Canadian cases were characterized by dark-colored urine. The California cattle displayed intermittent attacks characterized by falling and convulsions, interspersed with periods of depression. Older European literature and more recent reports from Australia suggest another species of *Sium* as poisonous, but again the evidence is less than satisfactory.

Order Santalales

Loranthaceae

Phoradendron villosum Nutt. Mistletoe

DESCRIPTION. A woody perennial, parasitic chiefly on oaks, forming a dense bushy growth 1 to 4 ft in diameter among oak branches, lighter green than the oak foliage. Leaves and stems hairy. Leaves opposite, oblong to

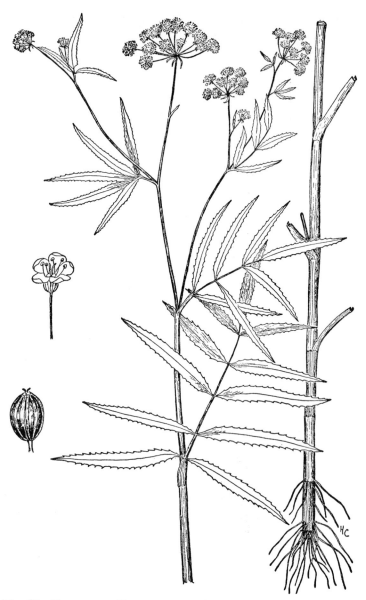

Fig. 91. *Sium suave*. Water parsnip. Upper and lower portions of flowering stem, with details of flower and fruit. Courtesy of The Macmillan Company.

obovate, ½ to 1½ in. long, inconspicuously 3- to 5-veined, leathery. Inflorescence a small spike less than 1 in. long; flowers small, inconspicuous. Fruit a small, pinkish-white berry.

DISTRIBUTION AND HABITAT. Parasitic on oaks, Pacific Coast states, east to Arizona.

POISONOUS PRINCIPLE. Probably the pressor amines beta-phenylethylamine and tyramine.

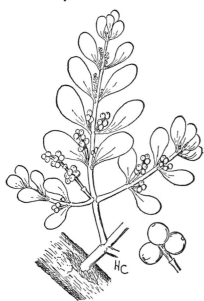

Fig. 92. *Phoradendron flavescens.* Mistletoe. Fruiting branch with detail of berries. Courtesy of The Macmillan Company.

TOXICITY, SYMPTOMS, AND LESIONS. Mistletoe has been toxic to animals browsing among oak branches. Thirteen of a herd of 30 Herefords were lost in California under such circumstances (1673). The animals died suddenly without displaying any characteristic symptoms. No significant lesions were observed on post mortem. Cattle usually leave mistletoe alone, but in this instance were observed avidly to seek it out. All poisoned animals had one- to two-week-old calves at side, which may account for development of an appetite for mistletoe.

Several other species of *Phoradendron* are found in North America. One, *P. flavescens* (Pursh) Nutt., is the familiar mistletoe of Christmas. This species is a parasite of a variety of deciduous trees in the southeastern United States. Its berries are considered by some (816) to be poisonous. The National Clearinghouse for Poison Control Centers has reported (237) a fatality following ingestion of a tea brewed from the berries. Death occurred about 10 hr after symptoms of acute gastroenteritis and cardiovascular collapse. This species contains beta-phenylethylamine and tyramine. *Viscum album,* the European mistletoe, also contains these amines (1423) and is known to be poisonous.

Santalaceae

Comandra pallida A. DC. Bastard toadflax

This plant is (1591) a secondary or facultative selenium absorber. (See p. 45.)

Order Thymelaeales

Thymelaeaceae

Daphne spp. Daphne, mezereon, spurge laurel

DESCRIPTION, DISTRIBUTION, AND HABITAT. The species of Daphne are small woody shrubs, the larger not over 4 ft, the smaller not over 1 ft in height. Several species and hybrids are in cultivation as ornamentals. The flowers are small but showy, in clusters, usually fragrant, and composed of a colored tubular calyx with spreading lobes, corolla lacking. The leaves are simple and entire.

Daphne cneorum L. Small shrub with rose-colored flowers in terminal heads, persistent leaves, and orange-red "berries" (drupes).

Daphne laureola L. Shrub with yellowish-green flowers in axillary racemes, persistent foliage, and bluish-black fruit.

Daphne genkwa Sieb. & Zucc. Shrub with deciduous foliage, opposite

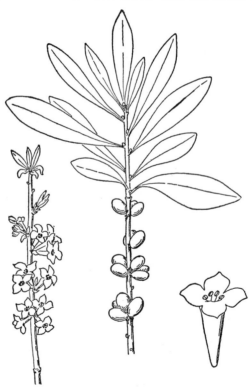

Fig. 93. *Daphne mezereum.* Daphne. Fruiting stem, with details of flowering stem and flower. Courtesy of The Macmillan Company.

leaves, purple flowers along the principal axes before leaves appear in the spring, and white fruit.

Daphne mezereum L. Shrub with deciduous foliage, alternate leaves, purple flowers along the principal axes before leaves appear in the spring, and scarlet fruit.

All are ornamentals, but *D. mezereum* may be found occasionally also naturalized in thickets, hedgerows, and along roadsides in the Northeast. Its "berries" are round, about $\frac{1}{4}$ in. in diameter, and attractive to children. A variety has white flowers and yellowish fruits.

POISONOUS PRINCIPLE. Species of *Daphne* contain a glycoside in which the aglycone is dihydroxycoumarin.

TOXICITY, SYMPTOMS, AND LESIONS. Daphne is among the oldest of plants recognized as poisonous. Reference to its toxicity may be found in Dioscorides and in all of the principal reference works on plant toxicity of the eighteenth and nineteenth centuries. Loss of human life to ingestion of the bark or fruit of daphne seems not to have been uncommon in earlier times, but recent literature contains few references to cases which have not been drawn from the older literature, and in the Western Hemisphere reports of poisoning are rare. In the United States, poisoning of a child by ingestion of an unknown number of "berries" from *Daphne mezereum* has been reported by Kingsbury (871) and human fatality has been reported from Nova Scotia (592).

Some idea of the potential toxicity of the plant may be gained from the fact that in Britain (574) six 10-week old pigs died after ingestion of an average of 3 "berries" each, even though vomition occurred. Experiments by Orfila, reported in 1814 (1206), showed that 12 grams of powdered bark was lethal to experimental dogs.

From these and other cases it appears that any species of daphne may prove highly toxic. The poisonous principle is contained throughout the plant, the "berries" and bark being the parts usually involved in poisoning and is not destroyed on drying. The plant is intensely acrid, producing vesication when the leaves are rubbed on the skin. Ingestion of parts of the plant produces a burning sensation in the mouth and corrosive lesions of the oral membranes. Forsyth (574) found lesions of inflammation and white patches with a burned appearance throughout the upper digestive tract in pigs. Vomition is common. Diarrhea, usually with blood and mucus, may be evidenced if death does not intervene. Stupor, weakness, and convulsions may also be observed.

CONDITIONS OF POISONING. The greatest danger of poisoning lies in the attractive appearance of the "berries" to children. There is also the danger of poisoning of livestock by clippings or prunings from ornamental plantings of daphne. Since only a few berries may kill a child, owners of daphne plants should be well aware of the danger in a single plant, and it would seem advisable to take positive measures for prevention of poisoning if children are in the neighborhood.

Additional reference: 607.

Order Loasales

Datiscaceae

Datisca glomerata (Presl.) Baill. Durango root

DESCRIPTION. Herbaceous perennial. Stems erect, clustered, to 5 (occasionally to 8) ft in height. Leaves alternate, divided, and sharply serrate, 5 to 6 in. long. Flowers dioecious, sessile in clusters in the leaf angles; corolla absent, calyx tubular in pistillate flowers, reduced in staminate. (Some pistillate flowers may bear a few stamens.) Fruit a capsule, ripening from a single-cavitied inferior ovary.

DISTRIBUTION AND HABITAT. Coast Ranges and the Sierra Nevada Mountains of southern California south into Mexico along stream beds or in washes.

POISONOUS PRINCIPLE. Unknown.

TOXICITY, SYMPTOMS, AND LESIONS. Experiments at the Davis campus of the University of California (1632) have established that the seeds, leaves, and seed capsules are highly toxic to cattle and sheep. A 750-lb heifer died 26 hours after being forced to consume 0.268 per cent of its weight (green-weight basis) of the plant. Roughly double the dosage produced death in a calf in 5 hours. Lesser amounts caused diarrhea and discomfort in both cattle and sheep. Symptoms consisted of diarrhea together with depression, weakness, and increased respiratory rate. Observed lesions in two animals consisted of moderate congestion (no hemorrhage) of the omasum, abomasum, and duodenum. It was concluded that the plant contained a toxic principle whose major effect was as a depressant, through action on the nervous system.

CONDITIONS OF POISONING. The experimental investigation was undertaken after the loss of 5 cattle on a ranch in Mariposa County, California. This loss followed a highway project during which two acres along a wet creek bottom had been fenced in with the original pasture. Much of the additional area was covered with durango root, the upper branches of which were heavily cropped. The plant is distasteful, and was not consumed in quantity until other pasturage had been exhausted. In the experimental work the plant was found particularly distasteful to sheep. It was also observed that animals normally may be expected to stop short of a lethal dose if any other feed is available.

Order Cucurbitales

Cucurbitaceae

Momordica charantia L. Wild balsam-apple, balsam pear, bitter gourd
This species is a creeping or climbing vine with palmately lobed leaves less than 6 in. across, and yellow, tubular flowers, the spreading portions of which are less than 1 in. across. Staminate and pistillate flowers are separate. Pistillate flowers form warty, ovoid fruits from 1½ to 5 in. long, tapering to a point at each end, orange or yellow at maturity. Pulp of the fruit is red; seeds are small, compressed.

This and another species (*M. balsamina* L.) with similar characteristics are inhabitants of sandy soils and waste grounds in the coastal plain from Florida to Texas.

Species of *Momordica* have records of toxicity, particularly to human beings, in Africa, Australia, and India (279, 810, 1533). The gourdlike fruits have been used in some areas as articles of diet. In some places and under some methods of preparation they are nontoxic. In general, however, the outer coat of the fruit, the seeds, and the foliage contain cathartic principles producing diarrhea and emesis, sometimes with serious consequences. According to Morton (1136), a small child was made ill after eating a whole fruit and did not recover completely for two months.

Fig. 94. *Cephalanthus occidentalis*. Buttonbush. Flowering shoot, with detail of flower. Courtesy of The Macmillan Company.

Order Rubiales

Rubiaceae

Cephalanthus occidentalis L. Buttonbush
This shrub, found in moist habitats throughout most of the United States, has been suspected (704) of causing poisoning of cattle in Indiana. Reference to it as possibly poisonous is found in several state poisonous-plants bulletins without documentation. Pammel (1217) lists it from earlier European work as containing a bitter glycosidic principle.

Additional reference: 913.

Caprifoliaceae

Sambucus spp. Elder, elderberry

Established elder plants are rather coarse bushes, to 12 ft tall, with opposite, pinnately compound foliage. The leaflets are lanceolate and serrate. The stems are stout, slightly woody, and characterized by a thick white or brown pith. Inflorescences are conspicuous, white, flat-topped in *S. canadensis* L., or ovoid in *S. pubens* Michx. Fruits are small berries, produced in large, conspicuous masses; purple-black or red (other colors in some varieties). Elder grows in moist or rich soils of eastern and central North America (*S. pubens* to Oregon and Alaska). Young growths may be confused with water hemlock (*Cicuta maculata*), but may be distinguished from that by the presence of opposite leaves and the absence of a bundle of tuberous roots.

Several species of elder have had bad reputations for many generations, yet cases of poisoning clearly caused by them have rarely been recorded. The American literature was reviewed by Pammel (1217) in 1911. Since then instances of poisoning in cattle (458), hogs (713), and the human being (663) after ingestion of elder have been suggested. Several supposedly active principles have been named from early chemical investigations of *Sambucus,* but are in need of confirmation.

The plant contains substances which are purgative if taken in moderate amount. Animals avoid elder, and thus poisoning is rare. The root, perhaps, is the most poisonous part, and may be responsible for mortality in hogs. Under unusual circumstances, the foliage or young growth may be ingested by cattle with harmful effect. Accidents involving children have occurred, either from ingestion of the roots or from using the stems of this or another species for blow-guns. The fresh berries used for various purposes by some persons appear the least toxic part of the plant and harmless when cooked. Uncooked berries may, nevertheless, produce nausea.

Order Campanulales

Campanulaceae

Lobelia spp. Lobelia, cardinal flower, Indian tobacco

The common lobelias are erect, mostly unbranched, annual or perennial herbs with alternate, simple, mostly lanceolate, decurrent leaves. The stem is prolonged upward into a raceme of numerous, alternately inserted flowers. The flower is strongly zygomorphic, and the corolla tubular. The corolla tube is prolonged into three downward and two erect lobes.

Lobelia cardinalis L., cardinal flower, is perennial, has very showy, deep red flowers, occurs wild along water courses or in damp soils throughout the eastern United States and southeastern Canada, and is frequently cultivated in flower gardens.

Lobelia siphilitica L., great lobelia or blue cardinal flower, is much like the preceding, except that the flowers are blue. Its habitat is as preceding,

Fig. 95. A-C, *Lobelia inflata*. Indian tobacco. Plant, with details of flower and seed. D-E, *Lobelia siphilitica*. Great lobelia. Flowering shoot, with detail of flower. Courtesy of The Macmillan Company.

but extends into moist open woods, and its range is centered as in the former, but is less extensive.

Lobelia berlandieri A. DC. Annual, erect or decumbent, few-leaved range plant of western Texas. Basal leaves form a rosette. Leaves become papery when dry. Flowers blue-purple with white center.

Lobelia inflata L., Indian tobacco, is annual, much branched, has inconspicuous blue flowers, which at maturity form more conspicuous inflated ovoid pods, and occurs as a weed of field and waste areas throughout the eastern United States and Canada.

Indian tobacco was so named by the first settlers from their observations that the Indians dried and smoked the leaves of this plant. This and other species indigenous to America were quickly found to possess considerable potency and they were employed in a variety of medicinals for various purposes. Cases of death from overdoses of medicinal preparations containing materials from these species were not infrequent, and they gained a considerable reputation as poisonous plants. Much of the information used by later authors may be traced to the writings of Millspaugh (1109). Cases of poisoning in human beings result from overdoses of the drug. Cases in animals are rarely reported. Recently, Dollahite and Allen have reported (437) field cases of poisoning of cattle and goats in which *Lobelia berlandieri* was incriminated. Feeding experiments with sheep and other animals proved the plant toxic at 0.5 per cent of the animal's weight administered daily for three days. Symptoms of sluggishness, salivation, diarrhea, anorexia, ulceration about the mouth, nasal discharge, and eventual coma, together with lesions of widely distributed hemorrhage and mild gastroenteritis are like those produced by an overdose of the alkaloid lobeline which was detected in the plant in ample quantity to account for the results.

Lobelia owes its activity to a variety of alkaloids. These have been investigated extensively with the result that fourteen related alkaloids have been isolated from *Lobelia inflata* alone (975, 977). Many of the same

$$\underset{\substack{| \\ C_6H_5}}{OCCH_2} \quad \underset{N}{\overset{CH_3}{|}} \quad \underset{\substack{| \\ C_6H_5}}{CH_2CHOH}$$

lobeline

alkaloids and some additional ones have been isolated from other species. They are pyridine alkaloids with structures not greatly different from that of nicotine.

Overdoses of the plant or extracts of the leaves or fruits produce vomition, sweating, pain, paralysis, depressed temperature, rapid but feeble pulse, collapse, coma, and death in the human being (61).

Order Asterales

Compositae

Achillea millefolium L. (probably including *A. lanulosa* Nutt.). Yarrow
A very common weed throughout the United States; aromatic with volatile oils, not generally considered poisonous but listed in Pammel (1217) and elsewhere as containing alkaloidal and glycosidal toxic principles. Hurst (810) cites a case (apparently circumstantial) of the death of a calf in 40 minutes after consuming a single plant.

Anthemis cotula L. Dog fennel, mayweed
Dog fennel is listed in several publications dealing with poisonous plants. It contains an acrid substance irritating to mucous membranes and is distasteful. As a weed in hay it has been suspected (935) of poisoning poultry. Losses in other classes of livestock have not been reported in the Western Hemisphere.

Artemisia spp. Sage, sagebrush
Several of the more than 200 species of *Artemisia* yield volatile oils useful in commerce (absinth, wormseed, santonica) and toxic if ingested in large amount. The western range sages are aromatic plants which are grazed heavily and generally considered desirable forage. Very heavy grazing on some species, however, has led to trouble.

Artemisia filifolia Torr. is the sand sagebrush found from Nebraska and Wyoming to Texas and Nevada. This species is credited (97) with causing a disease of horses known as "sage sickness." The disease develops in horses previously unaccustomed to sage, within a few days after being placed on sagebrush range. Symptoms include nervousness and a tendency to fall when forced to move. The latter may be attributed to an apparent partial paralysis of the forelimbs. Nothing more serious develops, the appetite is retained, and after a week or two the horses are able to consume large quantities of sand sage without developing further symptoms.

Artemisia spinescens D.C. Eat., another range sagebrush, has also come under suspicion (801, 1383). Feeding experiments (538) support the conclusion that this species may prove toxic under exceptional range conditions.

Aster spp. Aster
The following species of *Aster* are (1591) secondary or facultative selenium absorbers:

Aster adscendens Lindl.	*A. ericoides* L.
A. coerulescens DC.	*A. glaucoides* Blake
A. commutatus Gray	*A. laevis* var. *geyeri* Gray
	A. occidentalis (Nutt.) T. & G.

Some act as converters. Some of these species are common and palatable range plants. They may be dangerous in hay. (See selenium poisoning, p. 44, see also *Xylorrhiza*.)

Baccharis pteronioides DC. [= *B. ramulosa* (DC.) Gray]. Yerba-de-pasmo

DESCRIPTION. Perennial, resinous, spreading shrub, to 2 ft in height. Branches numerous, spreading, usually living only two years. Root a single tap root, often suckering. Leaves small, thick, from ⅛ to ¾ in. long, in clusters; larger leaves with a few coarse teeth, smaller ones almost linear. Plants dioecious, inflorescences appearing in April to May; male flowers in small, bell-shaped heads at the tips of densely leaved lateral branchlets, relatively inconspicuous. Female flowers borne similarly, more conspicuous through the formation of whitish down which projects from the mature female inflorescence as a dense tuft.

DISTRIBUTION AND HABITAT. Common in scattered stands in gravelly soils at elevations of 4000 to 6000 (occasionally to 7600) ft in central Arizona and New Mexico, west Texas, and south into Mexico.

POISONOUS PRINCIPLE. Unknown.

TOXICITY, SYMPTOMS, AND LESIONS. The plant experimentally has been shown (1004) toxic to sheep and is suspected of having caused cattle loss on the range. About 1 per cent green weight was shown lethal to sheep, producing symptoms and lesions that were not particularly characteristic. Symptoms in cattle on range have been described. Animals are stiff-gaited as though sore-footed. They lie down. Upon being aroused or driven, they exhibit more pronounced symptoms including trembling and convulsions. Death may be expected if a large amount of the plant has been consumed.

Baccharis glomeruliflora Pers. and *B. halimifolia* L. have experimentally been found (459) toxic. The former contains an active principle with some characteristics of a cardioactive glycoside.

CONDITIONS OF POISONING. Cases are rare because *Baccharis* is distasteful and occurs only in scattered, restricted stands. A large amount is required for fatal termination.

Bahia oppositifolia (Nutt.) DC. Plains bahia

DESCRIPTION. Small, gray-green perennial. Stems woody at base, much branched, to 6 in. tall. Leaves mostly opposite, the majority divided into 3 to 5 narrow segments. Flowers in small, tight composite heads, yellow in color.

DISTRIBUTION AND HABITAT. Dry soils from North Dakota and Montana to Texas and Arizona.

POISONOUS PRINCIPLE. Cyanogenetic glycoside.

TOXICITY, SYMPTOMS, AND LESIONS. A single feeding experiment each has been performed (413) with a sheep and a steer. Symptoms characteristic of cyanide poisoning were produced. Analysis of the plant showed it to contain about 30 mg cyanide potential per 100 g plant tissue.

CONDITIONS OF POISONING. Conclusive cases of poisoning on the range have not been reported. The toxicity of the plant, however, was discovered as the result of an investigation into the cause of death in a small herd of cattle in Colorado.

Baileya multiradiata Harv. & Gray. Desert baileya, cloth of gold

DESCRIPTION. A small showy plant that is annual in some situations and perennial in others, flowering from spring until late fall. Plant woolly, whitish, much branched from base, growing to 1 ft or a little more in height. Leaves numerous, alternate; those near the base of the plant with long petioles gradually expanded into an oblanceolate, irregularly lobed and divided blade; those in the upper portions, increasingly reduced to simple small oblanceolate, petioleless blades. Flowers aggregated in large, solitary, showy composite heads, several to many heads per plant. Heads 1 to 2 in. in diameter with 25 to 50 bright yellow, persistent ray florets, the rays of which bend backward with age.

DISTRIBUTION AND HABITAT. Locally common on sandy and gravelly soils in dry areas from Texas to southern California and south into Mexico. A major component of semidesert grass or shrub range in some areas.

POISONOUS PRINCIPLE. Unknown, water soluble (1035).

TOXICITY, SYMPTOMS, AND LESIONS. Poisoning by baileya results typically from ingestion of relatively large amounts of the green plant by sheep on range, over a relatively long period of time. Experimentally, for example, 41 lb of plant (green weight) produced death in a sheep after 25 days. In other experiments (432, 1035) the total amount of plant needed to produce death in sheep and goats varied from about 50 per cent to 150 per cent of the animal's weight, but approximated 1 to 2 per cent per day of the whole plant. The flowering and fruiting heads are about twice as toxic as and apparently less distasteful than the green leaves.

Symptoms include depression, anorexia, and green slobber about the mouth. Animals are sluggish and disinclined to move. If forced, they exhibit weakness, trembling, incoordination, and a rapid thumping heartbeat audible at a distance of several feet. One or more periods of prostration occur, during which the animal is unable to rise, or to remain standing if assisted to its feet. Death occurs several days or weeks after the appearance of symptoms unless corrective measures are taken. Slow recovery may be expected if poisoned animals are properly attended and the feed changed. Red urine and tendency to pneumonia in poisoned animals have been described (432).

Lesions consist primarily of widespread petechial hemorrhages and edema. Degenerative changes occur in liver and kidney, there are variable signs of gastroenteritis, ascites is common, and the brain may be congested and edematous.

CONDITIONS OF POISONING. Mortality as high as 25 per cent has occurred in bands of sheep in certain areas of Texas (432). The green plant is relatively distasteful to sheep, but the flower heads are relished and may be consumed even when ample acceptable forage is available. Losses among other classes of range livestock have not been reported, although goats have been poisoned experimentally with amounts similar to those poisoning sheep.

Additional reference: 1058.

Centaurea solstitialis L. Yellow star thistle

DESCRIPTION. Annual weed, branching from the base, to about 1 ft in height. Branches winged, divergently ascending. Leaves densely covered with cottony hair; basal leaves pinnatifid, stem leaves becoming linear, entire. Inflorescences (composite heads) terminal with ovoid spiny base and terminal spreading cluster of bright yellow florets.

DISTRIBUTION AND HABITAT. Introduced from the Mediterranean region, aggressively spreading and now found locally throughout much of the eastern, southern, and western portions of the United States in waste areas, roadsides, and as a weed of cultivation.

POISONOUS PRINCIPLE. Unknown.

TOXICITY, SYMPTOMS, AND LESIONS. This plant is responsible for the production of a nervous syndrome, "chewing disease" or nigropallidal encephalomalacia in horses. Symptoms in saddle or light harness horses appear (in experimental feedings) suddenly after ingestion of 50 to 150 per cent of the animal's weight of plant over a period of from one to three months. Lip twitches, tongue flicking, and involuntary chewing movements are observed. The mouth is commonly held open and the skin about the lips is puckered. Control of the tongue and swallowing reflex are unimpaired, but unless food is manually placed well back in the mouth, the animal is unable to eat. Except for occasional somnolence, animals appear otherwise normal.

Characteristic macroscopic lesions are uniform among animals at a given stage of the disease and consist of a nonprogressive focal necrosis of tissue in the anterior globus pallidus of the cerebrum and substantia nigra of the mesencephalon. Necrotic areas, up to about ¾ in. in greatest dimension, are yellowish and gelatinous in early stages and are sharply delineated. In later stages, changes associated with proliferation of a glial capsule about the necrotic area and the presence of scavenger cells occur. Degree of change appears closely correlated with duration of symptoms. Occasionally unilateral lesions were found and were associated with contralaterally oriented symptoms. Additional lesions commonly found include small mucosal ulcers in the mouth, caused probably by mechanical trauma from the spines about the heads of the plant, and occasionally edema of the muzzle from trauma associated with unsuccessful attempts to obtain food.

A discussion of microscopic pathology and its relation to nervous symptoms may be found in Cordy's papers (329, 330). He proposes a preliminary hypothesis that the plant possibly contains a substance inhibitory to the production or function of cytochrome oxidase and that the localization of lesions to specific areas in the brain results from the greater sensitivity of these areas to lack of cytochrome oxidase or its activity.

CONDITIONS OF POISONING. As presently reported, the disease has been observed only in saddle and light harness horses in central and northern California. Experimental feedings of sheep have been negative, and comparable symptoms have not been seen in other animals. Field cases occur among horses on poor, dry, summer pastures when *Centaurea* may be the only common plant remaining green. Cases have been observed in all months from May to December, except August. If allowed to progress to a natural conclusion, the disease eventually results in death through starvation or thirst.

Additional references: 1095, 1488.

Chrysothamnus nauseosus (Pall.) Britton. Rubber rabbitbrush

Several varieties of this brushy plant are common inhabitants of ranges from western Canada through the western United States into Mexico. It has been considered (1383) toxic to stock, and preliminary feeding experiments (801) support this conclusion. Other species of this genus constitute desirable range forage. Fortunately, this species appears to be the least palatable.

Conyza coulteri Gray. Conyza

A common annual of the ranges of the Trans-Pecos in Texas west into California and south into Mexico. Suspicion of this plant prompted feeding experiments (160) which demonstrated that the fresh green leaves were fatal in three days to a lamb when force-fed in the amount of 3 per cent of its weight. Symptoms and lesions were not described.

Eupatorium rugosum Houtt. Snakeroot, white snakeroot, richweed

(This plant has also been called *E. ageratoides* and *E. urticaefolium* in the poisonous-plants literature.)

INTRODUCTION. Since the days of the American Revolution an afebrile disease of human beings, characterized by weakness, nausea, and prostration, has occasionally reached epidemic proportions in certain areas of the United States, locally and sporadically causing loss of human life second to no other disease. It received many common names in the places where it occurred. In time, it became associated in the minds of the early settlers with the ingestion of milk from cattle that were themselves ill, and was designated "milksickness." The disease in cattle was usually termed "trembles" from its most obvious symptom. These associated diseases of livestock and human beings were first reported from North Carolina and

Fig. 96. *Eupatorium rugosum*. White snakeroot. Upper and lower parts of flowering plant, with details of a single head of flowers, a single flower, and fruit ("seed"). Courtesy of The Macmillan Company.

seemed to follow the settlers as the central states were inhabited. Milk-sickness reached a peak in incidence in the first half of the nineteenth century. It was so devastating in some areas that the human population was reduced to less than one-half its original number in one or a few years. On some occasions whole villages were abandoned (711), for it had been learned through painful experience that only certain limited areas produced milksickness. It is often stated that this disease was responsible for the death of Abraham Lincoln's mother.

Great in number and ingenuity were the causes advanced in explanation. Some thought poisonous plants culpable as evident in the first written accounts, and more than a score were named, each as the specific cause. Poison ivy (*Toxicodendron radicans*) was one of the chief contenders. Certain individuals believed that milksickness was caused by miasmas arising from the soil, from spider webs, or from other sources that now seem equally improbable. With wide acceptance of the pathogenicity of bacteria, milksickness, not having yielded conclusively to any other etiology, was added by most authorities to the ranks of bacterial diseases. Some experimental support for this view was forthcoming from reputable sources (847, 942, 988). The final recognition of milksickness as a disease produced by ingestion of milk, butter, or possibly meat from animals in turn poisoned by ingestion of snakeroot came about only when investigators eschewed preconceived ideas (of which a multitude were available), and refused to generalize beyond what was fully supported by their own results. Papers by Moseley (1137), Jordan and Harris (846, 847), Marsh and Clawson (988, 989), Wolf, Curtis, and Kaupp (1702), and Couch (344, 346, 347, 350, 353) constitute major contributions. Most of these papers contain a historical review of milksickness and trembles. More than 150 papers dealing with milksickness had appeared by the early twentieth century. In 1941, Moseley (1138) published a small book containing a review of all aspects of milksickness, trembles, and the so-called alkali disease of the Southwest. The latter is caused by a related genus, *Haplopappus* (*q.v.*), that contains the same toxic principle.

DESCRIPTION. Showy herbaceous perennial, forming erect, stiff, branched or unbranched stems, mostly 3 to 4 ft tall, from a shallow mat of fibrous, perennating roots. Leaves opposite, long-petioled, ovate to cordate, regularly longer than broad, thin, membranaceous, 3 to 6 in. in length; margin coarsely and sharply serrate; tip accuminate; blade strongly three-ribbed, especially on the undersurface. Flowers showy, snow white, small, in composite heads of 10 to 30 flowers, these grouped in open terminal corymbs.

Positive identification of *E. rugosum* is difficult and is based largely upon characteristics of the inflorescence and flower that are visible only with hand lens. There are more than 30 white-flowered species of *Eupa-*

torium. Eupatorium rugosum is particularly variable, being separated by some botanists into several varieties. Other species are not known to contain the toxic principle. Stress has been laid in the description above on characteristics most useful in separating this species from the others like it. Another useful characteristic is habitat. If positive identification of *E. rugosum* is required, the services of a specialist should be sought.

DISTRIBUTION AND HABITAT. *Eupatorium rugosum* in one or more of its varieties is found from eastern Canada to Saskatchewan, south to eastern Texas, Louisiana, Georgia, and Virginia. (The distribution of milksickness is more restricted; see later.) It is usually found in low, moist areas or

Fig. 97. *Eupatorium rugosum.* White snake-root.

bordering streams, often on rich or basic soils, almost always in open woods. In its southern range it is often found in abundance in wooded ravines or draws at moderate elevations, or on the northern slopes of wooded mountains. During the year or two following removal of timber from an area where it is established, it often forms dense stands to the exclusion of almost all other herbaceous plants. It will not persist on cultivated lands.

POISONOUS PRINCIPLE. Historically, several substances have been proposed as the toxic principle and later discarded. Considerable information characterizing the toxic fraction in extracts was thus accumulated, but it remained to the investigations of J. F. Couch, a chemist in the United States Department of Agriculture, first reported in 1927 (346, 347, 350), to come close to the present characterization of the toxic molecule. He found it to be a thick, straw-yellow oil with aromatic odor. For it, his analyses suggested the formula $C_{16}H_{22}O_3$. Chemically it was shown to have the reactions characteristic of an alcohol, to contain a phenyl nucleus, and to have a side chain containing two double bonds. This molecule proved difficult to handle, oxidizing readily in air, and a final structural formula was not determined. It was found to be readily soluble in alcohol, organic solvents, and in fats, but insoluble in water, acids, or alkalis. Its toxicity was proven by oral administration to various animals including sheep. In one case a suckling lamb was poisoned by the milk of its mother so poisoned. To this substance Couch gave the name, "tremetol." Tremetol occurs in the plant in combination with a resin acid of unknown structure. The acid, or other constituents of the plant, may exert a toxic action or modify the effect of tremetol. Couch considered tremetol itself "incapable of producing trembles when completely dry."

Couch has described (346) a test (710) for tremetol in plant or other materials based upon the development of a characteristic cherry-red color at the interface between petroleum ether and concentrated sulfuric acid when tremetol has been extracted in the former.

TOXICITY, SYMPTOMS, AND LESIONS: TREMBLES. Cases of trembles (that is, illness produced by direct ingestion of the plant) have experimentally been produced in sheep, cattle, horses, hogs (1702), fowl (454), and in a human being (1137), as well as in a variety of laboratory animals. It has been stated (1137, 1702) and disputed (988) that carnivorous animals may be poisoned from ingestion of meat from animals that have died of trembles. There is no doubt that suckling animals may be poisoned by tremetol excreted in the milk of animals obtaining it by ingestion of *Eupatorium,* and that symptoms may be observed in the offspring before they are manifested in the parent (347, 1702).

Useful figures for toxicity are not easily determined. Tremetol is excreted only slowly, and is, therefore, usually accumulated in the bodies of animals taking it in. Lactating animals appear to be less liable to poisoning because of a greater capacity for ridding themselves of the poisonous principle through their milk (1702). Many feeding experiments are on record with various classes of livestock. A major generalization from the resulting figures is the variation in individual tolerance of particular animals. With that reservation, the further generalizations may be made, that a total amount of green plant varying anywhere from slightly over 1 per cent

(454) to 20 per cent (394) of the animal's weight may be consumed before death, that time to onset of symptoms may vary from less than two days to as much as three weeks, that symptoms may not become apparent until as much as 11 days or more (394) after the last feeding with *Eupatorium,* that death follows the appearance of symptoms by a period varying between one day and three weeks, and that recovery is rare, slow, and often incomplete. Figures representing daily ingestion rates in cases of poisoning are more uniform. These vary mostly between 0.5 per cent and 1.5 per cent of the animal's weight, the larger figure in general associated with a quicker progression of the disease.

Although toxicity decreases with drying, an experiment (394) with *Eupatorium* hay six months after cutting showed it capable of producing trembles in horses and cattle. Other experiments (988) with dried *Eupatorium,* however, failed to demonstrate toxicity. Some of the variation in toxicity figures may be caused by seasonal or ecological variation in tremetol content of the plants.

Symptoms are comparable in various classes of livestock. The first symptom noticed is reluctance to move (one common name for trembles is "the slows") and sluggish behavior. Stiffness in walking or ataxia may be noticed. Shortly, if the animal is driven or made to exercise, it will abruptly stand still with feet wide apart as though to prop itself up, and begin to tremble, particularly about the flank and hind legs. Trembling becomes increasingly severe and more general, and the animal is prostrated in a natural recumbent position or with head extended on the ground. Usually, with complete relaxation in this fashion, trembling ceases. If the animal is made to get up, or does so voluntarily, another seizure of trembling occurs. Eventually in severe poisoning the animal remains prostrate, may struggle, and finally enters a comatose period of variable duration which is followed by death.

Additional symptoms of constipation, nausea, vomition, slobbering, loss of appetite, or labored or accelerated respiration may be observed at various points in the progression of the disease. Horses seem less likely to develop trembling and may go down without displaying this symptom (645). The same is true of an occasional animal in other classes of livestock. One of the effects of tremetol is to produce ketosis (347). Acetone odor may be detected on the breath and in the urine of severely poisoned animals. The blood-sugar level rises. In sheep, ketosis is not detectable until about 24 hours after onset of symptoms. This is held to indicate that ketosis is a result of poisoning and not in itself a cause of symptoms (347).

Consistent lesions in all classes of livestock include congestion and fatty degenerative changes, often extreme, in liver and kidney. Hemorrhages of variable extent may be found in the heart, in the gastrointestinal tract, and elsewhere. If the course of the disease can be countered before the stage at which obvious signs of ketosis appear, prognosis is good (353).

Measures to counter ketosis, relieve constipation if present, and promote elimination of the toxic principle are indicated.

TOXICITY, SYMPTOMS, AND LESIONS: MILKSICKNESS. Cases of milk-sickness in individuals or in families may still occur after ingestion of milk from a poisoned family cow, but the mass loss of human life of former times is impossible under current practices in animal husbandry and in pooling the milk from many producers. The disease is of gradual onset. A day or two of weakness and debility is followed by loss of appetite, abdominal pain, and severe, repeated vomiting. Obstinate constipation and severe thirst develop, the latter accompanied by repeated drinking, then loss of ingested water by vomiting. Muscular tremors or more general trembling is commonly observed. As the disease progresses, the characteristic odor of acetone appears on the breath. It has been stated that in milksickness areas doctors learned to diagnose the malady from this characteristic upon entering the house. In mortal cases delirium is followed by coma and death. At no stage does the temperature become significantly elevated; it is usually subnormal.

Mortality ranges between 10 and 25 per cent (847). Fatty degeneration of the liver is the most prominent lesion (847). When death does not occur, recovery is slow and uncertain. A patient slowly recovers his strength until recovery appears complete. Relapses following moderate exertion are, however, common and many terminate fatally. Many subjects who recover are incapacitated for several years or permanently for hard physical work.

CONDITIONS OF POISONING. The conditions which lead to ingestion of milk containing the poisonous principle and to cases of milksickness are obvious. In the older literature, butter and meat from severely poisoned animals were also considered responsible for producing milksickness in human beings.

Conditions which influence the incidence of trembles in animals include the following. Snakeroot is moderately distasteful to all classes of livestock, but in feeding experiments animals could be made to ingest large amounts if the plant was chopped up and mixed with desirable feed. A case is on record (454) in which poisoning occurred despite availability in the pasture of ample forage. It was concluded that animals sought the wooded area of the pasture for shade and while there consumed toxic amounts of snakeroot. Trembles is most prevalent in dry years or under other conditions, as unduly restricted pasturage, which result in a shortage of proper forage. The most dangerous season is late summer or early autumn, but cases may occur in any month that the plant is available. Poisoning has occurred from *Eupatorium* in hay (394), and it has been shown that the plant does not lose toxicity on being frosted (697). Because tremetol is excreted in the milk, milking animals are less apt to develop symptoms than dry livestock, but probably because of concentration in the milk, suckling animals may develop symptoms when no symptoms are apparent in the dam.

Milksickness and trembles are confined to an area smaller than the distribution of *Eupatorium*. Several authors have carefully searched the literature to determine the exact distribution of these diseases. They have found (346, 353, 847, 987) cases in North and South Carolina, Georgia, Alabama, Tennessee, Kentucky, extreme eastern Missouri, Illinois, Indiana, extreme southern Michigan, Ohio, West Virginia, and Maryland. The greatest number of cases has been recorded in North Carolina, Indiana, Illinois, and Ohio. Pennsylvania and New York (697) may also have had a few instances of milksickness. Trembles and milksickness occur in the Southwest from poisoning by *Haplopappus* (*q.v.*). Why cases have not occurred elsewhere in the *Eupatorium rugosum* range has not been explained.

Eupatorium wrightii Gray

This plant, without common name, is a woody, bushy, spreading, low-growing perennial of limited distribution in the Southwest. It is found on limestone formations at elevations between 5000 and 6000 ft in western Texas, southern New Mexico, southeastern Arizona, and northern Mexico. It has been incriminated (755) in unexplained losses of cattle, occasionally severe, in these areas over the last fifty years or more. Losses occur mainly in October following light frosts. No symptoms have ever been observed. The animals appear as though "shot and instantly killed." Symptoms similarly were absent in preliminary feeding experiments with goats and cattle in which small amounts of the plant resulted in death in a few hours.

Additional references: 379, 648, 696, 1380.

Florestina tripteris DC.

This annual herb with flesh-colored or white flowers and with palmately divided, alternate, petioled leaves is found in Texas and New Mexico. An experimental feeding to a sheep, made at the Texas Agricultural Experiment Station, showed 0.5 per cent of an animal's weight of leaves to be fatal in 33 minutes (158). HCN was detected in the plant by the picrate test and considered to be the toxic principle. Range cases are not reported.

Florensia cernua DC. Tarbush, blackbrush

DESCRIPTION. Perennial, much-branched, leafy shrub, to 6 ft in favorable habitats, or only 1 ft or less in dry locations. Plant strongly aromatic, especially when bruised. Leaves alternate, entire, ovate, to 1 in. in length. Composite heads small, solitary, yellow-flowered, rayless, pendant, inconspicuously borne in the angles of not greatly reduced leaves along

long terminal inflorescence axes. Achenes ("seeds") densely hairy, presented in small pendant clusters sticking out from the stem.

DISTRIBUTION AND HABITAT. Common, forming thickets on dry plains, hills, and mesas, from the counties just east of the Pecos River in Texas, west to Arizona, and south into Mexico.

POISONOUS PRINCIPLE. Unknown, alcohol insoluble.

TOXICITY, SYMPTOMS, AND LESIONS. Our knowledge of the toxic properties of tarbush rests upon the experimental investigations made by Mathews (1054) at the Texas Experiment Station prompted by range cases of severe loss in sheep and goats. In some instances as many as a quarter of the animals in large flocks were killed.

Experimental forced feeding of tarbush fruits to a relatively large number of sheep and goats showed the fruits lethal at about 1 per cent of the animal's weight. There was considerable variation in individual susceptibility, and a very small margin existed between toxic and lethal doses. The foliage in moderate quantity was not toxic.

Symptoms appear under range conditions a day or less after ingestion of a toxic amount of plant. Depending upon the acuteness of poisoning they may terminate in death within 24 to 72 hours, occasionally longer, or may be followed by rapid recovery after an animal has shown symptoms for several days to a week. Symptoms are somewhat modified by the severity of poisoning, but consist in general of loss of appetite, abdominal pain, reluctance to move, and occasionally some respiratory distress. In acute cases salivation may be observed. Animals remain on their feet until shortly before death, which occurs usually without struggle.

Lesions are characteristic and include severe congestion and ulceration of the abomasum and the first foot or so of the duodenum, and congestion of liver and kidney. Perforative ulceration with extensive necrosis and adhesions of the involved portion of the gut may be observed on necropsy in some cases.

CONDITIONS OF POISONING. *Flourensia* is distasteful and will not be browsed unless livestock are unusually hungry. Range cases are usually traced to conditions of improper management and are controllable by simple obvious corrections. Tarbush is useful in providing shade for animals on the range in summer and possibly has some forage value. Poisonings occur in the months of January, February, and March, after the fruit has matured (apparently the green fruit is not eaten) but before it falls from the plants.

Franseria discolor Nutt. White ragweed

Perennial, ragweedlike herb, Nebraska to Wyoming, south to Arizona and New Mexico. This plant has caused loss of life in stock by nitrate poisoning (804).

Grindelia spp. Gumweeds

Several species, but especially *Grindelia squarrosa* (Pursh) Dunal., are (1591) secondary or facultative selenium absorbers. (see p. 45.)

Gutierrezia microcephala (DC.) Gray [= *G. sarothrae* var. *microcephala* (L.) Benson, = *Xanthocephalum lucidum* Greene], *G. sarothrae* (Pursh) Britt. & Rusby (= *Xanthocephalum sarothrae* S. Shinners). Broomweed, perennial snakeweed, slinkweed, turpentine weed.

DESCRIPTION. Densely branched perennial resinous shrub, to 2 ft tall. Main stems woody, below leafless; bearing numerous herbaceous leafy branches on which the lower leaves are shed at maturity; branches ascending, hairless, ridged. Leaves numerous, alternate, linear, reflexed from the stem, ¾ to 2 in. long. Flowers in very small composite heads. Heads produced singly or in small clusters at the tips of numerous ascending ultimate branchlets, mostly at a single level in the upper periphery of the plant. Rays yellow, 4 to 5 per head; disc flowers 1 to 3 per head.

DISTRIBUTION AND HABITAT. Dry range and desert from Texas to California, north to Colorado and Idaho, south into Mexico. In range country an indication of improper grazing practices.

Fig. 98 . *Gutierrezia microcephala.* Broomweed.

POISONOUS PRINCIPLE. Saponin extracted from the plant and given by injection brings forth symptoms and lesions similar to those displayed in cases of poisoning by ingestion (443). The plants are most toxic in the stage of leaf formation.

TOXICITY, SYMPTOMS, AND LESIONS. Following persistent complaints concerning this plant, experiments were carried out at the Texas Experiment Station. At first toxicity was not demonstrated, but in 1933 positive results were obtained (1040, 1058). A second series of experiments was commenced in 1953, primarily to examine the abortifacient properties of the plant in relation to range animals (435, 440, 444).

Sheep and cattle especially have been poisoned in large numbers under range conditions in the Trans-Pecos and High Plateau areas of Texas. In acute cases death occurs, but more commonly the major result of poisoning is abortion. In some areas these plants are the major cause of abortion, contributing to losses which average between $2 million and $3 million annually in Texas (435).

In feeding experiments wide variation in individual susceptibility to snakeweed has been found. As little as 20 lb fresh snakeweed has produced abortion in cattle in 7 days. In other instances cattle have eaten as much as 1097 lb, aborting only after 117 days. Death has been produced in sheep, cattle, and goats by feeding between 10 and 20 per cent of their body weight of fresh snakeweed over periods of ½ to 2 weeks. Abortion and other reproductive disturbances were produced in sows fed 1½ lb snakeweed daily, but there was great variability in time before symptoms appeared and hence in total amount of snakeweed consumed. It is interesting to note that no effects were obtained in sows fed 1¼ lb daily over protracted periods. Poisoning also has been produced in various laboratory animals, of which the chick and rabbit appear most sensitive. The abortifacient properties of snakeweed are less readily demonstrated with sheep and goats than with cattle, swine, and rabbits.

The normal weight of Hereford calves is about 70 lb. In *Gutierrezia* poisoning as experienced on the range, cattle abort in various stages of term, or produce living but weak underweight calves, most of which perish unless exceptional effort is made to keep them alive. In experimental feedings of toxic *Gutierrezia,* only a very small number of cows gave birth to calves weighing over 60 lb and the majority weighed less than 50 lb. The placenta is commonly retained even in those cases where the calf appears normal. In occasional cases part of the placenta is passed but the calf retained. In a significant number of instances death of the cow follows parturition, either through effects of birth abnormalities or directly from the toxic effect of the plant. Pregnant cattle consuming relatively smaller or less toxic amounts of snakeweed may display periodic vulvar swelling and prematurely early udder development. Similar vulvar involvement and breeding or conception difficulties have been observed in sows. A natural case of abortion in sows pastured in a dense growth of *Gutierrezia* has been reported (435).

Symptoms in severely poisoned sheep and cattle include listlessness, anorexia, rough coat, diarrhea or constipation, mucus in feces, vaginal discharge, and often hematuria. In cattle a nasal discharge accompanied with crusted and peeling muzzle has been noted, while sheep have displayed minor icterus. Lesions are those of gastroenteritis accompanied by degenerative change in liver and kidneys. Microscopic examination of kidney tissue discloses severe toxic nephritis with necrosis if the disease progresses sufficiently before the animal dies. The liver displays an unusual diffuse hydropic degeneration of cells and ultimate necrosis. Some evidence of icterus is common in the subcutaneous fat and connective tissue. The spleen is congested, and there is a mild to severe gastroenteritis. The uterus is edematous, and hydrops may be observed in the fetal membranes.

Saponins administered parenterally evoke similar symptoms and lesions. Even by this route they cause visceral vasodilation, and mild gastroenteritis with or without hemorrhage.

CONDITIONS OF POISONING. It has been the observation of cattlemen, borne out in experimentation, that *Gutierrezia* is more toxic when growing on sandy soils that when on the range loam (so-called "hard") soils of Texas, even though the plant commonly grows more luxuriantly and in denser stands on the latter. Luxuriant stands of the growing plant may be eaten to some extent by range animals even when other vegetation is available, but poisoning usually occurs under conditions which force animals to concentrate on this species.

Additional reference: 1503.

Gutierrezia spp. Snakeweeds

The following species of *Gutierrezia* are (435) secondary or facultative selenium absorbers: *Gutierrezia sarothrae* (Pursh) Britt. and Rusby; *G. diversifolia* Greene. (See p. 45.)

Haplopappus heterophyllus (Gray) Blake (syn. *Aplopappus heterophyllus, Iscoma wrightii,* and *Bigelowia rusbeyi*). Rayless goldenrod, jimmy weed, burrow weed

DESCRIPTION. Erect, bushy, unbranched or sparingly branched, perennial, 2 to 4 ft tall. Stems numerous, arising from a perennating woody rootstalk. Leaves alternate, linear, sticky. Flowers yellow, borne in numerous, small, flat-topped, clustered heads at the stem tips; each head composed of 7 to 15 flowers.

DISTRIBUTION AND HABITAT. Common on dry rangelands, especially in river valleys, along drainage areas, and irrigation canals, from southern Colorado into Texas, Mexico, New Mexico, and Arizona.

POISONOUS PRINCIPLE. The higher alcohol, tremetol (351). The general chemical composition of this and a related species has been reported by Buehrer *et al.* (197) and Dermer and Cleverdon (420).

SYMPTOMS AND LESIONS. Ingestion of 1 to 1.5 per cent of an animal's weight of the green plant daily over the period of 1 to 3 weeks will produce symptoms in horses, cattle, and sheep. Death follows if the animal is not removed from access to the plant, but recovery may be expected otherwise. The first symptoms noticed are lassitude and depression, accompanied by a "humped-up" posture and stiff-legged walk when driven. The most characteristic and obvious symptom is trembling, especially of the muscles about the nose, hips, and shoulders. The whole body may shake. Final stages are characterized by general weakness. Attacks may be brought on by forced exercise and end in fatal collapse. Terminal respiration may consist of prolonged inspiration and forced expiration separated by a short pause. Death is quiet and may be preceded by prolonged coma. Constipation and more or less constant dribbling of urine are common secondary symptoms. In this syndrome it is usually possible to detect an acetone odor on the breath and to find measurable amounts of acetone in the blood and urine.

Post mortem findings are not spectacular but are constant. They include congestion of the abomasum and intestine. The liver is pale and the gall bladder distended. The histopathology has been detailed by Marsh et al (1023).

Symptoms and lesions do not differ in any important respect from those produced by *Eupatorium rugosum,* which is closely related to *Haplopappus* and contains the same toxic principle. The chemistry and physiological effects of tremetol are discussed under *Eupatorium.*

CONDITIONS OF POISONING. Loss of livestock has been severe in various sections of the Southwest, particularly in the Pecos and Rio Grande Valleys and the Trans-Pecos area of Texas. Poisoning is most common in late fall and winter, but animals may eat the plant at any time of year. In some places this species is the dominant plant. The toxic principle is excreted in the milk of lactating animals. Occasionally calves or other suckling animals may become poisoned while the parent does not display obvious symptoms. Ingestion of the milk from animals eating *Haplopappus* may cause tremetol poisoning (milksickness) in human beings. See discussion under *Eupatorium rugosum.*

Haplopappus fruticosus (Rose & Standl.) Blake (no common name) is a close relative of *H. heterophyllus.* It has a similar distribution and has also been shown to contain tremetol (353). *Haplopappus tenuisectus* (Greene) Blake & Benson and *H. hartwegii* Blake are also closely related and may be found to contain the same toxic principle.

Additional references: 846, 1010, 1500.

Helenium hoopesii Gray (= *Dugaldia hoopesii* Rydb.). Sneezeweed, orange sneezeweed

DESCRIPTION. Stout erect herbaceous perennial, 1 to 3 ft tall; rootstalk thick, perennating, reproducing the plant vegetatively by frequent offshoots, bearing few to several erect stems. Stems unbranched except at extremities. Leaves alternate, entire, lanceolate, parallel-veined; rootstalk leaves much longer and of more crowded insertion than those of the stem. Composite inflorescences borne singly at the tips of the ultimate branches, 2 to 3 in. broad; ray florets fertile, rays orange or golden yellow, slightly reflexed; disc nearly the same color or slightly darker, raised hemispherical.

DISTRIBUTION AND HABITAT. Mountain slopes and valleys mostly between 7000 and 10,800 ft, often forming dense stands in moist sunny localities. Native to undisturbed summer range, increasing in density with overgrazing. Present in the mountains of all states from the Rocky Mountains westward, except Montana and Washington.

POISONOUS PRINCIPLE. From studies in 1921, Marsh *et al.* announced (900) that toxicity resides in an easily decomposed glycoside, characterized as a white amorphous substance soluble in alcohol, to which they gave the name dugaldin. Plants retain their toxicity when dried.

TOXICITY, SYMPTOMS, AND LESIONS. Heavy losses in sheep from sneezeweed poisoning were the immediate reason for the establishment in 1915 of the United States Department of Agriculture's productive field station at Salina, Utah, for the investigation of poisonous plants. The detailed results of several years' study into poisoning by sneezeweed were published in 1921 (1003), and serve as the major basis of our knowledge of the poisonous nature of this species. Symptoms and lesions have also been described by Clawson (298).

It is possible to poison animals acutely with a single large dose of sneezeweed. In one experiment, about 5 per cent of the animal's weight of sneezeweed produced death in 3 days. That the plant contains a severe irritant was shown by the presence of irritation, necrosis, and eventual penetration into the intestinal wall in the areas of contact with the mass of ingested plants. Under range conditions poisoning results when animals consume moderate quantities of sneezeweed over an extended period of time. It has been possible to poison cattle experimentally, but natural losses are restricted almost entirely to sheep. Marsh *et al.* found considerable variation in the amount of sneezeweed necessary to produce symptoms in sheep and in the time before symptoms appeared. Averaging their several experimental poisonings they found that 2.17 lb sneezeweed per day per hundredweight of sheep resulted in overt symptoms after 21.6 days for a toxicity, total, of 45 per cent of an animal's weight of green plant. This agrees with results of Buck *et al.* (192), who produced severe illness and death in sheep fed 1 per cent of the animal's weight of *dry* plant per day for 8 days. Experimental feedings to cattle when averaged similarly gave toxicity values which were not appreciably different. Although sneezeweed appears somewhat cumulative in its toxic effect, daily consumption of amounts less than 1.5 lb even over prolonged periods of time fails to evoke symptoms or lesions (1003).

On the range, sneezeweed poisoning is known as "spewing sickness" from the principal symptoms observed. In experimental cases that have been watched closely, the first sign of poisoning is dullness and depression. In some instances this is followed solely by weakness. Such animals appear normal when lying down. Immediately after standing, they begin to tremble from weakness and are soon unable to keep their legs under them. Respiration and pulse become rapid and irregular during the time they are standing, but return to normal after the animal has been recumbent for a time. In other instances nausea with vomition is the prominent symptom. Often several or many animals in a band will stand with upturned head attempting to retain regurgitated material, which escapes in quantity from the corners of the mouth. Vomition is frequently accompanied by excessive salivation, belching, frothing, intestinal rumbling, and rapid and irregular pulse and respiration. Often, during vomition, ingesta enters the trachea, and coughing or more serious lung involvement results. Animals which do not evidence vomition usually recover if removed from access to sneezeweed. Vomition is usually the sign of permanent injury and often continues for some time after sneezeweed is no longer available. Animals which have been affected in this way usually do not die immediately, but lose flesh and wool, becoming prey to death from whatever particularly rigorous conditions may arise.

Post mortem examination usually reveals a variety of lesions but a few are found uniformly. They include gastrointestinal irritation, congestion of liver and kidney, and usually adhesions of necrotic areas in the lungs. The last-named is undoubtedly the result of respiratory involvement in vomiting animals. Microscopic examination reveals liver and kidney damage of variable characteristics. Elevated serum transaminase in poisoned animals is held by Buck et al. (192) to result from necrotic changes in the livers of poisoned animals.

CONDITIONS OF POISONING. Sneezeweed is a major economic problem for sheep raisers on the summer ranges of the central Rocky Mountains. It was estimated in 1944 (447) that nearly 8000 sheep die each year in Colorado alone from sneezeweed poisoning and that the problem is equally severe in Utah. Because of these severe losses and because it was apparent that artificial control of the plant would be impractical, studies (262, 263, 298, 447) were undertaken with bands of sheep to determine range practices which would keep sneezeweed losses to a minimum. This important experiment also had interesting results for those who study range ecology. It showed that good management practices such as loose herding, avoiding particularly dense areas of sneezeweed, careful culling, and evenly spread use of range, resulted in much fewer losses to sneezeweed, and in greater average weight of animals harvested from equal range allotments and equal original band size.

Sneezeweed is particularly dangerous in early spring and late fall. Many plants remain green right through the winter after other vegetation disappears and start growing early in the spring before new plants of other species appear. Sneezeweed is not relished by animals but will be consumed readily by sheep when other forage is scarce.

Additional species which have records or reputations for toxicity are the following.

Helenium autumnale L. Sneezeweed, bitterweed

DESCRIPTION. Fibrous-rooted, herbaceous perennial, 1 to 4½ ft tall. Stems winged, unbranched or branched near the top. Leaves sparsely small-toothed, lanceolate, 1½ to 6 in. long, ½ to 1½ in. broad, pinnately net-veined. Composite inflorescences borne singly at the tips of the ultimate branches, about 1 in. broad; ray florets mostly fertile, rays yellow, 3-lobed, reflexed at maturity; disc yellow, subglobose.

DISTRIBUTION AND HABITAT. Several varieties are recognized in this species. Taken together, their range extends throughout most of the United States and southern Canada. They are absent in the southwestern states. Typically they inhabit moist low areas, meadows, or neglected areas of scrub growth.

Fig. 99. *Helenium autumnale*. Sneezeweed. Detail of inflorescence.

Helenium nudiflorum Nutt. Sneezeweed

DESCRIPTION. As *H. autumnale,* except to 3½ ft tall; leaves entire, smaller, lanceolate-linear; heads with purple discs.

DISTRIBUTION AND HABITAT. Eastern United States, to Michigan and Texas. Habitat generally as *H. autumnale.*

Helenium tenuifolium Nutt. Sneezeweed

DESCRIPTION. Herbaceous annual, ½ to 1½ ft tall. Stems not winged. Leaves numerous, linear, ¾ to 3 in. long, ascending. Head as in *H. autumnale* except somewhat smaller, disc yellow or purple.

DISTRIBUTION AND HABITAT. Southeastern United States to Texas. Sandy soils of fields or waste areas or open woods.

Helenium microcephalum DC. Sneezeweed

DESCRIPTION. Annual. Leaves lanceolate, sparsely toothed below, entire above. Heads with rays equal in length or shorter than diameter of disc; disc yellow.

Fig. 100. *Helenium tenuifolium*. Sneezeweed. Plant, and detail of inflorescence.

DISTRIBUTION AND HABITAT. Moist ground, southern Texas and Mexico.

Among the 40-odd species of *Helenium* in the United States there is some taxonomic uncertainty. A general reputation for toxicity exists for all the species named above. In some cases this is backed with some published experimental or circumstantial evidence, but the exact species referred to is sometimes uncertain. The poisonous principle is unknown in all cases, or assumed to be dugaldin. King (864) cites the extraction of an unnamed principle similar in action to aconite.

Phares, in 1889, described (1269) experiments performed at the Mississippi Agricultural Experiment Station in which aqueous extracts of a plant were shown toxic to calves. These experiments were prompted by natural cases in sheep, horses, and mules. In these animals the plant is described as producing some weakness and dyspnea together with terminal "epileptiform spasms" or convulsions. Horses and mules were particularly susceptible, while sheep occasionally developed a taste for the plant after having once experienced it. The plant involved in producing these effects was identified as *H. autumnale,* and the description of symptoms has served as the basis for discussions under this species name in many poisonous-plants bulletins. The plant is described, however, as a perennial with purple disc. From this description, it was not *H. autumnale* as currently recognized, but more likely was *H. nudiflorum.*

Pammel (1219) cites two cases received by him from Iowa in which loss of sheep, cattle, and horses was involved. In his opinion (from material sent him) the plant involved was *H. autumnale*. Symptoms included frothing at the mouth and incoordination. Hansen (704) cites a case of poisoning in cattle in Indiana which he ascribed to this species. Labored breathing and convulsions were followed by death.

Chesnut (263) says that *H. tenuifolium* is suspected as a poisonous plant and that poisoning of human beings has occurred from consumption of bread made with flour which contained large quantities of the seeds of this plant as contaminant. West and Emmel (1661) consider this species toxic to livestock in Florida.

Feeding experiments reported but briefly (158, 159) have been performed at the Texas Agricultural Experiment Station with *H. microcephalum,* showing it toxic. Leaves were rapidly fatal to mature sheep at 0.25 per cent of their weight. Chronic poisoning resulted from feeding 0.0625 per cent daily and terminated after 57 days ($=$ 3.2 per cent total). A sheep was made very sick in a few hours after a single feeding at 0.125 per cent. The mature plant was found more toxic than the seedlings, and the winter basal rosette seemed to be not toxic at all.

Additional references: 274, 446.

Hymenoxys odorata DC. [syn. *Actinea odorata* (DC.) Kuntze]. Bitterweed, bitter rubberweed

DESCRIPTION. Annual weed ranging in size from a few inches to 2 ft; erect, much branching from the base. Stem usually purplish towards base. Leaves alternate, once to three times alternately divided into very narrow, glandular, wooly divisions not distinct from the petiole. Composite flower heads at tips of stem branches, bright yellow, ⅕ to ½ in. in diameter, with 60 or more disc florets and 6 to 10 ray florets; rays tipped with three lobes. Aboveground parts of plant bitter, unpleasant to the taste; root not so.

DISTRIBUTION AND HABITAT. Common in the semiarid range from southwest Kansas through western and central Texas into Mexico, Arizona, and New Mexico into southeast California.

This plant should not be confused with *Helenium tenuifolium*, which also is commonly called bitterweed and also is toxic.

POISONOUS PRINCIPLE. Unknown; apparently water soluble. The plant retains its toxicity on drying.

TOXICITY, SYMPTOMS, AND LESIONS. Bitterweed on ranges of the southwestern United States causes considerable loss of life in sheep. Experimental work has been done with it at the Texas Experiment Station (156, 721, 845) and by the U.S. Department of Agriculture (293). About 1 per cent of an animal's weight of green plant is lethal, whether ingested at one time or in fractional amounts daily over a period of one to several months. The former regimen produces symptoms and death within a day or two. The latter produces chronic symptoms and eventual death. The considerable variation in minimum lethal dose is not dependent on the nutritional history of the experimental animal. Bitterweed slowly increases in toxicity with maturity, but much greater increase in toxicity accompanies growth under drought conditions. For example, Boughton and Hardy (156) found that 1.3 per cent of an animal's weight of plant represented the minimum lethal dose in a season with normal rainfall but that only 0.5 per cent was lethal in the following season when bitterweed developed under drought conditions.

Symptoms are acute if produced experimentally by forced feeding of a single lethal dose and include anorexia, salivation, vomition, depression, and weakness. Produced, as on the range, through daily ingestion of small amounts, the symptoms are similar but less marked. A common symptom in range cases is a green salivary discharge and stain about the muzzle. Affected animals often lag behind the flock and may stand with arched back. Lesions are variable but usually include lung congestion, hemorrhages of the epicardium, inflammation of the abomasum and occasionally of other sections of the intestinal tract. Chronic cases may display few or no significant lesions.

CONDITIONS OF POISONING. Prior to about 1925, bitterweed was found in abundance only in localized basins and low areas of the range. Overstocking of range country, accompanied by destruction of perennial grasses and forbes, allowed the spread of bitterweed into vast areas of previously useful range. Cases of range poisoning, previously unknown, became severe (31) and prompted the experimental investigation summarized above. Cases are reported primarily from the Edwards Plateau of Texas. Here bitterweed starts growth from seed in December or January, and cases of poisoning follow until April or May when other forage becomes available. Bitterweed is distasteful to range livestock; probably for this reason it has not been known to produce natural cases of poisoning in cattle, horses, or goats although these animals may be poisoned experimentally. Under conditions of starvation sheep will turn to consumption of bitterweed and may develop a liking for it. In range cases symptoms usually appear after a month or so of access to the plant. If removed at the onset of symptoms, sheep may be expected to make an uneventful though slow recovery.

Hymenoxys richardsonii (Hook.) Cockerell [syn. *Actinea richardsonii* (Hook.) Kuntze, *Hymenoxys floribunda* Cockerell]. Pingue, Colorado rubberweed

DESCRIPTION. Perennial herb from a thick woody root; 6 to 18 in. tall; habit similar to preceding. Stems bearing a conspicuous dense mass of white or brownish hairs at ground level among the lower leaves. Leaves

Fig. 101. A-B, *Hymenoxys richardsonii*. Pingue. Plant with detail of disc floret, opened. C-E, *H. odorata*. Bitterweed. Plant, with details of head and single disc floret. Courtesy of The Macmillan Company.

bright green, divided as in the preceding species into narrow, glandular, but not woolly segments; basal leaves clustered, about 4 in. long; those on the stem alternate, about 2 in. long. Composite flowering heads golden yellow, ½ to 1 in. in diameter; otherwise as in preceding species.

DISTRIBUTION AND HABITAT. This species is widely distributed from Canada to Texas and westward to California and Oregon. Reports of toxicity appear to be confined to the entity botanically recognized by some as var. *floribunda*. This variety has a much more restricted distribution, being confined to northern New Mexico, northern Arizona, southern Utah, and southern Colorado, in dry soils, occasionally in dense stands, at elevations from 4000 to 10,000 ft.

POISONOUS PRINCIPLE. Unknown. Probably similar to, or the same as, that in the preceding species.

TOXICITY, SYMPTOMS, AND LESIONS. Pingue has caused extensive loss of sheep in Colorado, New Mexico, and Arizona. Experimental administration of pingue in single doses by forced feeding to sheep (1) has shown that the lethal dose is about 1.5 per cent of the animal's weight of green plant. Fed thus, an acute syndrome is produced, terminating in death in one or two days.

Symptoms of acute poisoning include salivation, anorexia, rumen stasis, depression, signs of severe abdominal pain, uneasiness, weakness, and prostration. There is some respiratory involvement. Lesions are those associated with gastrointestinal irritation and fatty degeneration of hepatic cells. Both symptoms and lesions are similar to those described for *H. odorata*.

CONDITIONS OF POISONING. Sheep are most commonly poisoned, although cattle and goats may also be affected. The plant is dangerous throughout its period of growth, but most cases occur in the spring before other forage becomes available, or in late fall. Pingue is distasteful and will not be eaten unless the animals are driven to it by starvation. There is evidence (1247) that a mineral unbalance in the diet may predispose to poisoning.

Hymenoxys lemmoni (Greene) Cockerell

This species, native to California, Utah, northeastern Arizona, and Nevada, has been fed experimentally at the Texas Experiment Station (550). It was clearly shown poisonous to sheep. One-half pound per sheep per day was consistently fatal within a few days; smaller amounts fed daily were equally fatal after longer periods of time. Like the other species, the plant is eaten only by sheep and only under drought conditions of semistarvation. Additional species may prove toxic when investigated (801).

Additional references: 338, 339, 985.

Lactuca scariola L. Wild lettuce

DESCRIPTION. Annual or winter-annual herbaceous weed, 2 to 4½ ft tall. Stems erect, without branches or few-branched, containing milky sap. Leaves alternate, the upper oblong, the lower pinnatifid, margins dentate, teeth bearing a terminal, sharp prickle. Inflorescences (composite heads) grouped into a large terminal panicle; heads numerous, small, with 6 to 30 flowers; individual flowers perfect, ligulate, pale yellow.

DISTRIBUTION AND HABITAT. Weed of grain crops and cultivated fields, also wild on waste or disturbed areas, especially with dry soils, through-out the northern United States and southern Canada.

POISONOUS PRINCIPLE. Historically, a number of active principles have been isolated, partially characterized, and named from this and other species of the same genus. However, the principle responsible for the disease described below is unidentified.

TOXICITY, SYMPTOMS, AND LESIONS. The Wyoming Experiment Station reports (97) that cattle develop symptoms and lesions of pulmonary emphysema after feeding on large quantities of young growth of prickly lettuce. Symptoms consist of severe dyspnea and weakness. In post mortem examination the lung tissue is found to be largely destroyed and the alveoli ruptured.

CONDITIONS OF POISONING. Poisoning seems to occur only under conditions in which very hungry animals are suddenly given access to large quantities of the young stages of this weed. Under these conditions a large amount will be consumed. The mature plant and the young stages after being dried appear to be nontoxic.

This and other species of *Lactuca* have been suspected in several countries of producing mild disorders in various classes of stock. The review by Hurst (810) may be consulted.

Machaeranthera ramosa A. Nels. Tansy aster

This plant is (1591) a secondary or facultative selenium absorber. Being palatable, succulent, and capable of containing very high concentrations of selenium, it is definitely dangerous to livestock. (See p. 45, see also *Xylorrhiza*.)

Oonopsis spp. Goldenweed

Of seven known species of *Oonopsis,* six have been examined and shown to accumulate selenium (1591). They are limited in habitat to soils containing selenium and, hence, are reliable indicators (see selenium, p. 44).

The goldenweeds are small, bushy, perennial herbs, mostly of dry range, with alternate, entire linear or lanceolate leaves and globose, terminal, solitary or cymose composite heads of yellow florets and yellow rays. They are closely related to *Haplopappus* (*q.v.*). The distribution of this genus is centered in the range country of Colorado and Wyoming. Some species extend into Kansas and South Dakota.

Feeding experiments performed at the Wyoming Agricultural Experiment Station with *O. condensata* A. Nels (97, 770) show that rela-

Fig. 102. *Oxytenia acerosa.* Copperweed. Flowering stem, with detail of "seed" (achene). Courtesy of The Macmillan Company.

tively small amounts (less than 3 per cent of the animal's weight for sheep) produce symptoms typical of acute selenium poisoning.

It is likely, however, that goldenweeds are not consumed under range conditions.

A goldenweed can readily act as a converter plant, causing other plants growing in its vicinity, or where it has previously grown, to be seleniferous.

Oxytenia acerosa Nutt. Copperweed

DESCRIPTION. Erect, stiff-stemmed perennial herb, 2 to 5 ft tall. Stems numerous, from a woody perennating rootstock, unbranched except in flowering, persisting after leaf drop. Leaves hairy, alternate-pinnately or irregularly divided into several linear, almost needlelike segments, or simple and needlelike towards extremities of plant. Inflorescence of small, few-flowered, composite heads, organized in dense terminal panicles; florets rayless, orange or yellow, sometimes white, individually inconspicuous, having *en masse* the general aspect of a goldenrod.

DISTRIBUTION AND HABITAT. Alkaline soils in draws or stream beds of desert ranges and foothills, southern California to southwestern Colorado, south to Colorado and New Mexico.

POISONOUS PRINCIPLE. Unknown. Stable on drying.

TOXICITY, SYMPTOMS, AND LESIONS. For many years occasional heavy losses of cattle in the same canyon in southwestern Colorado finally focussed attention upon copperweed. Experimental feedings at the Colorado Experiment Station (1580, 1581) and additional evidence from other states (28, 804) established its toxicity for cattle and sheep. About 0.5 per cent of an animal's weight of plant is lethal to cattle. Sheep may be somewhat less susceptible. Death occurs one to several days after ingestion of a lethal amount. The majority of poisoned animals die within a day of appearance of symptoms, but some linger in chronic condition for a week or longer. The occasional recovery is very slow.

Symptoms consist of anorexia, dullness, weakness, and coma, followed by death, usually without struggle. Lesions include degenerative changes in liver and later in kidney. Petechiation of the peritoneal membrane is common, and signs of gastrointestinal irritation may also be found.

CONDITIONS OF POISONING. Evidence suggests that the plant increases in toxicity with maturity. Cattle poisoning usually occurs in the fall when animals are being trailed from higher summer ranges through the draws where this species grows. Sheep have been poisoned in winter by eating the fallen leaves. Copperweed is not palatable.

Psathyrotes annua (Nutt.) Gray. Psathyrotes

This low-growing, yellow- to purple-flowered, much-branched herb of dry, sandy, often alkaline soils, especially of creek beds and dry washes, southern Utah to southeastern California and northwestern Mexico, has been tested experimentally for toxicity (122, 192). Single doses are lethal to sheep in less than 24 hrs. at 1.0 per cent or more of body weight. Symptoms include general weakness, incoordination, and depression. Coma precedes death without struggle. Fed daily, sublethal doses, sheep develop icterus.

The liver was the organ primarily affected in both acute and chronic syndromes. In the latter, the liver was swollen, with nutmeg appearance, and friable. Bile ducts were distended and few normal hepatic cells were found on microscopic examination.

Psathyrotes, thus, is highly poisonous. It may be eaten by livestock under adverse range conditions, but no natural cases of poisoning have yet been reported.

Psilostrophe gnaphalodes DC.
Psilostrophe tagetinae (Nutt.) Greene — Paperflowers
Psilostrophe sparsiflora (Gray) A. Nels.

DESCRIPTION. Bushy, woolly herbs with perennating taproot, 8 in. to 2 ft tall. Stem much branched, ribbed. Stem leaves alternate, oblanceolate to almost linear, mostly 2 in. long or shorter. Basal rosette leaves, if present, larger, pinnately dissected. Inflorescence a few-flowered composite head; heads grouped in corymbose clusters at stem tips, mostly surmounting foliage. Ray florets 3 to 4 per head; ray about as broad as long (about $\frac{3}{16}$ in.) in *P. gnaphalodes,* broader than long in the other species, yellow, terminated by 3 broadly rounded, pointed lobes; disc florets about twice as many as ray florets. Rays persistent as papery scales on mature achenes. *P. tagetinae* and *P. sparsiflora* intergrade. The latter is less woolly, and the heads are less tightly gathered in cymose clusters.

DISTRIBUTION AND HABITAT. These are plants of the open dry range.

Fig. 103. *Psilostrophe gnaphalodes.* Paperflower.

P. gnaphalodes is restricted to Texas. The others occur also in Utah, New Mexico, Arizona, and Mexico.

POISONOUS PRINCIPLE. Unknown. Stable on drying.

TOXICITY, SYMPTOMS, AND LESIONS. All three species have caused economically important loss of life in sheep on southwestern ranges. Cases in Texas led to several inconclusive experimental investigations of these plants, culminating in successful feeding experiments by Mathews at the Alpine substation (804).

Symptoms take the following form. Sheep appear in good condition at first but show some incoordination when running. They are found to be sluggish and without appetite. A violent cough is common, occasionally resulting in vomition. Vomition in a poisoned flock of sheep may be detected by the presence of a green stain about the muzzle. Eventually, depression and emaciation are followed by death.

No characteristic gross lesions were found on post mortem examination of the experimental animals and only occasionally was nephritis found in range cases. Nevertheless, in all instances microscopic examination of the kidney displayed albuminous degeneration of tubules with casts— which, however, were not extensive enough to completely occlude the tubule. Other lesions were not found.

CONDITIONS OF POISONING. All three species are poisonous, although it has not been established that they are of equal toxicity. Range observations indicate that *P. gnaphalodes* and *P. tagetinae* may be about equally toxic. These plants are not distasteful. In the feeding experiments, animals were disinclined to eat them for the first few days, but soon developed avidity for them. Under range conditions they are readily eaten during the winter by sheep. It was found that mature plants (flowering and fruiting) were much less toxic than the young green stages; a much larger amount over a longer period was necessary to bring on toxic symptoms, which were minor. Deaths were not produced with the mature stages, nor were kidney lesions.

Additional references: 803, 1037.

Rudbeckia laciniata L. Golden glow, cone flower, thimble weed

DESCRIPTION. Coarse herbaceous perennial; branching, 2 to 7 ft tall or rarely taller. Stem glabrous. Leaves alternate, large, petioled, usually hairy beneath, considerably varying in degree of incutting; basal leaves pinnately divided into 5 to 7 parts, those above progressively less divided, uppermost with 3 divisions, or entire, lanceolate at branching points beneath the inflorescences. Flowers in composite heads, occasionally one, usually several per plant; rays 6 to 16, yellow, 1¼ to 2½ in. long, drooping; disc conical or almost spherical, to ¾ in. in diameter, greenish-yellow or grayish.

DISTRIBUTION AND HABITAT. Moist rich soils, Quebec to Florida, west to Arizona to Montana. A double-flowered form, var. *hortensis* Bailey, is widely cultivated in perennial gardens.

POISONOUS PRINCIPLE. Unknown.

TOXICITY, SYMPTOMS, AND LESIONS. Toxicity of this plant was first suspected in 1873 (29). Since then it has been the subject of repeated circumstantial reports (608, 913, 1237, 1242) of toxicity to hogs, sheep, and horses. These reports have come from Kansas, Nebraska, Montana, Iowa, and Minnesota. In these reports symptoms were sketchily described and lesions not at all.

A series of experiments was undertaken at the Nebraska Experiment Station to determine the toxicity of this plant to hogs and sheep (1475). *Rudbeckia* was generally refused, but animals could be forced to consume small quantities after periods of starvation. Amounts of whole, nearly mature plant between 3 and 4 per cent of animal body weight produced symptoms after about 24 hours but not death in both hogs and sheep. In both species symptoms consisted of incoordination. Some evidence of abdominal pain was noticed in several of the hogs. Aimless wandering was observed in two of the experimental swine. The sheep displayed listlessness. Both species experienced increased respiratory rates. In these experiments the animals returned to normal after exhibiting symptoms for 24 to 36 hours and it was impossible to produce symptoms a second time with further feedings. Experiments with various laboratory animals in which some deaths were produced showed that the only consistent lesions were fatty degeneration of liver tissue.

Fig. 104. *Rudbeckia laciniata*. Golden glow. Courtesy of The Macmillan Company.

Rudbeckia occidentalis Nutt., western coneflower, which is found in the area bordered by Nevada, Washington, Montana, and Utah, is considered suspicious by Pammel (1217) and may have been the subject of the original report from Oregon (29).

Rudbeckia hirta L., the common black-eyed Susan, is said (913) to be responsible for poisoning in cattle and hogs in Indiana. Cattle showed symptoms of gastroenteritis; hogs, periods of coma or aimless wandering.

Additional reference: 277.

Sartwellia flaveriae Gray. Sartwellia

DESCRIPTION. Bushy, stiff-stemmed, much-branched annual herb, 6 in. to 2 ft tall. Leaves numerous, narrowly linear, entire, 1 to 2 in. long.

Inflorescence the composite head; heads very numerous, yellow, grouped in flat-topped cymose clusters; each head composed of 12 to 17 florets; ray florets 3 to 5, rays about $\frac{1}{16}$ in. long, almost as broad; corolla of disc floret slightly longer than ray of ray floret.

DISTRIBUTION AND HABITAT. Alkaline or very alkaline soils, western Texas and New Mexico; sometimes forming pure stands.

POISONOUS PRINCIPLE. Unknown.

TOXICITY, SYMPTOMS, AND LESIONS. Knowledge of the toxicity of sartwellia comes from the experimental investigation with goats by Mathews at the Alpine (Texas) experiment substation (1047). His investigation was prompted by range cases in Angora goats, characterized by gradual loss of weight despite normal appetite, distended abdomen, and, on post mortem, by ascites and extensive hepatic cirrhosis. Sartwellia was incriminated by association.

Mathews performed extensive and long-continued feeding experiments with several goats but was unable to reproduce the disease as found in range cases. An explanation may lie in the fact that he was unable to procure fresh material daily. Nevertheless his experiments demonstrated the toxic nature of the plant, even when dry, and that one of its effects was to produce liver damage. The plant was readily eaten. He found that amounts equivalent to 1.5 to 3 per cent of a goat's weight fed daily would produce anorexia after 6 to 28 days. If the plant was subsequently forced on the animal, death resulted. Post mortem examination showed liver necrosis with numerous grayish-yellow areas throughout, and albuminous degeneration in the kidneys. Histopathological examination of the liver displayed marked focal necrosis. Some pigment deposition was detected in both liver and kidney.

It was found that animals, left alone, would start eating sartwellia again after a few days. Either on the second period of sartwellia consumption or on a subsequent one, several animals developed a syndrome characterized by hydrothorax and pulmonary edema followed by death. In these animals the liver was found on gross examination to have only a slight yellowish cast. Microscopic examination, however, showed marked fatty infiltrative degeneration of liver and kidney epithelium together with fibrosis of the liver. There was neither marked necrosis nor marked cirrhosis. The yellowish cast of the liver was associated with the presence of a yellow pigment which came out in alcohol during preparation of liver specimens for the microscope.

A condition has been recognized in slaughterhouses which may be associated with the above. Occasionally it has been necessary to condemn livers from cattle (195) and lambs received at different slaughterhouses but originating from the area where sartwellia grows. In many cases the only gross distinguishing characteristic of condemned cattle livers was intense yellow or reddish-yellow pigmentation with slight swelling. In others, the livers were markedly cirrhotic as well as pigmented. The only other abnormality in these animals was concerned with hepatic lymph glands which were of a peculiar yellow, mottled appearance. Such pathologic bovine livers, when fed to rats, produced liver lesions in the latter. The yellow pigment was determined to be carotene. It was concluded (195) that these animals had been subjected to some specific liver irritant in the diet, probably from a plant, which produced parenchymatous degeneration followed by necrosis, fibrous changes, proliferation of bile ducts, and finally cirrhosis with calcification. The carotene probably accumulated secondarily.

Additional reference: 801.

Senecio spp. Groundsel, senecio

More than 1200 species of this genus are distributed widely over the world. About 25 of them have proven poisonous to livestock or human beings. It is likely that the list will grow, since toxic alkaloids have been isolated from a number of additional species. Nearly 50 species occur in North America. Seven have been suspected or have proven to be toxic.

Botanically, senecios are variable and difficult to describe faithfully. Two useful genus characters are the presence of a single whorl (sometimes subtended by a second, reduced whorl) of touching but not overlapping bracts forming a cup under the head, and the production of seed in both disc and ray florets. In cases where senecio poisoning is suspected, the services of a taxonomic botanist should be sought for accurate species identification.

Descriptions, distributions, and habitats of poisonous species are as follows.

Senecio integerrimus Nutt. (297)

Perennial; stems solitary, erect, from perennating crown, leafy mostly below middle, 1 to 3 ft tall. Lower leaves mostly ovate or obovate, entire to dentate, petiolate, blades 1 to 5 in. long; stem leaves fewer, reduced, very different. Composite heads relatively few, in terminal flat-topped open clusters; rays 5 to 12, yellow or creamy white. Woods and slopes; British Columbia to Montana, Rocky Mountains, and California.

Senecio jacobaea L. Stinking willie (841, 1267, 1646)

Biennial, winter annual, or occasionally perennial, erect, coarse, unbranched (except at inflorescence) herb, 1 to 4 ft tall. Stems evenly leafy. Leaves deeply, irregularly 2 to 3 times pinnately divided, larger to 9 in. long and 4 in. wide. Composite heads numerous, in showy, terminal flat-topped clusters; head about ½ in. tall; individual rays to ½ in.

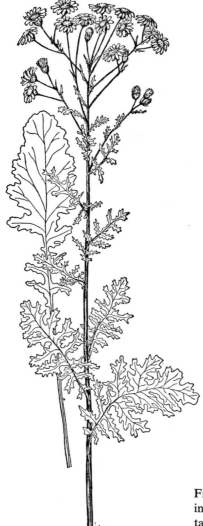

Fig. 105. *Senecio jacobaea*. Stinking willie. Flowering shoot, with detail of leaf. Courtesy of The Macmillan Company.

long, yellow. A troublesome introduced weed of pastures and meadows; Gaspé and Maritime Provinces to Massachusetts; Pacific coast; local elsewhere.

Senecio longilobus Benth.[2] Wooly groundsel, thread-leaf groundsel (297, 1036, 1041)

Shrubby, erect, branched, wooly-white perennial, leafy throughout, mostly 1 to 2 ft tall. Leaves narrowly linear, thick, white, occasionally pinnately lobed, to 4 in. long. Composite heads numerous in flat-topped terminal clusters; rays 13, yellow, ⅜ in. long. Common range plant; Colorado and Utah south to Texas and Mexico.

Fig. 106. *Senecio longilobus*. Wooly groundsel. Photograph of plant, and detail of inflorescences.

Senecio plattensis Nutt. (713)

Perennial; stems 1 to several from perennating rhizome, 6 in. to 1½ ft tall. Basal leaves obovate or oblanceolate, crenate to slightly pinnately cut, firm, thick, to 3 in. long and 2 in. wide. Composite heads in flat-topped terminal clusters; rays showy, yellow. Dry limy soils, prairies, rocky ground; Vermont and Ontario to Saskatchewan and Indiana, south to Virginia, Louisiana, and Texas.

Senecio riddellii Torr. & Gray.[2] Riddell's groundsel (198, 248, 297, 738, 1036, 1612)

Bright green, herbaceous perennial; stems glabrous, leafy above, branched, 1½ ft tall. Leaves threadlike, pinnately suboppositely lobed; lobes threadlike. Composite heads numerous, in flat-topped, terminal

[2] *Senecio longilobus* and *S. riddellii* are not considered separate species by some botanists.

clusters; rays 6 to 8, yellow ½ in. long. Range: Nebraska and Colorado to New Mexico and Texas.

Senecio spartioides Torr. & Gray. Broom groundsel (297, 404)

Coarse, bushy perennial, leafy throughout, woody below, 6 in. to 2 ft tall. Leaves mostly entire, narrowly linear, to 3 in. long. Heads loosely grouped, numerous, narrow; rays relatively few, yellow, ½ in. long. Valleys, plains; Wyoming to Nebraska, south to Arizona and Texas.

Senecio vulgaris L. Common groundsel

This species is a common, annual, garden weed. It is leafy throughout and the leaves are coarsely toothed or pinnately divided. It has not been found poisonous in North America, but has been so considered elsewhere (1533).

Senecio glabellus Poir. (= *S. lobatus* Pers.) Bitterweed

This plant of wet soils in the area between Texas, Illinois, Florida, and North Carolina has been suspected (1136) of poisoning cattle in Florida.

HISTORICAL. Several diseases of livestock characterized by liver lesions had been recognized under various names in various parts of the world when it was shown that a species of *Senecio* was responsible for one of them. This led to the discovery of the etiological relation of several species of *Senecio* to others, and to the association of *Senecio* with more recently discovered diseases of human beings and animals. The early history has been reviewed by Van Es *et al.* (1612).

A disease of horses loosely termed "stomach staggers" had been recognized in Wales in the early 1800's and was associated by the farmers with *Senecio jacobaea* (626). In the Western Hemisphere, Pictou disease of cattle had been known in Nova Scotia before about 1860 when it first caused serious losses (1267). It, too, was associated with *Senecio jacobaea* by the residents of that area. Elsewhere, the Winton disease of horses and cattle in New Zealand, the Molteno disease of cattle and dunziekte of horses in South Africa, sirasyke in Norway, and others unnamed were described with characteristic and similar liver lesions. Considerable effort was made to determine the etiology and to formulate control for Pictou disease. The etiological relationships of bacteria to many diseases were being discovered at that time, and the assumption of a similar relationship in this case undoubtedly delayed the discovery of the true cause. The Canadian government for several years purchased and caused to be slaughtered animals which showed signs of Pictou disease, in a mistaken attempt to prevent its spread.

The break came with experiments by Gilruth in 1902 (626) which indicated that Winton disease of horses and cattle in New Zealand was, as the farmers there suspected, caused by ingestion of *Senecio jacobaea*.

Further experiments by Gilruth in New Zealand and by Pethick in Nova Scotia soon firmly established that *Senecio jacobaea* was the cause of Winton disease and Pictou disease, both of which were characterized by almost exactly similar symptoms and lesions.

Since then, by either experiment or circumstance, species of *Senecio* have become associated with the other diseases named above. A number of more recently recognized diseases have also been linked with *Senecio:* the "walking disease" of horses in Nebraska with *S. riddellii;* bread poisoning of man in South Africa with *S. burchellii, S. ilicifolius,* and others (1531); ždar disease of horses in Czechoslovakia with *S. erraticus* (1620); and venous occlusive disease of animals in the West Indies with species of *Senecio* (774). Other enzootic liver diseases of similar pathology have been traced to species of *Crotalaria, Heliotrope,* and *Amsinckia* (*q.v.*). Venous occlusive disease of human beings in the West Indies and elsewhere is presumptively assigned to ingestion of senecio alkaloids, although the exact source is still uncertain (772, 774, 1539). Senecio alkaloids experimentally have also been shown to provoke some of the characteristics of kwashiorkor ("red body disease") in human beings (1407).

POISONOUS PRINCIPLE. Not all species of *Senecio* are toxic. Undoubtedly those that are owe their toxicity to the presence of one or more alkaloids, although this relationship has been proved only in certain cases. Hosking and Brandt (789) and Rosenfeld and Beath (1365) have reviewed the early chemical investigations of the senecio alkaloids. These compounds have provoked much interest among chemists and pharmacologists, and the exact chemical structure and physiological effect of many are known. For chemistry the review by Leonard (919) and Culvenor *et al.* (387) may be consulted. Hill has briefly reviewed diseases traced to pyrrolizidine alkaloids (772).

Despite their large number, senecio alkaloids belong to a single group, the pyrrolizidine alkaloids. On hydrolysis these alkamine esters break apart to yield a nitrogen-containing fraction, the necine, and another, a mono- or dicarboxylic necic acid. Neither breakdown product is hepatotoxic, but the necine in sufficient quantity may produce death. There are about ten necines and a considerably larger number of necic acids, which may be joined in various combinations. One of the common and more complex senecio alkaloids is retrorsine, composed of retronecine and isatinecic acid. Presence of the corresponding amine N-oxides has been detected in some instances. The nitrogen oxides are hepatotoxic, but the liver lesions they produce may vary somewhat from those produced by the alkaloids.

Pyrrolizidine alkaloids occur also in several species of *Crotalaria* and *Heliotropium,* and in a number of other genera including *Echium* (*q.v.*). Where specifically known, the gross physiological effect of this group of alkaloids in provoking liver lesions is remarkably uniform. Molecularly, the presence of a double bond in the 1, 2 position of the pyrrolizidine ring appears essential to toxicity (1408).

TOXICITY. Discussion will be confined to experiments performed since 1920. Feeding experiments have been conducted with *Senecio riddellii* by Van Es *et al.* (1612), Mathews (1036, 1039), Carpenter (248), and

retrorsine

Vardiman (1613); with *S. integerrimus* by Clawson (297), with *S. longilobus* by Clawson (297) and Mathews (1036), with *S. jacobaea* by Murnane (1150), and Markson (979), and with *S. spartioides* by Huffman (404) and Clawson (297).

In summary, it has been found that doses of 1 to 5 per cent of an animal's weight fed at one time or over a few days will bring on acute poisoning. For example, Mathews killed a cow in 18 hours with 3.2 per cent of its weight of plants. Acute poisoning is not unknown under natural conditions (e.g., 243), but is rare. Chronic cases are brought on by smaller daily, but larger total, doses obtained over the course of several weeks or months, both experimentally and under natural conditions. In most cases the amount of plant consumed by cattle and horses before chronic symptoms appeared varied between 12 per cent and 156 per cent, with symptoms appearing in less than a month or not until after 5 months. Variation depends in part on species of *Senecio,* species of animal, and stage of growth of the plant. *Senecio riddellii* and *S. longilobus* have been proved about equally toxic (1036). These species are the most troublesome on western ranges. They have an average toxicity of about 30 per cent in cattle and horses, with symptoms appearing in one to two months. *Senecio integerrimus* and *S. jacobaea* are less toxic. On the basis of limited feeding experiments, (297, 404), *S. spartioides* appears highly toxic.

Cattle and horses are about equally sensitive to the toxic effects of a given species of *Senecio.* Sheep and goats are more resistant but have been poisoned experimentally (297, 1036). It was found that 1 to 4 per cent per day of *S. longilobus* would provoke symptoms only after about a month. Thus, roughly twice as much is required for the same effect as in cattle or horses.

SYMPTOMS. A latent period is commonly observed in natural chronic cases. Most natural cases in cattle and horses in North America are of the type in which a relatively small amount of plant is consumed daily over an extended period of time. Under these circumstances the effect of the plant is not only cumulative, but progressive, and the complex degenerative and regenerative changes that take place in the liver may not result in the appearance of symptoms until several months after the animal no longer has access to the plant. Liver-function tests after cattle no longer had access to *Senecio* gave (931) normal values at first, but became positive for liver dysfunction several weeks later. Latent periods approaching six months in length have been observed (445, 1039). During the latent period animals may gain weight (297, 1036) and may appear in excellent condition immediately before the appearance of symptoms.

In chronic poisoning of horses, symptoms often appear abruptly. The affected animal stands apart, appearing depressed or sluggish and without appetite. The disease in many cases runs its course to a fatal termination within a week, although some animals linger longer. The animal becomes rapidly worse. Yellow or muddy discoloration of the visible mucous membranes is observed, and a peculiar, sweetish, yet unpleasant odor emanates from the skin. Weakness, uneasiness, signs of abdominal pain, emaciation, and reduced sensibility occur. In some cases a depraved appetite is evidenced by chewing at mangers, fences, or dirt. Diarrhea or darkly stained urine may or may not be present. At this juncture the disease may go one of two ways (298). In some instances weakness and depression increase and the animal dies quietly. In others restlessness increases and the animal starts walking aimlessly, not avoiding objects in its path. Most fences will not deter such an animal; a building or similar object will not be avoided. Animals will lean or push against such structures, sometimes becoming frenzied. In many instances death results when animals become entangled in fences or walk over the edge of a ravine.

Chronic poisoning in cattle is similar in most respects. The same peculiar odor has been noted in the milk (841) and about the skin. In some cases the odor seems to be associated principally with areas of subdermal edema commonly noted in cattle (297). In more severe instances seepage of serum through the skin occurs at these sites, and they are usually uncomfortable to the animal. This lesion may represent a photosensitive reaction resulting from liver damage.

Poisoned cattle generally display roughened coat and dry, scaly muzzle. Tenesmus associated with either constipation or diarrhea is common and may result in prolapse. Sometimes ascites may be found. As in horses, cattle may remain quiet or become agitated. If the latter, they may become dangerously aggressive, attacking even automobiles.

Chronic senecio poisoning of human beings in Africa has been described by Steyn (1531, 1533) and Selzer et al. (1436). It is similar to venous occlusive disease of human beings in the West Indies and elsewhere (774). Prominent symptoms include ascites, enlarged liver, abdominal pain, nausea, vomition, headache, apathy, and emaciation. Diarrhea may be present, and both diarrhea and vomitus may be bloodstained. Jaundice is rare.

Sheep are rarely poisoned. In those few experimental cases on record (297) the symptoms and lesions are similar to those in cattle.

Where acute poisoning is known, it is similar in most respects to the acute termination of chronic poisoning. Chronic and acute poisonings may be differentiated by their histories and on post mortem by the type of liver injury.

LESIONS. Senecio poisoning is almost entirely the result of specific liver injury produced by the senecio alkaloids. The exact appearance of the liver depends largely upon the duration of the disease. In acute poisoning necrosis and severe hemorrhage into the lobules is observed (297). If the initial damage is less severe, regenerative changes take place. Thus long-standing chronic cases on post mortem examination display fibrotic or cirrhotic livers, and intermediate cases are characterized by a variety of balances between destruction of hepatic cells and formation of connective tissue. Markson has closely followed the ontogeny of pathology in cattle (979).

In the usual chronic range case in horses or cattle, the liver is about normal in size. It is finely mottled with areas of differing color and presents a general off-color appearance. It may be grossly fibrotic.

In horses, a pathological liver and hepatic lymph nodes are the principal findings. In cattle additional lesions are found. Typically the gall bladder is tremendously enlarged and filled with thick, mucilaginous bile. Mathews (1036) found nearly 8 quarts of bile in one instance. Accumulation of bile is associated with increased production, since the bile duct is not obstructed and large quantities of bile are found in the intestine. There may be some abdominal distension and ascites in cattle. Often widespread or sometimes localized edematous swelling of visceral mucosae is found. The membranes become gelatinous and sometimes as much as an inch in thickness. Petechial or larger hemorrhage may be found in various sites. Sometimes in cattle and frequently in man hemorrhage into the digestive tract occurs. Degenerative changes may be detected grossly and histologically in the kidneys of cattle.

Experiments with crude or refined senecio alkaloids and laboratory animals have been performed by a number of persons in an attempt to isolate and describe the specific toxic effect in the liver. The several alkaloids employed, whether from *Crotalaria, Heliotropium,* or *Senecio,* are grossly similar in effect. Differences in toxicity and some differences in effect have been correlated with elements of chemical structure by Schoental and Magee (1410, 1411), and Culvenor *et al.* (387). Harris *et al.* (724) considered primary a toxic necrosis produced in hepatic cells by senecio alkaloids. Rosenfeld and Beath (1365), on the other hand, ascribed primary toxic effect to capillary damage and resulting hemorrhage, particularly in the liver. Selzer *et al.* (1437), after reviewing previous concepts, describe almost simultaneous appearance of necrosis of hepatic cells and vascular damage with hemorrhage, and conclude that the alkaloids have a dual toxic effect. Others also have distinguished separate toxic effects. Pyrrolizidine alkaloids have been found by Gallagher and Koch (595) to have an inhibiting effect at the neuromuscular junction. Nitrogen oxides were without similar effect. Level of dosage also can be used to identify separate effects: large doses produce necrosis of liver cells, while smaller doses produce distinct cellular changes which do not involve or include necrosis (202).

Several investigators (297, 1036, 1612) have remarked on the increased size and chaotic arrangement of hepatic cells. Bull (200) applied the term megalocytosis to this condition and considered it the most characteristic effect of senecio alkaloids. In such cells the nucleus increases greatly in size without undergoing mitosis, and becomes polyploid. Increase in chromatin and DNA may be detected.

An approach has been undertaken to learn the fundamental biochemical lesion. With purified alkaloid and laboratory animals, it has been shown (282) that exposure to the alkaloid is followed by sudden and complete loss of activity of pyridine-nucleotide-dependent enzyme systems in the liver and thereby loss of ability of mitochondria to oxidize certain substrates. Christie and LePage (282) suggest that the alkaloid decreases the binding powers of mitochondrial enzymes and of proteins dissolved in cytoplasm for pyridine nucleotides and reduces diphospho-pyridine-nucleotide synthesis. Culvenor *et al.* hypothesize that pyrrolizidine alkaloids owe their activity in cell nuclei to their ability to act in the cell as alkylating agents.

Since the liver does not usually increase in size during poisoning, the presence of megalocytes may indicate death of many hepatic cells. This, together with an increased death rate of megalocytes, is held to give rise to the fibrosis commonly observed. These cells, or structures resulting from them, are considered by some (467, 776, 1365) as neoplasms. In some cases malignancies may arise in the livers of poisoned animals. There appears to be some derangement in the normal process of mitosis on the part of megalocytes, which may be at the root of neoplasm development, but single doses of alkaloids, although giving rise to liver pathology, do not normally result in malignant tumors (1411). The mechanism by which venous occlusion occurs has been described as proliferation of vascular endothelium (1437), or subendothelial swelling (107) of medium and small hepatic veins. In either event, this gives rise to pronounced sinusoidal centrilobular congestion, resulting damage, and nonportal fibrosis. These effects are considered (107) specific for the pyrrolizidine alkaloids of *Crotalaria* and *Senecio,* and therefore, the general name venous occlusive disease may be applied to poisoning by these plants or by alkaloids from them, whether encountered in man or animal. These lesions produce several kinds of gross changes in physiology. The most significant, in the opinion of Bull (201) is the loss of the capacity of the liver to form urea. Death is, then, the direct result of increased blood ammonia concentration and ammonia intoxication.

In many experiments with laboratory animals, difference in susceptibility to poisoning has been noticed between the sexes (205). This may be related to steroid characteristics of the alkaloids.

Re-examination of preserved liver specimens from Van Es's walking disease of horses in Nebraska, from *Senecio*-poisoned cattle in England, and from animals poisoned by *Senecio* in South Africa (774, 776) has shown that the basic lesion is identical in all cases and that it is equivalent with venous occlusive disease of human beings.

CONDITIONS OF POISONING. In North America most poisoning by *Senecio* occurs on the range or pasture. Instances of heavy mortality in horses (1612) and cattle (1036) are on record, but because of the insidious nature of the disease and the latent period associated with it, probably a great deal of *Senecio* poisoning goes unrecognized (404). *Senecio riddellii* and *S. longilobus* (if they are different) account for the majority of cases. *Senecio integerrimus* is probably not toxic under range conditions because it is not highly toxic and is short-lived, appearing seasonally when range forage is usually plentiful (297). No *Senecio* is palatable to livestock. *Senecio longilobus* stays green longer and is succulent in winter. Young stages are consumed unselectively with grasses by grazing cattle in spring. There is some evidence that young stages of *Senecio,* and particularly young leaves, are the most highly toxic (297, 307, 1532). Statistically, incidence of poisoning is seasonal, with the majority of cases occurring in summer, but individual cases may be found in almost any month, often long after *Senecio* has become unavailable. Sheep are often used for controlling the plant because of their greater resistance. This is sometimes a risky practice. Sheep mortality under natural conditions has occurred (1150), and it has been shown (200) that progressive liver damage takes place during yearly grazing on *S. jacobaea* even though it may not result in clinical poisoning.

Senecio alkaloids are not destroyed on drying or during silage fermentation. In other countries, hay is a frequent source of poisoning (445, 1513). Cases from silage are fewer but are apt to be more spectacular (445, 931). One instance of poisoning from lucern cubes containing large admixtures of *Senecio* has been reported (268). If the use of pellets or cubes becomes more general, greater care will be necessary in keeping them free of poisonous weeds since they thwart the natural selectivity of the animal.

Human poisoning comes from two different sources. In Africa *Senecio* poisoning is usually traced (1531) to bread made from flour contaminated with seeds or fragments of *Senecio*. In the West Indies, it is presumed (774) that poisoning results from the native practice of brewing a supposedly medicinal "tea" from various indigenous plants. Several times it has been noted that protein deficiency in the diet seems to predispose to venous occlusive disease in human beings.

When an outbreak of *Senecio* poisoning is diagnosed in a herd of cattle on the death of the first animal, it may be assumed that additional cases will follow if all animals have been handled similarly. Thus considerable economic advantage may be had from detecting and marketing incipient cases before symptoms appear. Liver biopsy has proved an effective, though time-consuming, method of detecting incipient cases (110, 1614). Liver-function tests, if handled judiciously and skillfully, might serve the same purpose with greater ease (931), but are less reliable. Treatment of race horses with crystalline methionine was remarkably effective in two instances (1334).

Additional references: 188, 234, 403.

Sideranthus grindelioides (Nutt.) Rydb. Ironweed
This plant is (1591) a secondary or facultative selenium absorber and is known to be grazed by sheep during the fall and winter months. (See p. 45.)

Silybum marianum (L.) Gaertn. Variegated thistle, milk thistle, bull thistle, St. Mary's thistle
DESCRIPTION. Coarse, erect, annual or biennial herb, 2 to 6 ft tall. Stems branched above. Leaves alternate decurrent, pinnately veined and lobed; major veins extending beyond margin as yellow, woody, sharp-pointed spines; upper surface more or less marked with conspicuous white patches; lower leaves 6 to 12 in. long, half as wide. Inflorescence a large composite head, singly terminating each stem; heads purple, to 2 in. in diameter, spiny; florets numerous, ray florets absent.

DISTRIBUTION AND HABITAT. Used rarely as a garden plant; occasionally found as an escape from cultivation; widely naturalized in pastures and waste places in California.

POISONOUS PRINCIPLE. Nitrate. (See nitrate poisoning, p. 38.)

TOXICITY, SYMPTOMS, AND LESIONS. Heavy losses of cattle and sheep in Australia have occurred after ingestion of this species (810). Symptoms and lesions were those of nitrate poisoning. In California a number of deaths have been reported in cattle (857). Feeding tests confirmed the toxicity of variegated thistle. Symptoms and lesions were those of nitrate poisoning.

Nitrate content is variable. In one sample of leaves, 10 per cent nitrate content was detected. In the experimental animals the level of blood methemoglobin increased in proportion as the plant was fed.

CONDITIONS OF POISONING. Variegated thistle has been considered moderately useful as forage under some circumstances. This opinion should be reversed. It is not particularly palatable to cattle, and when growing on fertile soil may accumulate dangerous levels of nitrate.

Solidago spp. Goldenrods

Several reports of goldenrod toxicity to horses appeared at the close of the nineteenth century. Cases, some involving severe loss, were described in Pennsylvania, Wisconsin, and New Jersey (726, 747, 1374, 1429). Loss was associated with the practice of pasturing horses in areas where there were dense stands of goldenrod. It was noted that some horses developed an appetite for these plants, which they normally avoid, and that only such horses were affected. Symptoms developed some time after horses had access to the plant and death followed typically within 2 weeks to 2 months. Emaciation was most prominently noted, although appetite remained normal throughout most of the course of the disease. Other symptoms include some edema of legs and abdomen, dullness, and unsteadiness. Lesions consisted of enlarged spleen and some hemorrhaging, detected in the gastrointestinal tract and elsewhere. The blood appeared, in the language of the time, "disintegrated."

In the minds of the persons involved, the disease was definitely connected with the presence of a severe infestation of rust on the goldenrod. The rust was identified (747, 1374) as *Coleosporium solidagenis* (Schw.) Thüm., and the goldenrod was *Solidago odora* Ait. The latter identification was disputed by Rusby (1374). *Coleosporium solidagenis* is found on several species of *Solidago* and also on another composite, *Veronia noveboracensis* (L.) Michx. (ironweed). This plant was being used at that time to produce abortion in human beings and had been suggested (916) as a possible cause of abortion in cattle. It is interesting to note in this connection that abortion in cattle in Virginia has more recently been suggestively linked (589) with ingestion by them of *Solidago speciosa* Nutt. infected with a fungus that was tentatively identified as a species of *Coleosporium*.

Experiments performed at the Wyoming Agricultural Experiment

Station (97) show that relatively small amounts of range goldenrods *Solidago mollis* Bartl. and *"S. coccinna"* [= *S. concinna* A. Nels. (?)] are toxic to sheep. In these cases toxicity is derived from the irritant nature of resinous constituents of the plants, and symptoms consist of vomition, accelerated respiration, and general distress, followed by death if sufficient plant has been consumed. In the experiments doses of 1 lb of the partially air-dried plant given 4 hours apart produced death in a sheep after 12 hours.

In Nevada western goldenrod, identified as *Solidago spectabilis* (D.C. Eat.) Gray, has been suspected by stockmen of producing loss in sheep and cattle. Investigations by the Nevada Agricultural Experiment Station (547, 548) have confirmed its toxicity, which is developed in the leaves of the plant at, but not before, the time of flowering. A hemolytic substance was extracted and partially characterized.

Losses in sheep have occurred in Montana from an unidentified goldenrod (1655). Losses followed several instances when half-starved sheep were moved from dry range to pastures containing thick patches of goldenrod, particularly during late fall and early winter.

Tanacetum vulgare L. Tansy

This species, sometimes grown as an herb, has been used as the source of an antihelminthic and abortifacient ethereal oil since the Middle Ages. It is found in old gardens, herb gardens, and as an escape throughout North America. Loss of life in human beings after symptoms of severe gastritis and convulsions has occasionally followed injudicious use of a medicinal extract from this plant (1158). Abortion in cattle has circumstantially been linked with consumption of tansy in Pennsylvania (658). The plant is rarely touched by animals.

Tetradymia canescens DC. Spineless horsebrush
Tetradymia glabrata Gray. Littleleaf horsebrush, spring rabbitbrush, coal oil brush

DESCRIPTION. Densely branched, woody shrubs, to about 3 ft tall (sometimes more in *T. glabrata*). Inflorescence the composite head, produced in large numbers on short peduncles about the periphery of the plant; each head composed of 4 yellow florets which soon become interspersed with large amounts of straw-colored, threadlike bristles growing straight upward from the fruits. *Tetradymia canescens:* stem and leaves covered with dense, persistent woolly hair imparting a whitish cast. Leaves alternate, single, linear or barely lanceolate, about 1 in. long. *Tetradymia glabrata:* stems and leaves at first covered with white wooly hairs which are deciduous and soon absent. Leaves of two types; primary leaves on new growth single, alternate, linear, sharp-pointed, slightly less than ½ in. long, soon deciduous; secondary leaves clustered in angles of shed primary leaves, fleshier, blunt-tipped, slightly less than ½ in. long.

Both species produce vegetative growth, flower, and become dormant very early in the season. *Tetradymia glabrata* flowers in April and May; *T. canescens* in May, June, and early July. New vegetative growth appears at about the same time that winter snows melt.

DISTRIBUTION AND HABITAT. Both species are plants of dry desert and sagebrush ranges. *Tetradymia glabrata:* southern Oregon and Idaho to eastern California, Nevada, and western Utah. *Tetradymia canescens:* similar distribution, but extending into southeastern Washington, Montana, Wyoming, and northern New Mexico.

POISONOUS PRINCIPLE. Unknown. Soluble in petroleum ether, not stable to drying (541).

TOXICITY, SYMPTOMS, AND LESIONS. Both species of horsebrush produce liver injury in sheep. Losses of more than a thousand head at a single time have occurred (541). Additional symptoms of photosensitization (see p. 52) may or may not develop depending upon severity of poisoning, presence of green feed in the diet, and access of sunlight to the skin. On the range, both types of poisoning (liver injury with photosensitization or liver injury alone) are common and frequently occur in the same band at the same time.

Experimental feedings have been performed at the Nevada Experiment Station (539, 541) and the Salina station of the U.S. Department of Agriculture (301, 950). *Tetradymia glabrata* has been used in most of these. It is about twice as toxic as *T. canescens* (1587). *Tetradymia glabrata* is toxic to sheep at about 0.5 per cent of the animal's weight, whether given in one feeding or in lesser amount repeatedly over a longer period of time. At this level, symptoms of photosensitization ("bighead") are usually developed but the animal does not always die. Larger amounts produce more severe liver damage and result in death without symptoms of photosensitization.

Range experience is in agreement. It is common for those animals in a band that have consumed a greater amount to develop symptoms after 16 to 24 hours and succumb within an hour or so after appearance of symptoms. Symptoms consist of anorexia, depression, twitching, incoordination, rapid, weak pulse, prostration, dyspnea, coma, and death. In the same band, a few hours later, other animals begin to show signs of photosensitization. Redness of the skin about the head, accompanied by uneasiness and itching, develops after a few hours into a typical case of bighead. Necropsy examination of acute cases presents a somewhat enlarged and engorged liver in which marked degenerative changes histologically may be found. Occasionally the capsule has ruptured and hemorrhage occurred. Icterus has not been reported. The kidney shows signs of low-grade nephritis. The gall bladder is distended. Petechial hemorrhages may be found in the subcutis and elsewhere. Necropsy examination of typical cases of photosensitization presents a similar picture except that liver lesions and regenerative changes have proceeded further. The liver may be somewhat smaller than normal and show more distinct signs of fatty degeneration.

In order for photosensitization to occur, liver damage must not be so severe that the animal dies before the syndrome has time to develop. Moreover, green feed must be present in the diet. Usually the leaves of young *Tetradymia* shoots provide enough green substance, but occasionally poisoning may occur early in the season before the leaves have fully developed, or from ingestion principally of flower heads. Under these circumstances photosensitization will not appear unless other green material is present in the diet. Photosensitization is not likely to develop in black-skinned animals, because sufficient light does not reach the capillaries of the skin to provoke the reaction.

Attempts to poison cattle experimentally have not been successful (541). Cattle have been fed *Tetradymia* without effect in amounts equalling a percentage of their weight several times greater than that necessary to poison sheep.

CONDITIONS OF POISONING. Neither species of *Tetradymia* is palatable to sheep. Poisoning occurs under conditions which force animals to consume it. Most severe losses have occurred when animals were being trailed from winter to summer ranges. Both species of horsebrush often occur in fairly dense stands. They produce new growth early in the season when other green forage is scarce. It is at this time, also, that they have greatest toxicity. If animals are trailed through stands of horsebrush without being given ample opportunity to find more acceptable grazing, poisoning may be expected. *Tetradymia glabrata* may occasionally cause losses in the fall from its second-growth leaves. According to Huffman (801) *Tetradymia axillaris* A. Nels. has capacity for producing photosensitization.

Additional references: 537, 804.

Viguiera annua (Jones) Blake. Annual goldeneye
DESCRIPTION. Branching, erect annual herb, mostly 1 to 2 ft tall. Leaves opposite, linear or linear-lanceolate, entire, ¾ to 1½ in. long and about ⅛ in. wide. Inflorescence the composite head; heads relatively few, somewhat clustered at the tips of the ultimate branches, bright yellow, showy, about 1 in. across.

DISTRIBUTION AND HABITAT. Weed of ranges, Western Texas to Arizona and Mexico, in some places providing a blanket of brilliant yellow over thousand of acres.

POISONOUS PRINCIPLE. Unknown.

TOXICITY, SYMPTOMS, AND LESIONS. Cattle losses in New Mexico have been associated with ingestion of large amounts of this plant (1185). Under conditions of unavailability of other forage, particularly in the fall when this species grows rapidly, it may be eaten in quantity. The symptoms suggest either cyanide or nitrate poisoning. As yet, animals other than cattle do not appear to have been poisoned. Losses are not high.

Xanthium spp. Cocklebur

Cocklebur may set seed without fertilization of the ovule. This type of asexual propagation tends to result in local populations in which the plants are all genetically equivalent, but which differ in minor characteristics from other similar populations. The most consistent differences have been found in the structure of the bur. On the basis of these differences, some botanical taxonomists separate the cockleburs into a score of species. Accurate determination usually requires having burs to examine. On the other hand, toxicity appears to be similar among all the kinds of cockleburs, and it is impossible to determine which particular kind was involved in most of the case reports and experimental work. If differences in bur structure are not used to separate species, only two or three species remain. The most common is *Xanthium strumarium* L.

DESCRIPTION. Coarse annual herbaceous weed, reaching 3 ft or more in height. Stems erect, branched, stout. Leaves alternate, petiolate, deltoid-ovate, more or less cordate, rough-surfaced, blades to ½ ft long, almost as wide; margins irregularly cut, toothed, lobed, or almost entire. Inflorescence a much-modified composite head; sexes separated. Male heads small, inconspicuous, without rays, grouped in terminal or axillary racemes. Female heads in axillary clusters below. Each female head is composed of but 2 florets which lack rays and are surrounded by a many-bracted, elongate involucre. This entire structure becomes the fruit. The tips of the involucral bracts turn outward and become more or less hooked woody spines. The resulting bur is characteristic of the genus. It is elongate, ovoid, yellowish-green, 2-beaked, densely coarse-spined, ¾ to 1¼ in long, and contains two elongate cavities oriented lengthwise. Only the seedling stage is poisonous. Germinating seedlings first develop two cotyledons which are linear-lanceolate and do not resemble the later leaves. Seedlings may be identified with certainty in the cotyledonary stage by the presence (below ground) of the characteristic persistent bur which usually remains attached to the seedling.

Xanthium spinosum L. (spiny clotbur) is quite different in appearance. It is smaller, bears lanceolate, trilobate leaves, and forms a conspicuous 3-pronged spine in each leaf angle.

DISTRIBUTION AND HABITAT. Both species are found throughout North America. *Xanthium strumarium* is the more common. They occur in fields and waste lands, but especially in areas where receding water has exposed previously submerged land, as along the shores of ponds or rivers and in flood plains.

POISONOUS PRINCIPLE. In 1881 the name xanthostrumarin was given

Fig. 107. *Xanthium strumarium.*
Cocklebur. Fruiting shoot, with details of seedlings and spiny fruit.
Courtesy of The Macmillan Company.

to the toxic fraction of glycosidic characteristics isolated from cocklebur seeds
(see 356). This name is found in much
recent literature. Nevertheless, a critical
pharmacological study (895) prompted
by cocklebur poisoning of livestock in
North Dakota, reported in 1950, has
proved beyond question that the poisonous principle in *Xanthium strumarium* is hydroquinone. The substance
has been recovered from the plant, and
the symptoms and lesions of cocklebur
poisoning can be reproduced in detail
by administration of synthetic hydroquinone. It has been impossible to
demonstrate that hydroquinone is present in glycosidic combination in the
plant.

TOXICITY, SYMPTOMS, AND LESIONS.
Cases of cocklebur poisoning in various
classes of livestock have been reported
fairly frequently from most areas of the
United States (573, 609, 873, 1335,
1655). Experimental feedings have been
performed at the experiment stations of
Kansas (872), Indiana (703), and
most extensively at the USDA experiment station at Salina, Utah (1021,
1022).

The poisonous principle is contained in the seeds, which are toxic at
about 0.3 per cent of an animal's weight. The seeds, however, rarely cause
poisoning because they are enclosed in the burs, which are not normally
eaten. The poisonous principle is distributed into the seedling as the seed
germinates. Plants in the cotyledonary stage of growth are toxic and at the
same time not unpalatable. As the first true leaves develop, toxicity decreases rapidly in the seedling. Cotyledonary plants are toxic when an
amount equivalent to about 1½ per cent of an animal's weight has been
ingested. Toxicity is not lost on drying.

Pigs are commonly poisoned under natural conditions. Symptoms include anorexia, depression, nausea, vomition, weakened heartbeat, muscular
weakness, prostration, and dyspnea. Opisthotonus, spasmodic running motions, or convulsions are sometimes displayed by severely poisoned, pros-

trated animals. Evidence of abdominal pain may be observed in pigs. Symptoms in other classes of livestock are similar, except that vomiting may not be accomplished by ruminants. Fowl, poisoned on the seeds, present few symptoms other than profound depression.

Symptoms, in the experimental work, appeared ½ to 2 days after administration of a toxic dose. Death is usual a few hours to 3 days after appearance of the first symptoms.

Gross lesions consist of abnormal coloration or other evidence of pathological condition in liver and kidney. Signs of gastrointestinal irritation are frequently present, especially in pigs. Histologically, the kidney shows changes characteristic of acute nephritis. In the liver, the picture is one of acute hepatitis together with hemorrhage. Hemorrhages may be found elsewhere, especially in the heart.

It appears that administration of fatty substances to animals, if accomplished shortly after ingestion of cocklebur sprouts, may prevent poisoning. Materials such as milk, lard, and linseed oil have been experimentally investigated (1022) and are recommended.

CONDITIONS OF POISONING. Cocklebur poisoning has occurred in all classes of domestic livestock. It is always associated with ingestion of seedlings in the cotyledonary stage of growth. This limits the conditions under which poisoning may be expected. Cocklebur seeds sprout readily when present in soil that has been under water but is drying out. Such conditions are found along streams, or about the shores of shallow ponds as the summer progresses. Frequently, as the shore area is extended by a receding water margin, there is a continual germination and sprouting of cocklebur seedlings which, as the water withdraws, provide potentially toxic forage over an extended period of time. Although cocklebur is an annual, its seeds may persist for more than a year before germinating. This must be taken into consideration when planning control measures for its eradication.

The burs of *Xanthium* may cause mechanical damage of various kinds if they become entagled in the wool of sheep or other animals.

Additional reference: 698.

Xylorrhiza parryi (Gray) Greene (= *Aster parryi* Gray)
Xylorrhiza villosa Nutt. (= *Aster xylorrhiza* T. &. G.)
Xylorrhiza venusta (Jones) Heller (= *Aster venusta* Jones)   } Woody a
Xylorrhiza tortifolia (Gray) Greene (= *Aster tortifolius* Gray)
Xylorrhiza glabriuscula Nutt. (= *Aster xylorrhiza* T. & G.)

These species of *Xylorrhiza* (there are only a few others) are reliable indicators of selenium in the soil (1591) (see selenium, p. 44). The others have not yet been tested. Some botanists feel that the criteria which distinguish woody asters are not sufficient to warrant placing the woody asters in a genus of their own, and prefer to place all asters in the genus *Aster*. The synonyms are given above. It is useful, however, in studying selenium-bearing plants, to maintain the separation, since then it can be stated, as far as is known, that all species of *Xylorrhiza* are selenium accumulators and selenium indicator plants. *Machaeranthera* (*q.v.*), a secondary selenium absorber, is closely related and is included in the genus *Aster* by those who use this designation in its broad connotation. Others put *Xylorrhiza* and *Machaeranthera* together under the name *Machaeranthera*.

DESCRIPTION. The species of *Xylorrhiza* resemble one another closely. The following description applies to the genus as a whole: Perennial herbs, 6 in. to 2 ft or more tall, each consisting of a clump of numerous herbaceous leafy stems; stems erect and spreading, from a single, thick, woody, perennating taproot. Leaves numerous, alternate, linear to oblanceolate, mostly 1 to 3 in. long; tip prolonged into a fine point. Inflorescence the composite head; heads numerous, showy, terminal on the branches, 1 to 2 in. across; rays white or light pink to lavender; disc yellow to brown.

DISTRIBUTION AND HABITAT. Most of the species are found, often over large acreages, on seleniferous soils of Colorado, Wyoming, and Utah ranges. *Xylorrhiza glabriuscula* enters South Dakota and *X. tortifolia* is limited to Arizona and California. Woody aster often becomes the dominant member of plant communities on seleniferous shale.

POISONOUS PRINCIPLE. Accumulated selenium.

TOXICITY, SYMPTOMS, AND LESIONS. *Xylorrhiza* varies in toxicity with the amount of selenium accumulated, which in turn depends in part on the selenium-supplying power of the soil. Depending upon the selenium content of the plant and the amount consumed, either acute or chronic selenium poisoning may occur. As little as about 1 per cent of an animal's weight of *Xylorrhiza parryi* has produced symptoms of acute selenium poisoning a few hours after being experimentally fed to sheep (97).

CONDITIONS OF POISONING. Extensive loss of life in range sheep has been attributed to ingestion of woody aster, especially *Xylorrhiza parryi* (84, 1298). It is difficult, however, to specify one plant as the major cause of selenium poisoning when several species of selenium-accumulating plants are present. *Xylorrhiza* is unpalatable to sheep and will not be eaten unless range forage is in short supply.

Order Fagales

Fagaceae

Fagus sylvatica L. European beech

This ornamental tree (not to be confused with the American beech, *F. grandifolia* Ehrh.) may be obtained in many varieties, several of which have been popular for planting in the United States. From time to time cases of poisoning in human beings from the seeds (beechnuts), and in animals from the cake after the seeds have been expressed for their oil content, have been reported in European countries (607). The poisonous principle is saponinlike and causes severe gastrointestinal distress. The oil is nontoxic.

Quercus spp. Oaks

DESCRIPTION. Woody perennial plants, of diverse habit and leaf characteristics, varying in size from large trees to shrubs not more than 3 ft tall. Some are deciduous; others, the "live oaks," retain their leaves through the winter. Despite such diversity, oaks may be recognized by the acorn. This characteristic fruit is matured from a tricarpellate, inferior ovary and is subtended by the "cup" composed of numerous overlapping, greatly reduced, scale leaves. Oaks are divided into two groups: the white oaks, which mature acorns in one season, and the black oaks, which require two years for maturation of the acorns.

Taxonomy and identification of oak species are difficult. In some reports on oak toxicity, species identification is not given. However, symptoms and lesions do not seem to vary significantly with species of oak or part of plant ingested. It may turn out that not all species of oak are toxic but many, among both white and black, clearly are. It seems most practical to consider all oaks potentially toxic until proven otherwise, and to discuss oak poisoning as a single syndrome regardless of species of oak responsible.

DISTRIBUTION AND HABITAT. Some 60 species of oaks occur in the United States and Canada. Oaks are found in almost all areas and habitats. Areas in which poisoning has been recorded are identified below.

POISONOUS PRINCIPLE. Toxicity of oak was attributed to its tannin content in the nineteenth century. Experimental feedings of tannins (1013) did not demonstrate toxicity but analysis of acorns (291) failed to reveal any toxic factor other than the tannin fraction. The latter proved toxic parenterally in laboratory animals. Dollahite and coworkers (441, 442, 792, 1275) followed this up with an experimental investigation using the rabbit (which reacts to oak poisoning like livestock) and a few ruminants. They found that *repeated* doses of tannin, whether extracted from an oak or procured commercially, produced symptoms and lesions approximating those of natural oak poisoning. They also demonstrated conclusively that oak tannin is hydrolyzed and taken into the blood stream from the gastrointestinal tract. Gallic acid was identified as the polyhydroxyphenol moiety of oak tannin which is, therefore, a tannin of the gallotannin class. Of several potential treatments, calcium hydroxide worked best in their experience, preventing poisoning in rabbits when added in the amount of one part to six parts tannic acid.

TOXICITY, SYMPTOMS, AND LESIONS. Oak poisoning is a severe economic problem on the ranges of the Southwest where annual losses greater than $10 million have been estimated (433), and occurs sporadically elsewhere. Toxicity of oak is low, but buds and immature leaves are relished by cattle, sheep, and goats and may be consumed almost exclusively. Under such circumstances symptoms appear in a week or more and rapidly become acute. They consist of anorexia, rumen stasis, constipation, rough coat and dry muzzle, abdominal pain, excessive thirst, and frequent urination. Cattle at first pass small amounts of hard, brownish-black pelleted feces. If the animal remains alive long enough, this changes to diarrhea, containing blood and mucus. Edematous swellings sometimes occur in the ventral portions of the body. Pulse becomes thin, rapid, and wiry before death, and there may be a brownish discharge from the nostrils. Fever is absent. Death takes place in more than 85 per cent of cases if effective treatment cannot be given. Symptoms usually last 3 to 10 days but an occasional death occurs within 24 hours.

Lesions principally are those of gastritis and nephritis. The abomasum and small intestine are inflamed and often severely hemorrhagic. Petechial hemorrhages are widely distributed among other organs and membranes of the body. Subcutaneous edema is common. Large amounts of fluid are commonly found in the body cavities, especially in acute cases.

Renal changes, however, constitute the most interesting lesion in this disease (1487). Grossly the kidney is enlarged and pale, with tense capsule. Some petechial hemorrhages may be present. Histologically, a majority of tubules are normal. Some are filled with precipitated albumin. The pathognomonic change is the presence in many of the proximal and ascending tubules of a mass which stains red with hematoxylon-eosin and contains regularly distributed degenerated nuclei. In these tubules, epithelial cells are lacking. It appears that the mass in the lumen of the tubules consists of disintegrated epithelial cells and proteinaceous precipitate, homogeneously distributed.

Degree of retention of blood urea nitrogen can be used as an index of renal damage. Other clinical changes in blood serum composition in poisoned animals have been reported (792). The level of tannins detected in blood serum seems more a function of absorption than of total amount ingested.

CONDITIONS OF POISONING. Poisoning of cattle and occasionally sheep and goats on the ranges of the southwestern United States is common, especially during drought years. Occasional cases may occur at any time of year, but the danger season is during the sprouting of new foliage on the range scrub oaks. The most dangerous period lasts for about four weeks during March and April. Species of oak commonly involved are shin or shinnery (*Q. havardii* Ryd.), Gambel's oak (*Q. gambelii* Nutt.), and *Q. breviloba* (Torr.) Sarg. (= *Q durandii* Buckl.) (153, 155, 704,

932). Experimental feedings have shown (433) that a diet of not more than 50 per cent oak browse not only may be harmless, but also may actually contribute to the nutrition of cattle under range condtions. On ranges where oak is the principal early browse, supplemental feeding of 3 lb alfalfa daily per animal over the danger period will prevent poisoning.

Occasional loss of livestock from oak poisoning has occurred elsewhere in widely scattered parts of North America and has been caused not only by young oak browse but also by sprouts in cutover areas, mature foliage on felled trees, acorns, and possibly by fallen leaves. Losses, mostly of cattle, have occurred in Illinois (1566), Virginia (558, 907), Iowa (868, 1218), Maryland (1335), Indiana (564), New York (457), and Wisconsin (1213). In most of these instances the species of oak has not been identified. Where identification was made, the following species were involved: *Quercus marilandica* Muenchh. (jack oak) (558), *Q. velutina* Lam. (yellow-barked oak) (1218), *Q, robur* L. (= *Q. pedunculata* Ehrh.) (European oak) (291), *Q. rubra* L. var. *borealis* (northern red oak) (1148), *Q, prinus* L. (chestnut oak) (907), *Q. stellata* Wang. (post oak) (907), and *Q. coccinea* Muenchh. (scarlet oak) (907). Oak poisoning in horses has been described by Duncan (457).

Acorn poisoning does not appear to be as common in North America (273, 868, 907) as in Europe. It occurs when animals are pastured in stands of oak in years when the acorn crop is heavy. As encountered in other parts of the world (574, 640, 932, 1148, 1559, 1590) it has involved cattle, sheep, horses, and swine. Craving for acorns may be developed and animals will avidly seek them out (640, 868, 907, 1590). Symptoms and lesions, in general, are similar to oak-foliage poisoning and are not to be confused with those of overeating (574). Milk flow is decreased and milk may be made bitter (574, 640). The practice, common in some areas, of feeding acorns to swine with only beneficial results indicates either that some species of oak are less toxic than others, that swine are more resistant to poisoning than other animals (1559), or that not enough acorns are consumed to provoke symptoms.

Additional references: 153, 155, 704, 1220, 1483, 1489.

Subclass Monocotyledoneae—Monocots
Order Liliales

Liliaceae

Allium cepa L. Cultivated onion
Culled fresh or rotten onions occasionally have caused livestock poisoning.

POISONOUS PRINCIPLE. One analysis (881) has characterized the toxic principle as alkaloidal.

TOXICITY, SYMPTOMS, AND LESIONS. Moderate or large amounts of raw or cooked onions in the diet provoke severe anemia. This was first discovered during experiments by the U.S. Public Health Service (1431) to test the value of onions against blacktongue in dogs. Unexpectedly, the consequence was the production of anemia when cooked or raw onions were added to the diet in an amount equal to or greater than 0.5 per cent of the animal's weight. Larger amounts of raw onions provoked rapid depression of the red-blood-cell count—sometimes to less than 2 million per milliliter. Counts nearly as low have been observed in poisoned cattle (1577).

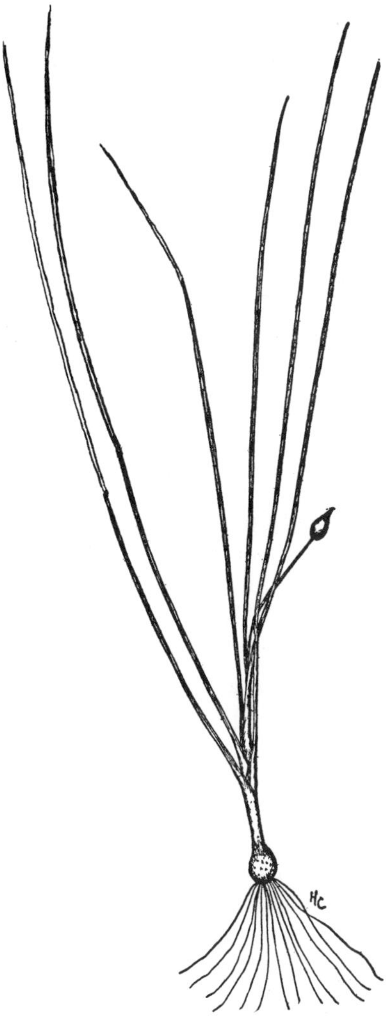

Symptoms in cattle and horses appear one to six or more days after the stock have had access to quantities of onions. They consist of hemoglobinuria, anemia, and icterus. In severe cases death follows quickly and may be precipitated by forcing the animals into sudden activity. Odor of onion is distinct throughout the tissues on necropsy. Older animals are often more severely affected than younger. Rapid recovery may be expected upon change of feed if the animals are not too severely poisoned. Sheep may be somewhat resistant. Only transient hemoglobinuria was observed (881) in one instance during which sheep consumed large quantities of onions.

CONDITIONS OF POISONING. Cattle and horses have been poisoned when run on fields of culled onions. Cases have also occurred after livestock have been given access to dumped cull onions. These are apparently equally poisonous whether fresh, frosted, or rotting. Livestock loss has been reported in Colorado and the Snake River Valley in Idaho.

Fig. 108. *Allium canadense*. Wild onion. Courtesy of The Macmillan Company.

Allium schoenoprasm L. Chives

In Japan, horses have been poisoned by eating chives. Poisoning occurs in early spring as the snow melts; at this time chives are among the first green plants to appear. Symptoms are similar to those produced in onion poisoning. Kobayashi (878) has described the histopathology which, in experimentally produced cases in horses, consisted primarily of degenerative changes in liver and kidney.

Allium canadense L. Wild onion

DESCRIPTION. A strong-scented bulbous herb, to 2 ft tall when in flower. Leaves linear, grasslike, arising from the small bulb. Inflorescence an umbel, borne terminally on a late-developing, leafless stem which arises between the leaves; individual flowers completely or mostly replaced by small bulblets, which are the usual means of propagation. Wild onions (there are many species more or less similar in general features) may be distinguished from other similar bulbous plants by their unmistakable onion odor.

DISTRIBUTION AND HABITAT. Native in rich woodlands or meadows in the northeastern and north-central states.

SYMPTOMS AND LESIONS. Ingestion of large amounts of plants of this species has caused death in cattle (1278) in Indiana. Symptoms and lesions were those of intense gastroenteritis, and death ensued within a few days. Onion poisoning may be detected by the onion odor in the tissues of the animal at necropsy.

Additional references: 465, 634.

Amianthium muscaetoxicum (Walt.) Gray [syn. *Chrosperma muscaetoxicum* (Walt.) Kuntze]. Staggergrass, fly poison, crow poison

DESCRIPTION. Perennial herb, growing from bulb 2 or 3 in. beneath the ground. Leaves in a clump, linear, ¼ to 1¼ in. wide, to 20 in. long. Flowering stem appearing later, to 4 ft tall, bearing few reduced leaves, terminating in a dense raceme; flowers white, 3-parted, turning greenish with age. Fruit a 3-parted capsule with abruptly turned-back tips. This plant may easily be confused with other, nonpoisonous species. In cases where poisoning is suspected, specimens should be obtained (flowering, if possible) and submitted to a specialist for positive identification.

DISTRIBUTION AND HABITAT. Open sandy woods, fields, and bogs from Florida to Oklahoma and north to New York (Long Island).

TOXIC PRINCIPLE. An alkaloid, as yet uncharacterized, but similar in many respects to the *Zigadenus* alkaloids (24).

TOXICITY, SYMPTOMS, AND LESIONS. Limited experimental feedings with sheep and cattle have established (1012) that both bulbs and leaves are dangerous to livestock. Only one death was produced (in a sheep). This resulted from administration of leaves equal to 0.5 per cent of the animal's weight. Symptoms were produced in sheep and cattle by various,

Fig. 109. *Amianthium muscaetoxicum*. Staggergrass. Plant, with details of inflorescence, flower, and fruit. Courtesy of The Macmillan Company.

but often considerably smaller, doses. Symptoms include salivation, nausea, rapid or irregular respiration, and weakness. Death is by respiratory failure. Necropsy findings are nonspecific.

CONDITIONS OF POISONING. Instances of loss of cattle have been reported in North Carolina. Loss occurs in the early spring, at which time the grasslike leaves of this plant may be the only available green feed. The plant is considered (127) to be among the ten most dangerous poisonous plants in that state.

Asparagus officinalis L. Cultivated asparagus

Dairy cattle have been poisoned when they accidentally gained access to fields of nearly mature asparagus (935). Symptoms and lesions were not reported.

Colchicum autumnale L. Autumn crocus

Colchicum is native to Great Britain and Europe, where its toxic nature has been known since the time of the Greek and Roman empires. This species is widely planted in gardens in the United States for its clusters of crocuslike flowers appearing in early autumn. The plant occasionally escapes cultivation and may be found naturalized in limited areas. The flowers are produced from an underground corm which is nourished in turn by the large lanceolate leaves that appear together with the seed pod in the spring. The leaves die back before flowering. The flowers, crocuslike in form and composition (but with superior ovary), are white or light purple.

Any part of the plant is toxic. The poisonous principle is the alkaloid colchicine and other closely related compounds (320, 1686). This alkaloid has limited use in medicine but has been extensively employed in genetic investigations for the production of polyploids in plants and some animals through its ability to inhibit spindle formation at metaphase in mitosis.

Fig. 110. *Colchicum autumnale*. Autumn crocus. Foliage of a single plant.

Loss of life in all classes of livestock and in human beings has been reported following ingestion of *Colchicum* in Europe (933). The symptoms and lesions are primarily those of gastrointestinal irritation. The alkaloid is heat stable. A few cases of livestock loss have occurred from hay containing the plant. The leaves are toxic at about 0.1 per cent of the animal's weight (933). Excretion of the toxic principle is slow. Small, subtoxic daily doses may build up the concentration of alkaloid in the body to a lethal level. A major pathway of excretion is via the milk in lactating animals. Thus poisoning of nursing animals or of human beings may take place after use of milk from poisoned animals. Livestock loss to this plant has not been reported in the United States or Canada.

Convallaria majalis L. Lily-of-the-valley

This familiar species is commonly planted in flower gardens for its raceme of fragrant, white, nodding, bellshaped flowers. The fruits ripen

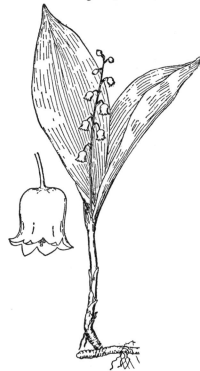

into rather conspicuous red berries, about ½ in. in diameter. If left undisturbed in favorable situations, this plant will spread, slowly forming a solid stand which excludes other species. It has the ability to persist when a garden is no longer cultivated and is frequently found about old cellar holes in the wild. A related species, *C. montana* Raf., is distributed as a native wild plant in the mountains between Virginia and Georgia.

Lily-of-the-valley, found also in Europe, has been considered a poisonous plant since almost the first publications dealing with this subject, and is listed as poisonous in many current publications. With the exception of undocumented reports of its toxicity to fowl (658), the American literature yields no cases of livestock loss and the foreign literature is almost as barren. A variety of names exist for compounds isolated and supposed toxic, especially in the older literature. Of these, the glycosides convallarin and convallamarin are most frequently listed. They were isolated and named

Fig. 111. *Convallaria majalis.* Lily-of-the-valley. Plant with detail of flower. Courtesy of The Macmillan Company.

by Walz in 1858 (3) and received empirical formulae. Definite toxicity of these glycosides and of convallatoxin has been determined with laboratory animals by several investigators (1499). Interest in them has been strong because of their digitalislike activity, and they are classed among the cardiac glycosides. The structure of the aglycone of convalla-

convallatoxigenin

toxin is shown here (268); the sugar is rhamnose. In addition to its digitalislike cardiac effect, the plant is said to have a purgative action.

Additional reference: 933.

Erythronium oregonum Appleg. (= *E. giganteum* Lindl.). Giant adder's tongue, dogtooth lily, fawn lily

This species, native from California to British Columbia, has been incriminated in poisoning of poultry in Vancouver (183). Bulbs were available to the birds, and pieces of them were found in the crop and intestine. Symptoms, appearing in 3 to 5 hours, consisted of a puffy crop, froth about the beak, and depression. Death occurred in 2 to 3 days.

Fritillaria meleagris L. Fritillaria, snake's-head

Occasionally found in rock gardens, as pot plants, or otherwise cultivated, this species has the reputation of having caused poisoning in Europe (574). It is said to contain a heart-depressant alkaloid.

Gloriosa superba L. Glory lily, climbing lily

This species of lily is native to tropical Africa and Asia. It is planted outdoors in the southern United States and treated elsewhere as a greenhouse plant. It has a record in Africa and elsewhere of having produced poisoning in the human being (1533, 1650). A physiologically active alka-

Fig. 112. *Gloriosa superba*. Glory lily. Photograph courtesy of Bailey Hortorium.

loid, first thought to be colchicine but recently shown closely related to it but not identical (1686), has been isolated. Ingestion of the plant is followed by symptoms similar to those of poisoning by the colchicine-containing *Colchicum autumnale.* They are those primarily of gastrointestinal irritation accompanied by excitatory nervous symptoms and oral parathesia. Death has occurred within 4 hours after ingestion of tubers from this plant.

Additional reference: 1660.

Hyacinthus orientalis L. Common garden hyacinth

When used as an emergency livestock feed in the Netherlands during World War II, the bulbs of this plant produced severe purgation in cattle (574).

Melanthium virginicum L. (syn. *M. hybridum* Walt.). Bunchflower

DESCRIPTION. Large herb, 2 to 5 ft tall, perennial from thick rhizome. Leaves linear, mostly basal, parallel-veined. Flowering stem bearing a few smaller leaves, terminating in a large panicle of greenish-yellow, 3-parted flowers.

DISTRIBUTION AND HABITAT. Marshes and wet woodlands, southern New England to Minnesota, south to Florida and Texas.

POISONOUS CHARACTERISTICS. Pammel (1217) cites several cases in Iowa that came to his attention in which this species was circumstantially incriminated. In all of these cases, horses were poisoned when fed hay containing bunchflower. Symptoms were nervous in character, including weakened heartbeat and respiration, nausea, slobbering, sweating, and weakness. No deaths occurred.

According to Hardin (719), sheep, cattle, and horses have been poisoned in the southeastern United States. Symptoms are similar and include anorexia, dyspnea, and stupor.

Nolina texana Wats. Sacahuista, sacahuiste, beargrass

DESCRIPTION. Perennial, in habit forming a distinctive large clump of growth consisting of numerous linear leaves growing densely upwards from a mostly underground stem, the outer portions curving back towards the ground. Stem woody, mostly buried, much branched; branches stubby, bearing leaves densely inserted; stem and branches together forming a trunklike structure, usually less than 6 in. tall, and as much as 1 ft in diameter. Leaves linear, about ¼ in. broad, to 5 ft long, bearing a prominent ridge in the concave upper surface; leaf, therefore, distinctly triangular in section near tip; margins minutely serrate. Flowering stems several to many, erect, borne among the leaves. Inflorescence paniculate; flowers numerous, white, long-lived, small, 6-parted. Fruit a capsule of 3 almost separate carpels.

DISTRIBUTION AND HABITAT. Rolling range lands and foothills, western Texas, Arizona, and Mexico.

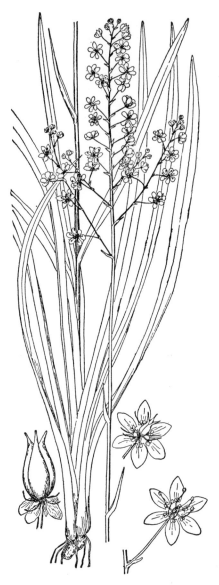

Fig. 113. *Melanthium virginicum*.
Bunchflower. Plant with details of
sterile flower, fertile flower, and
fruit. Courtesy of The Macmillan
Company.

Fig. 114. *Nolina texana.* Sacahuista.

Nolina microcarpa Wats., similar in appearance and distribution, also has been suspected (1185) of being poisonous to livestock in the same way as *N. texana*.

POISONOUS PRINCIPLE. Unknown. Stable to drying.

TOXICITY, SYMPTOMS, AND LESIONS. Sacahuista was the subject of extensive experimentation by Mathews (1049) at Alpine, Texas, following losses among livestock on the range. Practically all that is known of the toxic nature of the plant comes from his investigation.

Sacahuista blooms in the early spring when other succulent forage is not plentiful. The flowering buds, blooms, and fruit are avidly eaten by sheep, goats, and cattle on the range. The foliage also is eaten to some extent, particularly by cattle, but poisoning does not seem to follow ingestion of the foliage. The flowers, however, contain a principle that produces severe liver and kidney damage. Experimentally, Mathews found that the minimum toxic dose for sheep was about 1.1 per cent of the animal's weight of buds or blooms. Some experiments suggested that the toxic principle was not cumulative, but no experiments were performed in which poisoning resulted from single doses. Symptoms appeared several days after the first feeding. Since severe liver damage is involved, the minimum toxic dose and the minimum lethal dose are about equivalent. This is reflected under range conditions, where almost all animals that develop symptoms eventually succumb. Goats were found more susceptible than sheep to the toxic effects of the plant.

Anorexia and lassitude are noticed first. These are followed within a day or two by generalized icterus, which becomes intense. Animals seek shade and water. Yellow or red urine may occur. The latter may be hemoglobinuria, but according to Mathews is not hematuria. Discharges from the orbit and nostrils frequently occur. Progressive debilitation is followed by death, usually less than a week after the development of symptoms.

On the range, the symptoms and lesions of photosensitization frequently accompany those, as listed above, found in experimental feedings. Mathews was able to provoke photosensitization in his experimental animals by adding fresh green feed to the diet and exposing the animals to light. It was his conclusion that the addition of green feed resulted in the appearance of phylloerythrin, a normal digestive breakdown product of plant chlorophyll, in the peripheral circulation, that this was the photosensitizing pigment, and that liver dysfunction was responsible for its appearing in the peripheral circulation rather than being eliminated in the bile as normally. Only insignificant amounts of chlorophyll are present in the buds, blooms, and fruit of sacahuista.

Lesions, described in detail by Mathews, consisted essentially of fatty and albuminous degeneration in liver and kidney. In the liver, gross appearance was off-color and plugs of greenish material could be squeezed from the bile ducts on the cut surface. Degenerative changes were greatest about the central veins. Grossly, the kidneys appeared swollen, to twice normal in some cases, and off-color.

CONDITIONS OF POISONING. Although cattle and to a lesser extent sheep browse on the foliage of sacahuista during the winter months, poisonings seem to be associated only with the appearance of the blooms, which are avidly eaten. Thus the danger period is the period of blooming, which lasts for about three weeks in the spring. Severity of loss is closely correlated with abundance of bloom, which is quite variable from year to year with growing conditions. A heavy bloom occurs on the average only once every five or six years.

Ornithogalum umbellatum L. Star-of-Bethlehem, snowdrop

DESCRIPTION. Onionlike herb, perennating from bulb, about 1 ft tall. Leaves linear, erect, basally inserted at bulb, forming a clump. Single, leafless stem produced at flowering. Inflorescence corymbose, few-flowered; flowers showy, prominently bracted; perianth 6-membered, white. Fruit a 3-lobed, several-seeded capsule.

DISTRIBUTION AND HABITAT. Introduced from the Mediterranean region as a garden plant; now escaped and naturalized as a weed of grasslands and thickets from New England to North Carolina, Nebraska, and Kansas.

POISONOUS PRINCIPLE. Reports that colchicine is present in *Ornithogalum* come from early analyses in which the tests used were less than fully specific. Critical tests for colchicine in *Ornithogalum* have been negative

Fig. 115. *Ornithogalum umbellatum.* Star-of Bethlehem. Courtesy of The Macmillan Company.

(1686). It is likely that the plant contains another, perhaps closely related, alkaloid.

TOXICITY, SYMPTOMS, AND LESIONS. *Ornithogalum* bulbs have produced deaths in sheep and cattle in the United States (704, 1335). More than 1000 sheep were lost in a single year in Maryland. Only the small, white, onionlike bulbs seem involved. Animals have been observed to graze on the foliage without effect (1335). Symptoms in sheep include depression, salivation, and bloating.

CONDITIONS OF POISONING. Poisoning will not take place unless the bulbs have been brought to the surface. This may be accomplished by frost heaving (as in the winter losses in Maryland), plowing, rooting by swine, and the like. In other countries children have been poisoned after eating bulbs of related species.

Urginea maritima (L.) Baker. Squill, red squill

The bulb of this species is employed widely in commercial rodenticides. Rodenticides employing red squill are readily taken by rats and, in that animal, are not eliminated by vomiting. In man and most domestic animals red squill is distasteful or quickly vomited. Because of these safety features, poisoning of man and domestic animals by commercial preparations is rare.

Material for commercial use is obtained from countries about the Mediterranean where the plant is common. Recent attempts to introduce it into the United States appear successful (370). The raw bulb contains the same glycosides, of digitalislike effect, which account for the toxicity of the commercial preparation, hence care must be taken with commercial plantings to avoid accidents with farm animals. In the United States, southern California is best adapted for commercial plantings of red squill.

Species of the closely related genus *Scilla* are occasionally grown as ornamental plants in greenhouses or outdoors in mild regions. Several are toxic. These include *Scilla nonscripta* (L.) Hoffm. & Link (574) and *S. peruviana* L. (278).

Veratrum californicum Durand. False hellebore, corn-lily, skunk cabbage

Veratrum viride Ait. False hellebore, white hellebore, Indian poke

DESCRIPTION. Coarse erect herbs, 3 to 6 ft tall. Stems unbranched, leafy throughout, arising from a thickened, short, perennating rootstock.

Roots fibrous, coarse, numerous. Leaves alternate, in three ranks, broadly oval, or elliptical, becoming lanceolate above, entire, sheathing, parallel-veined, plaited, 6 to 12 in. long and 3 to 6 in. broad. Inflorescence a panicle, 8 in. to 2 ft long. Flowers numerous, about 1 in. across, but because of color, relatively inconspicuous. The two species are quite alike in most respects. *Veratrum californicum* has whitish flowers, and the branches of the panicle are erect. In *Veratrum viride,* the flowers are greenish-white and the lower panicle branches droop.

DISTRIBUTION AND HABITAT. *Veratrum viride* is found in low, moist habitats in open woods and pastures throughout North America. *Veratrum californicum* occupies a similar habitat in higher mountain valleys of the Pacific Coast and Northern Rocky Mountain states.

POISONOUS PRINCIPLE. *Veratrum* (particularly the European *Veratrum album* L.) has been considered a poisonous plant by all major authorities from Dioscorides to the present. *Veratrum viride* was widely used in the United States during the eighteenth and nineteenth centuries for various medicinal purposes and as the source of insecticide (1109). Several alkaloids were characterized, especially from the roots of *V. viride,* and were given names, but their structural chemistry failed to yield to many attempts (1624). Preparations of this species gradually fell into disuse because of their variable potency and occasionally unpredictable toxicity. The advent of better chemical procedures eventually made possible the separation and chemical identification in the 1950's of a number of alkaloids and other physiologically active compounds from several species of *Veratrum* (1564). Some of the alkaloids were found to have marked hypotensive properties in the human being. Lowering of blood pressure appears to be effected by dilatation of arterioles together with constriction in venous vascular beds. This is accompanied by slowing of the heart rate.

veratramine

The known *Veratrum* alkaloids are numerous and complex in structure. Some exist in the plant as glycoalkaloids; others occur as ester alkaloids. In both cases the alkamine is of steroid configuration. One of the well-established glycoalkaloids of *Veratrum* is veratrosine, of which the alkamine, represented here, is veratramine. The sugar is D-glucose. *Veratrum* alkaloids have been reviewed by Jeger and Prelog (830, 1292).

Fig. 116. Top, *Veratrum viride*. Center and Bottom, *Veratrum californicum*. False hellebores.

Manufacturing procedures have made available a drug of uniform potency and predictable action. *Veratrum* preparations now find use in animal and human medicine, in the latter especially as hypotensive agents of choice in certain crises associated with pregnancy. Their general use is limited by the frequency of unsatisfactory side effects such as nausea. *Veratrum viride* is the source of much of the drug currently employed medically. *Veratrum californicum* does not produce hypotensive alkaloids, at least in useful amount. Despite much pharmacological attention, little is known about the molecular source of toxicity as related to poisoning by either species under natural conditions.

TOXICITY, SYMPTOMS, AND LESIONS. Most instances of false-hellebore poisoning in the past occurred from misuse of medicinal preparations of the plant. On the other hand, scattered reports exist of poisoning in cattle, sheep, fowl, and the human being from accidental ingestion of the plant (both species) (274, 658, 935, 1335). A case of mass poisoning of Korean soldiers from soup made of *Veratrum japonicum* and other wild plants has been well described (1174). Despite variation in content of physiologically active principles, symptoms of acute poisoning seem remarkably constant. They consist of salivation, prostration, depressed heart action, and dyspnea. In human beings additional subjective symptoms including burning sensation of mouth and throat, hallucinations, and headache have been reported.

An entirely different syndrome has recently been traced to *Veratrum californicum* (49, 118, 123, 124). Congenital malformation in lambs had been known for many years on sheep ranches in southern Idaho. Deformed ("monkey-face") lambs accounted for 1 to 25 per cent of births in some flocks in certain years. The common name of the syndrome comes from the malformation which involves a greater or lesser extent of the face and cranium. In mild cases the face is shortened and the upper jaw and nose poorly developed so that the lower jaw and cranium appear to protrude and the face is dished in. Eyes are normal. In severe cases the eyes and nose are entirely lacking and the cerebrum rudimentary. Many animals are truly cycloptic with a single median eye; others possess two corneas in a single distorted sclera. Even when two apparently normal eyes are present, the scleral components are often fused into a single dumbell-shaped structure.

Monkey-face lambs carried to full term are usually borne alive and are apparently normal in all respects except that described. They usually die shortly after birth due to inability to breath or to feed. Often monkey-face lambs are carried several to many weeks past term, eventually dying and undergoing maceration *in utero*. When this happens, the dam dies shortly after.

Prior to 1957 the disease was believed to be of genetic origin. Often a monkey-face lamb is borne twin to a normal one. But experiments to demonstrate a genetic basis were negative.

Investigations of field cases and experimental feedings have now shown that the disease results when ewes feed on *Veratrum californicum* during the second and third weeks after conception. Feeding experiments also showed that the plant might produce direct toxic effects in the dam and might bring on abortion. Nothing is known of the compound which prevents normal development early in pregnancy.

CONDITIONS OF POISONING. The palatability of *Veratrum viride* is not clear. Conflicting statements indicate that both species are usually left strictly alone by livestock, but under some circumstances large amounts may be consumed. It appears that relatively large amounts are necessary to produce death, although smaller amounts may bring on symptoms. *Veratrum viride* produces young, succulent growth very early in spring, and it is at this time of year that danger of poisoning from this species is greatest. Fowl have been poisoned by greens thrown to them (658). *Veratrum californicum* is most dangerous in late summer because that is the time breeding commences. It is killed by frost and losses to monkey-face lambs may be eliminated by delaying breeding until after the first frost.

Additional reference: 537.

Zigadenus spp. (= Zygadenus). Death camas

The species of *Zigadenus,* about 15 in number, are separated with some difficulty and there has been confusion in identification of species described as poisonous. It has frequently been assumed that all species of *Zigadenus* are poisonous, but extensive experiments have shown considerable variation in toxicity among several of the well-tested species. Therefore it is useful or necessary to know which particular species is involved when assessing the potentiality for poisoning in a situation involving this genus, or in experimenting with it. A general description of the genus follows, together with habitat, distribution, and further characterization for each of the more important species.

DESCRIPTION. Perennial, glabrous herbs with mostly basal, grasslike leaves and underground perennating bulbs or rhizomes. Stems single, unbranched, produced at time of flowering, sparingly leafy, terminated by the inflorescence. Bulbs onionlike in structure, with a dark-colored outer coat. Leaves several to many, linear, flat, V-creased, never with hollow portions, distinctly paralleled-veined, sheathing at attachment. Inflorescence a terminal raceme or panicle of greenish white, yellow or pink flowers; perianth 6-membered, spreading; stamens 6; styles 3; floral parts persistent but withered as the fruit develops. Fruit a 3-cavitied capsule, separating into three members and opening inwardly at maturity.

Zigadenus densus (Desr.) Fern. Bulb thin, plant 1½ to 5 ft tall; raceme of pink to creamy white flowers (perianth members very short—about ¼ in.). Damp soils of pine woods and bogs, eastern Texas to Florida and Virginia.

Zigadenus elegans Pursh. Bulbous, 1 to 3 ft tall; raceme of white

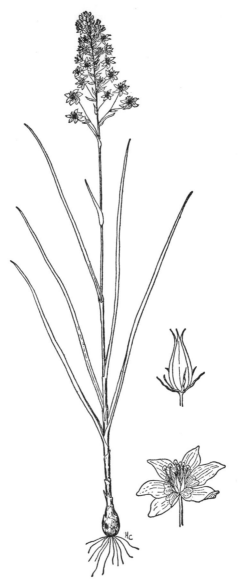

Fig. 117. *Zigadenus venenosus*. Death camas. Plant, with details of flower and fruit. Courtesy of The Macmillan Company.

flowers. Prairies and meadows, Minnesota south to Missouri, Oklahoma, northern Texas, westward (excluding California, western Oregon, and western Washington), north to Saskatchewan and Alaska.

Zigadenus fremontii Torr. Bulbous, 1 to 3 ft tall; panicle or raceme of yellowish-white flowers. Dry grassy or brushy slopes, California and southwestern Oregon.

Zigadenus gramineus Rydb. Bulbous, 8 to 15 in. tall; raceme of yellow-white flowers. Open hills and plains, Saskatchewan, western Montana, Idaho, Wyoming, Colorado, New Mexico, Utah, eastern Arizona, Nevada, and Washington.

Zigadenus nuttallii Gray. Bulbous, 1 to 2½ ft tall; raceme of yellow-white flowers; capsule distinctly ellipsoid. Prairies, Tennessee to northern Texas, Oklahoma, and Kansas.

Zigadenus paniculatus (Nutt.) Wats. Bulbous, ⅔ to 2 ft; most plants paniculate, flowers yellowish-white. Dry soils, eastern Washington, Idaho, western Wyoming, Utah, northern Arizona and New Mexico, Nevada, eastern California, and Oregon.

Zigadenus venenosus Wats. Bulbous, ⅔ to 2 ft tall; raceme of white flowers. Moist grassy meadows, California, Nevada, western Utah, southwestern Idaho, Oregon, western Washington to British Columbia.

Zigadenus plants may be immediately distinguished from wild onions (*Allium*), which they resemble, by the absence of onion odor.

The following table is provided to relate the species as here described with usage in major reports dealing with *Zigadenus* toxicity.

THE SPECIES HERE NAMED:	IS THE SAME AS:	IN:
Z. venenosus	Z. venenosus	225, 553, 894, 997
Z. gramineus	Z. venenosus	97, 273, 277, 1008
	Z. intermedius	277, 759, 760, 941, 1113
	Z. gramineus	95, 994, 997, 1081, 1330
Z. elegans	Z. coloradensis	1008

In general, the names of the remaining species have been used uniformly.

POISONOUS PRINCIPLE. Alkaloids were first extracted and partially characterized from species of *Zigadenus* at the beginning of the present century. Those investigations, and some subsequently, were prompted in part at least by the toxicity of the plants. Recently the interesting steriod configuration and some possibly useful pharmacological features of the alkaloids in *Zigadenus* have inspired further investigation of them, and their chemistry has been worked out in some detail. Reviews may be found in papers by Kupchan and Deliwala (894), Reid and Smith (1330), and Jeger and Prelog (830, 1292).

The several *Zigadenus* alkaloids are complex in structure. They are classed among the steroid alkaloids of the veratrum group (see also

Veratrum). These include glycoalkaloids and ester alkaloids, the alkamine having steroid configuration. One of the well-established ester alkaloids of *Zigadenus* is zygacine, which is represented here.

zygacine

TOXICITY, SYMPTOMS, AND LESIONS. Species of *Zigadenus* are among the most important poisonous plants in the western United States and western Canada. In many states they are responsible for the greatest loss of life in sheep on spring range of any poisonous plant. Extensive experimentation has been undertaken, especially by investigators at the experiment stations of Nevada (553), Wyoming (95, 97, 758, 760, 941, 1081), and the United States Department of Agriculture (273, 277, 994, 995, 997, 1008, 1015).

Most feeding experiments have been performed with sheep. Considerable variability in susceptibility of individual animal occurs, and there is undoubtedly some further variation with season and geographical location for a given species of *Zigadenus* (95). Nevertheless, enough experiments

AVERAGE TOXICITY OF ZIGADENUS SPECIES TO SHEEP

SPECIES	A	B	C	D
Z. gramineus	1½ hr	12 hr	0.4%	0.6%
Z. paniculatus	3¼	36	1.0	2.5
Z. venenosus	2½	29¼	0.4	2.0
Z. elegans	2	5¼	2.0	6.0
Z. nuttallii	7¾	48¾	0.2	0.5

A = average elapsed time between feeding and appearance of symptoms

B = average duration of symptoms

C = (average) minimum toxic dose, expressed as per cent of the animal's weight of green plant

D = (average) minimum lethal dose

have been performed that a relatively reliable figure for average toxicity to sheep may be given, as in the accompanying table, for each of the major troublesome species of death camas.

Several things are apparent. The species vary greatly in potential danger. For most species the time which elapses between feeding and appearance of symptoms is nearly equivalent, but the duration of sickness varies greatly. In some cases there is apparently a narrow margin between toxic and lethal doses, while in others the margin is wide. Under range conditions recovery is not uncommon.

Symptoms are markedly similar, irrespective not only of which plant species was responsible but also of the species of animal poisoned. They are best known for sheep. A definite progression may be observed. Excessive salivation is noted first and persists throughout most of the duration of poisoning. It is soon followed by obvious nausea, which is often accompanied by vomition. This stage is followed by muscular weakness with accompanying ataxia, trembling, and eventual prostration. The pulse becomes fast and weak and heart action is weakened. Signs of dyspnea are usual and often become severe. Some animals display cyanosis and spasmodic struggling for breath (which may be equivalent to the "convulsions" described by some authors). In severely poisoned animals a period during which the animal is comatose frequently occurs before death. The duration of coma is partly responsible for the variation in time elapsed between appearance of symptoms and death in the accompanying table. Some animals die within a few hours; others remain comatose for one or two days, sometimes longer, before death. Consistent, characteristic lesions are absent.

Cattle and horses are occasionally poisoned under range conditions, displaying essentially the same symptoms. In cattle salivation is sometimes less and nausea greater. Limited experiments (997) indicate that swine are highly susceptible to the toxic principle, but cases of swine poisoning are not encountered under natural conditions because of the promptness with which hogs expel the offending material by vomition. A case of poisoning in fowl has been described (1179). The chief symptoms were diarrhea, incoordination, prostration, and coma. Most birds died 24 to 48 hours after the appearance of symptoms.

Occasional cases of human poisoning may be found in the literature (225, 745, 1008). Most occurred during the years when the western country was being settled. The American Indians were aware of the toxic nature of the plant but occasionally both they and the settlers ate the bulb, mistaking it for edible plants with similar bulbs. The symptoms are those of gastrointestinal irritation and vasomotor collapse. A case has been described (225) in which poisoning followed ingestion of the flowers.

CONDITIONS OF POISONING. *Zigadenus* is distasteful to well-fed livestock. Nevertheless, individual instances of poisoning in sheep from species of this plant have occasionally been reported in which losses ranged between 500 and 2000 animals. Less spectacular losses are frequent. *Zigadenus* makes its early growth from food stored over winter in the bulb; hence it is among the first plants to appear in spring. The young stages are the most highly toxic (97), and the bulb, which is of equal or somewhat greater toxicity than the rest of the plant, may be pulled up and eaten with the foliage when the ground is wet. Conditions of management which promote poisoning include driving through infested ranges so that the animals have little time to feed selectively, unloading hungry animals in infested range, lambing in infested range, or placing animals on range where little other forage is available.

Zigadenus gramineus and *Z. paniculatus* account for the greatest number of losses in the areas where they occur. *Zigadenus nuttallii* is highly toxic and has been responsible for extensive loss in cattle (1015) and some in horses (1130). Fortunately it is geographically more restricted than the others. Although less toxic, *Z. elegans* has definitely produced occasional loss (97, 1081). In California, *Z. fremontii* has poisoned animals (1383). *Zigadenus densus* is considered among the more dangerous plants in North Carolina (127) but specific instances of loss have not been cited.

It was an early idea that the toxic principle of death camas was excreted in the milk of poisoned animals. Tests (95, 553) show, however, that this is not so. The greater mortality among lambs nursing poisoned ewes is probably the result of reduced milk flow together with other exigencies of the range.

Beath *et al.* (97) have developed an effective symptomatic treatment for death-camas poisoning in range sheep. They found that injection of 2 mg atropine sulfate and 8 mg picrotoxin per 100-lb sheep, if done as soon as possible after onset of symptoms, is beneficial. Reappearance of symptoms may be treated by a second dose. In some areas this formulation is commercially available as "death-camas tablets."

Additional references: 135, 1080, 1562.

Juncaceae

Juncus inflexus L. Blue rush

This species occurs relatively sparingly in the northeastern and north-central United States. In England (574) it produces an unusual syndrome in cattle which, after being forced to eat it by lack of other forage, develop a craving for it and engorge themselves with it to the exclusion of all else. Loss of condition and blindness come on rapidly and the animal becomes hypersensitive to stimuli, responding with convulsions. Death is the result of cerebral hemorrhage during convulsions.

Amaryllidaceae

Agave lecheguilla Torr. Lechuguilla

DESCRIPTION. Perennial, stemless in the vegetative condition. Leaves 10 to 30, fleshy, bayonetlike, erect, attached in a whorl to a short, broad, perennating stem crown at ground level; each leaf 1 to 1½ in. wide at base, tapering to a sharp point, 12 to 20 in. long, with recurving marginal serrations. After 10 to 15 years of vegetative growth, the plant flowers once, producing a large, spikelike terminal panicle on a thick stalk 6 to 12 ft tall, and then dies. New plants may be formed from the seeds and also by offsets from the parent plant. Flowers tubular with 3 sepals, 3 petals, 6 stamens, and a 3-carpellate pistil which matures into a leathery capsule containing many black, flattened seeds in its 3 cavities.

DISTRIBUTION AND HABITAT. This species is found in western Texas, southern New Mexico, and south into Mexico on dry hills, especially low limestone hills, dry valleys, and bordering canyons; especially abundant in the Trans-Pecos area of Texas.

POISONOUS PRINCIPLE. Unknown substance(s) producing hepatogenic photosensitization. Saponins [smilagenin (1640)].

TOXICITY, SYMPTOMS, AND LESIONS. Sheep and goats are poisoned most frequently under range conditions; cattle rarely. Horses are not known to be poisoned. Under range conditions the first symptom observed is list-lessness followed by the development of pronounced icterus and yellowish discharge about the eyes and nostrils. A purplish zone may appear beneath the coronary band of the hoof. Urine is often dark-colored. Eventual coma of short duration precedes death. Typical symptoms and lesions of photo-sensitization may or may not be produced during the period of illness, depending on the several factors involved (see discussion, p. 56). Principal lesions are those of acute toxic hepatitis and nephritis. Gross pathology and histopathology have been detailed by Mathews (1043).

In experimental work it has been shown that ½ to 1 lb of lechuguilla fed daily to sheep or goats produces symptoms of photosensitization in less than a week and death from the effects of liver and kidney damage in 1 to 2 weeks. Symptoms and lesions of experimental cases are similar to those found on the range.

Chemical procedures and further experimentation with laboratory animals led Mathews to the conclusion that the hepato-nephro-toxin was a saponin. It is water soluble, is not inactivated by boiling (cf. *Nolina*), and in itself is not photodynamic. A separate photodynamic substance was isolated and was shown to be independent of liver and kidney damage in its action. Its wavelength of activation was found to be similar to that of the photodynamic pigment in buckwheat (*Fagopyrum*), but it has not been identified chemically.

Thus it is possible that the photosensitization produced by lechuguilla is of two sources: (a) indirectly from an unknown substance (possibly phylloerythrin) abnormally present in the peripheral circulation after liver and kidney dysfunction, or (b) directly from a separate photodynamic pigment present in lechuguilla. The saponin from *Agave* produces visceral vasodilation, mild gastroenteritis, and often hemorrhage administered parenterally in experiments with rabbits (443). It is an abortifacient in small amounts.

CONDITIONS OF POISONING. Range animals are usually poisoned during the spring months, especially in drought years, but some cases may occur at any season. Sheep and goats under drought conditions on the range do not avoid the plant. In severe outbreaks of poisoning morbidity may reach 30 per cent and usually mortality approaches the morbidity rate. Liver damage and associated symptoms account for the severity of the outbreaks; photosensitization is secondary in importance.

Additional references: 848, 1044, 1045.

Galanthus nivalis L. Snowdrop
The common snowdrop is among the earliest of spring-flowering garden plants. During World War II, the bulbs of this plant proved poisonous when fed to livestock in the Netherlands as a substitute for unavailable feeds (574).

Fig. 118. *Galanthus nivalis*. Snowdrop.

Narcissus spp. Narcissus, daffodil, jonquil
Narcissus bulbs contain active principles which produce severe gastroenteritis, vomition, and purging, sometimes accompanied by nervous symptoms such as trembling or convulsions. Poisoning has occurred in human beings (1698) from small amounts of the bulbs and in livestock (574) when bulbs were fed as emergency feed in the Netherlands during World War II.

Other genera of the *Amaryllidaceae,* in common cultivation as ornamentals, contain alkaloids (1378, 1689). Species of some of these (including *Amaryllis, Crinum, Haemanthus,* and *Nerine*) have proven poisonous to livestock in other parts of the world.

Zephyranthes atamasco Herb. Atamasco lily, rain lily

DESCRIPTION. Handsome bulbous perennial herb, often forming clumps of several plants. Bulb onionlike, brown-coated, white-fleshed, about 1 in. in diameter, usually 1 to 2 in. beneath the soil. Leaves several, flat, linear, 4 to 10 in. long, bluish-green, borne from bulb. Flower single, erect, terminal on leafless stem; perianth 6-membered, each member 2 to 3 in. long, white or pink; stamens 6, anthers yellow. Fruit a 3-angled capsule.

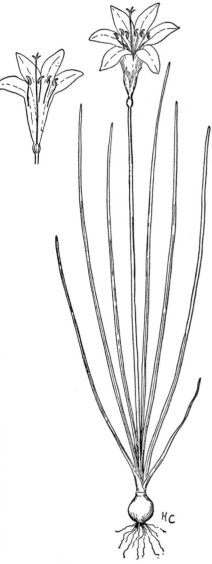

DISTRIBUTION AND HABITAT. Moist wooded areas or grassy fields mostly in the Coastal Plain of Mississippi to Florida and Virginia.

TOXICITY, SYMPTOMS, AND LESIONS. Observations made before the present century have given this plant a reputation for producing "staggers" in horses (273). It has been only recently, however, that feeding experiments (1661) have confirmed the toxicity of atamasco lily. The bulb is the most poisonous portion of the plant and is usually involved in cases of poisoning. Bulbs have proved fatal to steers at 0.5 to 0.75 per cent of the animal's weight. Cases of poisoning also have been described for horses and fowl.

Symptoms appear in less than 48 hours. They consist of softened feces, often with bloody mucus, staggering, collapse, and death. Lesions have not been reported.

CONDITIONS OF POISONING. Atamasco lily often covers large areas of land. The leaves appear in late fall or early spring. The plant flowers in spring. The foliage or bulbs may be consumed, particularly in spring when the ground is wet and other forage is in short supply.

Fig. 119. *Zephyranthes atamasco*. Atamasco lily. Plant, with detail of dissected flower. Courtesy of The Macmillan Company.

Haemodoraceae

Lacnanthes tinctoria Ellis (= *Gyrotheca tinctoria* Salisb.). Bloodwort, redroot

This large herb with grasslike leaves and characteristic short red rootstock and roots is a weed of cranberry bogs and is also found in swamps and

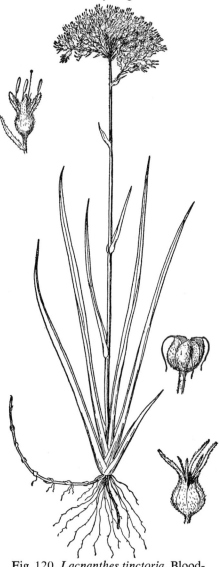

Fig. 120. *Lacnanthes tinctoria*. Bloodwort. Plant, with details of flower, young fruit, and old fruit. Courtesy of The Macmillan Company.

marshes from Massachusetts to Florida. In many earlier and more recent publications on poisonous plants this species is listed as poisonous to hogs, producing symptoms in white-skinned animals only. It is said to cause the bones in white-skinned animals to become pink. As one so often finds when tracing back statements that have originated in early literature, the final resting place is less than satisfactory. Blum (138) has made such a search for this species and finds that all reports apparently stem from a description, based on second-hand information, by Charles Darwin and published in *Origin of Species*. The original source of information appears to be the orally communicated beliefs of some Virginia "squatters."

The reported characteristics of the syndrome are similar to those of congenital porphyria.

Iris spp. Iris, flag

Garden iris are familiar plants. Wild iris may easily be recognized when in flower from the similarity of their flowers to those of cultivated varieties, but otherwise are easily confused with plants of marshy habitat that have similar large, parallel-veined, sharp-pointed leaves, such as sweet flag (*Acorus*), cattail (*Typha*), or some of the larger sedges (*Carix*). The combination of long, linear, erect, parallel-veined, two-ranked leaves with thick, fleshy, mostly horizontal rootstalks serves to separate iris from the

Fig. 121. *Iris versicolor*. Blue flag. Photograph of a flower.

others. Wild iris are found characteristically in moist soils as along stream banks, in marshes, or moist mountain meadows.

Various iris have been found to contain an irritant principle in the leaves or particularly in the rootstalks which produces gastroenteritis if ingested in sufficient, relatively large, amount. Cases on record include fatal poisoning of calves in British Columbia from a cultivated, but botanically unidentified, iris (185), and experimental poisoning of laboratory animals in Wyoming with *Iris missouriensis* Nutt. (97) prompted by the wide distribution and observed palatability of that species under range conditions. In the latter, dyspnea was the major symptom. Older literature usually emphasizes the purgative qualities of various species including *Iris versicolor* L., the common wild iris of the eastern United States and Canada (713, 1217). Poisonings produced by additional species may be found in the world literature (for example, 574). Iris may be poisonous fresh or in hay.

Order Arales

Araceae

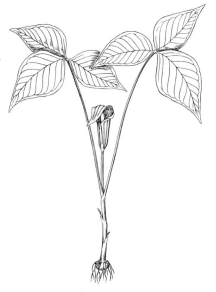

> *Arisaema spp.* Jack-in-the-pulpit, Indian turnip
>
> The jack-in-the-pulpit of the northeastern and north-central United States and southern Canada [*A. atrorubens* (Ait.) Blume, *A. triphyllum* (L.) Schott, and *A. stewardsonii* Britt.] and several other wild members of the *Araceae* [especially *Calla palustris* L., wild calla, and *Symplocarpus foetidus* (L.) Nutt., skunk cabbage] form needlelike crystals of calcium oxalate, particularly in the rhizome, which if taken into the mouth become embedded in the mucous membranes and provoke intense irritation and a burning sensation. Ingestion of more than the first mouthful rarely occurs.

Fig. 122. *Arisaema triphyllum*. Jack-in-the-pulpit. Courtesy of Cornell Extension Bulletin No. 538.

Mortality in human beings and livestock is not known, although mortality has been produced experimentally in animals (1335). (See also *Dieffenbachia.*)

Additional references: 592, 658.

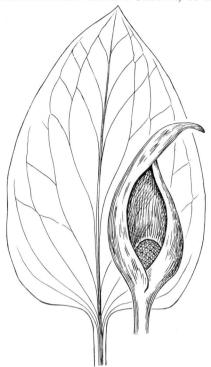

Fig. 123. *Symplocarpus foetidus.* Skunk cabbage. Leaf, with detail of inflorescence. Courtesy of Cornell Extension Bulletin No. 538.

Colocasia antiquorum Schott, *C. esculenta* Schott. Elephants-ear

These species are grown commercially for their tropical foliage; the second is grown also for its edible tuber (taro or dasheen). They are tropical plants, and are rarely found escaped from cultivation in the extreme southeastern United States.

Like *Arisaema* these plants contain crystals of calcium oxalate in their tissues. A case is on record (641) of severe irritation of the mouth and tongue in cattle after grazing on the foliage.

Among the most common of house plants are those that are usually called philodendron. Many of these belong botanically to the genus *Philodendron* (which has many species), but others do not. *Philodendron* is a member of the *Araceae,* and like its relatives, may contain an irritant principle. Greer has reported (655) 72 cases of "philodendrum" poisoning in cats with 37 deaths. Symptoms were debilitation and listlessness with complete destruction of kidney function, but no apparent pain.

Dieffenbachia seguine Schott., *D. picta* Schott. Dumbcane

This is a common ornamental plant grown in conservatories, houses, and especially in restaurants and hotel lobbies throughout the United States, hardy outdoors in southern Florida. It has the general appearance of sugar cane or banana, resemblances which have prompted persons to taste it. Stems green, conspicuously girdled with mostly evenly spaced leaf scars, from 2 to 6 ft tall. Leaves large; blades entire, oblong, entirely green or variously mottled, in horticultural varieties, with white, yellow, light green, or darker green.

Biting into, chewing, or tasting this plant rapidly produces irritation and burning of the surface of the mouth, tongue, and lips, copious salivation, and edematous swelling which may make the tongue immobile (whence

Fig. 124. *Dieffenbachia seguine*. Dumbcane.

the common name), may interfere with swallowing and breathing, and may last for several days or a week or more (23, 67).

The source of toxicity is not clear. Irritating capacity has generally been ascribed to the presence of numerous sharp, microscopic needles of calcium oxalate which pervade the plant tissues (129). It was held these had a partially mechanical and partially chemical action. This explanation has been called in question on the grounds that calcium oxalate crystals are present in both leaves and stem but only the latter produces the toxic reaction, and on the basis of experiments (see 1283) in which a toxic protein fraction has been isolated. Extracts are lethal to laboratory animals by injection (67).

Other cultivated aroids with irritant juice include *Alocasia, Caladium,* and *Xanthosoma* (1136). Cases of severe poisoning from these genera have not been reported in the United States or Canada.

Additional references: 1371, 1660.

Order Graminales

Cyperaceae

Scirpus americanus Pers. [= *S. americanus* var. *polyphyllus* (Boeck.) Beetle]. Bulrush, three-square

This and other species of rushes have been suspected on field evidence of producing pulmonary emphysema in Wyoming cattle (97). Symptoms and lesions are similar to, if not identical with, those produced by *Lactuca scariola* (*q.v.*). *Scirpus americanus* has also been suspected of poisoning cattle in Australia (810).

Gramineae

Avena sativa L. Cultivated oats

Cultivated oats are responsible for four different types of livestock poisoning.

I. *Nitrate.* Ingestion of oat hay has caused serious cattle loss in Montana, Colorado, Wyoming, the Dakotas, and elsewhere. Recorded losses date back to before 1900. In 1937 and 1938 a group at Colorado, investigating some severe losses (1178, 1576) reproduced them experimentally in cattle by feeding oat hay, but were unable to determine the toxic principle. In 1939, workers at Wyoming established (163) that toxic oat hay possessed high nitrate content and that the toxic principle was nitrite formed by reduction of nitrate in the hay. Toxic amounts, symptoms, lesions, and treatment are discussed under nitrate poisoning, p. 38.

Oat hay is one of the most common sources of plant poisoning by nitrate. Hay which has been grown under conditions that might promote a high nitrate content should be analyzed chemically before being fed. Evidence suggests (1178) that moisture on outdoor hay stacks may promote bacterial reduction of nitrate in the stack to the far more toxic nitrite. Cattle are more prone to poisoning than other classes of livestock, but similar poisoning in swine has been reported (1490). Turkeys have been poisoned by pasturage on oat stubble (1343).

II. *Grass Tetany.* Oats are among those crops, a lush growth of which can produce a mineral imbalance upon ingestion by ruminants. (See grass tetany, p. 504.)

III. *Photosensitization.* "Sunscald" has been reported (1472) as common in the Southeast among hogs pastured on oats in fall and winter.

Cases are noticed particularly after the pasturage has become wet. White or thinly haired areas of skin are affected. Intense itching is followed by necrosis and sloughing of skin. In severe cases the ears may be lost. In the one chemical examination reported, a positive test was obtained for hematoporphyrin in the urine. Photosensitization of goats and sheep on oat pasturage has been observed (1404) in Texas.

IV. *Smutty Oats.* Two reports from the nineteenth century incriminate smutty oats in poisoning of horses and cattle (1101, 1681). Severe mortality in horses was associated with feeding smutted oat grain, while cattle mortality resulted from ingestion of oat hay that had been cut before the grain matured because of developing smut infestation. In horses the symptoms were those primarily of paralysis, terminal convulsions, and death in 4 to 48 hours. In cattle, excitement and some gastroenteritis were noted, with death occurring in about 18 hours. Lesions were not reported. The fungus *Gibberella saubinetii* infecting oat grain has proved distasteful and possibly toxic to horses (see *Hordeum,* p. 482).

Additional references: 162, 164.

Cynodon dactylon (L.) Pers. Bermuda grass
DESCRIPTION. Long-lived perennial grass, seldom setting seed; propagating by runners, much branched, spreading, to 1 ft tall. Inflorescences terminal, upwardly divergent, rigid, slender spikes; 3 to 6 spikes in each cluster.

DISTRIBUTION AND HABITAT. Common throughout southern United States, west to Arizona and California, north to Virginia and Maryland. Locally distributed beyond this range. Bermuda grass is cultivated for hay and pasture purposes and also as a lawn grass in the south-central states. Several named varieties have been developed. The wild strain of Bermuda grass is a serious weed of cultivation in some areas of the Southeast.

TOXICITY, SYMPTOMS, AND LESIONS. Bermuda grass has been incriminated, but not proven the etiological factor, in several different toxemic syndromes.

In Florida, cattle pastured on Everglades pastures containing mainly Bermuda grass have for several years (615, 862, 863) occasionally developed photosensitization. As many as 600 head have been burned at one time and occasionally mortality has been heavy. The urine commonly is reddish-brown, and post mortem lesions include variable icterus and enlarged, granular-surfaced liver. Pastures, examined after certain severe attacks, were found to contain Bermuda grass to the exclusion of almost everything else. Cases often occur following the first frosts when killed grass has become molded and new growth is commencing. The role of the mold, if any, has not been demonstrated.

In southwest Georgia, northern Florida, and southeast Alabama a situation has been known for some 20 years (48, 616) in which cattle display a variety of symptoms, uniformly including posterior paralysis. Stimulation caudal to the lumbar region produces no reaction. Mortality is not uncommon after animals become prostrate. Icterus has been noted in some cases; otherwise post mortem examinations have shown nothing diagnostic. Cases occur after the first frosts in the fall and early winter. They are not always associated with Bermuda grass. Examination of offending pastures, however, has not led to the recognition of any other plant as toxic. The disease locally is known as "Bermuda-grass poisoning" or "downers."

In Oklahoma, a nervous disturbance in cattle associated with mature Bermuda-grass pastures has been reported (1666). All ages of cattle may be affected. It is characterized by nervousness, muscular twitching, especially of the flank, wildness, and eventual inability to stand. Cases occur in late fall on mature grass. In this they differ from the similar disease termed grass tetany (p. 504), which occurs after ingestion of lush young pasturage. Blood mineral content of affected animals in Bermuda-grass poisoning has been investigated. No abnormal levels or imbalances were found.

Symptoms appear within a few days to a week or slightly longer after cattle are placed on mature Bermuda grass. They disappear within a similar period of time if the cattle are removed, but may return with further access to Bermuda-grass pasturage. In some herds 70 to 80 per cent of the cattle are affected. Feeding experiments with steers have duplicated the characteristics of field cases.

Examination of the grass for ergot demonstrated that many fungi were present but no ergot sclerotia were found. Cultures of unidentified fungi isolated from the heads and upper stems of the grass were able to provoke nervous symptoms when fed experimentally. Fungi isolated from other parts of the grass did not do so. It has been suggested, therefore, that control may be achieved by clipping the heads as they form.

Eragrostis cilianensis (All.) Link [= *E. megastachya* (Koel.) Link].
Love grass, stink grass

The listing of this strongly scented, widely distributed, common grass as a poisonous plant rests upon a single account (609) of its toxicity to horses when fed in large quantities, fresh or in hay, over a long period of time. No further information is given.

Festuca arundinacea Schreb. [= *Festuca elatior* var. *arundinacea* (Schreb.) Celak.] Fescue, tall fescue

DESCRIPTION. A coarse perennial grass, deeply rooted, in vigorous clumps, reaching 3 to 4 ft in height when mature. Leaves broad, dark green, ribbed and rough on the upper surface; leaf sheath smooth, ligule short. Inflorescence paniculate, nodding, to 1 ft in length; spikelets many-flowered.

Tall fescue was introduced into the United States from Europe and is now widely naturalized. Two selected strains, Kentucky 31 and Alta fescue, are planted as forage crops.

DISTRIBUTION AND HABITAT. The wild form and the two selected strains are widely distributed throughout the country and may be found both in unimproved pastures and as forage crops. They do best in wet, heavy soils of high organic content, and are strongly drought-resistant.

POISONOUS PRINCIPLE. Alkaloids similar to those in ergot have been detected in nonheaded fescue plants (954, 1594).

TOXICITY, SYMPTOMS, AND LESIONS. In 1949 it was reported from New Zealand (391) that fescue caused gangrene of the extremities in cattle similar to that caused by ingestion of ergot (*Claviceps*). A similar situation had existed in the United States for several decades but had remained undiagnosed (636). Now gangrenous fescue poisoning ("fescue foot") has been recognized to occur from the Pacific Northwest to Missouri and throughout the southeastern United States. The disease has been reviewed by Yates (1709).

Fescue foot is a disease of cattle. Horses seem immune (391). Symptoms of lameness usually appear in a week and a half to two weeks or sometimes longer. One or both hind feet become gangrenous as in gangrenous ergotism. In severe cases the front feet, the tip of the tail, or the tips of the ears may be affected. Fescue retains all or most of its toxicity when made into hay. In experimental feedings of hay (391), 178 lb produced lameness in one instance in 15 days.

Resistance to poisoning seems variable within a herd. Sometimes lameness disappears from a herd without change of forage if the overt signs of gangrene have not appeared (44). Occasionally an animal which has developed lameness will recover spontaneously while the condition of other animals on the same diet become worse (391). In warm climates animals seem abnormally distressed by hot weather (1093) and there is evidence that cold intensifies the severity of the gangrenous attack in a cold climate (636). If poisoning runs its most destructive course, it will terminate in death.

In most cases the symptoms and lesions of fescue foot in cattle are comparable with those produced by ingestion of *Claviceps* sclerotia. In a few instances (44, 834, 1649) lesions of patchy necrosis of the skin, similar to that which occurs in photosensitization, have been observed above the gangrenous portion of the limb.

In ergot poisoning the sclerotial stage, associated with flowering of the host grass, appears to be the only part of the fungus life cycle in which toxic alkaloids are produced. Repeated examination of poisonous fescue for sclerotia has failed to demonstrate their presence. Fescue pastures are often poisonous before the grass has headed, and there is no sharp seasonal incidence of poisoning as there would be if sclerotia were involved. Alkaloids (954, 1594) have been detected in nonheaded, poisonous fescue. Identification of these alkaloids with alkaloids of ergot has not been made, but it has been shown (954) that the spectroscopic transmission characteristics of alkaloids obtained from fescue match closely those of ergot alkaloids. Fescue alkaloids have been shown (1594) capable of producing vasoconstriction and uterine contraction in the cat, but they apparently differ from ergot alkaloids in some of their physiological reactions. The *Claviceps* sclerotium owes its dark color to the presence of a characteristic pigment sclererythrin, which has also been detected in poisonous fescue extracts (954). It appears therefore that toxicity of fescue may be produced by an as yet unidentified fungus parasitic on it, and not by the grass itself.

CONDITIONS OF POISONING. Poisoning takes place when cattle are placed on fescue pasture or mixed pastures where they must eat fescue. Not all fescue pastures are poisonous (1093), and occasionally, pastures which have been poisonous are found nontoxic at a later date. Fescue pastures need not be headed to be poisonous. Fescue is not particularly palatable to cattle, and poisoning is more apt to occur in mixed pastures after conditions develop which force the animals to eat large quantities of fescue. These conditions include drought, to which fescue is resistant, and snow which covers shorter grasses. Fescue hay may be poisonous (391, 1093).

Fescue may accumulate dangerous levels of nitrates (see nitrate poisoning).

Additional references: 1369, 1516.

Festuca rubra var. *commutata* Gaud. (= *F. fallax* Thuill.) Chewings fescue

This grass is used in turf and lawn seed mixtures. Seed is grown commercially in New Zealand and in Oregon. In Oregon, screenings of chewings fescue seed heavily infested with nematode galls (*Anguina agrostis*) have caused fatal poisoning of sheep, cattle, and hogs and have produced symptoms in horses (669, 720, 1444). Experimental feedings with sheep and rats established that uninfested chewings fescue seed was nontoxic in amounts equal to those of infested screenings which produced symptoms and death. Poisonings and deaths in livestock fed heavily nematode infested chewings fescue hay in the milk stage have also been reported (597).

Symptoms in sheep and cattle are similar and equivalent whether produced naturally or experimentally (1444). They are primarily nervous in character and consist of ataxia, muscular trembling, and falling. Symptoms in sheep appear in about 6 to 10 days after consumption of 10 per cent or less of an animal's weight of screenings. Abortion was common in pregnant ewes. Lesions consist primarily of widely distributed hemorrhages, especially prominent in the large intestine, heart, and gall bladder or may be entirely absent. Gangrene, similar to that produced by ergot sclerotia (see *Claviceps*), was induced by experimental feedings in rats (669).

The poisonous principle is unknown. It is alcohol soluble and heat stable. Ground, filtered nematodes injected into the jugular vein of an experimental sheep failed to elicit symptoms. No fungi were found in the screenings.

Glyceria striata (Lam.) Hitchc. Fowl mannagrass

This grass of wet areas has been reported (1335) to have a high cyanogenetic potential. It has been incriminated in a case resulting in the death of several calves in Maryland.

Hilaria rigida (Thurb.) Benth. ex Scribn. Galleta grass

DESCRIPTION. Erect, stiff-stemmed perennial grass, forming open clumps from a woody rhizome; 1½ to 2½ ft tall. Stem surface wooly with pubescence in the short distances not covered by the sheathing leaf bases. Leaves narrow, blades spreading, stiff; sheathing bases much less hairy than stems. Inflorescence a somewhat obtruding spike 1½ to 3 in. long; spikelets sessile, wooly, in groups of three, alternately inserted.

DISTRIBUTION AND HABITAT. Common on dry lands and desert ranges, to 4000 ft, California to Utah, Arizona, and Mexico.

This range grass is considered moderately palatable forage on the ranges where it is common. However, it has been incriminated, largely by absence of any other known etiological factor, in instances of cattle loss in California where nearly two score animals died on the range (1318). Losses were characterized by sudden deaths in feeder cattle. Under range conditions, symptoms were rarely observed. Post mortem examination of several animals uniformly displayed evidence of stasis and severe irritation in the rumen, reticulum, and omasum. These organs were filled with dry, flaky ingesta consisting almost entirely of galleta grass. Diagnostic lesions in other organs were not found.

Ranges where losses occurred had a history of sporadic unexplained losses dating back to 1837. They were examined carefully for signs of poisonous materials of human or geological origin, with negative results. Botanical examination did not disclose any plant known capable of producing the syndrome found (although *Senecio douglasii* was present). In severely affected herds, losses ceased when animals were moved elsewhere. Toxicological analyses of stomach contents were negative as were the results of examinations for parasites or pathogenic bacteria.

These results pointed to the conclusion that ingestion of galleta grass, perhaps accompanied by restricted access to water, was responsible for

the losses found. Galleta grass has also been under suspicion in Arizona as a poisonous plant.

See also *Claviceps*.

Holcus lanatus L. Velvet grass

This perennial meadow or pasture grass was listed in 1932 by Couch (352) among species dangerous to livestock by virtue of their cyanogenetic capacity. In a similar list, published in 1937 (356), he omitted it. No cases are on record in the United States.

Hordeum jubatum L. Squirreltail grass, foxtail grass, wild barley

This widely distributed and locally common biennial or perennial grass occurs from Northern Canada and Alaska southward throughout most of the United States to Virginia and Texas. Of the many plants which cause injury to animals by purely mechanical means, this is one of the worst, having produced serious loss of life in sheep, particularly in the Rocky Mountain and northern Plains states. The long, slender, wiry bristles extending from the flowering spike bear reversely directed, almost microscopic teeth. Once the sharp tip of a bristle penetrates flesh, the teeth prevent it from coming out, and, together with movements of the animal, cause it to work its way further into the flesh.

Injury is recorded in cattle and horses (1173) but the plant is particularly dangerous to sheep (551, 1173, 1246). Most trouble occurs from feeding hay containing large amounts of this grass, particularly when fed in racks which force sheep to put their muzzles into the mass of hay

Fig. 125. *Holcus lanatus*. Velvet grass. Plant, with details of spikelet, and grain. Courtesy of The Macmillan Company.

while feeding. Bristles easily penetrate the delicate tissues inside the mouth or about the eyes. They also may work their way through the skin in the ears, face, neck, or back. Infection following these injuries results in abscesses and necrosis followed by sloughing of affected tissues. Deaths

Fig. 126. *Hordeum jubatum*. Squirreltail grass. Drawing of plant, with details of awned spikelets, and awn barbs. Photograph showing habit and detail of inflorescence. Courtesy of The Macmillan Company.

are not uncommon when animals are blinded and unable to find feed, or when the oral tissues become sore or damaged sufficiently to prevent feeding. Additional economic loss is sustained by ranchers through downgrading of wool or pelts from effects of this plant.

Hordeum vulgare L. Cultivated barley

Grain barley is subject to infection by a variety of fungi. When infected with *Gibberella saubinetii* (Mont.) Sacc., the imperfect stage of which is *Fusarium graminearum* Schw., it is toxic to certain species of animals.

Infection may be detected in heads of barley by loss of green color of infected spikelets followed by yellowing and browning. Eventually reddish mold growth may be observed on the surface. If the fungus undergoes sexual reproduction in the grain, small black bodies, the perithecia, will be observed scattered on the surface of the kernel. These appear ovoid or subconical with magnification. An individual kernel when blighted is shrunken and shrivelled to a degree dependent upon the severity of infection and the stage of development when initially infected. Barley blighted in this way is termed scabby. When parasitized by *Gibberella saubinetii,* the grains tend to develop bluish-black tips which impart a darkened or off-color appearance to mixtures in which they appear.

Crop years in which the barley harvest averages as high as 4 or 5 per cent scabby kernels are infrequent and are correlated with seasons in which prolonged moist periods occur at the time of flowering. Such a year was 1928. In some localities the proportion of scabby barley reached as high as 80 per cent (1352). Almost immediately following harvest of this crop difficulties arose in feeding it to pigs. Complaints were entered against barley grown in Indiana, Ohio, Illinois, Wisconsin, and Iowa (967). From the 1928 harvest, appreciable tonnages were exported to Germany, Belgium, and the Netherlands and were the source of further difficulties. Following complaints, the German Ministry of Food and Agriculture decreed that imported American barley must undergo tests for toxicity before being offered for use.

Extensive feeding experiments were undertaken in the United States, Germany, and elsewhere (280, 423, 967, 1088, 1140, 1141, 1352, 1353). They may be summarized as follows. Barley of which more than 5 per cent of the kernels are infected with *Gibberella saubinetii* is distasteful to hogs and will be refused unless the animal is starving. If hogs ingest it, even in relatively small quantities, intoxication and vomition occur. In a typical feeding experiment, hogs starved for 24 hours or longer might be induced to consume a few mouthfuls of a grain mixture containing less than half scabby barley. They refused more, and would look elsewhere for something to eat. After a short time they would appear drowsy and lie down, only to arise again and wander aimlessly about after a few minutes. This process would be repeated several times in the course of 30 to 45 minutes, either becoming progressively more intense, ending in vomition, or gradually decreasing in intensity, ending in complete recovery. Vomition, if it occurred, was usually repeated 6 to 8 times over the course of an hour or longer, becoming less severe and terminating in recovery. Further experiments showed that the toxic principle could be extracted in water, concentrated, and if given by stomach tube or by injection could produce vomition within a matter of minutes and in a few instances produced death. No deaths were recorded in natural cases. The extract of 15 g of

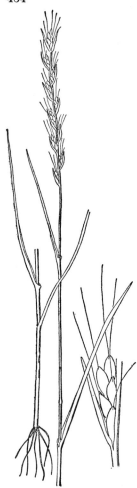

parasitized kernels administered by stomach tube was sufficient in one experiment (280) to produce vomition in a 100-lb pig (for toxicity of 0.03 per cent).

Scabby barley and oats were found distasteful to horses and mules and were refused by these animals. They were also distasteful to and were refused by rats and guinea pigs in experimental work with these laboratory animals. Rats could be sickened and even killed with scabby barley, but guinea pigs reacted only with weight losses to both scabby and nonscabby barley, but more severely to the former. The dog and human being are also sensitive to the poisonous principle in scabby barley.

Cattle and other ruminants appear immune to the toxic effects of scabby barley and will eat it readily even in amounts as high as 56 per cent of their rations (1352). Results with poultry have been equivocal. Poultry find scabby barley distasteful in large amount and will refuse it, with concomitant weight losses. Possibly toxic effects beyond weight loss have been reported both in some feeding experiments and in some natural cases, but have not been observed in other instances.

Feeding experiments with pigs using scabby barley parasitized by certain other genera of fungi, but not with *Gibberella saubinetii,* have produced no indication of toxicity (280). Experiments or observation of natural feeding with oats, corn, and possibly wheat parasitized by *Gibberella saubinetii* have yielded evidence of toxicity similar to that of barley parasitized by this fungus (244, 1352).

Fig. 127. *Lolium temulentum.* Darnel. Plant, with detail of spikelet. Courtesy of The Macmillan Company.

Lolium temulentum L. Darnel

DESCRIPTION. Erect annual weedy grass, often growing in clumps, 1½ to 4 ft tall. Leaf sheaths overlapping on stem. Inflorescence a stiff, erect, flattened spike, 4 to 8 in. tall, terminating the stem. Individual grass flowers in groups of 4 to 7 (the spikelet), alternately inserted on the spikelet axis in two ranks, hence spikelet flattened. Spikelets inserted on spike axis similarly. Spikelets sessile, subtended by a single bract which lies against and exceeds the spikelet in length.

DISTRIBUTION AND HABITAT. Adventive weed in poorly cultivated crops, especially grains, and waste fields, throughout the eastern United States, southeastern Canada, and on the Pacific Coast.

Darnel was much feared and highly publicized as a weed and as a poisonous plant in earlier times. References to it in these roles may be found in such authors as Ovid, Virgil, Shakespeare, Plautus, Dioscorides, and the Bible. These and other early writings about darnel have been reviewed by Leeman (914). It was generally understood that human beings would be poisoned by ingestion of flour or baked products containing seeds of darnel as contaminant. Contamination was also undesirable because of the strong taste of darnel seeds, which resulted in inferior bread, although darnel seeds were sometimes added to beer as a flavoring.

Cornevin, just before the turn of the present century, presented an extensive discussion, supplemented with some experimental observations, of the toxicity of darnel seed to human beings and livestock (335). Figures are quoted concerning the toxicity of the seed to human beings (1 oz to produce symptoms) and to various classes of livestock, found not equally susceptible. At about the same time, chemical investigations into the nature of the toxic principle resulted in the addition of several names to the literature, the most important of which was the alkaloid, temuline, investigated by Hofmeister. These results, because of their age, are in need of reconfirmation. Toxicity was thought to be present only in the seed. Cornevin presented details of darnel starch-grain structure by which it was possible to detect darnel in flour.

Also by the turn of the present century it had been discovered that seeds of darnel were commonly infected with a fungus. The thought was soon voiced (587) that the fungus contributed to the toxicity of the seed.

Further experiments and investigations have taken place, particularly in Africa and New Zealand, but the result has been to make less clear what had seemed well established as reviewed above. In South Africa darnel is common, and bread made with flour containing appreciable quantities of it is regularly eaten. Investigations were prompted by reports of bread poisoning, but in no case was it possible to demonstrate that the toxicity came from darnel. Instead it was found that *Senecio* (*q.v.*) was almost always responsible for bread poisoning. Experiments with laboratory animals using both infected and uninfected darnel seed were uniformly negative (1531).

A series of mycological papers has come from work of Neill in New Zealand (1171, 1172). He found a fungus, similar to that in darnel in other species of *Lolium* and in other grasses. His work was originally prompted by reports of toxicity of *Lolium perenne* L. (perennial rye grass), but although feeding experiments were carried out from time to time

486

444486

(see also 316), both with infected and with fungus-free material, no poisonings were ever produced.

In *Lolium temulentum,* the fungus does not produce sexual stages (which are necessary for complete indentification). Instead it forms a sterile hyphal stage which has been recognized as *Endoconidium temulentum* Prill. & Del. The fungus in *L. perenne,* which in the plant also forms an *Endoconidium* stage, has been cultured on artificial medium and made to form a sexual stage. The latter is identified by Neill as *Phialea temulenta* Prill. & Del. (an ascomycete).

Classical darnel poisoning was only occasionally fatal. Symptoms in man consisted of apathy, giddiness, or a feeling of intoxication, accompanied by ataxia, various abnormal sensations, mydriasis, nausea, vomition, gastric pain, and diarrhea.

Despite the fact that darnel is locally common in some parts of North America, no cases of typical darnel poisoning have been reported (see 1229). Occasional cases ascribed to ingestion of darnel seed have been reported in European literature [see review by Forsyth (574)]. Even in Europe poisoning is very rare.

In connection with investigations into forage poisoning in the Willamette Valley of Oregon from a variety of causes, Shaw and Muth (1444) associated a nervous syndrome in ewes with rye-grass (*Lolium perenne*) stubble pasturage, and in cattle with the feeding of rye-grass screenings. In both cases the syndrome was similar to that produced by acute ergotism, but on close examination no evidence of ergot was found. Pathognomonic lesions were absent in the several cattle that died.

Panicum spp. Panic-grasses
This genus of agriculturally important grasses contains close to 100 species. Feeding experiments with several species following outbreaks of hepatogenic photosensitization in Australia, South Africa (180), South America, and elsewhere (284) have occasionally had positive results. No cases have been reported in North America.

Setaria lutescens (Wiegel) Hubb. [= *S. glauca* (L.) Beauv.]. Yellow bristle grass, foxtail grass, pigeon grass
This species is a common weed of cultivation and waste areas throughout much of North America. Its spike is cylindrical, yellowish, and composed of numerous, tightly packed, mostly single-flowered spikelets. Subtending each spikelet is a tuft of 5 or more fine, wiry bristles which exceed the spikelet in length, thus giving the spike a fuzzy-surfaced general appearance. Each bristle bears tiny upwardly directed barbs or points. The bristles easily penetrate flesh and are kept there by the barbs.

That this species can produce mechanical injury of the oral tissues in livestock has been casually known for a long time. Recently a study was reported (63) in which lesions were described in detail and experimentally

Fig. 128. Grasses which cause mechanical injury. A-C, *Stipa spartea.* Porcupine grass. D-E, *Aristida dichotoma.* Poverty grass. F-G, *Aristida oligantha.* Wire grass. Courtesy of The Macmillan Company.

reproduced. The study was prompted by the gross similarity of lesions to those found in several vesicular diseases.

Relatively small amounts of *S. lutescens* in hay (in this study, 1.8 per cent) result in rapidly developing, relatively extensive ulceration of oral tissues. Ulcers average ½ in. in diameter and are surrounded by a white, raised rim. These and smaller discolored areas in the tissues are found to contain bristles of *Setaria* when examined closely.

Horses are somewhat more susceptible to injury because of the softer nature of the oral tissues, but lesions are easily produced in cattle as well. Other grasses which may inflict similar injury include *Hordeum jubatum* (*q.v.*) and species of *Aristida* (poverty grass, etc.) and *Stipa* (needle grass, etc.), which are particularly troublesome on dry range lands.

Sorghum spp. Johnson grass, Columbus grass, sudan grass, sorghum

AGRICULTURAL SIGNIFICANCE OF SORGHUM (GENUS). Members of the sorghum group of grasses have been cultivated since antiquity in Africa and Asia. Selection and hybridization have produced hundreds of recognized strains, the genetic background of which is usually obscure. Botanical treatment varies. Commonly the members of this group are divided into the cultivated sorghums and sudan grass, which are annual, and Johnson grass, which is a perennial weedy grass of the southern states. Since 1950 Columbus grass, a cold-sensitive, cultivated perennial, has gained some popularity.

The cultivated sorghums (*Sorghum vulgare* Pers.) are further divided into saccharin or forage sorghums, grain sorghums, and broom corn. Named and unnamed varieties exist within each category, and the first two botanically are closely related. Saccharin sorghums were once much used as a source of syrup in the United States; now they are used mainly for forage. They are also called sweet or cane sorghums or sorgo. The grain sorghums may be utilized either for grain or for forage. Names applied to various grain sorghums include kafir corn, hegari, milo, and many others. Bailey (54) treats the major types of sorghums as named botanical varieties.

Sorghums were first introduced into the United States in 1855. Toxicity was recognized in 1900 (779) and correctly ascribed to the presence of a cyanogenetic glycoside in 1902 (1476). Simultaneously, the same conclusion was reached independently in Britain (462). Since 1902 cyanide poisoning from sorghum has been confirmed in a number of countries where it is grown as a forage crop, such as Australia, India, Africa, and Italy.

Johnson grass is generally classed as a weed and has been declared noxious in several southern states. It is a troublesome perennial in the cotton-growing areas and is difficult to eradicate. Nevertheless, Johnson, grass is utilized in some places as a forage and hay crop. It was introduced to South Carolina in 1830. Wide distribution throughout the South followed, partly intentionally. The plant is hardy (perennial) to about 35° North Latitude. It is identified botanically by the name *Sorghum halepense* (L.) Pers. It was suspected of having caused cattle mortality as early as 1902 (58).

The desirable qualities of Johnson grass led to a search for a plant

Fig. 129. *Sorghum halepense*. Johnson grass. Plant, with details of portion of fruiting branch, and grains. Courtesy of The Macmillan Company.

which combined these qualities with an annual or nonweedy character of growth. Sudan grass was brought into the United States from Khartum, Sudan, in 1909 and was quickly found to be a valuable forage plant. Livestock losses were first reported in 1919 (1222, 1555). Sudan grass is more closely related to sorghum than is Johnson grass. It is commonly treated botanically as a variety of *Sorghum vulgare* (var. *sudanense* Hitchc.) but some consider it sufficiently different to warrant consideration as a separate species.

In 1936 a plant was discovered in Argentina having some of the characteristics of sudan grass and others of Johnson grass (714). It was botanically described and named by Parodi in 1943. He concluded that it had arisen as a natural hybrid between a cultivated sorghum and Johnson grass, and named it *Sorghum* X *almum* Parodi (the X signifying its hybrid nature as required under the international rules of botanical nomenclature). Seed was distributed to several continents. It entered the United States from South Africa in 1952 under the South African name of Columbus grass. Prior to that time it had been studied by the United States Department of Agriculture, but plantings had been discontinued because of its potentially troublesome nature. Additional importations have been made by commercial interests and seed of the plant, in several strains, is now widely available. *Sorghum almum* is a useful forage crop under some conditions. It is perennial in the far South but does not have the aggressive nature of Johnson grass. Winter killing to a greater or lesser degree limits its use as a perennial grass in Oklahoma and northward. Its usefulness is largely cancelled, however, by the fact that it is impossible to distinguish the seed of *Sorghum almum* from that of Johnson grass, and hence impossible to be sure that Johnson grass seed, prohibited as a noxious weed by the seed laws of several southern states, is actually absent in *Sorghum almum* seed. Furthermore, there is danger that *Sorghum almum* may hybridize with Johnson grass to produce dangerously weedy offspring. Compared with sudan grass, *Sorghum almum* has a distinctly higher HCN potential. Already some livestock loss has been reported (714).

Members of the genus *Sorghum* are coarse grasses. Grain and saccharin sorghums are coarser than sudan grass and the other species. Immature sorghums have the appearance of young corn plants. Grain and saccharin sorghums intergrade, but most commercial strains may be distinguished by the nature of the terminal fruiting panicle. In grain sorghums it is dense and compact; the panicle of the saccharin sorghums has an open structure. Other characteristics and general distributions for the cultivated sorghums are described in various USDA publications and elsewhere.

Experimental hybridization and selection for superior forage characteristics is a continuing process. A number of named crosses involving Johnson grass and sorghum have been selected and introduced. Designations such as perennial sweet sudan grass or sorgrass have been used. Attention has been given in such selections to the HCN potential, and generally only those of low potential have been developed.

Johnson grass occurs as a weed from Florida to Texas and California, north to Iowa and New England. It is rarely sown, although large acreages on alluvial bottom lands are managed as perennial hay fields or pastures. Stems are coarse, erect, ½ to ¾ in. thick at base, 3 to 6 ft tall. Plants propagate in part by free production of lateral stems arising from the root crown. Leaf blades are ½ to 1 in. broad and 1 to 1½ ft long. The plant is topped by a very open, large, lacy panicle. The main axis bears whorls of laterals which in turn bear spikelets. Spikelets are of two types. The fertile ones are plump, sessile, and frequently tipped with a dry coarse hair (awn). The sterile ones are about twice as numerous, stemmed, and less plump.

POISONOUS PRINCIPLE. The cyanogenetic glycoside dhurrin (462, 915) is present in greater or lesser amount in various sorghums, sudan grass,

dhurrin

Johnson grass, and *Sorghum almum*. In almost every instance, loss is the result of cyanide poisoning.

Forage sorghums also may accumulate toxic levels of nitrates (1200). Sudan grass has caused nitrate poisoning (1255). Photosensitization has been reported (583) in sheep grazing sudan grass. From the absence of icterus it is fair to assume the presence of a photodynamic pigment in the plant.

TOXICITY, SYMPTOMS, AND LESIONS. *Cyanide poisoning.* Cyanide potential (amount of nitrile glycoside in the plant) varies with a number of factors. Environmental factors which tend to result in higher HCN potential include high available nitrogen and low phosphorus in the soil, and drought, which results in slowed or stunted growth (161, 583, 1279, 1690, 1691). To a degree, the darker green the plant is, the higher cyanide content it has (1279). Age of plant is also important. Young growth tends to have the highest HCN potential (583, 1027). The concentration of cyanide remains level or usually increases slightly to the time when pollination takes place, then drops rapidly. Leaves usually have a higher cyanide potential than stems.

Inheritance is generally more important than environment, age, or part of plant in determining cyanide potential. Before selection for cyanide potential was used in breeding programs, the sorghums, taken as a whole, had the highest cyanide potential and caused the greatest numbers of mortalities. Sudan grass, in general, had considerably less potential. Johnson grass was intermediate. *Sorghum almum* has been found to have a potential near that of the more potent sorghums. Varietal differences in cyanide potential had been demonstrated in 1919 (312) but it was not until 1937 and 1938 that experiments to determine whether these variations were inherited were performed (308, 1358). Selfed (inbred) lines clearly showed distinct differences in cyanide potential. A strain of low cyanide potential displayed cyanide content varying somewhat with environmental and other factors, but always distinctly lower than the cyanide potential of a high-cyanide strain. Since then, low-cyanide-potential, named strains of forage sorghums (such as Rancher) and of sudan grass (such as Piper) have been developed at various agricultural experiment stations. Danger of cyanide poisoning from use of these strains is nil, no matter what the environmental or management factors. Genetic work has been reviewed by Carlson (243).

Analyses of cyanide level in sorghums and sudan grass are common in the literature. The older ones may be used only in a general way, since defects in techniques resulted in variable and unknown loss of cyanide during measurement. Comparative figures for strains of commercial sorghums, sudan grass, *Sorghum almum,* and Johnson grass, grown in Texas are presented by Gangstad (598). Cyanide potential in some commercial forage sorghums may reach as high as 0.34 per cent (582) (0.02 per cent is considered the threshold of danger). As little as ½ lb of forage at this level might prove fatal. Sudan-grass strains generally have one-third to one-tenth the cyanide potential of average sorghum strains (1556, 1625, 1626). Georgia's Tift strain, developed for disease resistance, has a high cyanide potential among sudan grasses. *Sorghum almum* has a high potential; one strain was found to have 0.1 per cent cyanide at the time when measured (598).

The symptoms and lesions of cyanide poisoning are discussed elsewhere (p. 26).

A geographical pattern was early discerned in loss of livestock by sorghum forage poisoning. It was generally confined to the area bounded by Colorado, South Dakota, Indiana, Missouri, and Oklahoma (451, 452, 579, 583, 702, 779, 1222, 1263), although loss has occurred also in Saskatchewan (233) and Maryland (1335) and was suspected also in Florida (312). Greater loss correlated with drier years. Almost all mortality involved cattle, but sheep (582) and horses (702, 1335) have been poisoned by forage sorghums. The great majority of cases occurred at pasture, although hay has proved toxic (452) occasionally.

Sudan-grass poisoning has occurred in the same general geographic area, and likewise is almost always limited to cattle on pasture (1222, 1554, 1625). Loss from toxic hay (1625) has been reported.

Johnson-grass poisoning is less common, and more widely scattered. Cattle mortality, sometimes extensive, has been reported from California, Arizona (375), Texas (1032), and Alabama (1676) and horse mortality in Maryland (1335). *Sorghum almum* has killed cattle (714).

Nitrate. After livestock loss in India, Pease (1255) found white crystals of nitrate in the stems of sorghum plants involved. Olson and Whithead have also found potentially toxic amounts of nitrate in forage sorghum (1200). Losses to ingestion of sudan grass of high nitrate content have been reported by Franzke in South Dakota (583). Symptoms and lesions are those of nitrate poisoning (see p. 38).

Photosensitization. Sheep have developed photosensitivity while grazing on sudan-grass pastures in California (793) and Texas (1046). Symptoms and lesions were those of primary photosensitization (see p. 52) and ceased when the animals were removed from the sudan grass.

CONDITIONS OF POISONING. Whether or not poisoning will take place depends on a large number of variables: cyanide potential of the plant, amount eaten, rate of ingestion, degree of enzymatic release of HCN before or during digestion, amount of inactivation of HCN before absorption, rate of absorption (dependent on amount of ingesta and moisture), and rate of excretion. The relationship of these factors to particular conditions of management is obvious (161). Most losses have occurred when hungry animals have been put on pasturage of high cyanide content. The latter most often is young, dark-green growth, stunted by insufficient moisture, frequently less than 1 ft tall. Second growth is commonly involved. These statements apply generally to forage sorghums, sudan grass, Johnson grass, and *Sorghum almum*.

The frequency of cattle poisoning compared with that of other animals may be explained by conditions in the rumen which promote greater and more rapid enzymatic breakdown of the cyanogenetic glycoside as compared with the digestive process in other animals. These may include the activity of the microflora and the nearly neutral pH of the rumen. Enzymatic release of cyanide from sorghums is greatest *in vitro* at pH's between 4.1 and 5.1 (358), but cyanide once released in a slightly acid medium is subject to further reaction to yield ammonium formate or some other less toxic compound (358, 1556).

Only rarely has poisoning followed use of sorghum or sudan-grass hay. In the curing process a greater or lesser amount of cyanide potential is lost (312, 451, 583, 1626). Quick-dried hay may retain a large proportion (161). Complete drying inactivates the enzyme involved in cyanide release.

Frost-damaged sorghum has been incriminated in some losses (583, 702, 1555). Frosting causes cellular damage and joins enzyme with cyanogenetic substrate so that there is immediate release and build-up in just-frosted plants of an appreciable quantity of free HCN. As the plants wilt, however, free HCN is lost. Nevertheless, plants containing free HCN are always more dangerous than those with an equivalent potential toxicity in glycosidic form, since in the free form the HCN is totally and immediately available for absorption into the bloodstream.

No cases of mortality after ingestion of sorghum silage have been reported. Several experiments have been made (171, 583) which show that properly cured silage may still have dangerous levels of cyanide potential if the starting material was high in cyanide. But during fermentation it appears that glycoside breakdown is complete and that all cyanide potential of such silage occurs as free HCN. This is rapidly lost to the air when the silage is opened up and spread out for feeding.

To determine whether suspected sorghum or sudan-grass forage is safe or not, the following observations may be useful. Pasturage may be safely used if yellow (as opposed to dark green), if more than 2 ft tall, or if forming fruiting heads. Under some circumstances, however, patches of dangerous plants may occur in pastures that are otherwise acceptable. Analyses may be made of suspected plants if facilities are available. If the analysis gives a figure of 20 mg HCN per 100 g plant tissue, or higher, toxicity may be expected. In the absence of such facilities, a test animal may be used. It has been noted (161) that a cow whose appetite has been partially satiated will usually stop eating sorghums of dangerous cyanide content after a few minutes and before a toxic amount has been ingested.

Additional references: 357, 359, 676, 1280, 1687.

Stipa robusta Scribn. ($=$ *S. vaseyi* Scribn.). Sleepygrass

DESCRIPTION. Stout, perennial grass, forming erect clumps mostly 2 to 4 ft tall. Leaves flat $\frac{5}{16}$ in. wide, up to 2 ft long. Inflorescence a green or greenish-yellow terminal panicle, to 1 ft long; branches several at each node, variable in length, bearing several spikelets, strongly directed upward, hence panicle compact and narrow; spikelets narrow, about ½ in. long, tipped by a long, dry, twisted awn; awns about 1 in. long.

DISTRIBUTION AND HABITAT. Dry plains, hills, and open woods, Colorado to Texas, Arizona, and Mexico.

POISONOUS PRINCIPLE. Unknown. Some attempts to extract the active principle have been reported (922).

TOXICITY, SYMPTOMS, AND LESIONS. Reports of the toxicity of sleepygrass to horses in New Mexico date back to 1887. Ingestion of a moderate amount produces a profound, but not lethal, somnolent or stuporous condition sometimes lasting several days. In times when the horse was the principal means of travel, serious delay and inconvenience occasionally befell those unaware of the danger in this plant (55, 69, 735).

Following a number of field reports and correspondence concerning the toxicity of sleepygrass to horses, the United States Department of

Agriculture undertook feeding experiments at the Salina (Utah) experiment station and in the field (998). It was found that 0.6 per cent of an animal's weight of plant (green-weight basis) was the least toxic dose for the horse and produced transitory depression or drowsiness. One per cent was the average effective single dose. Larger amounts provoked somewhat, but not proportionately, greater symptoms. Symptoms appeared in 6 to 24 hours and lasted 24 to 48 hours. Field cases have been reported in which as much as a week elapsed before all signs of poisoning had disappeared. Great variation in degree of sleepiness was found. Mildly poisoned animals were dejected, inactive, and withdrawn. With greater dose animals became somnolent, presenting symptoms of drooping head, closed eyes, and irregularity of gait if forced to move. Severely poisoned animals lie on the sternum or flat on the side with head resting on the ground. These horses are in profound slumber from which they can be raised only momentarily with great difficulty. In such animals the pulse and respiration become weak and irregular. A definite rise in temperature has been recorded in many instances.

Despite field reports of toxicity to cattle, doses of active material up to 3.4 per cent of an animal's weight in a single day failed to bring out symptoms. In sheep, doses of about 2 per cent of an animal's weight provoked depression and a rise in temperature, but not sleepiness.

CONDITIONS OF POISONING. Reports of poisoning have come from only a portion of the area in which *Stipa robusta* is found, namely the Sacramento and Sierra Blanca Mountains of New Mexico. Material collected from several other areas failed to bring on poisoning although given in more than adequate amount in feeding experiments (998). The plant retains full toxicity on drying. Sleepygrass was readily and repeatedly taken by horses during the feeding experiments, but it is generally believed among ranchers that horses once poisoned will refuse subsequently to graze the plant.

Zea mays L. Corn, Indian corn, maize

Corn, used as grain, forage or silage, has been responsible for a variety of disease syndromes in livestock. Difficulties arising from feeding or pasturing moldy corn and from abnormally high nitrate content in corn forage were recognized prior to 1900. Investigations of moldy corn poisoning are discussed under fungus toxicoses (p. 72).

POISONINGS ARISING FROM HIGH NITRATE CONTENT OF CORN FORAGE OR SILAGE. Corn, as many of the Gramineae, tends to accumulate nitrates under certain conditions. Factors promoting abnormal uptake of nitrates are discussed on p. 39. Analyses of corn (165, 1200, 1667, 1669) from seedling to mature plant indicate that nitrate accumulation is greatest in the stalk and that highest concentration is reached before tasseling. Nitrate content is sharply reduced during the formation of grain. Conditions which retard fruiting, such as drought, late planting, or early frost, can result in corn forage which will be harvested or pastured when dangerous.

(a) *Nitrate poisoning.* Poisoning of cattle after ingestion of corn forage containing lethal levels of nitrate was recognized in the United States as early as 1895 (1064). Nitrate crystals were observed on the corn stalks, which burned like a fuse when ignited. Analyses (165) in recent years have discovered concentrations of nitrate (as KNO_3) as high as 8 per cent in stalks. Sporadic cases of cattle loss with classical symptoms of nitrate poisoning have occurred from time to time in the United States, particularly in the Midwest and Great Plains states during drought years (1064, 1667, 1668, 1669). Cattle are frequently poisoned. Sheep, tending to feed selectively on the leaves as opposed to the more toxic stalks, are less liable to poisoning (165).

Symptoms and lesions of nitrate poisoning are discussed on p. 40.

(b) *Nitrogen dioxide and nitrogen tetroxide from corn silage fermentation.* In recent years, syndromes have been described in which symptoms and lesions other than those of classical nitrate poisoning occur, yet which are traced to high nitrate content of the plants ingested. High nitrate content of ensilage corn may be responsible for unusual fermentation in the silo. Partial reduction of nitrate at acid pH by bacteria gives rise to several oxides of nitrogen which are evolved as a pungent, yellowish-brown, toxic gas (165, 417, 940, 1265, 1667, 1668, 1696). It is probable that upon reaction with air, the principal product is nitrogen dioxide (NO_2) forming, by polymerization, a mixture with nitrogen tetroxide at usual temperatures (940). Industry tolerance standards for this gas allow not more than 10 to 25 ppm in the atmosphere. Silage-generated concentrations of 151 ppm have been measured in an average case (1266) and have reached concentrations greater than 100,000 (381, 940, 1265). The gas is derived almost entirely from the nitrate content of the plants (940) and as evolved is concentrated in the upper layers of silage. It discolors plant material, unpainted woodwork, and other objects, turning them yellow-brown. Nitrogen dioxide is heavier than air, flows down delivery chutes, and tends to collect around the bases of silos, especially at chutes or in small silage delivery rooms where it may be observed as a yellowish fog. Flies and other animals in such rooms or areas will quickly be killed. The loss of occasional chickens (940, 1266) and pigs (940) under such circumstances has been reported. Nitrogen-dioxide production commences within a few hours, reaches a maximum rate in $1\frac{1}{2}$ to 2 days, and continues at an increasingly reduced rate for about a week after silo filling begins (940).

Although the first published report of nitrogen-dioxide poisoning came from inquiries into loss of animal life, the disease has received its most thorough investigation following loss of human life (417, 940). Nitrogen-dioxide poisoning in human beings may result from exposure to gas from a number of industrial sources. From such poisonings it is clear that clinical and pathological characteristics may vary over a broad, apparently continuous spectrum, depending on concentration of toxic gas and duration of exposure. The few reported cases of poisoning in human beings from fumes generated from silage (termed "silo-filler's disease") suggest similar variation.

Acute cases terminate fatally from effects of pulmonary edema within a few hours to a very few days following a massive exposure. More typical is the situation in which coughing and some respiratory distress may be noted upon exposure. Although these symptoms, together with weakness and dyspnea, persist for some time, the subject is not totally incapacitated during a latent period of 2 to 3 weeks. At that juncture fever, often with chills, severe dyspnea, serious ineffective cough, and cyanosis develop. Antibiotics, oxygen, and bronchodilators are of little or no use. Death (or occasionally spontaneous recovery) occurs 3½ to 6 weeks after exposure. X-ray examination reveals uniform, discrete nodulation in the lungs. Blood examination shows marked neutrophilic leukocytosis. Otherwise the usual tests give normal values. Lung nodules consist of small bronchi or bronchioles, the lumens of which have become occluded by a fibrous cellular mass. Less severe cases show the characteristics of bronchopneumonia.

Treatment of two cases of bronchiolitis obliterans in the acute stages, as described above, with full doses of adrenocortical steroids brought dramatic relief (940).

(c) *Pulmonary adenomatosis in cattle.* Since 1932 a disease in cattle has been recognized (1115, 1116, 1430) which is characterized by development of pulmonary edema and emphysema. The disease, diagnosed as pulmonary adenomatosis, has been reported from Texas and Iowa. Attempts to correlate its incidence with a particular feed have not been fruitful. It was first thought to be caused by a fungus on corn forage, sweet potatoes, alfalfa hay, corn silage, commercial mixtures, and other feeds, then (1116) by a food allergy. Ultimately, resemblances to "silo-filler's disease" led Seaton (1430) to consider the possibility of nitrogen dioxide as its source. He reproduced the characteristics of the disease by administering nitrogen-dioxide gas to an experimental animal.

The symptoms include increase in rate and depth of breathing, distinct expiratory grunt, and discharge of thick brownish mucus from the nostrils. Subcutaneous emphysema of neck and shoulders may be observed. Lungs are uniformly greatly enlarged, bearing the imprint of the rib cage on their surface. They are edematous, of "meaty" consistency, and easily cut. Histological examination discloses extensive alveolar edema and pulmonary emphysema with large bullae in the interlobular septa. The trachea and bronchi bear numerous petechial hemorrhages. The source of the nitrogen dioxide, if it be the cause of the syndrome, is not clear. Seaton has postulated the possibility of its production in the rumen of the poisoned animal from forages high in nitrate.

In most cases the formation of nitrogen gases in silage is beneficial, since by reducing nitrate content it reduces the possibility of nitrate poisoning. Obviously, precautions must be taken to ensure that poisonings of human beings or animals will not occur during the relatively brief period of gas evolution. Evolution of nitrogen gases in tightly closed silos may be a factor in occasional silo explosions, and it has been suggested (261), further, that production of nitrocelluloses by reactions between nitrates and organic matter of the silage may partially explain some unusually violent explosions.

(d) *Nitrosohemoglobin and miscellaneous.* There remain a number of cases of apparent intoxication in livestock following ingestion of corn of high nitrate content which do not present the symptoms characteristic of nitrate poisoning. In some cases, they have some of the characteristics of moldy corn poisoning (see fungus toxicoses, p. 72), but are not associated with obviously molded corn. The extensive study of the amount, form, and distribution of nitrogen in corn under various field conditions reported by Whitehead *et al.* (1669) was undertaken in an effort to find previously unreported compounds, such as alkaloids, in corn which might be held responsible for toxicity in cases where the blood of poisoned animals did not contain significant concentrations of methemoglobin. Results of the study were inconclusive on this point, however, since definitely toxic corn could not be obtained.

Schwarte *et al.* in 1939 (1422) described cases of loss of cattle in Iowa from corn late in the year after a dry growing season. Symptoms included rapid, labored respiration, trembling, and death with 24 hours—often within 5 or 6 hours of appearance of symptoms. Post mortem findings included some subcutaneous petechial hemorrhaging, petechial hemorrhages of the heart, swollen liver and kidney, and some yellow, edematous swellings about the gall bladder and hepatic ligaments. They were unable to demonstrate an infectious agent, hydrocyanic acid, or methemoglobin (the blood was not dark-colored). The corn forage was not molded.

Aitken, in 1952 (12), recalled cattle poisoning from corn forage in the drought years of the middle 1930's and cited several cases. He noted a spotty incidence among animals on a given field, with younger animals more frequently involved than older. Most cases occurred in November in herds after they had been on stunted or frosted—but not molded—corn for a week or ten days. Cases stopped almost immediately on removal, but mortality approached 100 per cent in poisoned animals. He noted widely distributed petechial and ecchymotic hemorrhaging, a bluish, slightly swollen liver, and amber edematous thickening of the wall of the gall bladder. To his knowledge, no explanation had ever been offered for these widespread and not uncommon cases.

Olson and Whitehead in 1953 (1201) thought those cases of poisoning from sound corn forage in which the blood was not darkened were due to a definite toxic factor in the corn which had not yet been discovered.

Recently it has been suggested (261) that a nitroso radical may be formed in the rumen of cattle ingesting forage of high nitrate content, with consequent formation of nitrosohemoglobin in the blood. This compound does not have the ability to transport oxygen sufficiently well to meet the demands of the tissues, but its color is not the characteristic dark brown of methemoglobin. Case described (261) a simple test for nitrosohemoglobin to distinguish it from carbon-monoxide hemoglobin, which it resembles in color, function, and some other characteristics. He implied that the mortality of hundreds of cattle in Missouri in 1954 as described by Brady *et al.* (165) and Case (255) and in Iowa in 1939 as described by Schwarte *et al.* (1422) were caused by this compound. In his description of poisonings, Case (255) noted that the corn was molded with gray and green molds, and also that the corn contained a high nitrate level. He was unable to obtain satisfactory results with treatments specific for nitrate poisoning. Symptoms and lesions included excitement, or depression, and extensive internal hemorrhaging. In cases described by Schwarte *et al.* (1422) and by Aitken (12) the corn was not molded. Elder (480) has suggested that cases examined by him of cattle loss in Wisconsin were the same as those reported by Case. Young stock were especially susceptible and when poisoned showed excitement with terminal depression and lesions similar to those described by Case. The blood was not darkened, and fungi were thought not to be involved. The corn was shown to have a high nitrate content and the presence of nitrosohemoglobin in the blood was suspected. Spectrographic analysis confirmed these poisonings to be associated with nitrosohemoglobin in the blood of poisoned animals.

POISONINGS ARISING FROM CYANOGENETIC GLYCOSIDES IN CORN. Corn has long been suspected as a potential poisoner by hydrocyanic acid. This belief is probably reinforced by the close genetic relationship of corn and sorghum. Corn forage was suspected (1533) of producing heavy mortality in cattle in Nebraska in this way many years ago, but no conclusive experiments were made at that time. In 1902, suspicions of corn toxicity prompted examination (1297) for hydrocyanic acid, with negative results, and for the enzyme capable of releasing HCN from glycosidic combination, with positive results. In a large number of tests in South Africa (1533)

HCN was detected only rarely, and then under unusual soil and climatic conditions.

VULVOVAGINITIS IN SWINE. Vulvovaginitis previously unreported in swine was common in areas of Iowa, Illinois, Minnesota, South Dakota, and Indiana in 1926 and 1927 but has occurred only rarely since. It was associated with feeding of heavily molded corn produced in an abnormally short growing season with much wet weather just before harvest. The fungi involved were not identified.

Experimental feeding of suspect ear corn (223, 854, 1086) produced symptoms and lesions typical of the disease in nature in 2 days to a week. Gilts from sucklings to 150 lb or more were involved. Occasionally a brood sow showed some symptoms of the disease. Symptoms, well reviewed by McNutt et al. (1086), commence with enlargement of the vulva, which becomes tense and swollen from the body. The lips separate and vaginal prolapse commences. As the vagina is everted, its weight pulls forth more anterior portions. The organ becomes pendant, reaching a length of up to six inches and diameter of four. During the initial stages in this process the animal does not appear discomforted and its appetite remains normal. Itching may occur, with injury as a consequence, and in any event, complications resulting in necrosis, septicemia, and gangrene develop. Urination may be difficult. In severe cases straining may involve the rectum in prolapse. In fully developed cases death is usual, resulting from one or another complication such as hemorrhage, septicemia, uremic poisoning, or the like. Post mortem examination reveals no gross abnormalities other than those observable before death.

In some instances male pigs seem completely unaffected. In others there may be minor or greater swelling of the prepuce, occasionally sufficiently severe to cause difficult urination (1243). In one instance (880) mammary involvement in male pigs was noted. Similar involvement in female pigs has occasionally been observed, and it has been noted (1313) that suckling animals may exhibit symptoms of the disease even though not eating corn. The toxic factor appears to be water soluble in that water extracts were found (854) capable of producing symptoms. Gilts with vulvitis removed from offending corn before vaginal prolapse make a slow recovery, beginning after several days and requiring several weeks for completion (880).

Examinations repeatedly made for infectiousness have been negative. It has been suggested (880) that the moldy corn may produce some estrogen-like compound which causes the effects characteristic of this syndrome.

MISCELLANEOUS. Corn artificially infested with *Gibberella saubinetii* (Mont.) Sacc. (= *Fusarium graminearum* Schw.) produced vomition when fed to hogs experimentally. See *Hordeum,* scabby barley poisoning, p. 482.

Order Juncaginales

Juncaginaceae

Triglochin maritima L. } Arrowgrass
Triglochin palustris L.

DESCRIPTION. Herbaceous, perennial, grasslike plants, forming clumps of leaves from a very short basal stem. Leaves long-linear, thick (not flat as in true grasses), somewhat fleshy, unjointed, sheathing at base. Inflorescence a raceme, pedicels short, hence appearing as though a spike, terminating a single, unbranched, unjointed flowering stem which projects stiffly well beyond the somewhat lax leaves; flowers numerous, small; perianth greenish, 6-membered, small, soon lost. Fruit composed of 3 to 6 capsules, each the product of a single carpel, splitting apart at maturity.

It is difficult to pick out individual plants of arrowgrass in a field of grasses until the time of flowering, when the characteristic inflorescence makes them clearly obvious. Arrowgrasses may be distinguished from true grasses (Gramineae) by their thick, fleshy leaves. In section, arrowgrass leaves are flattened on one surface, round on the other. The leaves of most rushes (another group with which arrowgrasses might be confused) are usually round and wiry in texture.

Triglochin maritima is larger (the flowering stems reach 3 ft or slightly more in height) and usually commoner than *T. palustris* (flowering stems reach 2 ft or slightly more).

DISTRIBUTION AND HABITAT. Arrowgrass clumps sometimes occur singly, but more commonly form associations to the exclusion of other plants. Such areas of arrowgrass may be small and irregular or may cover several acres. Both species occur in damp soils, marshes, or sloughs, usually where the soil is alkaline or the water calcareous or brackish. They may be found in locations where they are under water or partially under water throughout all or part of the growing season. *Triglochin maritima* occurs from Alaska and Labrador southward, along the shore or in appropriate habitats inland, to Delaware, Pennsylvania, Illinois, Nebraska, New Mexico, and Mexico. *Triglochin palustris* has a similar distribution except that it is not found as far south in the eastern United States.

POISONOUS PRINCIPLE. *Triglochin maritima* has been shown to release HCN and to owe its toxicity entirely to its cyanogenetic capacity (92, 554). Repeated attempts to isolate a cyanogenetic glycoside from it have been unsuccessful. Some other unusual results of chemical analyses of *Triglochin* lend weight to the thought that HCN may not be present in the plant in the glycosidic form usually characteristic of cyanogenetic plants.

TOXICITY, SYMPTOMS, AND LESIONS. Symptoms and lesions in livestock are those of typical cyanide poisoning (see cyanogenetic glycosides,

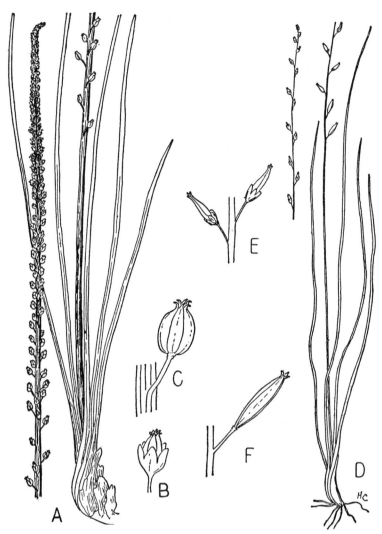

Fig. 130. Arrow grass. A-C, *Triglochin maritima*. Plant, with details of flower and fruit. D-F, *T. palustris*. Plant, with details of flower and fruit. Courtesy of The Macmillan Company.

p. 23). Experimental investigations of arrowgrass have been made by the Nevada (554) and Wyoming (92, 97) experiment stations and by the U.S. Department of Agriculture at the Salina, Utah station (302, 1019). In all cases, the more common species (*T. maritima*) was employed.

Potential toxicity varies with cyanide potential of the plant, speed of HCN release, and speed with which a potentially toxic dose is consumed.

Analyses of arrowgrass have shown considerable variation in cyanide content. Cyanide content of about 50 mg per 100 g green arrowgrass is potentially lethal in amounts as small as 0.5 per cent of an animal's weight. At higher content the amount required is proportionately less.

Variation in cyanide potential is related to a number of factors. Most important appears to be the adequacy of moisture during growth. Highest cyanide content was found in plants subjected to drought conditions throughout the growing period. In arrowgrass, drought conditions are not necessarily associated with stunted growth; plants of normal or vigorous appearance may be highly toxic. Plants which have been partially submerged throughout the entire growing period may be expected to be one-fifth to one-tenth as toxic. Frosted or wilted plants may have reduced cyanide potential (92) but may still be dangerous (1546).

Drying causes some reduction in cyanide potential. Concentration of cyanide potential in a given amount of arrowgrass by evaporation of water during drying is usually more than offset by accompanying release and loss of HCN. This means that hay is usually less toxic, pound for pound, than the arrowgrass from which it was made, although quickly cured material may have an equal cyanide potential (92). Chemically, however, the HCN in hay may be more quickly and totally available than in the green plant. Hay stored for several months gradually loses all its cyanide potential.

CONDITIONS OF POISONING. Poisoning of sheep and cattle has been reported from British Columbia (1081) to Nebraska (1019), California (1383), and New Mexico (754). Most cases occur when hungry sheep or cattle have access to the green plant, which is not particularly unpalatable. *Triglochin maritima,* being more common, is usually involved, but losses have also been attributed (1081) to *T. palustris.*

Order Pandanales

Typhaceae

Typha latifolia L. Common cattail

This common weed of moist soils, marshes, and ponds is recognized by its irislike leaves and its terminal, fat-cigar shaped, brown-surfaced spike of densely packed, woolly fibers. It has been suspected in a case in which several horses were fatally poisoned in Indiana (713). Symptoms included stiffness, disinclination to move, profuse perspiration, and muscular trembling.

GRASS TETANY

The terms *grass tetany, grass staggers, wheat pasture poisoning, protein poisoning,* and *hypomagnesemia* have been applied to a syndrome in live-stock which has been of economic concern in several parts of North America. Despite some differences in typical history, symptoms, and lesions in this disease as it occurs in geographically separated locations, certain important features are identical throughout, and the syndrome associated with the several common names is now generally accepted as a single entity. Its exact cause is unknown. It is always associated with imbalance in the ionic components of blood serum—especially reduced magnesium levels—and generally with ingestion of lush forage or pasturage.

This disease occurs primarily in cattle, sometimes in sheep, and rarely in horses and has been reported from various sections of the United States. In the Southeast, it is commonly called grass staggers, and is associated with pasturing of dairy and beef cattle on lush, rank, young growth of pasture grass in early spring (211, 1096, 1180, 1467). In the same general area, sheep exhibit similar symptoms on lush winter forage crops of oats and rye (73, 211). In the western plains states, development of tetany in cattle, occasionally in sheep, and possibly in horses (1596) is associated with ingestion of lush "wild" range grasses in the spring. In the winter-wheat growing area of the Southwest, centering in the panhandles of Texas and Oklahoma, similar symptoms in cattle are associated with inges-tion of lush young growth of wheat forage (385, 1328, 1462, 1463, 1464). Here the disease popularly is termed wheat poisoning, wheat pasture poisoning, or protein poisoning. In the Northwest, it has occurred in cattle during the winter months near the coast, where the mild winter climate in certain years promotes a luxuriant growth of young grass (1162) and in

504

California on lush growth following rains after an extended dry period (808). A similar disease is known in the Netherlands, Scandinavian countries, England, and New Zealand. Heavy losses in cattle and occasionally in sheep have been experienced. The particular species of plant involved, whether "wild" or cultivated, seems unimportant (15, 75). Losses usually stop coincident with maturation of the forage (1596).

Hypomagnesemia has been considered by most investigators as one of the most significant aspects, if not the most significant, of the syndrome. The disease may be separated into two types: acute and chronic. The chronic type (15, 18, 1607) is usually detected clinically by serum magnesium levels, which are well below normal, but which are usually not accompanied by gross symptoms. It appears that animals may have considerable powers of adaptation to gradually reduced magnesium levels. Chronic hypomagnesemia is often found in herds during winter months and is usually not associated with ingestion of lush forage. This discussion is confined to the acute syndrome, in which symptoms are clearly presented.

In general, symptoms may appear within a week or less or may not be developed for as long as six months on lush pasturage. Rarely, symptoms may appear on forage that is not lush. Animals in later stages of pregnancy, or recently post partum, are affected primarily or else seem predisposed to earlier and more severe symptoms. There is some evidence (1024) that older animals are more prone to the disease than younger, and that conditions of inclement weather may predispose (18, 1024). Grass tetany may occur much more frequently on some farms than on neighboring ones over a period of years. Much attention has been given to analyzing the differences in forage under such circumstances. Little has come to light other than the general observation of a tendency for grass tetany to be associated with practices of high fertilization and to appear in herds at times of low planes of nutrition or nutritional stress (15).

In cattle, the first symptoms are excitement, incoordination, and anorexia. Muscular twitching appears and salivation or grinding of the teeth may be noted. Animals may become belligerent; staggering increases and is followed by prostration. Tetanic seizures become general and are accompanied by dyspnea and increased heartbeat. Convulsions, interspersed with periodic remissions, occur terminally. Coma may precede death. Symptoms are similar in sheep. Death usually occurs within 6 to 10 hours after appearance of symptoms. Necropsy findings are variable and not characteristic.

Much experimental work has been performed to locate the exact source of difficulty. Results of various workers are not entirely in agreement. In typical cases it has been found that abnormal levels exist in certain blood components. Principal among these are drastically lowered magnesium and calcium levels, while blood-serum protein and possibly phosphorus may be elevated. Calcium may drop to 3.5 mg per 100 ml serum (9 to 12 mg normal) and magnesium to 0.5 mg per 100 ml serum (2 to 3 mg normal) (1180, 1328). Of these, the lowered magnesium level appears physiologically the more important. Hypomagnesemia in this syndrome is not the result of inadequate dietary levels of magnesium (389, 1096). However, excess of magnesium oxide added to the diet is an effective preventative if each animal is made to consume sufficient amounts and if the practice is continued regularly through the danger period (15, 36) (magnesium levels may drop to the danger point as abruptly as within 48 hours and there is no build-up of magnesium reserves in the tissues by prior high-magnesium diets). Heavy fertilization of dangerous pastures with magnesium also may partially reduce the incidence of disease (1528).

The metabolism and role of magnesium in the body is poorly understood. Levels of magnesium normally remain remarkably constant throughout health and disease and great variation in diet. How a constant level is maintained is not known.

Grass tetany appears to be the result of failure by animals to absorb enough magnesium from an adequate diet. Absorption of magnesium might be curtailed or prevented by reactions such as precipitation or chelation of magnesium before absorption from the intestine. It has been shown (739, 740) that rumen ammonia level is raised from a normal 10 to 20 mg per 100 ml to 40 to 50 mg per 100 ml and maintained at that level when animals are put on lush pasturage. This appears to be the most characteristic change associated with a change to lush forage (740). At this level, small amounts of ammonia may be detected in jugular blood. Coincident with increased ruminal ammonia production, urinary excretion of magnesium falls dramatically. It can also be shown (740) that the ultrafiltrable (absorbable) magnesium level of the absorptive small intestine falls from a normal 5 to 15 mg per 100 ml digesta to practically nothing. Nitrogenous substances normally are reduced to ammonia in the rumen. Ammonia is regularly utilized by the ruminal flora and also absorbed into the bloodstream to be changed to urea in the liver. An abrupt rise in ammonia content of the rumen when lush forage, rich in crude protein, is ingested, indicates inability of these processes to maintain the lower, normal level. Artificially raising the rumen ammonia level of hay- and grain-fed animals by adding ammonia to the rumen provokes some of the same changes in the blood as in hypomagnesemia. Under these conditions dietary magnesium may be converted to the relatively insoluble hydroxide. Attempts to induce hypomagnesemia by feeding large quantities of urea have been negative (281, 1697).

Experiments by Kunkel et al. (893) and Fontenot et al. (559) corroborate the view that diet in wheat pasture poisoning somehow reduces or prevents absorption of magnesium. Well-controlled diets high in potassium or in potassium and protein were fed ruminants and compared with control diets of normal composition. Serious hypomagnesemia was not produced, but significant elevation of fecal magnesium and depression of serum levels occurred in the experimental animals.

Little attention has been given the role of the low level of serum calcium in this disease. It has been thought that the relatively greater shortage of magnesium than of calcium is responsible for the greater tetanic and convulsive symptoms of grass tetany compared with parturient paresis (1094) but the widely varying values of serum magnesium in some observations (385, 1024) do not bear this out.

Effective treatment is usually obtained by injections of calcium gluconate (often supplemented with magnesium) if begun within the first two or three hours from the onset of symptoms, but in some situations response to this therapy has been below expectations (1467). Udder insufflation also is effective (73, 1024, 1464, 1607).

Additional references: 390, 407, 717, 1083.

BIBLIOGRAPHY

1. Aanes, W. A. Pingue (*Hymenoxys richardsonii*) Poisoning in Sheep. *Am. J. Vet. Res.*, **22**: 47. 1961.
2. Abbott, B. C., and D. Ballantine. The Toxin from *Gymnodinium veneficum* Ballantine. *J. Mar. Biol. Assoc. U.K.*, **36**: 169. 1957.
3. Abderhalden, E., ed. Handbuch der biologischen Arbeitsmethoden, Abt. 1, *Kohlenhydrate Teil*, **5**: 1004. 1922.
4. Adams, R. Marihuana. *Science*, **92**: 115. 1940.
5. Adams, R., T. A. Geissman, D. J. Butterbaugh, and E. C. Kirkpatrick. Structure of Gossypol. XV. An Interpretation of its Reactions. *J. Am. Chem. Soc.*, **60**: 2193. 1938.
6. Adams, R., and N. J. Leonard. Structure of Monocrotaline. XI. Proof of the Structure of Retronecine. *J. Am. Chem. Soc.*, **66**: 257. 1944.
7. Adams, R., and E. F. Rogers. The Structure of Monocrotaline, the Alkaloid in *Crotalaria spectabilis* and *Crotalaria retusa*. I. *J. Am. Chem. Soc.*, **61**: 2815. 1939.
8. Adler, H. E. Indigestion from an Unbalanced Kiawe (Mesquite) Bean Diet. *J. Am. Vet. Med. Assoc.*, **115**: 263. 1949.
9. Affleck, H. Jack Bean Poisoning in Cattle. *Rhodesia Agr. J.*, **58**: 21. 1961.
10. Ainsworth, G. C. *Medical Mycology*. Pitman, New York. 1952.
11. Ainsworth, G. C., and P. K. C. Austwick. Fungal Diseases of Animals. Commonw. Agr. Bur., Bur. Anim. Health (England), *Rev. Ser.* 6. 1959.
12. Aitkin, W. A. Cornstalk Poisoning. *J. Am. Vet. Med. Assoc.*, **121**: 402. 1952.
13. *Albany Evening News*, August 27, 28, 29, 30, 31; Sept. 5, 10, 1923.
14. Alberts, H. W. Poisoning of Livestock by Plants. Alaska Agr. Expt. Sta., *Rept.*, **1930**: 35. 1931.
15. Allcroft, R. Hypomagnesaemia in Cattle. *Vet. Res.*, **66**: 517. 1954.
16. Allcroft, R., and R. B. A. Carnaghan. Groundnut Toxicity: an Examination for Toxin in Human Food Products from Animals Fed Toxic Groundnut Meal. *Vet. Rec.*, **75**: 259. 1963.

17. Allcroft, R., and G. Lewis. Groundnut Toxicity in Cattle: Experimental Poisoning of Calves and a Report on Clinical Effects in Older Cattle. *Vet. Rec.,* **75**: 487. 1963.
18. Allcroft, W. M. Seasonal Hypomagnesaemia of the Bovine Without Clinical Symptoms. *Vet. J.,* **103**: 75. 1947.
19. Allen, C. E., and D. S. Dow. The Biological Assessment of the Value of Rapeseed Oil Meal as a Dietary Component. *Sci. Agr.,* **32**: 403. 1952.
20. Allen, J. R., G. R. Childs, and W. W. Cravens. *Crotalaria spectabilis* Toxicity in Chickens. *Proc. Soc. Expt. Biol. Med.* (N.Y.), **104**: 434. 1960.
21. Allen, M. R., and W. D. Kitts. The Effect of Yellow Pine (*Pinus Ponderosa* Laws) Needles on the Reproductivity of the Laboratory Female Mouse. *Canad. J. Anim. Sci.,* **41**: 1. 1961.
22. Allen, W. E. "Red Water" in La Jolla Bay in 1945. *Trans. Am. Microsc. Soc.,* **65**: 149. 1946.
23. Allen, P. H. Poisonous and Injurious Plants of Panama. *Am. J. Trop. Med. Suppl.,* **23**: 1. 1943.
24. Alsberg, C. L. The Toxic Action of *Amianthium muscaetoxicum. J. Pharm. and Exptl. Therapeut.,* **3**: 473. 1912.
25. Anderson, M. S., H. W. Lakin, K. C. Beeson, F. F. Smith, and E. Thacker. Selenium in Agriculture. USDA, *Handbook* 200. 1961.
26. Anderson, W. A. Halogeton Poisoning in a Ewe. *J. Am. Vet. Med. Assoc.,* **130**: 330. 1957.
27. Anet, E. F. L. J., B. Lythgoe, M. H. Silk, and S. Trippett. Oenanthotoxin and Cicutoxin. Isolation and Structure. *J. Chem. Soc.* (London), **1953**: 309. 1953.
28. Animal Disease and Parasite Research Division. 16 Plants Poisonous to Livestock in the Western States. USDA, *Farmers' Bull.,* 2106. 1958.
29. Anonymous. A Poisonous Composite Plant. *Pharm. J.,* (S. 3) **4**: 518. 1873.
30. Anonymous. The Danger of Eating Rhubarb Leaves. *Sci. Amer.,* **117**: 82. 1917.
31. Anonymous Items. *Science,* **77**(1998): 10. 1933.
32. Anonymous. Yearling Heifers Poisoned by Privet. *New Zealand J. Agr.,* **59**: 430. 1939.
33. Anonymous. Mushroom Poisoning. *M.S.C.* (Mich. State Col.) *Vet.,* **1**: 88. 1941.
34. Anonymous. Unusual Case of Hemlock Poisoning in Swine. *California Vet.,* **5**(2): 25. 1951.
35. Anonymous (W. Binns and L. F. James). Crooked Calf Disease. *Agr. Res.,* **8**(12): 12. 1960.
36. Anonymous. Hypomagnesaemia. Ministry of Agr., Fisheries, and Food (London), *Anim. Health Leafl.* 49. 1960.
37. Anonymous. Pine Needles May Cause Abortion in Beef Cows. *Rocky Mt. Vet.,* **8**(4): 9. 1960.
38. Appleman, D. Preliminary Report on Toxicity of Avocado Leaves. *California Avocado Soc. Yearbook,* **1944**: 37. 1944.
39. Archibald, R. McG., H. J. Smith, and J. D. Smith. Brazilian Groundnut Toxicosis in Canadian Broiler Chickens. *Canad. Vet. J.,* **3**: 322. 1962.

40. Arizona Agricultural Experiment Station. *Cercocarpus* and *Acacia* Species Lethal by HCN. Ariz. Agr. Expt. Sta., *Ann. Rept.,* **45**: 44. 1934.
41. Armer, W. Halogeton—A Stock Poisoning Weed. Arizona Agr. Expt. Sta., *Extension Circ.* 197. 1952.
42. Arnold, H. L. *Poisonous Plants of Hawaii.* Tongg Publishing Company, Honolulu, Hawaii. 1944.
43. Arnold, H. L., W. S. Middleton, and K. K. Chen. The Action of Thevetin, a Cardiac Glucosid, and its Clinical Application. *Am. J. Med. Sci.,* **189**: 193. 1935.
44. Ashley, G. Fescue Poisoning of Cattle on Florida Muck Land. *J. Am. Vet. Med. Assoc.,* **132**: 493. 1958.
45. Ashworth, C. T., and M. F. Mason. Observations on the Pathological Changes Produced by a Toxic Substance Present in Blue-green Algae (*Microcystis aeruginosa*). *Am. J. Path.,* **22**: 369. 1946.
46. Astwood, E. B., M. A. Greer, and M. G. Ettlinger. L-5-vinyl-2-thiooxazolidone, an Antithyroid Compound from Yellow Turnip and from Brassica Seeds. *J. Biol. Chem.,* **181**: 121. 1949.
47. Atal, C. K., and A. E. Schwarting. A Note on the Variability of Alkaloid Content of Domestic Ergot. *J. Am. Pharm. Assoc.* (Sci. ed.), **46**: 451. 1957.
48. Atwood, M. B. A Paralysis of Cows of Unknown Etiology ("Downer Cows," "Bermuda Grass Poisoning"). *Georgia Vet.,* **5**(1). 1953.
49. Babbott, F. L., Jr., W. Binns, and T. H. Ingalls. Field Studies of Cyclopian Malformations in Sheep. *Arch. Environ. Health,* **5**: 109. 1962.
50. Bachelor, F. W., R. F. C. Brown, and G. Büchi. The Constitution of Ring A in Aconitine. *Tetrahedron Letters,* **1960**(10): 1. 1960.
51. Bachhuber, T. E., and J. J. Lalich. Production of Dissecting Aneurysms in Rats Fed *Lathyrus odoratus. Science,* **120**: 712. 1954.
52. Bachhuber, T. E., J. J. Lalich, D. M. Angevine, E. D. Schilling, and F. N. Strong. Lathyrus Factor Activity of Beta-Aminopropionitrile and Related Compounds. *Proc. Soc. Exptl. Biol. Med.,* **89**: 294. 1955.
53. Bacon, A. E. An Experiment with the Fruit of Red Baneberry. *Rhodora,* **5**: 77. 1903.
54. Bailey, L. H. *Manual of Cultivated Plants.* Macmillan, New York. 1949.
55. Bailey, V. Sleepy Grass and its Effects on Horses. *Science,* **17**: 392. 1903.
56. Bailey, W. S., and A. H. Groth, Jr. The Relationship of Hepatitis X of Dogs and Moldy Corn Poisoning of Swine. *J. Am. Vet. Med. Assoc.,* **134**: 514. 1959.
57. Baker, C. J. L., and A. Eden. Studies on the Oxalate Content of the Leaves of Certain Varieties of *Beta vulgaris. J. Agric. Sci.,* **44**: 394. 1954.
58. Ball, C. R. Johnson Grass: Report of Investigations Made During the Season of 1901. USDA, Bur. Pl. Ind., *Bull.* 11. 1902.
59. Ballantine, D., and B. C. Abbott. Toxic Marine Flagellates; Their Occurrence and Physiological Effects on Animals. *J. Gen. Microbiol.,* **16**: 274. 1957.
60. Balthrop, E., W. B. Gallagher, T. F. McDonald, and S. Camariotes. Tung Nut Poisoning. *J. Florida Med. Assoc.,* **40**: 813. 1954.

61. Bamford, F. *Poisons, Their Isolation and Identification*. Blakiston Company, Philadelphia. 3rd ed., 1951.
62. Bandeline, F. J., and W. Malesh. Alkaloids of *Chelidonium majus* L., Leaves and Stems I. *J. Am. Pharm. Assoc.* (Sci. ed.), **45**: 702. 1956.
63. Bankowski, R. A., R. W. Wichmann, and E. E. Stuart. Stomatitis of Cattle and Horses Due to Yellow Bristle Grass (*Setaria lutescens*). *J. Am. Vet. Med. Assoc.*, **129**: 149. 1956.
64. Barber, M. A. Poisoning Due to the Papaw (*Asimina triloba*). *J. Am. Med. Assoc.*, **45**: 2013. 1905.
65. Barger, G. *Ergot and Ergotism*. Gurney and Jackson, London. 1931.
66. Barkley, F. A. A Monographic Study of *Rhus* and its Immediate Allies in North and Central America, Including the West Indies. *Ann. Missouri Bot. Gard.*, **24**: 265. 1937.
67. Barnes, B. A., and L. E. Fox. Poisoning with *Dieffenbachia*. *J. Hist. Med.*, **10**: 173. 1955.
68. Barnes, M. F. Black Locust Poisoning of Chickens. *J. Am. Vet. Med. Assoc.*, **59**: 370. 1921.
69. Barnes, W. C. *Western Grazing Grounds and Forest Ranges*. The Breeder's Gazette, Chicago. 1913.
70. Barnett, B. D., H. R. Bird, J. J. Lalich, and F. M. Strong. Toxicity of Beta-Aminopropionitrile for Turkey Poults. *Proc. Soc. Exp. Biol. Med.*, **94**: 67. 1957.
71. Barr, A. G., and C. S. Davies. An Unusual Case of Poisoning in a Sow and Litter. *Vet. Rec.*, **75**: 457. 1963.
72. Barr, C. G., H. W. Reuszer, and F. Thorp, Jr. The Chemical Composition of *Suckleya suckleyana*. *Science*, **90**: 497. 1939.
73. Barrentine, B. F., and E. G. Morrison. Grass Tetany in Sheep Grazing Winter Forages. *Proc. Assoc. Southern Agr. Workers,* **50**: 64. 1953.
74. Barshad, I. Molybdenum Content of Pasture Plants in Relation to Toxicity to Cattle. *Soil Sci.*, **66**: 187. 1948.
75. Bartlett, S., B. B. Brown, A. S. Foot, S. J. Rowland, R. Allcroft, and W. H. Parr. The Influence of Fertilizer Treatment of Grasslands on the Incidence of Hypomagnesaemia in Milking Cows. *Brit. Vet. J.*, **110**: 3. 1954.
76. Barton, D. H. R., and P. de Mayo. Triterpenoids. XV. The Constitution of Icterogenin, a Physiologically Active Triterpenoid. *Chem. Soc.*, **1954**: 887.
77. Barton, D. H. R., and P. de Mayo. Triterpenoids. XVI. The Constitution of Rehmannic Acid. *J. Chem. Soc.* (London), **1954**: 900. 1954.
78. Barton, D. H. R., P. de Mayo, and J. C. Orr. Triterpenoids. XXIII. The Nature of Lantadene A. *J. Chem. Soc.* (London), **1956**: 4160. 1956.
79. Barton, D. H. R., P. de Mayo, E. W. Warnhoff, O. Jeger, and G. W. Perold. Triterpenoids. XIX. The Constitution of Lantadene B. *J. Chem. Soc.* (London), **1954**: 3689. 1954.
80. Baxter, C. M. Broadleaf Milkweed Poisoning. *Cornell Vet.*, **34**: 256. 1944.
81. Baxter, J. N., B. Lythgoe, B. Scales, S. Trippett, and B. K. Blount. Taxine—I, The Major Alkaloid of the Yew, *Taxus baccata* L. *Proc. Chem. Soc.* (London), **1958**: 9. 1958.

82. Baxter, J. T. Suspected Fodderbeet Poisoning in Pigs. *Vet. Rec.*, **68:** 236. 1956.
83. Beath, O. A. The Chemical Examination of Three Species of Larkspurs. Wyoming Agr. Expt. Sta., *Bull.* 120. 1919.
84. Beath, O. A. Chemical and Pharmacological Examination of the Woody Aster. Wyoming Agr. Expt. Sta., *Bull.* 123. 1920.
85. Beath, O. A. The Chemical Examination of the Silvery Lupine. Wyoming Agr. Expt. Sta., *Bull.* 125. 1920.
86. Beath, O. A. Poisonous Plants of Wyoming. Wyoming Agr. Expt. Sta., *Bull.* 126. 1921.
87. Beath, O. A. Chemical Examination of Three Delphiniums. Wyoming Agr. Expt. Sta., *Bull.* 143. 1925.
88. Beath, O. A. Chemical Study of the Silvery Lupine. Wyoming Agr. Expt. Sta., *Bull.* 144. 1925.
89. Beath, O. A. Economic Potential and Botanic Limitation of Some Selenium-bearing Plants. Wyoming Agr. Expt. Sta., *Bull.* 360. 1959.
90. Beath, O. A. Private communication to R. W. Pohl, Iowa State University, Ames. 1960.
91. Beath, O. A., J. H. Draize, and H. F. Eppson. Three Poisonous Vetches. Wyoming Agr. Expt. Sta., *Bull.* 189. 1932.
92. Beath, O. A., J. H. Draize, and H. F. Eppson. Arrow Grass, Chemical and Physiological Considerations. Wyoming Agr. Expt. Sta., *Bull.* 193. 1933.
93. Beath, O. A., J. H. Draize, H. F. Eppson, C. S. Gilbert, and O. C. McCreary. Certain Poisonous Plants of Wyoming Activated by Selenium and Their Association with Respect to Soil Types. *J. Am. Pharm. Assoc.*, **23:** 94. 1934.
94. Beath, O. A., and H. F. Eppson. The Form of Selenium in Some Vegetation. Wyoming Agr. Expt. Sta., *Bull.* 278. 1947.
95. Beath, O. A., H. F. Eppson, J. H. Draize, and R. S. Justice. Three Species of Zygadenus (Death Camas). Wyoming Agr. Expt. Sta., *Bull.* 194. 1933.
96. Beath, O. A., C. S. Gilbert, and H. F. Eppson. The Use of Indicator Plants in Locating Seleniferous Areas in Western United States. I. General. *Am. J. Bot.*, **26:** 257. 1939. II. Correlation Studies by States. **26:** 296. III. Further Studies. **27:** 564. 1940. IV. Progress Report. **28:** 887. 1941.
97. Beath, O. A., C. S. Gilbert, H. F. Eppson, and I. Rosenfeld. Poisonous Plants and Livestock Poisoning. Wyoming Agr. Expt. Sta., *Bull.* 324. 1953.
98. Becker, D. E., C. R. Adams, S. W. Terrill, and R. J. Meade. The Influence of Heat Treatment and Solvent upon the Nutritive Value of Soybean Oil Meal for Swine. *J. Anim. Sci.*, **12:** 107. 1953.
99. Becker, R. B., W. M. Neal, and P. T. Dix Arnold. Value of Crotalaria as Feed. Florida Agr. Expt. Sta., *Bull.* 361: 33. 1941.
100. Becker, R. B., W. M. Neal, P. T. Dix Arnold, and A. L. Shealy. A Study of the Palatability and Possible Toxicity of 11 Species of Crotalaria, Especially of *C. spectabilis* Roth. *J. Agr. Res.*, **50:** 911. 1935.
101. Bein, S. J. The Relationship of Total Phosphorus Concentration in Sea Water to Red Tide Blooms. *Bull. Marine Sci. Gulf Caribb.*, **7:** 316. 1957.

102. Bell, A. T., L. G. Newton, S. L. Everist, and J. Legg. *Acacia georginae* Poisoning of Cattle and Sheep. *Austral. Vet. J.*, **31**: 249. 1955.

103. Bell, E. A. Alpha, Gamma-Diaminobutyric Acid in Seeds of Twelve Species of *Lathyrus* and Identification of a New Natural Amino-Acid, L-Homoargenine, in Seeds of Other Species Toxic to Man and Domestic Animals. *Nature* (London), **193**: 1078. 1962.

104. Bellue, M. K. Nitrate Accumulation in Toxic Quantity Discovered in California Weeds. California Dept. Agr., *Bull.* 41: 103. 1952.

105. Bellue, M. K. Halogeton Invades California. California Dept. Agr., *Bull.* 38: 32. 1949.

106. Bennetts, H. W. Lupinosis. *J. Agr. West Australia,* 1(4th ser.): 47. 1960.

107. Berry, D. M., and G. Bras. Venous Occlusion of the Liver in Crotalaria and Senecio Poisoning. *N. Am. Vet.*, **38**: 323. 1957.

108. Bessey, C. E. Popular Descriptions of Some Harmful Plants. *Bull. Iowa Agr. College Dept. Botany,* **1884**: 110. 1884.

109. Bessey, C. E. Notes on the Poisonous Plants of Nebraska. Soc. Prom. Agric. Sci., *Proceedings,* **23**: 34. 1901.

110. Betty, R. W., and L. M. Markson. Liver Biopsy in the Diagnosis of Ragwort (*Senecio jacobaea*) Poisoning in a Herd of Cattle. *Vet. Rec.,* **66**: 398. 1954.

111. Bierer, B. W., and W. H. Rhodes. Corn Cockle, Cockleburs, and Coffee Beans as Poultry Ration Contaminants. *J. Am. Vet. Med. Assoc.,* **137**: 352. 1960.

112. Bierer, B. W., and W. H. Rhodes. Poultry Ration Contaminants. *J. Am. Vet. Med. Assoc.,* **137**: 352. 1960.

113. Bierer, B. W., and J. B. Thomas. An Early Report on Crotalaria Poisoning. *J. Am. Vet. Med. Assoc.,* **136**: 332. 1960.

114. Bierer, B. W., C. L. Vickers, W. H. Rhodes, and J. B. Thomas. Comparison of the Toxic Effects of *Crotalaria spectabilis* and *Crotalaria giant striata* as Complete Contaminants. *J. Am. Vet. Med. Assoc.,* **136**: 318. 1960.

115. Biester, H. E., L. H. Schwarte, and C. H. Reddy. Further Studies on Moldy Corn Poisoning (Leucoencephalomalacia) in Horses. *Vet. Med.,* **35**: 636. 1940.

116. Biggs, A. I. The Spectrophotometric Detection of *Cannabis sativa* Resin. *J. Pharmacy and Pharmacol.,* **5**: 18. 1953.

117. Binns, H. R. Cottonseed Poisoning of Pigs. *J. Comp. Path. Exptl. Therapeut.,* **51**: 297. 1938.

118. Binns, W., W. A. Anderson, and D. J. Sullivan. Further Observations on a Congenital Cyclopian-Type Malformation in Lambs. *J. Am. Vet. Med. Assoc.,* **137**: 515. 1960.

119. Binns, W., and L. F. James. A Congenital Deformity in Calves, Similar to "Crooked Calf Disease," Has Been Experimentally Produced by Feeding Heifers Lupine and Lead. *Proc. Am. Soc. Anim. Prod.* (Western Sect.), **12**(66): 1. 1961.

120. Binns, W., and L. F. James. Halogeton and Other Oxalic Acid Poisonings. *Proc. Am. Col. Vet. Toxicol.,* **1960**: 5. 1961.

121. Binns, W., L. F. James, K. C. Beeson, and R. W. Holley. A Congenital Deformity Experimentally Produced in Calves by Feeding Lupine and Lead. *Proc. Am. Col. Vet. Toxicol.,* 1961: 29. 1961.

122. Binns, W., L. F. James, and J. L. Shupe. *Psathyrotes annua,* Poisonous Plant for Sheep. *Vet. Med.,* 57: 509. 1962.

123. Binns, W., L. F. James, J. L. Shupe, and E. J. Thacker. Cyclopian-Type Malformation in Lambs. *Arch. Environ. Health,* 5: 106. 1962.

124. Binns, W., E. J. Thacker, L. F. James, and W. T. Huffman. A Congenital Cyclopian-Type Malformation in Lambs. *J. Am. Vet. Med. Assoc.,* 134: 180. 1959.

125. Birchir, I. G. Possible Warfarin Poisoning. *Vet. Med.,* 46: 416. 1951.

126. Bishop, C. T., E. F. L. J. Anet, and P. R. Gorham. Isolation and Identification of the Fast-death Factor in *Microcystis aeruginosa* NRC-1 *Canad. J. Biochem. Physiol.,* 37: 453. 1959.

127. Biswell, H. H., and J. E. Foster. Stock-poisoning Plants of North Carolina. North Carolina Agr. Expt. Sta., *Bull.* 342. Rev. 1953.

128. Bjornson, C. B., P. McIlwain, D. F. Eveleth, and F. M. Bolin. Sources of Nitrate Intoxication. *Vet Med.,* 56: 198. 1961.

129. Black, O. F. Calcium Oxalate in the Dasheen. *Am. J. Bot.,* 5: 447. 1918.

130. Black, O. F., W. W. Eggleston, and J. W. Kelly. Toxicity of *Bikukulla formosa* (Western Bleedingheart). *J. Agr. Res.,* 40: 917. 1930.

131. Black, O. F., W. W. Eggleston, J. W. Kelly, and H. C. Turner. Poisonous Properties of *Bikukulla cucullaria* (Dutchman's Breeches) and *B. canadensis* (Squirrel Corn). *J. Agr. Res.,* 23: 69. 1923.

132. Black, W. L., and K. W. Parker. Toxicity Tests on African Rue (*Peganum harmala*). New Mexico Agr. Expt. Sta., *Bull.* 240. 1936.

133. Blakely, R. L., and I. E. Coop. The Metabolism and Toxicity of Cyanides and Cyanogenetic Glucosides in Sheep. II. Detoxication of Hydrocyanic Acid. *New Zealand J. Science and Techn.* (Sect. A), 31(3): 1. 1949.

134. Blakeway, J. Bracken Poisoning in Pigs. *Vet. J.,* 80: 89. 1924.

135. Blankinship, J. W. The Loco and Some Other Poisonous Plants in Montana. Montana Agr. Expt. Sta., *Bull.* 45. 1903.

136. Block, S. S., R. L. Stephens, A. Barreto, and W. A. Murrill. Chemical Identification of the Amanita Toxin in Mushrooms. *Science,* 121: 505. 1955.

137. Blum, H. F. Domestic Animal Diseases Produced by Light. *J. Am. Vet. Med. Assoc.,* 93: 185. 138.

138. Blum, H. F. Photodynamic Action and Diseases Caused by Light. *Am. Chem. Soc.,* Monograph ser. Reinhold Publ. Corp., New York. 1941.

139. Blumstein, G. L. Buckwheat Sensitivity. *J. Allergy,* 7: 74. 1935.

140. Boatner, C. H., A. M. Altschul, G. W. Irving, Jr., E. R. Pollard, and H. C. Schaefer. The Nutritive Value of Cottenseed for Chicks as Affected by Methods of Processing and Content of Pigment Glands. *Poultry Sci.,* 27: 315. 1948.

141. Boatner, C. H., C. M. Hall, R. T. O'Connor, and L. E. Castillion. The Pigment Glands of Cottonseed. II. Nature and Properties of the Gland Wall. *Bot. Gaz.,* 108: 484. 1947.

142. Boatner, C. H., C. M. Hall, R. T. O'Connor, and L. E. Castillion. The Pigment Glands of Cottonseed. III. Distribution of the Pigments in the Seed Kernel. *Bot. Gaz.,* **109**: 108. 1947.

143. Boddie, G. F. Toxicological Problems in Veterinary Practice. *Vet. Rec.,* **59**: 470. 1947.

144. Bohmont, D., and O. A. Beath. We've Stalemated Halogeton. Wyoming Agr. Expt. Sta., *Wyo. Roundup,* 1(3): 3. 1954.

145. Bolin, F. M. Green Potatoes Can Kill Sheep. *N. Dakota* (Agr. Expt. Sta.) *Farm Res.,* **22**(7): 15. 1962.

146. Bolton, B. L., A. D. Bergner, J. J. O'Neill, and P. F. Wagley. Effect of a Shellfish Poison on End Plate Potentials. *Bull. Johns Hopkins Hosp.,* **105**: 233. 1959.

147. Bomhard, M. L. Leaf Venation as a Means of Distinguishing *Cicuta* from *Angelica. J. Wash. Acad. Sci.,* **26**: 102. 1936.

148. Bond, R. M., and J. C. Medcof. Epidemic Shellfish Poisoning in New Brunswick, 1957. *Canad. Med. Assoc. J.,* **79**: 19. 1958.

149. Bonisteel, W. J. Polyploidy in Relation to Chemical Analysis. *J. Am. Pharm. Assoc.* (Sci. ed.), **29**: 404. 1940.

150. Borchers, R. Castor Bean Oil Meal. I. Destruction of the Toxic Factor. *Poultry Sci.,* **28**: 568. 1939.

151. Bossenmaier, E. F., T. A. Olson, M. E. Rueger, and W. H. Marshall. Some Field and Laboratory Aspects of Duck Sickness at Whitewaters Lake, Manitoba. *Trans. N. Am. Wildlife Conf.,* **19**: 163. 1954.

152. Bosshart, J. K., and W. A. Hagan. A Fatal Unidentified Cattle Disease in New York State. *Cornell Vet.,* **10**: 102. 1920.

153. Boughton, I. B. Oak Brush Poisoning. *Texas Vet. Bull.,* **5**(4): 2. 1943.

154. Boughton, I. B., and W. T. Hardy. Mescalbean (*Sophora secundiflora*) Poisonous for Livestock. Texas Agr. Expt. Sta., *Bull.* 519. 1935.

155. Boughton, I. B., and W. T. Hardy. Oak Poisoning in Range Cattle and Sheep. *J. Am. Vet. Med. Assoc.,* **89**: 157. 1936.

156. Boughton, I. B., and W. T. Hardy. Toxicity of Bitterweed (*Actinea odorata*) for Sheep. Texas Agr. Expt. Sta., *Bull.* 552. 1937.

157. Boughton, I. B., and W. T. Hardy. Toxicity of the Coffee Bean (*Sesbania vesicaria*) for Sheep. *J. Am. Vet. Med. Assoc.,* **95**: 239. 1939.

158. Boughton, I. B., and W. T. Hardy. Feeding Trials of Suspected Plants. Texas Agr. Expt. Sta., *Ann. Rept.,* **52**: 239. 1939.

159. Boughton, I. B., and W. T. Hardy. Feeding Trials of Suspected Plants. Texas Agr. Expt. Sta. *Ann. Rept.* **53**: 236. 1940.

160. Boughton, I. B., and W. T. Hardy. Feeding Trials of Suspected Plants. Texas Agr. Expt. Sta., *Ann. Rept.,* **54**: 159. 1941.

161. Boyd, F. T., O. S. Aamodt, G. Bohstedt, E. Truog. Sudan Grass Management for Control of Cyanide Poisoning. *Am. Soc. Agron.,* **30**: 569. 1938.

162. Bradley, W. B., O. A. Beath, and H. F. Eppson. Oat Hay Poisoning. *Science,* **89**: 365. 1939.

163. Bradley, W. B., H. F. Eppson, and O. A. Beath. Livestock Poisoning by Oat Hay and Other Plants Containing Nitrate. Wyoming Agr. Expt. Sta., *Bull.* 241. 1940.

164. Bradley, W. B., H. F. Eppson, and O. A. Beath. Methylene Blue as an Antidote for Poisoning by Oat Hay and Other Plants Containing Nitrates. *J. Am. Vet. Med. Assoc.,* **96**: 41. 1940.

165. Brady, D. E., J. E. Comfort, J. F. Lasley, and W. H. Pfander. Forage Poisoning in Missouri Due to Excessive Amounts of Nitrate. Missouri Agr. Expt. Sta., *Bull.* 652: 19. 1955.

166. Brakenridge, D. T. Nitrate Poisoning Caused by Turnips and Redroot. *New Zealand Vet. J.,* **4**: 165. 1956.

167. Brandenburg, T. O., and F. M. Shigley. "Water Bloom" as a Cause of Poisoning of Livestock in North Dakota. *J. Am. Vet. Med. Assoc.,* **110**: 384. 1947.

168. Breed, F. Plant Poisoning in Swine. *Norden News,* **19**(3): 6. 1945.

169. Breniman, G. W., A. L. Neumann, G. S. Smith, and H. A. Jordon. Nitrate and Nitrite Contents of Corn Forages and Silages as Influenced by Nitrogen Fertility, Seeding Rate, and Various Silage Additives. *Proc. Am. Soc. Anim. Prod.* (Western Sect), **1961**(XL): 1. 1961.

170. Brentzel, W. E. Ergot on Grains and Grasses. North Dakota Agr. Extension Service, *Circ.* 109. 1932.

171. Briese, R. R., and J. F. Couch. Hydrocyanic Acid in Sorghum Silage. *Vet. Med.,* **35**: 86. 1940.

172. Brink, R. A., and W. L. Roberts. The Coumarin Content of *Melilotus dentata. Science,* **86**: 41. 1937.

173. Britton, J. W., and H. Goss. Chronic Molybdenum Poisoning in Cattle. *J. Am. Vet. Med. Assoc.,* **108**: 176. 1946.

174. Brodie, D. A. Poison Parsnip in Western Washington. Washington Agr. Expt. Sta., *Bull.* 45. 1901.

175. Broerman, A. Poisoning of Cattle by Sweet Clover Hay. *J. Am. Vet. Med. Assoc.,* **67**: 367. 1925.

176. Bromberg, W. Marihuana: A Psychiatric Study. *J. Am. Med. Assoc.,* **113**: 4. 1939.

177. Brown, H. B. Life History and Poisonous Properties of *Claviceps paspali. J. Agr. Res.,* **7**: 401. 1916.

178. Brown, H. B., and E. M. Ranck. Forage Poisoning due to *Claviceps paspali* on *Paspalum.* Mississippi. Agr. Expt. Sta., *Tech. Bull.* 6. 1915.

179. Brown, J. M., A. Savage, and A. D. Robinson. A Report on Some Investigations into the Cause of Sweet Clover (*Melilotus*) Disease. *Sci. Agr.,* **13**: 561. 1933.

180. Brown, J. M. M. *et al.* Advances in "Geeldikkop" (*Tribulosis ovis*) Research. I. The History of "Geeldikkop" Research. *J. South African Vet. Med. Assoc.,* **30**: 97. 1959; II. Field Investigations—The Mobile Laboratory and Experimental Facilities. *Ibid.,* **30**: 395. 1959; III. The Epizootology of "Geeldikkop." *Ibid.,* **30**: 403. 1959; IV. The Pathology of Geeldikkop—Part I. *Ibid.,* **31**: 179. 1960.

181. Brown, J. M. M. and P. J. de Wet. A Preliminary Report on the Occurrence of Selenosis in South Africa and its Possible Role in the Aetiology of Tribulosis (Geeldikkop), Enzootic Icterus, and Some Other Disease

Conditions Encountered in the Karoo Areas. *Onderstepoort J. Vet. Res.,* **29:** 111. 1962.

182. Brown, R. G., and F. E. Hull. *Taxus* (Yew) Poisoning of Cattle. *J. Am. Vet. Med. Assoc.,* **118:** 398. 1951.

183. Bruce, E. A. *Astragalus campestris* and Other Stock Poisoning Plants of British Columbia. Canada Dept. Agr., *Bull.* 88(n.s.). 1927.

184. Bruce, E. A. Fagopyrismus (Buckwheat Poisoning) and Similar Affections. *J. Am. Vet. Med. Assoc.,* **52:** 189. 1917.

185. Bruce, E. A. Iris Poisoning of Calves. *J. Am. Vet. Med. Assoc.,* **56:** 72. 1919.

186. Bruce, E. A. Hydrangea Poisoning. *J. Am. Med. Assoc.,* **58:** 313. 1920.

187. Bruere, N. Nitrate-nitrite Poisoning on Second-Growth Rape. *New Zealand Vet. J.,* **4:** 128. 1956.

188. Bruun-Hanssen, C. F. The Experimental Production of Hepatic Veno-occlusive Disease in Rats. *Acta Path. Microbiol. Scand.,* **53:** 329. 1961.

189. Buck, R. W. Mushroom Poisoning Since 1924 in the United States. *Mycologia,* **53:** 538. 1961 (and processed supplements).

190. Buck, W. B., W. Binns, L. James, and M. C. Williams. Feeding of Herbicide-Treated Plants. *J. Am. Vet. Med. Assoc.,* **138:** 320. 1961.

191. Buck, W. B., J. W. Dollahite, and T. J. Allen. Silver-leafed Nightshade Poisoning. *J. Am. Vet. Med. Assoc.,* **137:** 348. 1960.

192. Buck, W. B., L. F. James, and W. Binns. Changes in Serum Transaminase Activities Associated with Plant and Mineral Toxicity in Sheep and Cattle. *Cornell Vet.,* **51:** 568. 1961.

193. Buck, W. B., L. F. James, and W. Binns. Changes in Serum Transaminase Activities Associated with Plant and Mineral Toxicity in Sheep and Cattle. *Proc. Am. Col. Vet. Toxicol.,* **1961:** 13. 1961.

194. Buckingham, J. L. Poisoning in a Pig by Hemlock (*Conium maculatum*). *Vet. J.,* **92:** 301. 1936.

195. Buckley, J. S., E. C. Joss, G. T. Creech, and J. F. Couch. Carotenosis of Bovine Livers Associated with Parenchymatous Degeneration. *J. Agr. Res.,* **40:** 991. 1930.

196. Buckley, S. S., and W. G. MacCallum. Acute Hemorrhagic Encephalitis Prevalent among Horses in Maryland. *Am. Vet. Rev.,* **25:** 99. 1901

197. Buehrer, T. F., C. M. Mason, and J. A. Crowder. The Chemical Composition of Rayless Goldenrod. (*Aplopappus hartwegi*). *Am. J. Pharm.,* **111:** 105. 1939.

198. Bukey, F. S., and R. W. Cunningham. A Study of *Senecio riddellii. J. Am. Pharm. Assoc.* (Sci. ed.), **22:** 399. 1933.

199. Bull, L. B. Poisoning of Sheep by Soursobs (*Oxalis cernua*): Chronic Oxalic Acid Poisoning. *Austral. Vet. J.,* **5:** 60. 1929.

200. Bull, L. B. The Histological Evidence of Liver Damage from Pyrrolizidine Alkaloids. *Austral. Vet. J.,* **31:** 33. 1955.

201. Bull, L. B. Liver Disease in Livestock from Intake of Hepatotoxic Substances. *Austral. Vet. J.,* **37:** 126. 1961.

202. Bull, L. B., and A. T. Dick. The Chronic Pathological Effects on the

Liver of the Rat of the Pyrrolizidine Alkaloids Heliotrine, Lasiocarpine, and their N-Oxides. *J. Path. and Bact.,* **78**: 483. 1959.

203. Bull, L. B., and A. T. Dick. The Function of Total Dose in the Production of Chronic Lethal Liver Disease in Rats by Periodic Injection of the Pyrrolizidine Alkaloid, Heliotrine. *Austral. J. Expt. Biol.,* **38**: 515. 1960.

204. Bull, L. B., A. T. Dick, J. C. Keast, and G. Edgar. An Experimental Investigation of the Hepatotoxic and Other Effects on Sheep of Consumption of *Heliotropium europaeum* L.: Heliotrope Poisoning of Sheep. *Austral. J. Agr. Res.,* **7**: 281. 1956.

205. Bull, L. B., A. T. Dick, and J. S. McKenzie. The Acute Toxic Effects of Heliotrine and Lasiocarpine, and Their N-Oxides, on the Rat. *J. Path. Bact.,* **75**: 17. 1958.

206. Bull, L. B., E. S. Rogers, J. C. Keast, and A. T. Dick. Heliotropium Poisoning in Cattle. *Austral. Vet. J.,* **37**: 37. 1961.

207. Bunyea, H. Treatments of Cyanide Poisoning of Sheep and Cattle. *J. Am. Vet. Med. Assoc.,* **86**: 656. 1935.

208. Burgess, P. S. Range Livestock Losses from Poisonous Plants. Arizona Agr. Expt. Sta., *Ann. Rept.,* **45**: 44. 1934.

209. Burke, J. M., J. Marchisotto, J. J. A. McLaughlin, and L. Provasoli. Analysis of the Toxin Produced by *Gonyaulax catenella* in Axenic Pure Culture. *Ann. N.Y. Acad. Sci.,* **90**: 837. 1960.

210. Burns, P. W. Clinical Diagnosis in Veterinary Toxicology. *Proc. Am. Col. Vet. Toxicol.,* **1961**: 5. 1961.

211. Burns, M. J. Grass Tetany (Hypomagnesaemia). *Auburn Vet.,* **13**: 118. 1957.

212. Burnside, J. E. A Case of Suspected Mushroom Poisoning in Cattle. *Georgia Vet.,* **5**(1): 13. 1953.

213. Burnside, J. E. Photosensitization in Cattle, a Case Report. *Georgia Vet.,* **5**(4): 10. 1953.

214. Burnside, J. E. Animal Poisoning and Diagnosis. *Vet. Med.,* **49**: 136. 1954.

215. Burnside, J. E. Procedure for Qualitative Determination of Hydrocyanic Acid by the Sodium Picrate Test. *Georgia Vet.,* **6**(3): 10. 1954.

216. Burnside, J. E. Simple Test for Bracken Poisoning. *Georgia Vet.,* **6**(4): 15. 1954.

217. Burnside, J. E., P. H. Langer, M. B. Atwood, and R. A. Bennett. Tifton Diagnostic Laboratory Notes. *Georgia Vet.,* **5**(5): 3. 1953.

218. Burnside, J. E., W. L. Sippel, J. Forgacs, W. T. Carll, M. B. Atwood, and E. R. Doll. A Disease of Swine and Cattle Caused by Eating Moldy Corn. II. Experimental Production with Pure Cultures of Molds. *Am. J. Vet. Res.,* **18**: 817. 1957.

219. Burton, H. A. Mushroom Poisoning in Cattle. *Vet Med.,* **39**: 290. 1944.

220. Butcher, J. E., F. A. Branson, W. E. Booth, and R. L. Warden. Loco— The Taxonomy of the Plants, A Review of Literature, and a Report of Current Montana Research. Montana Agr. Expt. Sta., *Mimeo. Circ.* 72. 1953.

221. Butler, T. Notes on a Feeding Experiment to Produce Leucoencephalitis in a Horse with Positive Results. *Am. Vet. Rev.,* **26:** 748. 1902.
222. Butler, W. J. Pulmonary Emphysema or Asthma in Cattle. *Lederle Vet. Bull.,* **9:** 11. 1940.
223. Buxton, E. A. Mycotic Vaginitis in Gilts. *Vet. Med.,* **22:** 451. 1927.
224. Byrns, K. V. Dermatitis of White Pigs Associated with Lucerne and Trefoil Grazing. *Agr. Gaz. New S. Wales,* **48:** 214. 1937.
225. Cameron, K. Death Camas Poisoning. *Northwest Med.,* **1952:** 682. 1952.
226. Camp, B. J., and C. M. Lyman. The Chemistry of the Toxic Principle of *Acacia berlandieri* (Guajillo Bush). *Min. Am. Col. Vet. Toxicol.,* **1960:** 34 (Jan). 1960.
227. Camp, B. J., and C. M. Lyman. The Isolation of N-Methyl Beta-Phenylethylamine from *Acacia berlandieri. J. Am. Pharm. Assoc.* (Sci. ed.), **45:** 719. 1956.
228. Camp, B. J., and C. M. Lyman. The Toxic Agent Isolated from *Acacia berlandieri,* N-Methyl Beta-Phenylethylamine. *Southw. Vet.,* **10:** 133. 1957.
229. Campbell, H. A., and K. P. Link. Studies on the Hemorrhagic Sweet Clover Disease. IV. *J. Biol. Chem.,* **138:** 21. 1941.
230. Campbell, H. A., W. L. Roberts, W. K. Smith, and K. P. Link. Studies on the Hemorrhagic Sweet Clover Disease. I. *J. Biol. Chem.,* **136:** 47. 1940.
231. Campbell, H. A., W. K. Smith, W. L. Roberts, and K. P. Link. Studies on the Hemorrhagic Sweet Clover Disease. II. *J. Biol. Chem.,* **138:** 1. 1941.
232. Campbell, H. H. The Whorled Milkweed as a Poisonous Plant for Poultry. California Dept. Agr., *Monthly Bull.,* **20:** 577. 1931.
233. Campbell, J. B., R. W. Lodge, and A. C. Budd. Poisonous Plants of the Canadian Prairies. Canada Dept. Agr., *Publ. 900.* 1954.
234. Campbell, J. G. Variation of Liver Function in Immature Fowls and Susceptibility to Seneciphylline. *J. Path. and Bact.,* **80:** 399. 1960.
235. Cann, H. M., and H. L. Verhulst. Poisonous Plants. *Natl. Clearinghouse Pois. Contr. Cent.,* Sept. 1958: 2.
236. Cann. H. M., and H. L. Verhulst. Mushroom Poisoning. *Natl. Clearinghouse Pois. Contr. Cent.,* Oct. 1958: 1.
237. Cann, H. M., and H. L. Verhulst. Toxic Hazards at Christmas. *Natl. Clearinghouse Pois. Contr. Cent.,* Dec. 1959: 1.
238. Cannon. H. L., and J. M. Bowles. Contamination of Vegetation by Tetraethyl Lead. *Science,* **137:** 765. 1962.
239. Cardassis, J. Intoxication des Équidés par *Cannabis indica. Rec. Méd, Vét.,* **127:** 971. 1951.
240, Care, A. D. Goitrogenic Activity in Linseed. *New Zealand J. Sci. and Tech.* (Sect. A), **36:** 321. 1955.
241. Carey, J. C. Black Nightshade Poisoning in Swine. *N. Am. Vet.,* **36:** 466. 1955.
242. Carlson, C. W., E. Gruenthner, W. Kohlmeyer, and O. E. Olson. Some Effects of Selenium, Arsenicals, and Vitamin B_{12} on Chick Growth. *Poultry Sci.,* **33:** 768. 1954.

243. Carlson, I. T. Inheritance of Hydrocyanic Acid Production in Crosses Between Sorghum and Sudan Grass. *Agron. J.,* **50:** 302. 1958.
244. Carll, W. T., and J. Forgacs. The Significance of Fungi in Hyperkeratosis. *Military Surgeon,* **115:** 187. 1954.
245. Carll, W. T., J. Forgacs, and A. S. Herring. Toxic Aspergilli Isolated from a Food Concentrate. *Vet. Med.,* **48:** 324. 1953.
246. Carll, W. T., J. Forgacs, and A. S. Herring. Toxocity of Fungi Isolated from a Food Concentrate. *Am. J. Hygiene,* **60:** 8. 1954.
247. Carll, W. T., J. Forgacs, A. S. Herring, and B. G. Mahlandt. Toxicity of *Aspergillus fumigatus* Substances to Animals. *Vet. Med.,* **50:** 210. 1955.
248. Carpenter, P. T. Acute Senecio Poisoning. *Vet. Bull.* (U.S. Army), **32:** 32. 1938.
249. Carpenter, K. J., A. T. Phillipson, and W. Thomson. Experiments with Dried Bracken (*Pteris aquilina*). *British Vet. J.,* **106:** 292. 1950.
250. Carroll, L. K. Isolation of an Anti-thyroid Compound from Rapeseed (*Brassica napus*). *Proc. Soc. Exptl. Biol. and Med.,* **71:** 622. 1949.
251. Carroll, M. N. Jr., L. E. Fox, and W. T. Ariail. Investigation of the Toxic Principles of *Hippomane mancinella* L. III. *J. Am. Pharm. Assoc.* (Sci. ed.), **46:** 93. 1957.
252. Carruth, F. E. Contribution to the Chemistry of Gossypol, the Toxic Principle of Cottonseed. *J. Am. Chem. Soc.,* **40:** 647. 1918.
253. Cary, C. A. Poisonous Action of Red Buckeye on Horses, Mules, Cattle, Hogs, and Fish. Alabama Agr. Expt. Sta., *Bull.* 218. 1922.
254. Cary, C. A., E. R. Miller, and G. R. Johnstone. Poisonous Plants of Alabama. Alabama Polytechnic Institute, *Ext. Circ.* 71. 1924.
255. Case, A. A. Cornstalk Intoxication. *Sheep Breeder and Sheepman,* **74**(10): 14. 1954.
256. Case, A. A. Malnutrition Complex. *Sheep Breeder and Sheepman,* **74**(11): 9. 1954.
257. Case, A. A. Nightshade Poisoning. *Southw. Vet.,* **9:** 140. 1955.
258. Case, A. A. Nightshade Poisoning. *Sheep Breeder,* **77**(8): 10. 1957.
259. Case, A. A. Abortion in a Swine Drove. *Sheep Breeder,* **77**(7): 12. 1957.
260. Case, A. A. Photosensitization Syndrome in Cattle, Sheep, and Swine. *N. American Vet.,* **38:** 161. 1957.
261. Case, A. A. Some Aspects of Nitrate Intoxication in Livestock. *J. Am. Vet. Med. Assoc.,* **130:** 323. 1957.
262. Cassady, J. T. Certain Ecological Characteristics of Orange Sneezeweed. *Ecology,* **21:** 87. 1940.
263. Cassady, J. T. Management for Prevention of Sneezeweed Poisoning. *Natl. Wool Grower,* **30**(5): 12. 1940.
264. Casselberry, N. H. Nightshade Poisoning of Swine. *Vet. Med.,* **34:** 444. 1939.
265. Chaudhuri, R. N. Tropical Medicine—Past, Present, and Future. *Brit. Med. J.,* **2:** 423. 1954.
266. Chen, K. K., and A. L. Chen. The Action of Crystalline Thevetin, a Cardiac Glucoside of *Thevetia neriifolia. J. Pharm. and Exptl. Therapeut.,* **51:** 23. 1934.

267. Chen, K. K., and A. L. Chen. The Constituents of Be-still Nuts, *Thevetia neriifolia. J. Biol. Chem.,* **105**: 231. 1934.

268. Chen, K. K., A. L. Chen, and R. Anderson. The Potency of Eleven Crystalline Cardiac Principles from Plants. *J. Am. Pharm. Assoc.,* **25**: 579. 1936.

269. Chen, K. K., and F. G. Henderson. Pharmacology of Sixty-four Cardiac Glycosides and Aglycones. *J. Pharm. and Exptl. Therapeut.,* **111**: 365. 1954.

270. Chervenka, C. H., and S. H. Wender. Chemical Studies on the Toxic Concentrate from the Big Bend Locoweed. *Proc. Oklahoma Acad. Sci.,* **31**: 99. 1950.

271. Chesney, A. M., T. A. Clawson, and B. Webster. Endemic Goiter in Rabbits. Incidence and Characteristics. *Bull. Johns Hopkins Hosp.,* **43**: 261. 1928.

272. Chesnut, V. K. Abrus Poisoning. *Asa Gray Bull.,* **5**: 35. 1897.

273. Chesnut, V. K. Preliminary Catalogue of Plants Poisonous to Stock. Bur. Anim. Ind. (USDA), *Ann. Rept.,* **15**: 387. 1898.

274. Chesnut, V. K. Principal Poisonous Plants of the United States. USDA, Div. Bot., *Bull.* 20. 1898.

275. Chesnut, V. K. Thirty Poisonous Plants of the United States. USDA, *Farmers' Bull.* 86. 1898.

276. Chesnut, V. K. Poisonous Properties of the Green-spored Lepiota. *Asa Gray Bull.,* **7**: 87. 1900.

277. Chesnut, V. K., and E. V. Wilcox. The Stock-poisoning Plants of Montana. USDA, Div. Bot., *Bull.* 26. 1901.

278. Chevalier, A. Scilles à Bulbes Comestibles ou Vénéneux. *Rev. Bot. Appl.,* **13**: 469. 1933.

279. Chopra, R. N., R. L. Badhwar, and S. Ghosh. *Poisonous Plants of India.* Indian Counc. Agr. Research, Sci. Monograph 17, Manager of Publications, Delhi, 1949.

280. Christensen, J. J., and H. C. H. Kernkamp. Studies on the Toxicity of Blighted Barley to Swine. Minnesota Agr. Expt. Sta., *Tech. Bull.* 113. 1936.

281. Christian, K. R., and V. J. Williams. Attempts to Produce Hypomagnesaemia in Dry Nonpregnant Sheep. *N. Zeal. J. Agr. Res.,* **3**: 389. 1960.

282. Christie, G. S., and R. N. LePage. Liver Damage in Acute Heliotrine Poisoning. I., II. *Biochem. J.,* **84**: 25; 202. 1962.

283. Church, M. B., and J. S. Buckley. Laboratory Feeding of Molds to Animals. *N. Am. Vet.,* **4**: 7. 1923.

284. Clare, N. T. *Photosensitization in Diseases of Domestic Animals.* Rev. ser. #3. Commonwealth Bur. Animal Health. Commonwealth Agr. Bureaux, Farnham Royal, Bucks, England. 1952.

285. Clare, N. T. Photosensitization in Animals. *Advances in Vet. Sci.,* **2**: 182. 1955.

286. Clark, E. D., and J. L. Kantor. Toxicological Experiments with Some of the Higher Fungi. *Mycologia,* **3**: 175. 1911.

287. Clark, E. D., and C. S. Smith. Toxicological Studies on *Clitocybe illudens* and *Inocybe infida*. *Mycologia,* **5**: 224. 1913.
288. Clark, E. P. Studies of Gossypol. II. Concerning the Nature of Carruth's D Gossypol. *J. Biol. Chem.,* **76**: 229. 1928.
289. Clark, M., E. K. Marshall, Jr., and L. G. Rowntree. Mushroom Poisoning. *J. Am. Med. Assoc.,* **64**: 1230. 1915.
290. Clarke, E. G. C. Poisoning by Castor Seed. *Vet. J.,* **103**: 273. 1947.
291. Clarke, E. G. C., and E. Cotchin. A Note on the Toxicity of the Acorn. *Brit. Vet. J.,* **112**: 135. 1956.
292. Clarke, E. G. C., and J. H. Jackson. The Use of Immune Serum in the Treatment of Ricin Poisoning. *Brit. Vet. J.,* **112**: 57. 1956.
293. Clawson, A. B. A Preliminary Report on the Poisonous Effects of Bitter Rubber Weed (*Actinea odorata*) on Sheep. *J. Agr. Res.,* **43**: 693. 1931.
294. Clawson, A. B. Two Lupines Shown to be Poisonous to Livestock. USDA, *Official Rec.,* **10**: 71. 1931.
295. Clawson, A. B. Additional Information Concerning Larkspur Poisoning. Supplement to USDA, *Farmers' Bull.* 988. 1933.
296. Clawson, A. B. Alpine Kalmia (*Kalmia microphylla*) as a Stock-poisoning Plant. USDA, *Tech. Bull.* 391. 1933.
297. Clawson, A. B. The American Groundsels, Species of Senecio as Stock-poisoning Plants. *Vet. Med.,* **28**: 105. 1933.
298. Clawson, A. B. Some Symptoms and Lesions Produced by Stock-poisoning Plants. *J. Am. Vet. Med. Assoc.,* **85**: 179. 1934.
299. Clawson, A. B., H. Bunyea, and J. F. Couch. Treatment for Livestock Poisoned by Hydrocyanic Acid. USDA, *Yearbook of Agr.,* **1935**: 247. 1935.
300. Clawson, A. B., J. F. Couch, and H. Bunyea. The Toxicity of Sodium Cyanide and the Efficiency of the Nitrite-Thiosulfate Combination as a Remedy for Poisoned Animals. *J. Wash. Acad. Sci.,* **25**: 357. 1935.
301. Clawson, A. B., and W. T. Huffman. Bighead in Sheep Caused by Plant Poisoning. *Natl. Wool Grower,* **27**(3): 13. 1937.
302. Clawson, A. B., and E. A. Moran. Toxicity of Arrowgrass for Sheep and Remedial Treatment. USDA, *Tech. Bull.* 580. 1937.
303. Claughton, W. P., and H. D. Claughton. Vetch Seed Poisoning. *Auburn Vet.,* **10**: 125. 1954.
304. Clec'h, L. Observations sur quelques cas d'intoxication d'origine alimentaire. *Rec. Méd. Vét.,* **132**: 468. 1956.
305. Clegg, F. G. A Convulsive Syndrome in Sheep. *Vet. Rec.,* **71**: 824. 1959.
306. Clegg, F. G., and R. K. Evans. Haemoglobinaemia of Cattle Associated with the Feeding of Brassicae Species. *Vet. Rec.,* **74**: 1169. 1962.
307. Cockburn, R. S., G. Eaton, J. R. Hudson, K. G. Morgan, E. C. Wood, and A. N. Worden. Acute Poisoning of Cattle by Common Ragwort (*Senecio jacobaea* L.). *Vet. Rec.,* **67**: 640. 1955.
308. Coleman, O. H., and D. W. Robertson. Preliminary Report on Inheritance of Differential Ability of Inbred Lines of Sudan Grass to Produce HCN. Colorado Agr. Expt. Sta., *Tech. Bull.* 24. 1938.

309. Coleman, R. G., G. M. Windrum, and E. M. Hutton. Studies on the Toxicity of *Indigofera endecaphylla.* III. *J. Nutr.* **70:** 267. 1960.

310. Collentine, G. C., and A. J. Quick. The Interrelationships of Vitamin K and Dicoumarin. *Am. J. Med. Sci.,* **222:** 7. 1951.

311. Collins, F. S. A Case of Boletus Poisoning. *Rhodora,* **1:** 21. 1899.

312. Collison, S. E. Prussic Acid in Sorghum. Florida Agr. Expt. Sta., *Bull.* 155. 1919.

313. Compère, R. Etude toxicologique du *Leucaena glauca* chez les Bovins. *Bull. Agr. du Congo Belge,* **50:** 1311. 1959.

314. Connor, A. B. Trials with Poisonous Plants. Texas Agr. Expt. Sta., *Ann. Rept.,* **42:** 140. 1929.

315. Connor, A. B. Swellhead of Sheep and Goats. Texas Agr. Expt. Sta., *Ann. Rept.,* **43:** 9. 1930.

316. Connor, H. E., and N. M. Adams. Poisonous Plants in New Zealand. Dept. Sci. and Ind. Res., *Bull.* 99. 1951.

317. Cook, C. D., and R. J. Haggerty. Mycetismus (*Amanita phalloides*). *N. Engl. J. Med.,* **262:** 832. 1960.

318. Cook, C. W., and D. H. Gates. Effects of Site and Season on Oxalate Content of Halogeton. *J. Range Management,* **13:** 97. 1960.

319. Cook, C. W., and L. A. Stoddart. The Halogeton Problem in Utah. Utah Agr. Expt. Sta., *Bull.* 364. 1953.

320. Cook, J. W., and J. D. Loudon. Colchicine. *In* Manske, R. H. E., and H. L. Holmes, eds., *The Alkaloids.* Academic Press, New York. Vol. II, 1952.

321. Cook, K. F. The Toxicity of Certain Species of Amanita to Guinea Pigs. *Mycologia,* **46:** 24. 1954.

322. Cook, W. B. The Isolation and Study of the Alkaloids of *Delphinium barbeyi* Huth. *Univ. Wyoming Publ.,* **17:** 105. 1951.

323. Cook, W. B., and O. A. Beath. The Alkaloids of *Delphinium barbeyi* H. *J. Am. Chem. Soc.,* **74:** 1411. 1952.

324. Cooke, A. The Toxic Constituent of *Indigofera endecaphylla. Arch. Biochem. and Biophys.,* **55:** 114. 1955.

325. Coop, I. E., and R. L. Blakley. The Metabolism and Toxicity of Cyanides and Cyanogenetic Glucosides in Sheep. I. Activity in the Rumen. *New Zealand J. Sci. and Tech.* (Sect. A), **30:** 277. 1949.

326. Coop, I. E., and R. L. Blakley. The Metabolism and Toxicity of Cyanides and Cyanogenetic Glucosides in Sheep. III. The Toxicity of Cyanides and Cyanogenetic Glucosides. *New Zealand J. Sci. and Tech.* (Sect. A), **31:** 44. 1950.

327. Copithorne, B. Suspected Poisoning of Goats by Hemlock (*Conium maculatum*). *Vet. Rec.,* **49:** 1018. 1937.

328. Cordy, D. R. The Pathology of Experimental Bracken Poisoning in Rats. *Cornell Vet.,* **42:** 108. 1952.

329. Cordy, D. R. Nigropallidal Encephalomalacia in Horses Associated with Ingestion of Yellow Star Thistle. *J. Neuropath. and Exptl. Neurol.,* **13:** 330. 1954.

330. Cordy, D. R. Nigropallidal Encephalomalacia (Chewing Disease) in

Horses on Rations High in Yellow Star Thistle. 91st Ann. Meeting Am. Vet. Med. Assoc., *Proceedings:* 149. 1954.

331. Cordy, D. R. Experimental Production and Control of Bracken Fern Poisoning in Rats. *J. Am. Vet. Med. Assoc.,* **130:** 333. 1957.

332. Core, E. L., J. H. Reitz, and W. H. Gillespie. The Poisonous Plants of West Virginia, A Preliminary Report. *Proc. W. Virginia Acad. Sci.,* **33:** 29. 1961.

333. Corkill, L. Cyanogenesis in White Clover (*Trifolium repens* L.). *New Zealand J. Sci. and Tech.* (Sect. A.), **34:** 1. 1952.

334. Cornevin, C. *Des Plantes Vénéneuses.* Firmin-Didot et Cie., Paris. 1887.

335. Cornevin, C. *Des Plantes Vénéneuses.* Firmin-Didot et Cie., Paris. 1893.

336. Cory, V. L. A New Loco from the Edwards Plateau of Texas. *Rhodora,* **32:** 4. 1930.

337. Cory, V. L. African Rue (*Peganum harmala*) in the United States. *Field and Lab.* **17:** 20. 1949.

338. Cory, V. L. Increase of Poison-bitterweed (*Hymenoxys odorata*) on Texas Range Lands. *Field and Lab.,* **19:** 39. 1951.

339. Cory, V. L., and W. H. Dameron. Range Studies of Bitterweed. *Southw. Sheep and Goat Raiser,* **7**(11): 8. 1937.

340. Coté, F. T. Rape Poisoning in Cattle. *Canad. J. Comp. Med.,* **8:** 38. 1944.

341. Cottingham, J. O. Notes on *Gyromitra esculenta* Fr. *Proc. Indiana Acad. Sci.,* **65:** 210. 1955.

342. Cotton, H. L. Algae Poisoning. *Am. J. Vet. Med.,* **9:** 903. 1914.

343. Couch, J. F. The Toxic Constituent of Greasewood (*Sarcobatus vermiculatus*). *Am. J. Pharm.,* **94:** 631. 1922.

344. Couch, J. F. Acidosis, Trembles, and Milksickness. *Science,* **64** (n.s.): 456. 1926.

345. Couch, J. F. Relative Toxicity of the Lupine Alkaloids. *J. Agr. Res.,* **32:** 51. 1926.

346. Couch, J. F. The Toxic Constituent of Richweed or White Snakeroot (*Eupatorium urticaefolium*). *J. Agr. Res.,* **35:** 547. 1927.

347. Couch, J. F. The Toxicity of Tremetol. *J. Am. Vet. Med. Assoc.,* **73:** 603. 1928.

348. Couch, J. F. A Contribution to the Study of Locoism. *J. Pharm. and Exptl. Therapeut.,* **36:** 55. 1929.

349. Couch, J. F. Experiments with Extracts from the Wooly-pod Milkweed (*Asclepias eriocarpa*). *Am. J. Pharm.,* **101:** 815. 1929.

350. Couch, J. F. Tremetol, the Compound that Produced "Trembles" (Milksickness). *J. Am. Chem. Soc.,* **51:** 3617. 1929.

351. Couch, J. F. The Toxic Constituent of Rayless Goldenrod. *J. Agr. Res.,* **40:** 649. 1930.

352. Couch, J. F. Poisoning of Livestock by Plants that Produce Hydrocyanic Acid. USDA, *Leaflet* 88. 1932.

353. Couch, J. F. Trembles (or Milksickness). USDA, *Circ.* 306. 1933.

354. Couch, J. F. Poisoning of Livestock by Plants that Produce Hydrocyanic Acid. USDA, *Leaflet* 88. 1934.

355. Couch, J. F. Deltaline, a New Alkaloid from *Delphinium occidentale* S. Wats. *J. Am. Chem. Soc.*, **58**: 684. 1936.

356. Couch, J. F. The Chemistry of Stock-poisoning Plants. *J. Chem. Ed.*, **14**: 16. 1937.

357. Couch, J. F., and R. R. Briese. Hydrogen Ion Concentration and Cyanogenesis in Sorghum. *Am. J. Pharm.*, **111**: 55; 151; 193. 1939.

358. Couch, J. F., R. R. Briese, and J. H. Martin. Hydrocyanic Acid Content of Sorghum Varieties. *J. Wash. Acad. Sci.*, **29**: 146. 1939.

359. Couch, J. F., and R. R. Briese. Cyanogenesis and Enzyme Activity in Sorghum Varieties. *J. Wash. Acad. Sci.*, **30**: 413. 1940.

360. Couch, J. F., H. Bunyea, and A. B. Clawson. The Relationship Between Time of Administration and Effectiveness of Remedies for Cyanide Poisoning. *J. Wash. Acad. Sci.*, **25**: 57. 1935.

361. Couch, J. F., A. B. Clawson, and H. Bunyea. The Toxicity for Sheep of Water Solutions of Hydrocyanic Acid and the Effectiveness of the Nitrite-Thiosulfate Combination as a Remedy. *J. Wash. Acad. Sci.*, **25**: 272. 1935.

362. Couch, J. R., W. Y. Chang, and C. M. Lyman. The Effect of Free Gossypol on Chick Growth. *Poultry Sci.*, **34**: 178. 1955.

363. Coulson, C. B., P. J. Davies, and W. C. Evans. Clinical Biochemistry of Farm Animals. II. Amino-acid and Protein Patterns of the Body Fluids of Cattle and Sheep in Disease. *J. Comp. Path.*, **70**: 199. 1960.

364. Courville, D. A., B. W. Halsted, D. W. Hessel. Marine Biotoxins: Isolation and Properties. *Chem. Rev.*, **58**: 235. 1958.

365. Covell, W. P., and W. F. Whedon. Effects of the Paralytic Shellfish Poison on Nerve Cells. *Arch. Path.*, **24**: 411. 1937.

366. Cover, M. S., W. J. Mellen, and E. Gill. Studies of Hemorrhagic Syndrome in Chickens. *Cornell Vet.*, **45**: 366. 1955.

367. Coville, F. V. Crimson Clover Hair Balls. USDA, Div. Bot., *Circ.* 8. 1896.

368. Coward, T. G. Acute, Fatal Poisoning in Sheep Due to Ingestion of Common Sorrel (*Rumex acetosa*). *Vet. Rec.*, **61**: 765. 1949.

369. Cox, D. H., D. L. Harris, and T. A. Richard. Chemical Identification of Crotalaria Poisoning in Horses. *J. Am. Vet. Med. Assoc.*, **133**: 425. 1958.

370. Crabtree, D. G. Red Squill—The Most Specific of the Raticides. *Econ. Bot.*, **1**: 394. 1947.

371. Craig, J. F., and G. O. Davies. Some Observations on Bracken Poisoning. *Vet. Rec.*, **52**: 499. 1940.

372. Craig, J. F., and D. Kehoe. Investigations as to the Poisonous Nature of Common Sorrel (*Rumex acetosa* Linn.) for Cattle. *J. Comp. Path. and Exptl. Therapeut.*, **34**: 27. 1921.

373. Craig, J. F., and D. Kehoe. Plant Poisoning. *Vet. Rec.*, **38**: 795. 1925.

374. Craig, R. A. Cornstalk Disease. Purdue (Indiana) Agr. Expt. Sta., *Circ.* 3. 1906.

375. Crawford, A. C. The Poisonous Action of Johnson Grass. USDA, Bur. Plant Ind., *Bull.* 90, pt. 4. 1906.

376. Crawford, A. C. The Larkspurs as Poisonous Plants. USDA, Bur. Plant Ind., *Bull.* 111, pt. 1. 1907.

377. Crawford, A. C. Barium, A Cause of Locoweed Disease. USDA, Bur. Plant Ind., *Bull.* 129. 1908.
378. Crawford, A. C. Mountain Laurel, a Poisonous Plant. USDA, Bur. Plant Ind., *Bull.* 121, *misc. paper* 2. 1908.
379. Crawford, A. C. The Supposed Relationship of White Snakeroot to Milksickness or "Trembles." USDA, Bur. Plant Ind., *Bull.* 121. 1908.
380. Crawford, A. C. A Poisonous Principle in Certain Cottonseed Meals. *J. Pharm. and Exptl. Therapeut.*, 1: 519. 1910.
381. Crawford, R. F., and W. K. Kennedy. Nitrates in Forage Crops and Silage. Cornell (New York Agr. Expt. Sta.) *Misc. Bull.* 37. 1960.
382. Crawshaw, H. A. Rape Blindness. *Vet. Rec.*, 65: 254. 1953.
383. Cromwell, B. T. Studies on the Synthesis of Hyoscyamine in *Atropa belladonna* L. and *Datura stramonium* L. *Biochem. J.*, 87: 717. 1943.
384. Cromwell, B. T. The Separation, Micro-estimation, and Distribution of the Alkaloids of Hemlock (*Conium maculatum* L). *Biochem. J.*, 64: 259. 1956.
385. Crookshank, H. H., and F. H. Sims, Serum Values in Wheat Pasture Poisoning Cases. *J. Animal Sci.*, 14: 964. 1955.
386. Culpepper, C. W. and H. H. Moon. Composition of Rhubarb at Different Stages of Maurity in Relation to its Use in Cooking and Canning. *J. Agr. Res.*, 46: 387. 1933.
387. Culvenor, C. C. J., A. T. Dann, and A. T. Dick. Alkylation as the Mechanism by which the Hepatotoxic Pyrrolizidine Alkaloids Act on Cell Nuclei. *Nature* (London), 195: 570. 1962.
388. Cunningham, H. M., J. M. Brown, and A. E. Edie. Molybdenum Poisoning of Cattle in the Swan River Valley of Manitoba. *Canad. J. Sci. Agr.*, 33: 254. 1953.
389. Cunningham, I. J. Grass Staggers and Magnesium Metabolism. *New Zealand J. Sci. and Tech.*, 18: 242. 1936.
390. Cunningham, I. J. The Distribution of Magnesium in the Animal Organism and the Effect of Dietary Magnesium. *New Zealand J. Sci. and Tech.*, 18: 419. 1936.
391. Cunningham, I. J. A Note on the Cause of Tall Fescue Lameness in Cattle. *Austral. Vet. J.*, 25: 27. 1949.
392. Cunningham, I. J., I. G. McIntosh, and J. B. Swan. The Nontoxicity of Milk and Meat from Ergotized Cattle. *New Zealand J. Sci. and Tech.* (Sect. A), 26: 125. 1944.
393. Cunningham, I. J., J. B. Swan, and C. S. M. Hopkirk. The Symptoms of Ergot Poisoning in Sheep. *New Zealand J. Sci. and Tech.* (Sect. A), 26: 121. 1944.
394. Curtis, R. S., and F. A. Wolf. *Eupatorium ageratoides*, the Cause of Trembles. *J. Agr. Res.*, 9: 397. 1917.
395. Dalton, P. J. Rape Blindness. *Vet. Rec.*, 65: 298. 1953.
396. Damseaux, J. Étude de trois légumineuses fourragères introduites au Congo belge en vue de l'alimentation du bétail. *Bull. Agr. du Congo Belge*, 47: 93. 1956.

397. Daniel, T. W., F. B. Volberg, V. L. Miller, J. H. Alswager, M. E. Ensminger, and A. A. Spielman. Chemical Composition and Digestibility of Flat Pea Forage in Three States of Maturity. *J. Anim. Sci.*, **5**: 80. 1946.

398. Dasler, W. Production of Experimental Lathyrism in the Rat by Two Different Beta-substituted Ethylamines. *Proc. Soc. Exptl. Biol. and Med.*, **88**: 196. 1955.

399. Dasler, W. Protective Action of Glutamine, Cysteine, and Other Substances Against Experimental Lathyrism in the Rat. *Proc. Soc. Exptl. Biol. and Med.*, **91**: 554. 1956.

400. Davidson, F. F. Poisoning of Wild and Domestic Animals by a Toxic Waterbloom of *Nostoc rivulare* Kuetz. *J. Am. Water Works Assoc.*, **51**: 1277. 1959.

401. Davidson, W. B. Selenium Poisoning. *Canad. J. Comp. Med.*, **4**: 19. 1940.

402. Davidson, W. B., J. L. Doughty, and J. L. Bolton. Nitrate Poisoning of Livestock. *Canad. J. Comp. Med.*, **5**: 303. 1941.

403. Davis, C. C. *Gymnodinium brevis* sp. nov., a Cause of Discolored Water and Animal Mortality in the Gulf of Mexico. *Bot. Gaz.*, **109**: 358. 1948.

404. Davis, C. L. Senecio Poisoning in Livestock. *Western Vet.*, **5**: 28. 1958.

405. Davis, D., *et al.* Discussion in Mod. Vet. Pract. Looseleaf Notebook on Small Animal Practice, F 4–2, and *Mod. Vet. Pract.*, **39**(7): 60. 1958.

406. Davis, G. K., N. R. Mehrhof, and R. S. McKinney. Effect of Tung Meal in Rations for Growing Chicks. *Poultry Sci.*, **25**: 74. 1946.

407. Davis, R. E., and H. R. Crookshank. Grass Tetany and Wheat-pasture Poisoning. USDA, *Yearbook of Agr.*, **1956**: 260. 1956.

408. Dawson, C. R. The Toxic Principle of Poison Ivy and Related Plants. *Rec. Chem. Prog.*, **15**: 38. 1954.

409. Dawson, C. R. Chemistry of Poison Ivy. *Trans. N.Y. Acad. Sci.* (Ser. II), **18**: 427. 1956.

410. Dayton, W. A. Historical Sketch of Barilla (*Halogeton glomeratus.*) *J. Range Management,* **4**: 375. 1951.

411. DeEds, F., R. H. Wilson, and A. M. Ambrose. Hazards and Potential Drugs. USDA, *Yearbook of Agr.*, **1950–1951**: 721. 1951.

412. Deem, A. W., and F. Thorp. Toxic Algae in Colorado. *J. Am. Vet. Med. Assoc.*, **95**: 542. 1939.

413. Deem, A. W., F. Thorp, and L. W. Durrell. Range Plant Newly Found to be Poisonous. *Science,* **89**: 435. 1939.

414. Deerness, J. The Personal Factor in Mushroom Poisoning. *Mycologia,* **3**: 75. 1911.

415. Deerness, J. Gyromitra Poisoning. *Mycologia,* **16**: 199. 1924.

416. Degen, A. von. Adonis-Vergiftung. *Fortschritte der Landwirtschaft,* **7**: 556. 1932.

417. Delaney, L. T., H. W. Schmidt, and C. F. Stroebel. Silo-filler's Disease. *Proc. Staff Meet. Mayo Clinic,* **31**: 189. 1956.

418. Delli Quadri, C. A. Disease Investigation Supervisor, County of Los Angeles, California. Personal communication, 1961.

419. Department of Animal Pathology. The Cornstalk Disease. Nebraska Agr. Expt. Sta., *Ann. Rept.,* **16**: 63. 1903.

420. Dermer, O. C., and R. Cleverdon. Studies on the Chemical Constituents of Rayless Goldenrod (*Aplopappus heterophyllus*). *Proc. Oklahoma Acad. Sci.,* **23**: 63. 1943.

421. Dick, A. T. Molybdenum in Animal Nutrition. *In* Bear, F. E., ed., Molybdenum in Plant and Animal Nutrition. *Soil Sci.,* **81**: 159. 1956.

422. Dickson, A. D., K. P. Link, B. H. Roche, and J. G. Dickson. Report on the Emetic Substances in Gibberella-infected Barley. *Phytopath.,* **20**: 132. 1930.

423. Dickson, J. G. Leaf and Head Blights of Cereals. In *Plant Diseases,* USDA, *Yearbook of Agr.,* **1953**: 344. 1953.

424. Dillenberg, H. O., and M. K. Dehnel. Toxic Waterbloom in Saskatchewan, 1959. *Canad. Med. Assoc. J.,* **83**: 1151. 1960.

425. Dillon, B. E. Acute Ergot Poisoning in Cattle. *J. Am. Vet. Med. Assoc.,* **126**: 136. 1955.

426. Dinwiddie, R. R. Unsound Corn and Forage as a Cause of Disease in Livestock. Arkansas Agr. Expt. Sta., *Bull.* 25. 1893.

427. Dinwiddie, R. R., and A. K. Short. Cottonseed Poisoning of Livestock. Arkansas Agr. Expt. Sta., *Bull.* 108: 395–410. 1911.

428. Diven, R. H., W. J. Pistor, R. E. Reed, R. J. Trautman, and R. E. Watts. The Determination of Serum or Plasma Nitrate and Nitrite. *Am. J. Vet. Res.,* **23**: 497. 1962.

429. Diven, R. H., R. E. Reed, R. J. Trautman, W. J. Pistor, and R. E. Watts. Experimentally Induced Nitrite Poisoning in Sheep. *Am. J. Vet. Res.,* **23**: 494. 1962.

430. Dodd, S. Trefoil Dermatitis. *J. Comp. Path. and Therapeut.,* **29**: 47. 1916.

431. Dollahite, J. W. Toxicity of *Drymaria arenarioides* for Cattle, Sheep, and Goats. *J. Am. Vet. Med. Assoc.,* **135**: 125. 1959.

432. Dollahite, J. W. Desert Baileya Poisoning in Sheep, Goats, and Rabbits. Texas Agr. Expt. Sta., *Prog. Rept.,* 2149. 1960.

433. Dollahite, J. W. Shin Oak (*Quercus havardi*) Poisoning in Cattle. *Southw. Vet.,* **14**: 198. 1961.

434. Dollahite, J. W. Ergotism Produced by Feeding *Claviceps cinerea* Growing on Tobosagrass (*Hilaria mutica*) and Galletagrass (*Hilaria jamesii*). *Southw. Vet.,* **16**: 295. 1963.

435. Dollahite, J. W., and T. J. Allen. Feeding Perennial Broomweed to Cattle, Sheep, Goats, Rabbits, Guinea Pigs, and Chickens. Texas Agr. Expt. Sta., *Prog. Rept.* 2105. 1959.

436. Dollahite, J. W., and T. J. Allen. Silverleaf Nightshade Poisoning in Livestock. Texas Agr. Expt. Sta., *Prog. Rept.* 2146. 1960.

437. Dollahite, J. W., and T. J. Allen. Poisoning of Cattle, Sheep and Goats with *Lobelia* and *Centaurium* species. *Southw. Vet.,* **15**: 126. 1962.

438. Dollahite, J. W., and W. V. Anthony. Malnutrition in Cattle on an Unbalanced Diet of Mesquite Beans. Texas Agr. Expt. Sta., *Prog. Rept.* 1931. 1957.

439. Dollahite, J. W., and W. V. Anthony. Toxicity of *Drymaria arenarioides* for Cattle, Sheep, and Goats. Texas Agr. Expt. Sta., *Prog. Rept.* 1911. 1956.

440. Dollahite, J. W., and W. V. Anthony. Experimental Production of Abortion, Premature Calves, and Retained Placentas by Feeding a Species of Perennial Broomweed. *Southw. Vet.,* **10**: 128. 1957.
441. Dollahite, J. W. and B. J. Camp. Calcium Hydroxide—An Antidote for Tannic Acid Poisoning in Rabbits. *Am. J. Vet. Res.,* **23**: 1271. 1962.
442. Dollahite, J. W., R. F. Pigeon, and B. J. Camp. The Toxicity of Gallic Acid, Pyrogallol, Tannic Acid, and *Quercus havardi* in the Rabbit. *Am. J. Vet. Res.,* **23**: 1264. 1962.
443. Dollahite, J. W., T. Shaver, and B. J. Camp. Injected Saponins as Abortifacients. *Am. J. Vet. Res.,* **23**: 1261. 1962.
444. Dollahite, J. W., and W. V. Anthony. Poisoning of Cattle with *Gutierrezia microcephala,* a Perennial Broomweed. *J. Am. Vet. Med. Assoc.,* **130**: 525. 1957.
445. Donald, L. G., and P. L. Shanks. Ragwort Poisoning from Silage. *Brit. Vet. J.,* **112**: 307. 1956.
446. Doran, C. W. Sneezeweed, Fifth Columnist in Sheep Production, Combatted by Management. *Colorado* (Agr. Expt. Sta.) *Farm Bull.,* **4** (3): 5. 1942.
447. Doran, C. W., and J. T. Cassady. Management of Sheep on Range Infested with Orange Sneezeweed. USDA, *Circ.* 691. 1944.
448. Dougherty, R. W., and R. M. Cello. Study of Toxic Factors in the Rumen Ingesta of Cows and Sheep. *Cornell Vet.,* **39**: 403. 1949.
449. Dougherty, R. W., and R. B. Christensen. In Vivo Absorption Studies of Hydrocyanic Acid of Plant Juice Origin. *Cornell Vet.,* **43**: 481. 1953.
450. Douglass, B. Mushroom Poisoning. *Torreya,* **17**: 171, 207. 1917.
451. Dowell, C. T. A Study of Cyanogenesis in *Sorghum vulgare.* Oklahoma Agr. Expt. Sta., *Bull.* 122. 1919.
452. Dowell, C. T. Cyanogenesis in *Andropogon sorghum. J. Agr. Res.,* **16**: 175. 1919.
453. Dowell, C. T., and P. Menaul. Effect of Autoclaving upon the Toxicity of Cottonseed Meal. *J. Agr. Res.,* **26**: 9. 1923.
454. Doyle, L. P., and F. L. Walkey. White Snakeroot Poisoning in Livestock. Indiana Agr. Expt. Sta., *Bull.* 270. 1923.
455. Drach, G. and Maloney, W. H. Toxicity of the Common Houseplant *Dieffenbachia. J. Am. Med. Assoc.,* **184**: 1047. 1963.
456. Driggers, J. C., G. K. Davis, and N. R. Mehrhof. Toxic Factor in Citrus Seed Meal. Florida Agr. Expt. Sta., *Bull.* 476. 1951.
457. Duncan, C. S. Oak Leaf Poisoning in Two Horses. *Cornell Vet.,* **51**: 159. 1961.
458. Duncan, W. H., and T. J. Jones. Poisonous Plants of Georgia. Univ. Georgia. Sch. Vet. Med., *Bull.,* **49** (13). 1949.
459. Duncan, W. H., P. L. Piercy, S. D. Feurt, and R. Starling. Toxicological Studies of Southeastern Plants. II Compositae. *Econ. Bot.,* **11**: 75. 1957.
460. Duncan, W. H., P. L. Piercy, R. J. Starling. Toxicological Studies of Southeastern Plants. I. Leguminosae. *Economic Bot.,* **9**: 243. 1955.
461. Dunne, G. T. Poisoning in Calves by Nascent Hydrocyanic Acid Evolved by Cake in Solution. *Vet. J.,* **80**: 40. 1924.

462. Dunstan, W. R., and T. A. Henry. Cyanogenesis in Plants. II. The Great Millet, *Sorghum vulgare. Proc. Roy. Soc.* (London), **70**: 153. 1902.
463. Dupuy, H. P., and J. G. Lee. The Isolation of a Material Capable of Producing Experimental Lathyrism. *J. Am. Pharm. Assoc.* (Sci. ed.), **43**: 61. 1954.
464. Durrell, L. W. Halogeton: A New Stock-poisoning Weed. Colorado Agr. Expt. Sta., *Circ.* 170-A. 1951.
465. Durrell, L. W., R. Jensen, and B. Klinger. Poisonous and Injurious Plants in Colorado. Colorado Agr. Expt. Sta., *Bull.* 412-A. 1952.
466. Dybing, O. Aconitum-Alkaloidenes Toksikologi. *Nord. Vet.*, **6**: 283, 1951.
467. Dybing, O., and S. Erichsen. Liver Changes in Rats after Administration of *Senecio aquaticus. Acta Path. et Microbiol. Scand.*, **47**: 1. 1959.
468. Dye, W. B. Chemical Studies on *Halogeton glomeratus. Weeds*, **4**: 55. 1956.
469. Dyer, I. A. Implications of Manganese Deficiency in the Etiology of Deformed Calves. *Proc. Am. Soc. Anim. Prod., West Sect.*, **12**(67): 1. 1961.
470. Eastwood, A. Ledum as a Poisonous Plant. *Leafl. Western Bot.*, **1**: 43. 1933.
471. Eaton, G. A Series of Cases of Poisoning in Cattle. *Vet. Rec.*, **53**: 145. 1941.
472. Eckles, C. H., C. P. Fitch, and J. L. Seal. Molds in Silage and Their Significance in the Production of Disease among Livestock. *J. Am. Vet. Med. Assoc.*, **64**: 716. 1924.
473. Editor. Toxicity of Jequirity Beans. *J. Am. Med. Assoc.*, **157**: 779. 1955.
474. Edwards, C. M. Some Observations on Plant Poisoning in Grazing Animals. *Vet. Rec.*, **61**: 864. 1949.
475. Edwards, E. P. Aconite Poisoning. *Vet. Rec.*, **5** (n.s.): 559. 1925.
476. Edwards, H. I. The Etiology and Epidemiology of Paralytic Shellfish Poisoning. *J. Milk and Food Tech.*, **19**: 331. 1956.
477. Edwards, J. D., Jr. Total Synthesis of Gossypol. *J. Am. Chem. Soc.*, **80**: 3798. 1958.
478. Eggleston, W. W., O. F. Black, and J. W. Kelly. A Botanical and Chemical Study of *Bikukulla eximia*, with a Key to North American Species of *Bikukulla. J. Agr. Res.*, **39**: 477. 1929.
479. Eggleston, W. W., O. F. Black, and J. W. Kelly. *Linum neomexicanum* (yellow pine flax) and One of Its Poisonous Constituents. *J. Agr. Res.*, **41**: 715. 1930.
480. Elder, C. Cornstalk Poisoning of Cattle. *J. Am. Vet. Med. Assoc.*, **130**: 331. 1957.
481. Elderfield, R. C. On Thevetin. *J. Biol. Chem.*, **115**: 247. 1936.
482. Ellis, M. M., H. L. Motley, M. D. Ellis, and R. O. Jones. Selenium Poisoning in Fishes. *Proc. Soc. Expt. Biol. Med.*, **36**: 519. 1937.
483. Eloire, A. Poisoning of Cart Horses by Field Wallflower (Wild Radish). *Vet. J.*, **78**: 209. 1922.
484. Emerick, R. J. and L. B. Embry, Effect of Chlortetracycline on Methemoglobinemia Resulting from the Ingestion of Sodium Nitrate by Ruminants. *J. Anim. Sci.*, **20**: 844. 1961.

485. Emery, Z. T. Report of Thirty-two Cases of Poisoning by Locust Bark. *New York Med. J.*, **45**: 92. 1887.

486. Emmel, M. W. The Toxicity of *Glottidium vesicarium* (Jacq.) Harper Seeds for the Fowl. *J. Am. Vet. Med. Assoc.*, **87**: 13. 1935.

487. Emmel, M. W. The Pathology of *Crotalaria spectabilis* Roth Seed Poisoning in the Domestic Fowl. *J. Am. Vet. Med. Assoc.*, **90**: 627. 1937.

488. Emmel, M. W. The Toxicity of *Crotalaria retusa* L. Seeds for the Domestic Fowl. *J. Am. Vet. Med. Assoc.*, **91**: 205. 1937.

489. Emmel, M. W. The Toxic Principle of *Aleurites Fordii* Hemsl. *J. Am. Vet. Med. Assoc.*, **103**: 162. 1943.

490. Emmel, M. W. The Toxicity of *Glottidium vesicarium* (Jacq.) Harper for cattle. *J. Am. Vet. Med. Assoc.*, **104**: 222. 1944.

491. Emmel, M. W. The Toxic Principle of the Species Aleurites. *J. Am. Vet. Med. Assoc.*, **111**: 386. 1947.

492. Emmel, M. W. The Toxic Principle of the Tung Tree. Florida Agr. Expt. Sta., *Bull.* 431. 1947.

493. Emmel, M. W. Crotalaria Poisoning in Cattle. *J. Am. Vet. Med. Assoc.*, **113**: 164. 1948.

494. Emmel, M. W., and D. W. Sanders. *Crotalaria spectabilis* and *C. retusa* Poisoning of Livestock. Florida Agr. Expt. Sta., *Press Bull.* 574. 1942.

495. Emmel, M. W., D. A. Sanders, and W. W. Henley. Additional Observations on the Toxicity of *Crotalaria spectabilis* Roth for Swine. *J. Am. Vet. Med. Assoc.*, **87**: 175. 1935.

496. Emmel, M. W., D. A. Sanders, and W. W. Henley. *Crotalaria spectabilis* Roth Seed Poisoning in Swine. *J. Am. Vet. Med. Assoc.*, **86**: 43. 1935.

497. Emmel, M. W., D. A. Sanders, and L. E. Swanson. The Toxicity of the Foliage of *Aleurites fordii* for Cattle. *J. Am. Vet. Med. Assoc.*, **101**: 136. 1943.

498. Emmel, M. W., and G. E. Ritchey. The Toxicity of *Indigofera endecaphylla* Jacq. for Rabbits. *J. Am. Soc. Agron.* 33: 675. 1941.

499. Eppson, H. F., M. W. Glenn, W. W. Ellis, and C. S. Gilbert. Nitrate in the Diet of Pregnant Ewes. *J. Am. Vet. Med. Assoc.*, **137**: 611. 1960.

500. Erickson, J. L. E., and J. H. Brown, Jr. A Study of the Toxic Properties of Tung Nuts. *J. Pharm. and Exptl. Therapeut.* **74**: 114.

501. Erickson, L. C., H. L. Morton, E. W. Tisdale, and G. Zappettini. The Present Status of the Halogeton Problem. *Weeds*, **1**: 321. 1952.

502. Erickson, L. C., E. W. Tisdale, H. L. Morton, and G. Zappettini. Halogeton—Intermountain Range Menace. Idaho Agr. Expt. Sta., *Circ.* 117. 1951.

503. Ettlinger, M. G., and J. E. Hodgkins. The Mustard Oil of Rape Seed, Allylcarbinyl Isothiocyanate, and Synthetic Isomers. *J. Am. Chem. Soc.*, **77**: 1831. 1955.

504. Evans, E. T. R. Kale and Rape Poisoning in Cattle. *Vet. Rec.*, **63**: 348. 1951.

505. Evans, E. T. R., and W. C. Evans. The Effect of the Inclusion of Bracken (*Pteris aquilina*) in the Diets of Rats. *Biochem. J., Proc.*, **44**: ix. 1949.

506. Evans, E. T. R., W. C. Evans, and L. E. Hughes. Developments in the Investigation into "Bracken Poisoning" in Cattle. *Vet. Rec.,* **63**: 444. 1951.

507. Evans, E. T. R., W. C. Evans, and H. E. Roberts. Studies on Bracken Poisoning in the Horse. *Brit. Vet. J.,* **107**: 364; 399. 1951.

508. Evans, I. A., and R. M. Howell. Bovine Bracken Poisoning. *Nature* (London), **194**: 584. 1962.

509. Evans, I. A., A. J. Thomas, W. C. Evans, and C. M. Edwards. Studies on Bracken Poisoning in Cattle. V. *Brit. Vet. J.,* **114**: 253. 1958.

510. Evans, W. C., and E. T. R. Evans. Studies on the Biochemistry of Pasture Plants. No. 3. The Effects of Inclusion of Bracken (*Pteris aquilina*) in the Diets of Rats, and the Problem of Bracken Poisoning in Farm Animals. *Brit. Vet. J.,* **105**: 175. 1949.

511. Evans. W. C., E. T. R. Evans, and L. E. Hughes. Studies on Bracken Poisoning in Cattle. I, II, III. *British Vet. J.,* **110**: 295; 365; 426. 1954.

512. Evans, W. C., I. A. Evans, R. F. E. Axford, G. Threlfall, D. A. Hemphreys, and A. J. Thomas. Studies on Bracken Poisoning in Cattle. VII. The Toxicity of Bracken Rhizomes. *Vet. Rec.,* **73**: 852. 1961.

513. Evans, W. C., I. A. Evans, A. G. Chamberlain, and A. J. Thomas. Studies on Bracken Poisoning in Cattle. VI. *Brit. Vet. J.,* **115**: 83. 1959.

514. Evans, W. C., I. A. Evans, C. M. Edwards, and A. J. Thomas. Bracken Poisoning of Cattle—Therapeutic Treatment. *Biochem. J., Proc.,* **65**: 6P. 1957.

515. Evans. W. C., I. A. Evans, A. J. Thomas, J. E. Watkins, and A. G. Chamberlain. Studies on Bracken Poisoning in Cattle. IV. *Brit. Vet. J.,* **114**: 180. 1958.

516. Evans, W. C., N. R. Jones, and R. A. Evans. The Mechanism of the Antianeurin Activity of Bracken (*Pteris aquilina*). *Biochem. J., Proc.,* **46**: xxxviii. 1950.

517. Evans, W. M. Report of Investigations of Cattle Poisoning around Payne Lake, Jefferson County, New York. *Cornell Vet.,* **26**: 337. 1936.

518. Ewan, J. A Synopsis of the North American Species of Delphinium. *Univ. Colorado Studies* (Ser. D), **2**: 55. 1945.

519. Fairbairn, J. W., and S. B. Challen. The Alkaloids of Hemlock (*Conium maculatum* L.). I. Distribution in Relation to the Development of the Fruit. *Biochem. J.,* **72**: 556. 1959.

520. Fairbairn, J. W., and P. N. Suwal. The Alkaloids of Hemlock (*Conium maculatum* L.). II. Evidence for a Rapid Turnover of the Major Alkaloids. *Phytochem.,* **1**: 38. 1961.

521. Farlow, W. G. Edible and Poisonous Fungi. USDA, Div. Veg. Physiol. and Path., *Bull.* 15. 1890.

522. Farlow, W. G., Poisonous Action of *Clathrus columnatus. Bot. Gaz.,* **15**: 45. 1890.

523. Farlow, W. G. Poisoning by *Agaricus illudens. Rhodora,* **1**: 43. 1899.

524. Faulkner, K. K., and J. W. H. Smith. Preliminary Studies of the Toxicity of Locoweed Extracts. *Proc. Oklahoma Acad. Sci.,* **31**: 48. 1950.

525. Featherly, H. I. Some Plants Poisonous to Livestock in Oklahoma, Oklahoma Agr. Expt. Sta., *Circ.* C-118. 1945.

526. Featherly, H. I., E. E. Harnden, O. C. Dermer, and H. C. Smith. *Glottidium vesicarium,* a Poisonous Plant in the Southwest. *Vet. Med.,* **38:** 478. 1943.

527. Fenley, J. M. How to Live with Halogeton by Limiting its Spread. Nevada Agr. Ext. Serv., *Bull.* 106. 1952.

528. Fernald, M. L. *Gray's Manual of Botany.* American Book Company, New York. 8th ed., 1950.

529. Fiddian, W. E. H. Fodder Beet: A Review. *Agriculture* (London), **58:** 258. 1951.

530. Fincher, M. G., and H. K. Fuller. Case Report, Photosensitization—Trifoliosis—Light Sensitization. *Cornell Vet.,* **32:** 95. 1942.

531. Fingerman, M., R. H. Forester, and J. H. Stover, Jr. Action of Shellfish Poison on Peripheral Nerve and Skeletal Muscle. *Proc. Soc. Exp. Biol. Med.,* **84:** 643. 1953.

532. Finnemore, H. The Constituents of Canadian Hemp. Part II. Cynotoxin. *Proc. Chem. Soc.* (London), **25:** 77. 1909.

533. Firkins, G. S. Toxic Algae Poisoning. *Iowa State Col. Vet.,* **15:** 151. 1953.

534. Fischer, O. E. Mushroom Poisoning. In: *The Agaricaceae of Michigan.* Mich. Geol. and Biol. Survey, *Publ.* 26 (Biol. ser. 5), Vol. 1: 825. 1918.

535. Fitch, C. P. Disease in Cattle Caused by Feeding Sweetclover Hay. *Rec. Proc. Am. Soc. Anim. Production,* **1923:** 37. 1924.

536. Fitch, C. P. L. M. Bishop, W. L. Boyd, R. A. Gortner, C. F. Rogers, and J. E. Tilden. "Water Bloom" as a Cause of Poisoning in Domestic Animals. *Cornell Vet.,* **24:** 30. 1934.

537. Fleming, C. E. Range Plants Poisonous to Sheep and Cattle in Nevada. Nevada Agr. Expt. Sta., *Bull.* 95. 1918.

538. Fleming, C. E. Poisonous Range Plants. Nevada Agr. Expt. Sta., *Ann. Rept.,* **1919:** 39. 1920.

539. Fleming, C. E. The Spring Rabbit-brush, a Range Plant Poisonous to Sheep. *Am. Sheep Breeder & Wool Grower,* **43:** 542; **44:** 126. 1923. 1924.

540. Fleming, C. E., and R. Dill. The Poisoning of Sheep on Mountain Grazing Ranges in Nevada by the Western Choke-cherry (*Prunus demissa*). Nevada Agr. Expt. Sta., *Bull.* 110. 1928.

541. Fleming, C. E., M. R. Miller, and L. R. Vawter. The Spring Rabbit-brush (*Tetradymia glabrata*), a Range Plant Poisonous to Sheep. Nevada Agr. Expt. Sta., *Bull.* 104. 1922.

542. Fleming, C. E., M. R. Miller, and L. R. Vawter. The Low Larkspur. Nevada Agr. Expt. Sta., *Bull.* 105. 1923.

543. Fleming, C. E., M. R. Miller, and L. R. Vawter. The Common Choke-cherry (*Prunus dimissa*) as a Plant Poisonous to Sheep and Cattle. Nevada Agr. Expt. Sta., *Bull.* 109. 1926.

544. Fleming, C. E., M. R. Miller, and L. R. Vawter. The Greasewood (*Sarcobatus vermiculatus*), a Range Plant Poisonous to Sheep. Nevada Agr. Expt. Sta., *Bull.* 115. 1928.

545. Fleming, C. E., M. R. Miller, and L. R. Vawter. The Fitweed (*Capnoides caseana*), a Poisonous Range Plant of the Northern Sierra Nevada Mountains. Nevada Agr. Expt. Sta., *Bull.* 121. 1931.

546. Fleming, C. E., M. R. Miller, L. R. Vawter, and W. Neilson. *Halogeton glomeratus*—A Desert Range Plant Poisonous to Sheep in Nevada. Nevada Agr. Expt. Sta., *Ann Rept.,* **1947:** 16. 1948.

547. Fleming, C. E., M. R. Miller, L. R. Vawter, and A. Young. Poisonous Range Plants. Nevada Agr. Expt. Sta., *Ann. Rept.,* **1928:** 21. 1931.

548. Fleming, C. E., M. R. Miller, L. R. Vawter, and A. Young. Poisonous Range Plants. Nevada Agr. Expt. Sta., *Ann. Rept.,* **1930:** 12. 1931.

549. Fleming, C. E., M. R. Miller, L. R. Vawter, and A. Young. Poisonous Plants. Nevada Agr. Expt. Sta., *Ann. Rept.,* **1933:** 10. 1934.

550. Fleming, C. E., M. R. Miller, L. R. Vawter, and A. Young. Poisonous Range Plants. Nevada Agr. Expt. Sta., *Ann. Rept.,* **1935:** 15. 1936.

551. Fleming, C. E., and N. F. Peterson. Don't Feed Foxtail Hay to Lambing Ewes. Nevada Agr. Expt. Sta., *Bull.* 97. 1919.

552. Fleming, C. E., N. F. Peterson, M. R. Miller, L. R. Vawter, and L. H. Wright. The Narrow-leaved Milkweed (*Asclepias mexicana*) and the Broad-leaved or Snowy Milkweed (*Asclepias speciosa*)—Plants Poisonous to Livestock in Nevada. Nev. Agr. Expt. Sta., *Bull.* 99. 1920.

553. Fleming, C. E., N. F. Peterson, M. R. Miller, and L. H. Wright. Death Camas (*Zygadenus paniculatus* and *Zygadenus venenosus*). Plants Poisonous to Sheep and Cattle. Nevada Agr. Expt. Sta., *Bull.* 101. 1921.

554. Fleming, C. E., N. F. Peterson, M. R. Miller, L. H. Wright, and R. C. Louck. Arrow-grass, a New Stock-poisoning Plant. Nevada Agr. Expt. Sta., *Bull.* 98. 1920.

555. Fleming, C. E., N. F. Peterson, M. R. Miller, L. H. Wright, and R. C. Louck. The Poison Parsnip or Water Hemlock. Nevada Agr. Expt. Sta., *Bull.* 100. 1920.

556. Fletcher, J. M. Bracken Poisoning in Cattle. *Vet. Rec.,* **56:** 478. 1944.

557. Foggie, A. Suspected Bracken Poisoning in Sheep. *Vet. Rec.,* **63:** 242. 1951.

558. Foley, O. F. "Mountain Disease" Possibly *Quercus* Poisoning. *Am. J. Vet. Med.,* **12:** 244. 1917.

559. Fontenot, J. P., R. W. Miller, C. K. Whitehair, and R. MacVicar. Effect of a High-protein High-potassium Ration on the Mineral Metabolism of Lambs. *J. Anim. Sci.,* **19:** 127. 1960.

560. Foote, P. A. and L. G. Gramling. A Chemical Investigation of the Seeds of *Glottidium vesicarium* (Jacq.) Harper. *J. Am. Pharm. Assoc.,* **29:** 311. 1940.

561. Forbes, E. B., and S. I. Bechdel. The Chemical Composition and Feeding Value of Laurel and Rhododendron, and the Conditions of Browsing in Forests Overstocked with Deer, in Relation to the Death of Young Deer. Pennsylvania Agr. Expt. Sta., *Bull.* **258:** 39. 1930.

562. Ford, W. W. Poisonous Mushrooms. *In* Peterson, F., W. S. Haines, and R. W. Webster. *Legal Medicine and Toxicology.* W. B. Saunders Co., Philadelphia. Vol. 2, 2nd ed., 1923.

563. Forebacher, S. Schachtelhalmvergiftung der Pferde—ein B_1 Avitaminose. *Schweiz. Arch. Tierheilk.,* **94:** 153. 1952.

564. Foreman, E. J. Is Shinnery Poisoning Hemorrhagic Septicemia? *Vet. Med.,* **17:** 689. 1922.

565. Forgacs, J. Toxicity of *Stachybotrys atra* for Animals. *Trans. New York Acad. Sci.* (Ser. 2), **20:** 787. 1958.

566. Forgacs, J., and W. T. Carll. Preliminary Mycotoxic Studies on Hemorrhagic Disease in Poultry. *Vet. Med.,* **50:** 172. 1955.

567. Forgacs, J. and W. T. Carll, Mycotoxicoses. *Adv. Vet. Sci.,* **7:** 274. 1962.

568. Forgacs, J., W. T. Carll, and A. S. Herring. Toxic Fungus Isolated from Feed Pellets. *Vet. Med.,* **48:** 410. 1953.

569. Forgacs, J., W. T. Carll, A. S. Herring, and B. G. Mahlandt. A Toxic *Aspergillus clavatus* Isolated from Feed Pellets. *Am. J. Hygiene,* **60:** 15. 1954.

570. Forgacs, J., H. Koch, and W. T. Carll. Further Mycotoxic Studies on Poultry Hemorrhagic Syndrome. *Poultry Sci.,* **34:** 1194. 1955.

571. Forgacs, J., H. Koch, W. T. Carll, and R. H. White-Stevens. Additional Studies on Relationship of Mycotoxicoses to the Poultry Hemorrhagic Syndrome. *Am. J. Vet. Res.,* **19:** 744. 1958.

572. Forgacs, J., H. Koch, W. T. Carll, and R. H. White-Stevens. Relationship of Toxic Fungi to Moldy-Feed Toxicosis in Poultry. *Avian Dis.,* **6:** 363. 1962.

573. Forrest, G. P. Cocklebur Poisoning. *J. Am. Vet. Med. Assoc.,* **93:** 42. 1938.

574. Forsyth, A. A. British Poisonous Plants. Ministry of Agr., Fisheries, and Food (London), *Bull.* 161. 1954.

575. Fowler, M. E. The Veterinarian's Role in Poison Plant Problems. *Mod. Vet. Pract.,* **43**(3): 40. 1962.

576. Fox, H. J., and W. H. France. Bracken Poisoning in Cattle. *Vet. Rec.,* **66:** 711. 1954.

577. Fox, M. W. Castor Seed Residue Poisoning in Dairy Cattle. *Vet. Rec.,* **73:** 885. 1961.

578. France, W. H. Bracken Poisoning in Cattle. *Vet. Rec.,* **67:** 802. 1955.

579. Francis, C. K. The Poisoning of Livestock While Feeding on Plants of the Sorghum Group. Oklahoma Agr. Expt. Sta., *Circ. Infor.* 38. 1915.

580. Franke, K. W. (*et al.* in part). A New Toxicant Occurring Naturally in Certain Samples of Plant Foodstuffs. I-IV. *J. Nutr.,* **8:** 597. 1934.

581. Franke, K. W., T. D. Rice, A. G. Johnson, and H. W. Schoening. Report on a Preliminary Field Survey of the So-called "Alkali Disease" of Livestock. USDA, *Circ.* 320. 1934.

582. Franzke, C. J. Rancher, a Low Hydrocyanic Acid Forage Sorghum. South Dakota Agr. Expt. Sta., *Circ.* 57. 1945.

583. Franzke, C. J., L. F. Puhr, and A. N. Hume. A Study of Sorghum with Reference to the Content of HCN. South Dakota Agr. Expt. Sta., *Tech. Bull.* 1. 1939.

584. Fraps, G. S., and E. C. Carlyle. Locoine, the Poisonous Principle of Locoweed (*Astragalus earlei*). Texas Agr. Expt. Sta., *Bull.* 537. 1936.

585. Fraps, G. S., and S. H. Wender. Studies on Toxic Substances of Loco-

weeds, *Astragalus earlei* and Others. Texas Agr. Expt. Sta., *Bull.* 650. 1944.

586. Fraser, C. M., and J. Nelson. Sweet Clover Poisoning in Newborn Calves. *J. Am. Vet. Med. Assoc.,* **135**: 283. 1959.

587. Freeman, E. M. The Seed Fungus of *Lolium temulentum,* the Darnel. *Proc. Roy. Soc.* (London), **71**: 27. 1902.

588. Freeman, V. A., and G. A. Brown. 1944. Pig Manamar for Growing and Fattening Pigs. Michigan Agr. Expt. Sta., *Quart. Bull.,* **26**: 177. 1944.

589. Freer, R. S. Toxic Effects of a *Solidago* Species on Cattle. *Proc. Virginia Acad. Sci.,* **27**: 97. 1949.

590. French, C. Pokeroot Poisoning. *New York Med. J.,* **72**: 653. 1900.

591. Fulmer, E. Part III. Effect of Feeding Cottonseed Meal upon the Health of Animals, etc. Washington Agr. Expt. Sta., *Bull.* 67: 28. 1905.

592. Fyles, F. Principal Poisonous Plants of Canada. Canada Dept. Agr., Exptl. Farms, *Bull.* 39 (2nd ser.). 1920.

593. Gabbai, Lisbonne, and Pourquier. Ergot Poisoning at Pont St. Esprit. *Brit. Med. J.,* **2**: 650. 1951.

594. Gaillard, G. E. The Modern Treatment of Poison Ivy. *N.Y. State J. Med.,* **56**: 2255. 1956.

595. Gallagher, C. H., and J. H. Koch. Action of Pyrrolizidine Alkaloids on the Neuro-muscular Junction. *Nature* (London), **183**: 1124. 1959.

596. Gallie, J. G. E., and J. D. Patterson. Charlock Poisoning of Lambs. *Vet. Rec.,* **57**: 198. 1945.

597. Galloway, J. H. Grass Seed Nematode Poisoning in Livestock. *J. Am. Vet. Med. Assoc.,* **139**: 1212. 1961.

598. Gangstad, E. O. Composition, Yield, and Grazing Studies of Sudan and Related Sorghums. Hoblitzelle Agr. Lab., Texas Res. Found., *Bull.* 7. 1959.

599. Ganther, H. E. and C. A. Baumann. Selenium Metabolism. II. *J. Nutr.,* **77**: 408. 1962.

600. Gardiner, E. E. A Comparison of the Toxicity to Poults and Chicks of a Certain Peanut Oil Meal. *Poultry Sci.,* **41**: 1348. 1962.

601. Gardiner, M. R. Lupinosis—An Iron Storage Disease of Sheep. *Austral. Vet. J.* **37**: 135. 1961.

602. Gardiner, W. W. Locust-tree Bark Poisoning. *Am. Vet. Rev.,* **27**: 599. 1903.

603. Gardner, A. F. Morphologic and Histochemical Studies of Skeletal Lesions in Rats Fed Sweet Pea (*Lathyrus odoratus*) Seeds. *Am. J. Vet. Res.,* **21**: 298. 1960.

604. Gardner, C. A. The Wedge-leaved Rattlepod. W. Austral. Dept. Agr., *Leafl.* 2015. 1952.

605. Gardner, C. A., and H. W. Bennetts. *The Toxic Plants of Western Australia.* West Australian Newspapers, Ltd., Perth. 1956.

606. Garner, G. B. Learn to Live with Nitrates. Missouri Agr. Expt. Sta., *Bull.* 708. 1958.

607. Garner, R. J. *Veterinary Toxicology.* Baillière, Tindall, and Cox, London (Williams and Wilkins Co., Baltimore). 1957.

608. Gates, F. C. Botanical Notes, 1928–1929. *Trans. Kansas Acad. Sci.,* **33**: 26. 1930.

609. Gates, F. C. Principal Poisonous Plants in Kansas. Kansas Agr. Expt. Sta., *Tech. Bull.* 25. 1930.

610. Gay, J. Drip from 'Glades Manchineel Tree Burns, Sap Kills. *Florida Grower,* **59**(10): 17. 1951.

611. Geary, T. Castor Bean Poisoning. *Vet. Rec.,* **62**: 472. 1950.

612. Geiger, B. J., H. Steenbock, and H. T. Parsons. Lathyrism in the Rat. *J. Nutr.,* **6**: 427. 1933.

613. Gettler, A. O., and J. O. Baine. The Toxicology of Cyanide. *Am. J. Med. Sci.,* **195**(n.s.): 182. 1938.

614. Gibbard, J., and J. Naubert. Paralytic Shellfish Poisoning on the Canadian Atlantic. *Am. J. Publ. Health,* **38**: 550. 1948.

615. Gibbons, W. J. Photosensitization in Cattle. *Auburn Vet.,* **9**: 177. 1953.

616. Gibbons, W. J. "Downer" or "Bermuda Grass Poisoning." *N. Am. Vet.,* **34**: 433. 1953.

617. Gibbons, W. J. Forage Poisoning. *Mod. Vet. Pract.,* **40**(15): 41; **40**(16): 43. 1959.

618. Gibbons, W. J., E. H. Durr, and S. A. Cox. An Outbreak of Cirrhosis of the Liver in Horses. *N. Am. Vet.,* **34**: 556. 1953.

619. Gibbons, W. J., J. F. Hokanson, A. M. Wiggins, and M. B. Schmitz. Cirrhosis of the Liver in Horses. *N. Am. Vet.,* **31**: 229. 1950.

620. Gilbert, C. S., H. F. Eppson, W. B. Bradley, and O. A. Beath. Nitrate Accumulation in Cultivated Plants and Weeds. Wyoming Agr. Expt. Sta., *Bull.* 277. 1946.

621. Gilfillan, F. A., and C. Otsuki. Toxicity in the Leaves of *Rhododendron californicum* Hook. *J. Am. Pharm. Assoc.* (Sci. ed.), **27**: 396. 1938.

622. Gilkey, H. M. Livestock-poisoning Plants. Oregon Agr. Expt. Sta., *Bull.* 564. 1958.

623. Gill, D. A., and P. McGregor. Laurel Poisoning in Stock. *New Zealand J. Agr.,* **37**: 407. 1928.

624. Gillam, W. G. The Effect on Livestock of Water Contaminated with Fresh Water Algae. *J. Am. Vet. Med. Assoc.,* **67**: 780. 1925.

625. Gillis, W. T., W. Ball, Sr., and W. Ball, Jr. Pieris Poisoning in Zoo Animals. *M.S.U.* (Michigan State Univ.) *Vet.,* **22**: 24. 1961.

626. Gilruth, J. A. Note on Cirrhosis of the Liver in Horses and Cattle, and its Production in the Latter Experimentally. *The Vet.,* **75**: 436. 1902.

627. Glasscock, R. S., T. J. Cunha, A. M. Pearson, J. E. Pace, and D. M. Buschman. Preliminary Observation on Citrus Seed Meal as a Protein Supplement for Fattening Steers and Swine. Florida Agr. Expt. Sta., *Circ.* S12. 1950.

628. Gleeson, L. N. Suspected Bracken Poisoning. *Vet. Rec.,* **56**: 374. 1944.

629. Glover, G. H. Larkspur and other Poisonous Plants. Colorado Agr. Expt. Sta., *Bull.* 113. 1906.

630. Glover, G. H. The Whorled Milkweed. *Am. J. Vet. Med.,* **12**: 303. 1917.

631. Glover, G. H., I. E. Newsom, and W. W. Robbins. A New Poisonous Plant. Colorado Agr. Expt. Sta., *Bull.* 246. 1918.

632. Gmelin, J. F. *Abhandlung von den giftigen Gewächsen.* Stettin, Ulm. 1775.
633. Goldberg, R. E. The Jimson Weed Menace. *Today's Health,* **29:** 38. 1951.
634. Goldsmith, W. W. Onion Poisoning in Cattle. *J. Comp. Path. and Therapeut.* **22:** 151. 1909.
635. González, M. H., and F. Martínez Martínez. Las Plantas Toxicas al Ganado en los Pastizales de Chihuahua. Sec. de Agr. y Ganaderia, Off. de Estud. Esp., *Foll. Divulg. 28* (Mexico). 1958.
636. Goodman, A. A. Fescue Foot in Cattle in Colorado. *J. Am. Vet. Med. Assoc.,* **121:** 289. 1952.
637. Gore, T. L., and E. J. Tracy. Mushroom Poisoning. *Military Surgeon,* **77:** 281. 1935.
638. Gorham, P. R. Toxic Waterblooms of Blue-green Algae. *Canad. Vet. J.,* **1:** 235. 1960.
639. Gorham, P. R. Laboratory Studies on the Toxins Produced by Waterblooms of Blue-green Algae. *Am. J. Publ. Health,* **52:** 2100. 1962.
640. Gould, G. N., and K. G. Morgan. Acorn Poisoning. *Vet. Rec.,* **14:** 33. 1934.
641. Gowanloch, J. N., and C. A. Brown. *Poisonous Snakes, Plants, and Black Widow Spider of Louisiana.* Louisiana Dept. Conservation, New Orleans. 1943.
642. Graf, E., H. Boeddeker, and R. Rosha. Taxin B. das Hauptalkaloid von *Taxus baccata* L. *Arch. der Pharm.,* **291:** 443. 1958.
643. Graham, R. Forage Poisoning in Horses, Cattle, and Mules, So-called Cerebro-spinal Meningitis and Commonly Termed "Staggers." Kentucky Agr. Expt. Sta., *Bull.* **167:** 369. 1913.
644. Graham, R. Cornstalk Disease Investigations. *Vet. Med.,* **31:** 46. 1936.
645. Graham, R., and I. B. Boughton. White Snakeroot Poisoning. Illinois Agr. Expt. Sta., *Circ.* 295. 1925.
646. Graham, R., A. L. Bruechner, and R. L. Pontius. Studies in Forage Poisoning. Kentucky Agr. Expt. Sta., *Bull.* 207. 1917.
647. Graham, R., A. L. Bruechner, and R. L. Pontius. Studies in Forage Poisoning. Kentucky Agr. Expt. Sta., *Bull.* 208. 1917.
648. Graham, R., and V. M. Michael. White Snakeroot Poisoning. Illinois Agr. Expt. Sta., *Circ.* 436. 1935.
649. Grahame, E., H. E. Albiston, and L. B. Bull. Investigations into the Etiology and Control of Enzootic (Toxaemic) Jaundice of Sheep. *Austral. Vet. J.,* **25:** 202. 1949.
650. Grant, G. A., and E. O. Hughes. Development of Toxicity in Blue-green Algae. *Canad. J. Publ. Health,* **44:** 334. 1953.
651. Gray, J. E., G. H. Snoeyenbos, and I. M. Reynolds. The Hemorrhagic Syndrom of Chickens. *J. Am. Vet. Med. Assoc.,* **125:** 144. 1954.
652. Gray, M. L. Isolation of *Listeria monocytogenes* from Oat Silage. *Science,* **132:** 1767. 1960.
653. Greenberg, J., D. J. Taylor, H. W. Bond, and J. F. Sherman. Toxicity of Amine-Extracted Soybean Oil Meal. *J. Agr. Food Chem.,* **7:** 573. 1959.

654. Greer, M. A., and E. B. Astwood. The Antithyroid Effect of Certain Foods in Man as Determined with Radioactive Iodine. *Endocrinology,* **43**: 105. 1948.
655. Greer, M. J. Plant Poisoning in Cats. *Mod. Vet. Pract.,* **42**(20): 62. 1961.
656. Gregor, A. Feeding of Beet Tops. Proc. Conf. on Metabolic Disorders, Brit. Vet. Assoc., *Publ.* No. 23: 132. 1952.
657. Gregory, T. S. Trial of Cobalt Administration for the Prevention of *Heliotropium* Poisoning. *Austral. Vet. J.,* **39**: 64. 1963.
658. Gress, E. M. Poisonous Plants of Pennsylvania. Penn. Dept. Agr., *Bull.* 18(5) (*Gen. Bull.* 531). 1935.
659. Griffiths, T. W. Apparent Hazards of High Concentrate Feeding to Beef Cattle. *Vet. Rec.,* **75**: 182. 1963.
660. Groh, H. Horsetail a Horse-poisoning Weed. Canada Dept. Agr., Dom. Exptl. Farms, *Circ.* 74. 1930.
661. Groh, H. The Distribution of Bracken in its Possible Relations to Bovine Haematuria in British Columbia. *Sci. Agr.,* **21**: 703. 1941.
662. Grossman, C. M., and B. Malbin. Mushroom Poisoning: A Review of the Literature and Report of Two Cases Caused by a Previously Undescribed Species. *Ann. of Internal Med.,* **40**: 249. 1954.
663. Grover, M. J. Personal communication. 1961.
664. Guilhon, J. L'Ergotisme des Animaux Domestiques. *Rev. Path. Gén. et Comp.,* **55**: 1467. 1955.
665. Gunter, G., R. H. Williams, C. C. David, and F. G. W. Smith. Catastropic Mass Mortality of Marine Animals and Coincident Phytoplankton Bloom on the West Coast of Florida, November 1946 to August 1947. *Ecol. Monogr.,* **18**: 309. 1948.
666. Gussow, H. T. Horsetail, *Equisetum arvense* L. Canada Dept. Agr., Dom. Exptl. Farms, *Rept.,* **1912**: 210. 1912.
667. Guth, E. P. A Phytochemical and Phytological Study of *Solanum Villosum. J. Am. Pharm. Assoc.,* **27**: 217. 1938.
668. Gwatkin, R., and I. W. Moynihan. Wild Mustard Seed Poisoning in Cattle. *Canad. J. Comp. Med. and Vet. Sci.,* **7**: 76. 1943.
669. Haag, J. R. Toxicity of Nematode Infested Chewings Fescue Seed. *Science,* **102**: 406. 1954.
670. Haag, J. R., B. Stearman, P. H. Weswig, R. I. Pierce, and J. R. Schubert. Mechanism of Thiamine Destruction by Bracken Fern. *Feder. Proc.,* **9**: 180. 1950.
671. Haag, J. R., and P. H. Weswig. Further Observations Concerning Antithiamine Activity in Plants. *Feder. Proc.,* **7**: 157. 1948.
672. Haag, J. R., P. H. Weswig, and A. M. Freed. Anti-thiamine Activity of Bracken Fern. *Feder. Proc.,* **6**: 408. 1947.
673. Habekost, R. C., I. M. Fraser, and B. W. Halsted. Observations on Toxic Marine Algae. *J. Wash. Acad. Sci.,* **45**: 101. 1955.
674. Hackbarth, J. Lupinosis in the Light of Old and New Evidence. *J. Austral. Inst. Agr. Sci.,* **27**: 61. 1961.
675. Hackett, W. Poisoning of Cattle with Horseradish. *J. Comp. Path. and Therapeut.* **30**: 138. 1917.

676. Hadley, F. B. The Sudan Grass Poisoning Problem. *Canad. J. Comp. Med.*, **2:** 169. 1938.

677. Hadley, F. B., and F. L. Kozelka. Antidotes for Hydrocyanic Acid Poisoning. *Vet. Med.*, **30:** 79. 1935.

678. Hadwen, S. So-called Staggers in Horses Caused by the Ingestion of *Pteris aquilina*, the Common Bracken. *J. Am. Vet. Med. Assoc.*, **50:** 702. 1917.

679. Hadwen, S., and E. A. Bruce. The Poisoning of Horses by the Common Bracken. *Vet. J.*, **76:** 98. 1920.

680. Hadwen, S., and E. A. Bruce. The Poisoning of Horses by the Common Bracken (*Pteris aqualina* L.). *Vet. J.*, **89:** 120. 1933.

681. Hagan, W. A. Further Studies of the Etiology of an Undiagnosed Disease of Cattle. *Cornell Vet.*, **12:** 43. 1922.

682. Hagan, W. A. Bracken Poisoning of Cattle. *Cornell Vet.*, **15:** 326. 1925.

683. Hagan, W. A., and A. Zeissig. Experimental Bracken Poisoning of Cattle. *Cornell Vet.*, **17:** 194. 1927.

684. Haggerty, D. R., and J. A. Conway. Report of Poisoning by *Cicuta maculata*. *New York State J. Med.*, **36:** 1511. 1936.

685. Hakim, S. A. E., V. Mijović, and J. Walker. Distribution of Certain Poppy-Fumaria Alkaloids and a Possible Link with the Incidence of Glaucoma. *Nature* (London), **189:** 198. 1961.

686. Hakim, S. A. E., V. Mijović, and J. Walker. Experimental Transmission of Sanguinarine in Milk: Detection of a Metabolic Product. *Nature* (London), **189:** 201. 1961.

687. Hale, F., and C. M. Lyman. Cottonseed as a Source of Animal Feedstuffs. *In* Bailey, A. E., ed., *Cottonseed and Cottonseed Products*. Interscience Publ., New York. 1948.

688. Hale, F., and C. M. Lyman. Effect of Protein Level in the Ration on Gossypol Tolerance in Growing—Fattening Pigs. *J. Anim. Sci.*, **16:** 364. 1957.

689. Hale, F., C. M. Lyman, and H. A. Smith. Use of Cottonseed Meal in Swine Rations. Texas Agr. Expt. Sta., *Bull.* 898. 1958.

690. Hall, A. E. Fatal Hemorrhages in Chickens, Possibly Due to Rape Pasture. *M. S. C.* (Michigan State College) *Vet.*, **14:** 148. 1954.

691. Halsted, B. D. Poisonous Plants in New Jersey, a Preliminary Report. New Jersey Agr. Expt. Sta., *Ann. Rept.*, **1895:** 351. 1895.

692. Halverson, A. W., P. L. Guss, and O. E. Olson. Effect of Sulfur Salts on Selenium Poisoning in the Rat., *J. Nutr.*, **77:** 459. 1962.

693. Halverson, A. W., and K. J. Monty. An Effect of Dietary Sulfate on Selenium Poisoning in the Rat. *J. Nutr.*, **70:** 100. 1960.

694. Halverson, J. O., and F. W. Sherwood. Investigations in the Feeding of Cottonseed Meal to Cattle. North Carolina Agr. Expt. Sta., *Tech. Bull.* 39. 1930.

695. Hansen, A. A. Robitin—A Potent Plant Poison. *Better Crops*, **2**(2): 22. 1924.

696. Hansen, A. A. Two Common Weeds that Cause Death. Purdue (Indiana) Agr. Expt. Sta., *Circ.* 110. 1923.

697. Hansen, A. A. A Unique Experiment with White Snakeroot. *J. Am. Vet. Med. Assoc.*, **65**: 224. 1924.
698. Hansen, A. A. Cocklebur Sprouts are Deadly. *Better Crops*, **2**(1): 28. 1924.
699. Hansen, A. A. Dutchman's-breeches. *Better Crops*, **2**(4): 26. 1924.
700. Hansen, A. A. Jimson Poisoning. *Better Crops*, **2**(6): 28. 1924.
701. Hansen, A. A. Mechanical Injuries Caused by Weeds and Other Plants. *Proc. Indiana Acad. Sci.*, **34**: 229. 1924.
702. Hansen, A. A. Prussic Acid Poisoning in Livestock. *Better Crops*, **2**(3): 26, 38. 1924.
703. Hansen, A. A. The Poison Plant Situation in Indiana. II. *J. Am. Vet. Med. Assoc.*, **66**: 80. 1924.
704. Hansen, A. A. The Poison Plant Situation in Indiana. III. *J. Am. Vet. Med. Assoc.*, **66**: 351. 1924.
705. Hansen, A. A. Two Fatal Cases of Potato Poisoning. *Science*, **61**: 340. 1925.
706. Hansen, A. A. Stock Poisoning by Plants in the Nightshade Family. *J. Am. Vet. Med. Assoc.*, **71**: 221. 1927.
707. Hansen, A. A. Cicuta or Water Hemlock Poisoning. *N. Am. Vet.*, **9**(6): 34. 1928.
708. Hansen, A. A. Potato Poisoning. *N. Am. Vet.*, **9**(7): 31. 1928.
709. Hansen, A. A. Stock Poisoning. *N. Am. Vet.*, **9**(5): 24. 1928.
710. Hansen, A. A. The Latest Developments in the Stock-poisoning Plants Situation in Indiana. *J. Am. Vet. Med. Assoc.*, **73**: 471. 1928.
711. Hansen, A. A. The Tragedy of Hindustan. *Nature Magazine*, **11**: 385. 1928.
712. Hansen, A. A. Trifoliosis and Similar Stock Diseases. *N. Am. Vet.* **9**(8): 34. 1928.
713. Hansen, A. A. Indiana Plants Injurious to Livestock. Purdue (Indiana) Agr. Expt. Sta., *Circ.* 175. 1930.
714. Hanson, A. A. *Sorghum almum.* (Remarks made at the Maryland Crop Improvement Assoc. Meeting, 1/14/59. Mimeographed.)
715. Hanson, L. E., W. R. Pritchard, C. E. Rehfeld, V. Perman, J. H. Sautter, and M. O. Schultze. Studies on Trichloroethylene-extracted Feeds. Experiments with Swine Fed Trichloroethylene-extracted Soybean Oil Meal. *J. Anim. Sci.*, **15**: 368. 1956.
716. Hanway, J. J., and A. J. Englehorn. Nitrate Accumulation in Some Iowa Crop Plants. *Agron. J.*, **50**: 331. 1958.
717. Harbaugh, F. G. and J. Dennis. The Blood Potassium and Calcium Levels of Cattle Grazing Wheat. *Am. J. Vet. Res.*, **8**: 396. 1947.
718. Hardikar, S. W. On Rhododendron Poisoning. *J. Pharm. and Exptl. Therapeut.*, **20**: 17. 1922.
719. Hardin, J. W. Poisonous Plants of North Carolina. North Carolina Agr. Expt. Sta., *Bull.* 414. 1961.
720. Hardison, J. R. Seed Disorders of Forage Plants. USDA, *Yearbook of Agr.*, **1953**: 272. 1953.

721. Hardy, W. T., V. L. Cory, H. Schmidt, and J. W. Dameron. Bitterweed Poisoning in Sheep. Texas Agr. Expt. Sta., *Bull.* 433. 1931.

722. Harms, R. H., C. F. Simpson, and P. W. Waldroup. Influence of Feeding Various Levels of Velvet Beans to Chicks and Laying Hens. *J. Nutr.,* **75:** 127. 1961.

723. Harris, F. W., and F. Cockburn. Alleged Poisoning by Potatoes. *Am. J. Pharm.,* **90:** 722. 1918.

724. Harris, P. N., R. C. Anderson, and K. K. Chen. The Action of Senecionine, Integerrimine, Jacobine, Longilobine, and Spartioidine, Especially on the Liver. *J. Pharm. and Exptl. Therapeut.,* **75:** 69. 1942.

725. Harris, P. N., R. C. Anderson, and K. K. Chen. The Action of Monocrotaline and Retronecine. *J. Pharm. and Exptl. Therapeut.,* **75:** 78. 1942.

726. Harshberger, J. W. *Pastoral and Agricultural Botany.* P. Blakiston's Son and Co., Philadelphia. 1920.

727. Hart, G. H., H. R. Guilbert, K. A. Wagnon, and H. Goss. "Acorn Calves." California Agr. Expt. Sta., *Bull.* 699. 1947.

728. Hart, L. "Petty Spurge" (*Euphorbia peplus*) not Harmful to Fowls. *Agr. Gazette of New South Wales,* **48:** 489. 1937.

729. Hart, L. The Toxicity of Seeds of *Argemone mexicana* for Fowls. *Austral. Vet. J.,* **17:** 69. 1941.

730. Hart, R. C. Animal Poisoning by Yew. Bull. Suppl. Material, *Clinical Toxicol. of Commercial Prod.* (by Gleason, Gosselin, and Hodge), Univ. of Rochester, 4(7): 12. 1960 (Processed).

731. Hart, R. C. Personal communication. 1960.

732. Hartwell, J. L., and A. W. Schrecker. The Chemistry of Podophyllum. *Fortschritte der Chemie Organischer Naturstoffe,* **15:** 83. 1958.

733. Harvey, R. B., A. H. Larson, R. H. Landon, W. L. Boyd, and L. C. Erickson. Weeds Poisonous to Livestock. Minnesota Agr. Expt. Sta., *Bull.* 388. 1944.

734. Hassall, C. H., and K. Reyle. Hypoglycin A and B, Two Biologically Active Polypeptides from *Blighia sapida. Biochem. J.,* **60:** 334. 1955.

735. Havard, V. The Sleepy Grass. *Garden and Forest,* **4:** 111. 1891.

736. Hawk, W. Hematuria in Dairy Heifers Probably Due to a Plant Toxin. *J. Am. Vet. Med. Assoc.,* **128:** 261. 1956.

737. Hayes, W. F. Probable Dallis Grass Poisoning. *Texas Vet. Bull.,* **10**(1): 5. 1948.

738. Hays, C. H., and L. Van Es. On the Nature, Cause, and Possible Prevention of the "Walking Disease" Among Horses and Cattle. (Unnumbered Publ. of:) Nebraska Dept. Agr., Bur. Anim. Ind., Lincoln, July 1, 1929.

739. Head, M. J., and J. A. F. Rook. Hypomagnesaemia in Dairy Cattle and its Possible Relationship to Ruminal Ammonia Production. *Nature* (London), **176:** 262. 1955.

740. Head, M. J., and J. A. F. Rook. Some Effects of Spring Grass on Rumen Digestion and Metabolism of the Dairy Cow. *Proc. Nutr. Soc.,* **16:** 25. 1957.

741. Heald, F. D., and A. T. Peters. Ergot and Ergotism. Nebraska Agr. Expt. Sta., *Press Bull.* 23. 1906.

742. Heath, G. B. S., and B. Wood. Bracken Poisoning in Cattle. *J. Comp. Path.*, **68:** 201. 1958.

743. Hedrick, U. P. A Plant that Poisons Cattle—*Cicuta.* Oregon Agr. Expt. Sta., *Bull.* 46. 1897.

744. Heftmann, E., and E. Mosettig. *Biochemistry of Steroids.* Reinhold Publ. Corp., New York. 1960.

745. Heller, A. A. The Death Camas. *Muhlenbergia*, **5:** 50. 1909.

746. Heller, C. A. *Edible and Poisonous Plants of Alaska.* Extension Service, Univ. Alaska, College. 1953.

747. Helmer, J. Acute Toxic Anemia—Was it Caused by *Coleosporium solidagenis* Thümen. *J. Comp. Med. and Vet. Arch.*, **14:** 150. 1893.

748. Helwig, D. M., and B. P. Setchell. Observations on the Diagnosis of Nitrite Poisoning in Sheep. *Austral. Vet. J.*, **36:** 14. 1960.

749. Hendershot, J. M. Ketosis in the Hawaiian Islands. *J. Am. Vet. Med. Assoc.*, **108:** 74. 1946.

750. Henderson, J. A., E. V. Evans, and R. A. McIntosh. The Antithiamine Action of *Equisetum. J. Am. Vet. Med. Assoc.*, **120:** 375. 1952.

751. Hendricks, H. V. Poisoning by False Morel (*Gyrometra esculenta*). *J. Am. Med. Assoc.*, **114:** 1625. 1940.

752. Hendrickson, J. M., and K. F. Hilbert. Pokeweed Berries not Poisonous for Chickens. *J. Am. Vet. Med. Assoc.*, **78:** 556. 1931.

753. Hercus, C. E., and H. D. Purves. Studies on Endemic and Experimental Goiter. *J. Hygiene*, **36:** 182. 1936.

754. Hershey, A. L. Some Poisonous Plants Problems of New Mexico. New Mexico Agr. Expt. Sta., *Bull.* 322. 1945.

755. Hershey, A. L. Another Poisonous Species of *Eupatorium. Colorado-Wyoming Acad. Sci. J.*, **4:** 52. 1949.

756. Hester, J. H. The Injurious Effects of Malva Plant. *Am. Vet. Rev.*, **30:** 106. 1906.

757. Heuser, G. F., and A. E. Schumacher. The Feeding of Corn Cockle to Chickens. *Poultry Sci.*, **21:** 86. 1942.

758. Heyl, F. W., and M. E. Herr. The Formula of Zygadenine. *J. Am. Chem. Soc.*, **71:** 1751. 1949.

759. Heyl, F. W., S. K. Loy, H. G. Knight, and O. L. Prien. The Chemical Examination of Death Camas. Wyoming Agr. Expt. Sta., *Bull.* 94. 1912.

760. Heyl, F. W., and L. C. Raiford. Analysis of *Zygadenus intermedius. J. Am. Chem. Soc.*, **33:** 206. 1911.

761. Heywang, B. W., and H. R. Bird. Supplements for Cottonseed Meal in Diets of Chickens. *Poultry Sci.*, **29:** 486. 1950.

762. Heywang, B. W., and H. R. Bird. The Effect of Alfalfa Saponin on the Growth, Diet Consumption, and Efficiency of Diet Utilization of Chicks. *Poultry Sci.*, **33:** 239. 1954.

763. Heywang, B. W., and H. R. Bird. Relationship Between the Weight of Chicks and Levels of Dietary Free Gossypol Supplied by Different Cottonseed Products. *Poultry Sci.*, **34:** 1239. 1955.

764. Heywang, B. W., H. R. Bird, and A. M. Altschul. The Effect of Pure Gossypol on Egg Hatchability and Weight. *Poultry Sci.*, **29:** 916. 1950.

765. Heywang, B. W., H. R. Bird, and R. P. Kupperman. The loss or Inactivation of Pure Gossypol in a Mixed Diet. *Poultry Sci.,* **31:** 35. 1952.
766. Heywang, B. W., C. A. Denton, and H. R. Bird. The Effect of the Dietary Level of Cottonseed Meal on Hatchability. *Poultry Sci.,* **28:** 610. 1949.
767. Hidiroglou, M. and H. J. Knutti, The Effects of Green Tall Buttercup in Roughage on the Growth and Health of Beef Cattle and Sheep. *Canad. J. Anim. Sci.,* **43:** 68. 1963.
768. Hill, E. G., K. P. Misra, T. H. Canfield, E. L. Johnson, V. Perman, W. R. Pritchard, J. H. Sautter, and M. O. Schultze. Studies on Trichloroethylene-Extracted Feeds. 8. *Poultry Sci.,* **35:** 686. 1956.
769. Hill, H. E. Fluorine Poisoning, *Auburn Vet.,* **7:** 127. 1951.
770. Hill, J. A. Chemistry Department, Wyoming Agr. Expt. Sta., *Ann. Rept.,* **44:** 17. 1933–34.
771. Hill, K. R. Hypoglycaemia and Fatty Metamorphosis of the Liver in the Vomiting Sickness of Jamaica. *J. Path. Bact.,* **60:** 334. 1953.
772. Hill, K. R. The World-wide Distribution of Seneciosis in Man and Animals. *Proc. Roy. Soc. Med.,* **53:** 281. 1960.
773. Hill, K. R. Comment on the Histological Appearances in Serial Liver Biopsies and Post-mortem Specimens. *Vet. Rec.,* **75:** 493. 1963.
774. Hill, K. R., and G. Bras. Geographic Pathology of Hepatitis. *In* Hartman, F. W., *et al.,* eds., *Hepatitis Frontiers.* Little, Brown & Co., Boston. 1957.
775. Hill, K. R., L. M. Markson, and R. Schoental. Discussion on Seneciosis in Man and Animals. *Proc. Roy. Soc. Med.* (Britain), **53:** 281. 1960.
776. Hill, K. R., and H. M. Martin. Hepatic Veno-occlusive Disease and Meglalocytosis in Senecio Poisoning of Horses. *Brit. Vet. J.,* **114:** 345. 1958.
777. Hill, R., and R. van Heyningen. Ranunculin: The Precursor of the Vesicant Substance of the Buttercup. *Biochem. J.,* **49:** 332. 1951.
778. Hill, R. K. Stereochemistry of the Hemlock Alkaloids. I & II. *J. Am. Chem. Soc.,* **80:** 1609. 1958.
779. Hiltner, R. S. The Fatal Effect of Green Sorghum. Nebraska Agr. Expt. Sta., *Bull.* 63. 1900.
780. Hocking, G. M. Henbane—Healing Herb of Hercules and of Apollo. *Econ. Bot.,* **1:** 306; **2:** 110. 1947, 1948.
781. Hogue, D. E., J. F. Proctor, and D. C. Maplesden. The Relationship Between Selenium, Muscular Dystrophy, and Other Factors in Animal Nutrition. *Proc. Cornell Nutrition Conf. for Feed Manuf.,* **1959:** 96. 1959.
782. Holm, G. C., D. F. Eveleth, and W. E. Dinusson. Trichloroethylene Soybean Meal Poisoning in Sheep. *J. Am. Vet. Med. Assoc.,* **122:** 380. 1953.
783. Holmes, H. L. The Chemistry of the Tropane Alkaloids. *In* Manske, R. H. R., and H. L. Holmes, eds., *The Alkaloids.* Academic Press, New York. Vol. I, 1950.
784. Holmes, R. L., and E. T. Rayner. Isolation of Two Nitrogen-free Toxins from Tung Kernels. *J. Am. Oil. Chem. Soc.,* **35:** 586. 1958.
785. Holmgren, A. H. Two Poisonous Milkweeds. Utah Agr. Expt. Sta., *Farm and Home Sci.,* **6**(2): 11. 1945.
786. Holtenius, P. Nitrite Poisoning in Sheep, with Special Reference to the

Detoxification of Nitrite in the Rumen. *Acta. Agr. Scandin.,* **7:** 113. 1957.

787. Holz, W. Der Alkaloidgehalt des Duwocks (*Equisetum palustre* L.) nach Wuchsstoffbehandlung und die sich daraus ergebenden Möglichkeiten zu seiner Bekämpfung. *Berlin. Biol. Bundesanst. f. Land- u. Forstwirt. Mitt.,* **87:** 51. 1957.

788. Horne, C. H. Dallis Grass Poisoning. *Texas Vet. Bull.,* **10**(3): 1. 1948.

789. Hosking, J. R., and C. W. Brandt. The Toxic Principle of Ragwort, *Senecio jacobaea. New Zealand J. Sci. and Tech.,* **17:** 638. 1936.

790. Hotson, J. W. Mushroom Poisoning at Seattle. *Mycologia,* **26:** 194. 1934.

791. Hotson, J. W., and E. Lewis. *Amanita pantherina* of Western Washington. *Mycologia,* **26:** 384. 1934.

792. Householder, G. T., and J. W. Dollahite. Some Clinical Biochemical Changes in the Blood Serum of Calves Fed *Quercus havardi. Southw. Vet.,* **16:** 107. 1963.

793. Howarth, J. A. Sudan Grass as a Photosensitizing Agent Causing Dermatitis in Sheep. *N. Am. Vet.,* **12**(1): 29. 1931.

794. Howes, F. N. Sources of Poisonous Honey. *Kew Bulletin,* **1949:** 167. 1949.

795. Huang, T. C., T. J. Cunha, and W. E. Ham. The Deleterious Effects of Flat Pea Seed for Rats. *Am. J. Vet. Res.,* **11:** 217. 1950.

796. Hubbs, J. C. Belladonna Poisoning in Pigs. *Vet. Med.,* **42:** 428. 1947.

797. Hudson, R. Poisoning by Horsetail (*Equisetum arvense*). *Vet. J.,* **80:** 40. 1924.

798. Huebner, C. F., and K. P. Link. Studies on the Hemorrhagic Sweet Clover Disease. VI. *J. Biol. Chem.,* **138:** 529. 1941.

799. Huey, I. B. Rape Poisoning in Cattle. *Irish Vet. J.,* **12:** 83. 1958.

800. Huffaker, C. B., and C. E. Kennett. A Ten-year Study of Vegetational Changes Associated with Biological Control of Klamath Weed. *J. Range Management,* **12:** 69. 1959.

801. Huffman, W. T. Personal communication. 1955.

802. Huffman, W. T. Personal communication. 1961.

803. Huffman, W. T., and J. F. Couch. Plants Poisonous to Livestock. USDA, *Yearbook of Agr.,* **1942:** 354. 1942.

804. Huffman, W. T., E. A. Moran, and W. Binns. Poisonous Plants. USDA, *Yearbook of Agr.,* **1956:** 118. 1956.

805. Hughes, E. O., P. R. Gorham, and A. Zehnder. Toxicity of a Unialgal Culture of *Microcystis aeruginosa. Canad. J. Microbiol.,* **4:** 225. 1958.

806. Hughes, H. T. Mustard Poisoning. *Vet. J.,* **80:** 43. 1924.

807. Hughes, J. D., and J. A. Clark. Stramonium Poisoning, a Report of Two Cases. *J. Am. Med. Assoc.,* **112:** 2500. 1939.

808. Hughes, J. P. and C. E. Cornelius. An Outbreak of Grass Tetany in Lactating Beef Cattle. *Cornell Vet.,* **50:** 26. 1960.

809. Humphreys, F. A., and R. J. Gibbons, Deaths of Mink Probably Shellfish Poisoning. *Canad. J. Comp. Med.,* **5:** 84. 1941.

810. Hurst, E. *The Poison Plants of New South Wales.* N.S.W. Poison Plants Committee, Sydney. 1942.

811. Hurt, L. M. Flaxstraw Impaction. Los Angeles County Livestock Dept., *Ann. Rept.*, **1942–1943**: 11.
812. Hurt, L. M. Avocado Poisoning. Los Angeles County Livestock Dept., *Ann. Rept.*, **1942–1943**: 44.
813. Hutner, S. H., and J. J. A. McLaughlin. Poisonous Tides. *Sci. American*, **199**(2): 92. 1958.
814. Hutton, E. M., G. M. Windrum, and C. C. Kratzing. Studies on the Toxicity of *Indigofera endecaphylla*. I. II. *J. Nutr.*, **64**: 321. 1958; **65**: 429. 1958.
815. Hutton, J. E. Favism. *J. Am. Med. Assoc.*, **109**: 1618. 1937.
816. Hyams, C. W. Medicinal Plants. North Carolina Agr. Expt. Sta., *Bull.* 150. 1898.
817. Hyams, T. A., and R. J. Mesler. Effects of a Synthetic Nitrate Concentrate Administered Orally to Cattle. *J. Am. Vet. Med. Assoc.*, **137**: 477. 1960.
818. Ince, J. W. Experiments Upon Flax Screenings. North Dakota Agr. Expt. Sta., *Special Bull.* 1: 393. 1911.
819. Ing, H. R. Mydriatic Alkaloids. *In* Manske, R. H. F., and H. L. Holmes, eds., *The Alkaloids*. Academic Press, New York. Vol. V, 1955.
820. Ing, H. R., and R. P. Patel. Local Anesthetics Derived from the Alkaloid Cytisine. *J. Pham. and Exptl. Therapeut.* **59**: 401. 1937.
821. Ingle, R. M., and D. P. deSylva. The Red Tide. Florida State Board Conserv., *Ed. Ser.* 1. Rev. 1955.
822. Ingram, W. M., and G. W. Prescott. *Illustrations of Fresh-water Algae Toxic to Animals*. Ohio-Tennesee Drainage Basins Off., Div. Water Pollution Control, Pub. Health Serv., Cincinnati, Ohio. 1952.
823. Ingram, W. M., and G. W. Prescott. Toxic Fresh-water Algae. *Am. Midl. Nat.*, **52**: 75. 1954.
824. Jacobson, C. A. Water Hemlock (*Cicuta*). Nevada Agr. Expt. Sta., *Tech. Bull.* 81. 1915.
825. Jacobziner, H., and H. W. Raybin. Internal Drug Poisonings Including Three Fatalities. *New York State J. Med.*, **60**: 3139. 1960.
826. Jacobziner, H., and H. W. Raybin. Fatal Salicylate Poisoning and Stramonium Poisoning. *New York State J. Med.*, **61**: 301. 1961.
827. Jacobziner, H., and H. W. Raybin. Plant and Insecticide Poisonings. *New York State J. Med.*, **61**: 2463. 1961.
828. James, L. F., and W. Binns. The Use of Mineral Supplements to Prevent Halogeton Poisoning in Sheep. *Proc. Am. Soc. Anim. Prod., West. Sect.*, **12**(68): 1. 1961.
829. Jeganathan, P. Toxic Effects of Feeding *Indigofera endecaphylla* (Jacq.) to Calves. *Ceylon Vet. J.*, 1: 83. 1953.
830. Jeger, O., and V. Prelog. Steroid Alkaloids: Veratrum Group. *In* Manske, R. H. F., ed., *The Alkaloids*. Academic Press, New York. Vol. VII, 1960.
831. Jeliffe, S. E. Some Notes on Poisoning by *Clitocybe dealbata* (Sow.) var. *sudorifica* (Peck). *New York State J. Med.*, **37**: 1357. 1937.
832. Jennings, R. E. Stramonium Poisoning. *J. Pediatrics*, **6**: 657. 1935.

833. Jensen, K. A., J. Conti, and A. Kjaer. *iso*Thiocyanates II. Volatile *iso*-Thiocyanates in Seeds and Roots of Various *Brassicae*. *Acta Chem. Scandinavica,* **7:** 1267. 1953.

834. Jensen, R., A. W. Deem, and D. Knaus. Fescue Lameness in Cattle. I. Experimental Production of the Disease. *Am. J. Vet. Res.,* **17:** 196. 1956.

835. Jensen, R., L. A. Griner, and O. R. Adams. Polioencephalomalacia in Cattle and Sheep. *J. Am. Vet. Med. Assoc.,* **129:** 311. 1956.

836. Johnson, A. Mintweed in the Northwest. *New South Wales Agr. Gaz.,* **63:** 453. 1952.

837. Johnson, A. G., and R. E. Vaughan. Ergot in Rye and How to Remove It. Wisconsin Agr. Ext. Serv., *Circ.* 94. 1918.

838. Johnson, E. P., and W. A. Archer. The Principal Stock-poisoning Plants of New Mexico. N. Mex. Agr. Expt. Sta., *Circ.* 71. 1922.

839. Johnson, H. W., R. Graham, and J. P. Torrey. A Note on the Non-poisonous Properties of Osage Oranges (*Maclura pomifera*). *J. Am. Vet. Med. Assoc.,* **86:** 667. 1935.

840. Johnston, A., and R. W. Peake. Effect of Selective Grazing by Sheep on the Control of Leafy Spurge (*Euphorbia esula* L.). *J. Range Management,* **12:** 192. 1960.

841. Johnston, W. Biliary Cirrhosis of the Liver in Cattle. *Proc. U.S. Vet. Med. Assoc.,* **30:** 120. 1893.

842. Jones, E. B., and C. M. Edwards. Ergot Poisoning in Young Cattle. *Vet. Rec.,* **65:** 156. 1953.

843. Jones, I., and E. V. Lynn. Differences in Species of Taxus. *J. Am. Pharm. Assoc.,* **22:** 528. 1933.

844. Jones, L. R. Are Our Native Horsetails or Ferns Poisonous? *Proc. Soc. Promotion Agr. Sci.,* **22:** 70. 1901.

845. Jones, S. E., W. H. Hill, and T. A. Bond. Control of the Bitterweed Plant Poisonous to Sheep in the Edwards Plateau Region. Texas Agr. Expt. Sta., *Bull.* 464. 1932.

846. Jordan, E. O., and N. M. Harris. The Cause of Milksickness or Trembles. *J. Am. Med. Assoc.,* **50:** 1665. 1908.

847. Jordan, E. O., and N. M. Harris. Milksickness. *J. Infect. Diseases,* **6:** 401. 1909.

848. Jungherr, E. Lechuguilla Fever of Sheep and Goats; a Form of Swellhead in West Texas. *Cornell Vet.,* **21:** 227. 1931.

849. Kalkus, J. W., H. A. Tripeer, and J. R. Fuller. Enzootic Hepatic Cirrhosis of Horses (Walking Disease) in the Pacific Northwest. *J. Am. Vet. Med. Assoc.,* **68:** 285–289. 1925.

850. Kaneko, J. J., C. E. Cornelius, and N. F. Baker. Erythrocyte Survival in Experimental Molybdenosis of Sheep. *Proc. Soc. Expt. Biol. Med.,* **107:** 924. 1961.

851. Kauffman, C. H. The Agaricaceae of Michigan, Vol. 1. Mich. Geol. and Biol. Survey, *Publ.* 26 (Biol. Ser. 5). 1918.

852. Keech, M. K. Electron Microscope Study of the Lathyritic Rat Aorta. *J. Biophysic. and Biochem. Cytol.,* **7:** 539. 1960.

853. Keil, H., D. Wasserman, and C. R. Dawson. Mango Dermatitis and its Relationship to Poison Ivy Hypersensitivity. *Ann. Allergy*, **4**: 268. 1946.

854. Keilholz, F. J. Spoiled Feed Shown to be Cause of Pig Trouble. Illinois Agr. Expt. Sta., *Ann. Rept.*, **41**: 144. 1928.

855. Kelly, J. W., C. W. Barber, D. D. Pate, and C. H. Hill. Effect of Feeding Crotalaria Seed to Young Chickens. *J. Am. Vet. Med. Assoc.*, **139**: 1215. 1961.

856. Kelsey, H. P., and W. A. Dayton. *Standardized Plant Names.* J. Horace McFarland Co., Harrisburg, Penn. 2nd ed., 1942.

857. Kendrick, J. W., J. Tucker, and S. A. Peoples. Nitrate Poisoning in Cattle Due to Ingestion of Variegated Thistle, *Silybum marianum. J. Am. Vet. Med. Assoc.*, **126**: 53. 1955.

858. Kennedy, P. C. Tarweed Poisoning in Swine. *J. Am. Vet. Med. Assoc.*, **130**: 305. 1957.

859. Kenten, R. H. The Partial Purification and Properties of a Thiaminase from Bracken [*Pteridium aquilinum* (L.) Kuhn]. *Biochem. J.*, **67**: 25. 1957.

860. Kerman, W. R. Impaction in Horses Due to Ingestion of Pea Straw. *J. Am. Vet. Med. Assoc.*, **95**: 237. 1939.

861. Kern, H. Die Gifte von *Equisetum palustre* L. Berlin. *Biol. Bundesanst. f. Land- u. Forstwirt. Mitt.*, **87**: 49. 1957.

862. Kidder, R. W., D. W. Beardsley, and T. C. Erwin. Photosensitization in Cattle Grazing Bermuda Grass. Assoc. of Southern Agric. Workers, *Proc.*, **48**: 80. 1951.

863. Kidder, R. W., D. W. Beardsley, and T. C. Erwin. Photosensitization in Cattle Grazing Frosted Common Bermuda Grass. Florida Agr. Expt. Sta., *Bull.* 630. 1961.

864. King, E. D., Jr. Poisonous Plants of the South. *J. Am. Vet. Med. Assoc.*, **57**: 302. 1920.

865. King, E. D., Jr. Jimson Weed Poisoning. *J. Am. Vet. Med. Assoc.*, **64**: 98. 1923.

866. King, J. M. Personal communication. 1960.

867. King, W. A., H. A. Campbell, I. W. Rupel, P. H. Phillips, and G. Bohstedt. The Effect of Alfalfa Lipids on the Progress of Sweet Clover Poisoning in Cattle. *J. Dairy Sci.*, **24**: 1. 1941.

868. Kingery, B. W., W. R. Richter, and R. M. Dingel. Acorn Poisoning in Cattle. *Iowa State Univ. Vet.*, **22**: 30. 1959.

869. Kingsbury, J. M. Plants Poisonous to Livestock. A Review. *J. Dairy Sci.*, **41**: 875. 1958.

870. Kingsbury, J. M. Toxicity of *Apocynum* (Dogbane) to Stock; a Correction. *Cornell Vet.*, **49**: 285. 1959.

871. Kingsbury, J. M. Knowledge of Poisonous Plants in the United States—Brief History and Conclusions. *Econ. Bot.*, **15**: 119. 1961.

872. Kingsley, A. T. Cocklebur Cotyledons Poisonous. *Vet. Med.*, **15**: 544. 1920.

873. Kinsley, A. T. Cocklebur Poisoning in Swine. *Vet. Med.*, **17**: 282. 1922.

874. Kirby-Smith, J. L. Mango Dermatitis. *Am. J. Trop. Med.*, **18**: 373. 1938.
875. Kjaer, A., J. Conti, and K. A. Jensen. *iso*Thiocyanates III. The Volatile *iso*Thiocyanates in Seeds of Rape (*Brassica napus* L.). *Acta Chem. Scandinavica*, **7**: 1271. 1953.
876. Kjaer, A., J. Conti, and I. Larsen. *iso*Thiocyanates IV. A Systematic Investigation of the Occurrence and Chemical Nature of Volatile *iso*-Thiocyanates in Seeds of Various Plants. *Acta Chem. Scandinavica*, **7**: 1276. 1953.
877. Kligman, A. M. Poison Ivy (*Rhus*) Dermatitis. *A.M.A. Arch. Derm.*, **77**: 149. 1958.
878. Kobayashi, T. Studies on the Histo-pathologic Changes of Experimental Cases of the "Ezonegi-poisoning" in Horses. *Japanese J. Vet. Sci.*, **12**: 209. 1950.
879. Kobert, R. *Lehrbuch der Intoxikationen*. Ferdinand Enke, Stuttgart. 1902.
880. Koen, J. S., and H. C. Smith. An Unusual Case of Genital Involvement in Swine Associated with Eating Moldy Corn. *Vet. Med.*, **40**: 131. 1945.
881. Koger, L. M. Onion Poisoning in Cattle. *J. Am. Vet. Med. Assoc.*, **129**: 75. 1956.
882. Köhler, H., and W. Grünberg. Zur Pathologie der Vergiftung mit *Taxus baccata* unter besonderer Berücksichtigung der Vergiftung beim Kängaruh. *Archiv f. Expt. Vetmed.*, **14**: 1149. 1960.
883. Kohman, E. F. Oxalic Acid in Foods and its Behavior and Fate in the Diet. *J. Nutrition*, **18**: 233. 1939.
884. Kon, G. A. R., and H. R. Soper. Sapogenins. VIII. The Sapogenin of Fuller's Herb. *J. Chem. Soc.* (London), **1940** (I): 617. 1940.
885. Kretschmer, A. E., Jr. Nitrate Accumulation in Everglades Forages. *Agron. J.*, **50**: 314. 1958.
886. Kretschmer, A. E., Jr., and R. J. Allen, Jr. Molybdenum in Everglades Soils and Plants. *Proc. Soil Sci. Soc. Am.*, **20**: 253. 1956.
887. Krieger, L. C. C. Note on the Reputed Poisonous Properties of *Coprinus comatus*. *Mycologia*, **3**: 200. 1911.
888. Krieger, L. C. C. Common Mushrooms of the United States. *National Geographic*, **37**: 387. 1920.
889. Krieger, L. C. C. A Popular Guide to the Higher Fungi (Mushrooms) of New York State. N.Y.S. Museum, *Handbook* 11. 1935.
890. Krog, N. E. Middleport, N.Y. Personal communication. 1961.
891. Kuder, R. C. Larkspurs, Delphiniums, and Chemistry. *J. Chem. Ed.*, **24**: 418. 1947.
892. Kummer, H. 1952. Vergiftungen bei Pferden durch *Adonis* in Luzerneheu. *Tierärztliche Umschau*, **7**: 430. 1952.
893. Kunkel, H. O., K. H. Burns, and B. J. Camp. A Study of Sheep Fed High Levels of Potassium Bicarbonate with Particular Reference to Induce Hypomagnesemia. *J. Anim. Sci.*, **12**: 451. 1953.
894. Kupchan, S. M., and C. V. Deliwala. Zygadenus Alkaloids. III. Active Principles of *Zygadenus venenosus*. *J. Am. Chem. Soc.*, **75**: 1025. 1953.
895. Kuzel, N. R., and C. E. Miller. A Phytochemical Study of *Xanthium canadense*. *J. Am. Pharm. Assoc.* (Sci. ed.), **39**: 202. 1950.

896. Ladd, E. F. Water Hemlock Poisoning. North Dakota Agr. Expt. Sta., *Bull.* 44. 1900.

897. Ladd, E. F., and A. K. Johnson. Are Flaxseed Screenings Poisonous to Stock? North Dakota Agr. Expt. Sta., *Special Bull.* 1: 316. 1911.

898. Lagacé, A. 1961. White Muscle Disease in Lambs. *J. Am. Vet. Med. Assoc.,* **138**: 188.

899. Lalich, J. J., B. D. Barnett, and H. R. Bird. Production of Aortic Rupture in Turkey Poults Fed Beta-Aminopropionitrile. *A.M.A.Arch. Path.,* **64**: 643. 1957.

900. Langley, H. R. Bracken Poisoning in Cattle. *Vet. Rec.,* **56**: 518. 1944.

901. Langs, R. J., and M. B. Strauss. Oral Prophylaxis against Poison Ivy Dermatitis with Aqua Ivy Tablets. *J. Allergy,* **30**: 130. 1959.

902. Lantow, J. L. The Poisoning of Livestock by *Drymaria pachyphylla.* New Mexico Agr. Expt. Sta., *Bull.* 173. 1923.

903. Latour, H. Aspects Actuels et Diagnostic de l'Ergotisme chez l'Homme, *Rev. Path. Gén. et Comp.,* **55**: 1444. 1955.

904. Lavers, D. W. Green Cestrum—A Plant Poisonous to Stock. *Queensland Agr. J.,* **76**: 160. 1953.

905. Lauter, W. M., and P. A. Foote. Investigation of the Toxic Principles of *Hippomane mancinella* L. II. Preliminary Isolation of a Toxic Principle of the Fruit. *J. Am. Pharm. Assoc.* (Sci. ed.), **44**: 361. 1955.

906. Lauter, W. M., L. E. Fox, and W. T. Ariail. Investigation of the Toxic Principles of *Hippomane mancinella* L. I. Historical Review. *J. Am. Pharm. Assoc.* (Sci. ed.), **41**: 199. 1952.

907. Lawrence, G. E. Personal communication. 1960.

908. Lawrence, W. E. The Principal Stock-poisoning Plants of Oregon. Oregon Agr. Expt. Sta., *Bull.* 187. 1922.

909. LeBreton, E. and Y. Moulé. Méchanisme d'action des toxalbumines végé-tales et notamment de la ricine. *Bull. Soc. Chem. Biologique,* **31**: 94. 1949.

910. Lee, J. G. Experimental Lathyrism Produced by Feeding Singletary Pea (*Lathyrus pusillus*) Seed. *J. Nutr.,* **40**: 487. 1950.

911. Lee, J. G., H. P. Dupuy, and H. E. Rolfs. Dietary Protein and the De-velopment of Rat Lathyrism. *J. Nutr.,* **58**: 433. 1956.

912. Lee, J. G., and J. A. Watson, Jr. The Detoxication of Tung Meal. *J. Am. Oil Chem. Soc.,* **30**: 32. 1953.

913. Lee, O. C., and L. P. Doyle. Indiana Plants Poisonous and Injurious to Livestock. Purdue Agr. Ext. Service, *Ext. Bull.* 240 (rev.). Not dated.

914. Leemann, A. C. A Short Summary of our Botanical Knowledge of *Lolium temulentum* L. *Onderstepoort J. Vet. Sci. Anim. Ind.,* **1**: 213. 1933.

915. Leemann, A. C. Hydrocyanic Acid in Grasses. *Onderstepoort J. Vet. Sci. Anim. Ind.,* **5**: 97. 1935.

916. Leidy, J. Iron-weed as a Cause of Abortion. *J. Comp. Med. and Surg.,* **8**: 95. 1887.

917. Leighton, R. E., W. B. Anthony, J. S. Huff, and I. W. Rupel. Relation of Breed and Free Gossypol Levels to Cottonseed Meal Toxicity in Dairy Calves. *J. Dairy Sci.,* **36**: 601. 1953.

918. Leonard, N. J. Lupin Alkaloids. *In* Manske, R. H. F., and H. L. Holmes, eds., *The Alkaloids*. Academic Press, New York. Vol. III, 1953.

919. Leonard, N. J. Senecio Alkaloids. *In* Manske, R. H. F., and H. L. Holmes, eds., *The Alkaloids*. Academic Press, New York. Vol. I, 1950; Vol. VI, 1960.

920. Leonard, N. J. Lupin Alkaloids. *In* Manske, R. H. F., ed., *The Alkaloids*. Academic Press, New York. Vol. VII, 1960.

921. Lerner, M. Marihuana: Tetrahydrocannabinol and Related Compounds. *Science,* **140:** 175. 1963.

922. Lescohier, A. W. Some Observations on the Physiological Action of Sleepy Grass. *Merck's Rept.,* **20:** 273. 1911.

923. Levene, C. I. Studies on the Mode of Action of Lathyrogenic Compounds. *J. Exp. Med.,* **116:** 119. 1962.

924. Lewis, D. The Metabolism of Nitrate and Nitrite in the Sheep. II. *Biochem. J.,* **49:** 149. 1951.

925. Lewis, H. B., and M. B. Esterer. Experimental Lathyrism in the White Rat. *Proc. Soc. Exptl. Biol. and Med.,* **53:** 263. 1943.

926. Lewis, H. B., R. S. Fajans, M. B. Esterer, C. Schen, and M. Oliphat. The Nutritive Value of Some Legumes. Lathyrism in the Rat. *J. Nutr.,* **36:** 537. 1948.

927. Lewis, H. B., and A. R. Schulert. Experimental Lathyrism in the White Rat and Mouse. *Proc. Soc. Exptl. Biol. and Med.,* **71:** 440. 1949.

928. Lillie, R. J., and H. R. Bird. Effect of Oral Administration of Pure Gossypol and of Pigment Glands of Cottonseed on Mortality and Growth of Chicks. *Poultry Sci.,* **29:** 390. 1950.

929. Link, K. P. The Discovery of Dicoumarol and Its Sequels. *Circulation,* **19:** 97. 1959.

930. Little, E. L. A Study of Poisonous Drymaria on Southern New Mexico Ranges. *Ecology,* **18:** 416. 1937.

931. Lloyd, J. R. The Use of a Liver Function Test in the Prognosis of Ragwort Poisoning in Cattle. *Vet. Rec.,* **69:** 623. 1957.

932. Lloyd, L. W. W. Acorn Poisoning. *Vet. J.,* **76:** 113. 1920.

933. Long, H. C. *Plants Poisonous to Livestock*. Cambridge (England) Univ. Press. 1917.

934. Lorenz, F. W. Egg Deterioration Due to Ingestion by Hens of Malvaceous Materials. *Poultry Sci.,* **18:** 295. 1939.

935. Los Angeles County Live Stock Department. *Poisonous and Injurious Plants of Los Angeles County*. County of Los Angeles, California. 1938.

936. Lott, D. G. The Use of Thiamin in Mare's Tail Poisoning of Horses. *Canad. J. Comp. Med.,* **15:** 274. 1951.

937. Louw, P. G. J. Lantanin, the Active Principle of *Lantana camara* L. I. *Onderstepoort J. Vet. Sci. Anim. Ind.,* **18:** 197. 1943.

938. Louw, P. G. J. Lantadene A, The Active Principle of *Lantana camara* L. II. Isolation of Lantadene B, and the Oxygen Functions of Lantadene A and Lantadene B. *Onderstepoort J. Vet. Sci. Anim. Ind.,* **23:** 233. 1948.

939. Louw, P. G. J. The Active Constituents of the Poisonous Algae, *Microcystis toxica* Stephens. *South African Ind. Chem.,* **4:** 62. 1950.

940. Lowry, T., and L. M. Schuman. "Silo-filler's Disease"—A Syndrome Caused by Nitrogen Dioxide. *J. Am. Med. Assoc.*, 162: 153. 1956.
941. Loy, S. K., F. W. Heyl, and F. E. Hepner. Zygadenine, the Crystalline Alkaloid of *Zygadenus intermedius*. Wyoming Agr. Expt. Sta., *Bull.* 101. 1913.
942. Luckhardt, A. B. Additional Notes on the Bacteriology and Pathology of Milksickness. *J. Infect. Diseases*, 6: 492. 1909.
943. Luisada, A. Favism. *Medicine*, 20: 229. 1941.
944. Lumb, J. W. Ergotism of Cattle in Kansas. *J. Am. Vet. Med. Assoc.*, 81: 812. 1932.
945. Luttrell, G. W. Annotated Bibliography on the Geology of Selenium. U.S. Geol. Surv., *Bull.* 1019-M: 867. 1959.
946. Lyman, C. M., B. P. Baliga, and M. Slay. Reactions of Proteins with Gossypol. *Arch. Biochem. and Biophysics*, 84: 486. 1959.
947. Lyman, C. M., A. S. El-Nockrashy, and J. W. Dollahite. Gossyverdurin: A New Pigment Found in Cottonseed Pigment Glands. *Science*, 138: 992. 1962.
948. Lynch, J. Bracken Poisoning. *Vet. Rec.*, 47: 1067. 1935.
949. Lynch, S. J., E. Larson, and D. D. Doughty. A Study of the Edibility of Akee (*Blighia sapida*) Fruit of Florida. *Proc. Florida State Hort. Soc.*, 64: 281. 1951.
950. Lytle, W. H. Big Head, Solar Eczema or Photosensitization of Sheep. *Vet. Med.*, 32: 266. 1937.
951. Lytle, W. H. Animals May Get Potato Poisoning. Oregon Dept. Agr., *Bull.* 138: 12. 1943.
952. Lytle, W. H. Fern (Bracken) and Fern Poisoning. Oregon Dept. Agr., *Bull.* 140: 8. 1943.
953. Maag, D. D., J. S. Orsborn, and J. R. Clopton. The Effect of Sodium Selenite on Cattle. *Am. J. Vet. Res.*, 21: 1049. 1960.
954. Maag, D. D., and J. W. Tobiska. Fescue Lameness in Cattle. II. Ergot Alkaloids in Tall Fescue Grass. *Am. J. Vet. Res.*, 17: 202. 1956.
955. Macbeth, A. K. Studies of the Glucosides. Part IV. Aesculin. *J. Chem. Soc.* (London), 1931: 1288. 1931.
956. MacDonald, D. W. Algal Poisoning in Beef Cattle. *Canad. Vet. J.*, 1: 108. 1960.
957. Macdonald, H. Hemlock Poisoning in Horses. *Vet. Rec.*, 49: 1211. 1937.
958. MacDonald, H. E. Photosensitization. *Canad. J. Comp. Med.*, 18: 228. 1954.
959. Macdonald, J. Macrocarpa Poisoning. *New Zealand Vet. J.*, 4: 30. 1956.
960. MacDonald, M. A. Pine Needle Abortion in Range Beef Cattle. *J. Range Management*, 5: 150. 1952.
961. MacDonald, M. A. Timber Milk Vetch Poisoning on British Columbia Ranges. *J. Range Management*, 52: 16. 1952.
962. Machlin, L. J., C. A. Denton, and H. R. Bird. Supplementation with Vitamin B_{12} and Amino Acids of Chick Diets Containing Soybean or Cottonseed Meal. *Poultry Sci.*, 31: 110. 1952.

963. MacKinnon, A. F. Report on Algae Poisoning. *Canad. J. Comp. Med. Vet. Sci.,* **14:** 208. 1950.

964. Macy, I. G., and L. B. Mendel. Comparative Studies on the Physiological Value and Toxicity of Cottonseed and Some of its Products. *J. Pharm. and Exptl. Therapeut.,* **16:** 345. 1920.

965. Madsen, D. E., and H. M. Nielsen. Parturient Hemoglobinemia of Dairy Cows. *J. Am. Vet. Med. Assoc.,* **94:** 577. 1939.

966. Madsen, D. E., and H. M. Nielsen. The Production of Parturient Hemoglobinemia by Low Phosphorus Intake. *J. Am. Vet. Med. Assoc.,* **105:** 22. 1944.

967. Mains, E. B., C. M. Vestal, and P. B. Curtis. Scab of Small Grains and Feeding Trouble in Indiana in 1928. *Proc. Indiana Acad. Sci.,* **39:** 101. 1930.

968. Maki, L. R., and J. O. Tucker. Acute Pulmonary Emphysema of Cattle. II. *Am. J. Vet. Res.,* **23:** 824. 1962.

969. Mann, G. E., W. H. Hoffman, Jr., and A. M. Ambrose. Detoxification and Toxicological Studies of Tung Meal. *J. Agr. Food Chem.,* **2:** 258. 1954.

970. Manske, R. H. F. The Alkaloids of Fumaraceous Plants. II. *Dicentra cucullaria* (L.) Bernh. *Canad. J. Res.,* **7:** 265. 1932.

971. Manske, R. H. F. Minor Alkaloids of Unknown Structure. *In* Manske, R. H. F., ed., *The Alkaloids.* Academic Press, New York. Vol. V, 1955.

972. Manske, R. H. F., and W. R. Ashford. The Protoberberine Alkaloids. *In* Manske, R. H. F., and H. L. Holmes, eds., *The Alkaloids.* Academic Press, New York. Vol. IV, 1954.

973. Manske, R. H. F., and H. L. Holmes, eds. *The Alkaloids.* Academic Press, New York. Vol. IV, 1954.

974. Manske, R. H. F., and H. L. Holmes, eds. *The Alkaloids.* Academic Press, New York. Vol. I, 1950; Vol. V, 1955.

975. Marion, L. The Pyridine Alkaloids, *In* Manske, R. H. F., and H. L. Holmes, eds., *The Alkaloids.* Academic Press, New York. Vol. I, 1950.

976. Marion, L. The Indole Alkaloids. *In* Manske, R. H. F., and H. L. Holmes, eds., *The Alkaloids.* Academic Press, New York. Vol. II, 1952.

977. Marion, L. The Pyridine Alkaloids. *In* Manske, R. H. F., ed., *The Alkaloids.* Academic Press, New York. Vol. VI, 1960.

978. Marker, R. E., R. B. Wagner, P. R. Ulshafer, E. L. Wittbecker, D. P. J. Goldsmith, and C. H. Ruof. Steroidal Sapogenins. *J. Am. Chem. Soc.,* **69:** 2167. 1947.

979. Markson, L. M. The Pathogenesis of the Hepatic Lesion in Calves Poisoned Experimentally with *Senecio jacobaea. Proc. Roy. Soc. Med.,* **53:** 283. 1960.

980. Marsh, C. D. The Locoweed Disease of the Plains. USDA, Bur. Anim. Ind., *Bull.* 112. 1909.

981. Marsh, C. D. Menziesia, a New Stock-poisoning Plant of the Northwestern States. USDA, Bur. Plant Ind., *Prelim. Notice.* (June 10) 1914.

982. Marsh, C. D. The Locoweed Disease. USDA, *Farmers' Bull.* 1054. 1919.

983. Marsh, C. D. A New Sheep-poisoning Plant of the Southern States. USDA, *Dept. Circ.* 82. 1920.

984. Marsh, C. D. The Whorled Milkweed, a Plant Poisonous to Livestock. USDA, *Dept. Circ.* 101. 1920.

985. Marsh, C. D. Stock-poisoning Plants of the Range. USDA, *Dept. Bull* 1245. 1924.

986. Marsh, C. D. Stock-poisoning Plants of the Range. USDA, *Dept. Bull.* 1245. 1924; rev. 1929.

987. Marsh, C. D. Trembles. USDA, *Farmers' Bull.* 1593. 1929.

988. Marsh, C. D., and A. B. Clawson. *Eupatorium urticaefolium* as a Poisonous Plant. *J. Agr. Res.,* 11: 699. 1917.

989. Marsh, C. D., and A. B. Clawson. White Snakeroot (*Eupatorium urticaefolium*) as a Stock-poisoning Plant. USDA, Bur. Anim. Ind., *Bull.* 26. 1918.

990. Marsh, C. D., and A. B. Clawson. *Daubentonia longifolia* (Coffee Bean), a Poisonous Plant. *J. Agr. Res.,* 20: 507. 1920.

991. Marsh, C. D., and A. B. Clawson. *Astragalus tetrapterus,* a New Poisonous Plant of Utah and Nevada. USDA, *Dept. Circ.* 81. 1920.

992. Marsh, C. D., and A. B. Clawson. Poisonous Properties of the Whorled Milkweeds *Asclepias pumila* and *A. verticillata* var. *geyeri.* USDA, *Dept. Bull.* 942. 1921.

993. Marsh, C. D., and A. B. Clawson. Mexican Whorled Milkweed (*Asclepias mexicana*) as a Poisonous Plant. USDA, *Dept. Bull.* 969. 1921.

994. Marsh, C. D., and A. B. Clawson. The Death Camas Species, *Zygadenus paniculatus* and *Z. elegans* as Poisonous Plants. USDA, *Dept. Bull.* 1012. 1922.

995. Marsh, C. D., and A. B. Clawson. The Stock Poisoning Death Camas. USDA, *Farmers' Bull.* 1273. 1922.

996. Marsh, C. D., and A. B. Clawson. The Woolly-pod Milkweed (*Asclepias eriocarpa*) as a Poisonous Plant. USDA, *Dept. Bull.* 1212. 1924.

997. Marsh, C. D., and A. B. Clawson. Meadow Death Camas (*Zygadenus venenosus*) as a Poisonous Plant. USDA, *Dept. Bull.* 1240. 1924.

998. Marsh, C. D., and A. B. Clawson. Sleepy Grass (*Stipa vaseyi*) as a Stock-poisoning Plant. USDA, *Tech. Bull.* 114. 1929.

999. Marsh, C. D., and A. B. Clawson. Toxic Effect of St. Johnswort (*Hypericum perforatum*) on Cattle and Sheep. USDA, *Tech. Bull.* 202. 1930.

1000. Marsh, C. D., and A. B. Clawson. Mountain Laurel (*Kalmia latifolia*) and Sheep Laurel (*Kalmia angustifolia*) as Stock-poisoning Plants. USDA, *Tech. Bull.* 219. 1930.

1001. Marsh, C. D., A. B. Clawson, and J. F. Couch. Greasewood as a Poisonous Plant. USDA, *Dept. Circ.* 279. 1923.

1002. Marsh, C. D., A. B. Clawson, J. F. Couch, and W. W. Eggleston. Whorled Milkweed (*Asclepias galioides*) as a Poisonous Plant. USDA, *Dept. Bull.* 800. 1920.

1003. Marsh, C. D., A. B. Clawson, J. F. Couch, and H. Marsh. Western Sneezeweed (*Helenium hoopesii*) as a Poisonous Plant. USDA, *Dept. Bull.* 947. 1921.

1004. Marsh, C. D., A. B. Clawson, and W. W. Eggleston. *Baccharis pteronio-*

ides as a Poisonous Plant of the Southwest. *J. Am. Vet. Med. Assoc.,* **57**: 430. 1920.

1005. Marsh, C. D., A. B. Clawson, and W. W. Eggleston. The Locoweed Disease. USDA, *Farmers' Bull.* 1054, rev. 1936.

1006. Marsh, C. D., A. B. Clawson, and H. Marsh. Larkspur, or "Poison Weed." USDA, *Farmers' Bull.* 531. 1913.

1007. Marsh, C. D., A. B. Clawson, and H. Marsh. *Cicuta,* or Water Hemlock. USDA, *Dept. Bull.* 69. 1914.

1008. Marsh, C. D., A. B. Clawson, and H. Marsh. *Zygadenus,* or Death Camas. USDA, *Dept. Bull.* 125. 1915.

1009. Marsh, C. D., A. B. Clawson, and H. Marsh. Larkspur Poisoning of Livestock. USDA, *Dept. Bull.* 365. 1916.

1010. Marsh, C. D., A. B. Clawson, and H. Marsh. Lupines as Poisonous Plants. USDA, *Dept. Bull.* 405. 1916.

1011. Marsh, C. D., A. B. Clawson, and H. Marsh. *Cicuta* (Water Hemlock) as a Poisonous Plant. Bur. Anim. Ind., USDA, *Circ.* A-15. 1917.

1012. Marsh, C. D., A. B. Clawson, and H. Marsh. Staggergrass (*Chroosperma muscaetoxicum*) as a Poisonous Plant. USDA, *Dept. Bull.* 710. 1918.

1013. Marsh, C. D., A. B. Clawson, and H. Marsh. Oak-leaf Poisoning of Domestic Animals. USDA, *Dept. Bull.* 767. 1919.

1014. Marsh, C. D., A. B. Clawson, and H. Marsh. Larkspur or "Poison Weed." USDA, *Farmers' Bull.* 988. Published 1918, reprinted with corrections 1923, rev. 1929, rev. 1934.

1015. Marsh, C. D., A. B. Clawson, and G. C. Roe. Nuttall's Death Camas (*Zygadenus nuttallii*) as a Poisonous Plant. USDA, *Dept. Bull.* 1376. 1926.

1016. Marsh, C. D., A. B. Clawson, and G. C. Roe. Wild Tobaccos (*Nicotiana trigonophylla* Dunal and *Nicotiana attenuata* Torrey) as Stock-poisoning Plants. USDA, *Tech. Bull.* 22. 1927.

1017. Marsh, C. D., A. B. Clawson, and G. C. Roe. Coyotillo (*Karwinskia humboldtiana*) as a Poisonous Plant. USDA, *Tech. Bull.* 29. 1928.

1018. Marsh, C. D., A. B. Clawson, G. C. Roe. Four Species of Range Plants Not Poisonous to Livestock. USDA, *Tech. Bull.* 93. 1928.

1019. Marsh, C. D., A. B. Clawson, and G. C. Roe. Arrow Grass (*Triglochin maritima*) as a Stock-poisoning Plant. USDA, *Tech. Bull.* 113. 1929.

1020. Marsh, C. D., G. C. Roe. The "Alkali Disease" of Livestock in the Pecos Valley. USDA, *Dept. Circ.* 180. 1921.

1021. Marsh, C. D., G. C. Roe, and A. B. Clawson. Livestock Poisoning by Cocklebur. USDA, *Dept. Circ.* 283. 1923.

1022. Marsh, C. D., G. C. Roe, and A. B. Clawson. Cockleburs (Species of Xanthium) as Poisonous Plants. USDA, *Dept. Bull.* 1274. 1924.

1023. Marsh, C. D., G. C. Roe, and A. B. Clawson. Rayless Goldenrod (*Aplopappus heterophyllus*) as a Poisonous Plant. USDA, *Dept. Bull.* 1391. 1926.

1024. Marshak, R. R. Some Metabolic Derangements Associated with Magnesium Metabolism in Cattle. *J. Am. Vet. Med. Assoc.,* **133**: 539. 1958.

1025. Marshall, H. T. Locoweed Disease of Sheep. Univ. of Virginia Publ., *Bull. Philosoph. Soc., Sci. Series*, 1: 373. 1914.

1026. Martin, J. G. Mycetism (Mushroom Poisoning) in a Dog: Case Report. *Vet. Med.*, **51**: 227. 1956.

1027. Martin, J. H., J. F. Couch, and R. R. Briese. Hydrocyanic Content of Different Parts of the Sorghum Plant. *J. Am. Soc. Agronomy*, **30**: 725.

1028. Mason, M. F., and R. E. Wheeler. Observations Upon the Toxicity of Blue-green Algae. *Fed. Proc. Am. Soc. Biol. Chem.*, 1: 124. 1942.

1029. Massey, A. B. Poisonous Plants in Virginia. Virginia Polytechnic Institute Agr. Ext. Serv., *Bull.* 222. 1954.

1030. Mathams, R. H., and A. K. Sutherland. The Oxalate Content of Some Queensland Pasture Plants. *Queensland J. Agr. Sci.*, **9**: 317. 1952.

1031. Mathews, F. P. Miscellaneous Poisonous Plants. Texas Agr. Expt. Sta., *Ann. Rept.*, **45**: 11. 1932.

1032. Mathews, F. P. Johnson Grass (*Sorghum halepense*) Poisoning. *J. Am. Vet. Med. Assoc.*, **81**: 663. 1932.

1033. Mathews, F. P. Locoism in Domestic Animals. Texas Agr. Expt. Sta., *Bull.* 456. 1932.

1034. Mathews, F. P. The Toxicity of *Drymaria pachyphylla* for Cattle, Sheep, and Goats. *J. Am. Vet. Med. Assoc.*, **83**: 255. 1933.

1035. Mathews, F. P. The Toxicity of *Baileya multiradiata* for Sheep and Goats. *J. Am. Vet. Med. Assoc.*, **83**: 673. 1933.

1036. Mathews, F. P. Poisoning of Cattle by Species of Groundsel (*Senecio longilobus* Benth. and *Senecio riddellii* Torr. and Gray). Texas Agr. Expt. Sta., *Bull.* 481. 1933.

1037. Mathews, F. P. *Psilostrophe tagetinae* and *Psilostrophe gnaphalodes*, Two Plants Poisonous to Sheep and Cattle on the Ranges of the Southwest. Texas Agr. Expt. Sta., *Bull.* 500. 1934.

1038. Mathews, F. P., and H. Schmidt. Miscellaneous Poisonous Plants. Texas Agr. Expt. Sta., *Ann. Rept.*, **47**: 12. 1934.

1039. Mathews, F. P. Miscellaneous Poisonous Plants. Texas Agr. Expt. Sta., *Ann. Rept.*, **48**: 16. 1935.

1040. Mathews, F. P. The Toxicity of Broomweed (*Gutierrezia microcephala*) for Sheep, Cattle, and Goats. *J. Am. Vet. Med. Assoc.*, **41**: 55. 1936.

1041. Mathews, F. P. Senecio Poisoning. Texas Agr. Expt. Sta., *Ann. Rept.*, **50**: 16. 1937.

1042. Mathews, F. P. Photosensitization and the Photodynamic Diseases of Man and the Lower Animals. *Arch. Path.*, **23**: 399. 1937.

1043. Mathews, F. P. Lechuguilla (*Agave lecheguilla*) Poisoning in Sheep, Goats, and Laboratory Animals. Texas Agr. Expt. Sta., *Bull.* 554. 1937.

1044. Mathews, F. P. Lechuguilla (*Agave lecheguilla*) Poisoning in Sheep and Goats. *J. Am. Vet. Med. Assoc.*, **93**: 168. 1938.

1045. Mathews, F. P. An Experimental Investigation of Lechuguilla Poisoning. *Arch. Path.*, **25**: 661. 1938.

1046. Mathews, F. P. Poisonous Plants in the Davis Mountain Area. Texas Agr. Expt. Sta., *Ann. Rept.*, **51**: 13. 1938.

1047. Mathews, F. P. The Toxicity of *Sartwellia flaveriae* to Goats. *J. Agr. Res.*, **61**: 287. 1940.

1048. Mathews, F. P. The Toxicity of Red-stemmed Peavine (= *Astragalus emoryanus*) for Cattle, Sheep, and Goats. *J. Am. Vet. Med. Assoc.*, **97**: 125. 1940.

1049. Mathews, F. P. Poisoning in Sheep and Goats by Sacahuiste (*Nolina texana*) Buds and Blooms. Texas Agr. Expt. Sta., *Bull.* 585. 1940.

1050. Mathews, F. P. Poisonous Plants in the Davis Mountains. Texas Agr. Expt. Sta., *Ann. Rept.*, **54**: 93. 1941.

1051. Mathews, F. P. Whitebrush (*Lippia ligustrina*) Poisoning in Horses. *J. Am. Vet. Med. Assoc.*, **101**: 35. 1942.

1052. Mathews, F. P. Fern (*Notholaena sinuata*, var. *crenata*) Poisoning in Sheep, Goats, and Cattle—The So-Called "Jimmies" of the Trans Pecos. Texas Agr. Expt. Sta., *Bull.* 611. 1942.

1053. Mathews, F. P. The Toxicity of *Kallstroemia hirsutissima* (Carpet Weed) for Cattle, Sheep, and Goats. *J. Am. Vet. Med. Assoc.* **105**: 152. 1944.

1054. Mathews, F. P. The Toxicity of the Ripe Fruit of Blackbrush or Tarbrush (*Flourensia cernua*) for Sheep and Goats. Texas Agr. Expt. Sta., *Bull.* 664. 1944.

1055. Mathews, F. P. The Toxicity of a Spurge (*Phyllanthus abnormis*) for Cattle, Sheep, and Goats. *Cornell Vet.*, **35**: 336. 1945.

1056. Mathews, F. P. A Comparison of the Toxicity of *Notholaena sinuata* and *N. sinuata* var. *cochisensis. Rhodora*, **47**: 393. 1945.

1057. Mathews, F. P. The Poisonous Astragali. *The Veterinary Student* (Iowa State College), **9**: 26. 1946.

1058. Mathews, F. P., and H. Schmidt. Miscellaneous Poisonous Plants. Texas Agr. Expt. Sta., *Ann. Rept.*, **47**: 12. 1934.

1059. Matsumoto, H., and G. D. Sherman. A Rapid Colorimetric Method for the Determination of Mimosine. *Arch. Biochem. and Biophys.*, **33**: 195. 1951.

1060. Matsumoto, H., E. G. Smith, and G. D. Sherman. The Effect of Elevated Temperatures on the Mimosine Content and Toxicity of Koa Haole (*Leucaena glauca*). *Arch. Biochem. and Biophys.*, **33**: 201. 1951.

1061. May, W. L. Whorled Milkweed the Worst Stock-poisoning Plant in Colorado. Col. Agr. Expt. Sta., *Bull.* 255. 1920.

1062. Mayer, C. F. Endemic Panmyelotoxicoses in the Russian Grain Belt. *Military Surgeon,* **113**: 173; 295. 1953.

1063. Mayo, N. S. Enzootic Cerebritis or "Staggers" of Horses. Kansas Agr. Expt. Sta., *Bull.* 24. 1891.

1064. Mayo, N. S. Cattle Poisoning by Nitrate of Potash. Kansas Agr. Expt. Sta., *Bull.* 49: 3. 1895.

1065. Mayo, N. S. Sweet Clover Hay Poisoning. *J. Am. Vet. Med. Assoc.*, **65**: 229. 1924.

1066. McCapes, D. B. Bottom Disease. *Am. Vet. Rev.*, **14**: 532. 1890.

1067. McCrary, C. M., and G. E. Taylor. A Comparison of Manamar and Cottonseed Meal in the Ration of Dairy Cattle. Michigan Agr. Expt. Sta., *Quart. Bull.*, **26**: 178. 1944.

1068. McCulloch, E. C. The Experimental Production of Hepatic Cirrhosis by the Seed of *Amsinckia intermedia. Science,* **91**: 95. 1940.
1069. McCulloch, E. C. Hepatic Cirrhosis of Horses, Swine, and Cattle Due to the Ingestion of Seeds of the Tarweed, *Amsinckia intermedia. J. Am. Vet. Med. Assoc.,* **96**: 5. 1940.
1070. McCulloch, E. C. Nutlets of *Amsinckia intermedia* Toxic to Swine, Horses, and Cattle. *Madroño,* **5**: 202. 1940.
1071. McDonald, P. A. Cases of Lantana Poisoning Seen. *Georgia Vet.,* **7**(3): 18. 1955.
1072. McFarren, E. F., M. L. Schafer, J. E. Campbell, K. H. Lewis, E. T. Jensen, and E. J. Schantz. Public Health Significance of Paralytic Shellfish Poison: A Review of Literature and Unpublished Research. *Proc. Natl. Shellfisheries Assoc.,* **47**: 114. 1956 (publ. 1957).
1073. McIlroy, R. J. *The Plant Glycosides.* Edward Arnold and Co., London. 1951.
1074. McIntosh, R. A. May Apple Poisoning in a Cow. *Rept. Ontario Vet. Col.,* **1927**: 18. 1928.
1075. McIntosh, R. A. Ergotism. *Rept. Ontario Vet. Col.,* **1927**: 20. 1928.
1076. McKay, G. F., J. J. Lalich, E. D. Schilling, and F. M. Strong. A Crystalline "Lathyrus Factor" from *Lathyrus odoratus. Arch. Biochem. and Biophys.,* **52**: 313. 1954.
1077. McKee, R., and C. R. Enlow. Crotalaria, a New Legume for the South. USDA, *Circ.* 137. 1931.
1078. McKinney, L. L. *et 6 al.* S-(Dichlorovinyl)-L-Cysteine: An Agent Causing Fatal Aplastic Anemia in Calves. *J. Am. Chem. Soc.,* **79**: 3932. 1957.
1079. McLauchlan, D. Bracken Poisoning. *Vet. Rec.,* **63**: 241. 1951.
1080. McLaughlin, A. R. Responses of Sheep to *Zygadenus gramineus. Science,* **73**: 135. 1931.
1081. McLean, A., and H. H. Nicholson. Stock Poisoning Plants of the British Columbia Ranges. Canada Dept. Agr., *Publ.* 1037. 1958.
1082. McLeod, J. A., and G. F. Bondar. A Case of Suspected Algal Poisoning in Manitoba. *Canad. J. Publ. Health,* **43**: 347. 1952.
1083. McMillan, W. N., and W. Langham. Grazing Winter Wheat with Special Reference to the Mineral Blood Picture. *J. Animal Sci.,* **1**: 14. 1942.
1084. McNair, J. B. *Rhus Dermatitis, its Pathology, and Chemotherapy.* University of Chicago Press. 1923.
1085. McNair, J. B. The Taxonomic and Climate Distribution of Alkaloids. *Bull. Torrey Bot. Club,* **62**: 219. 1935.
1086. McNutt, S. H., P. Purwin, and C. Murray. Vulvovaginitis in Swine. *J. Am. Vet. Med. Assoc.,* **73**: 484. 1928.
1087. Medcof, J. C., A. H. Leim, A. B. Needler, A. W. H. Needler, J. Gibbard, and J. Naubert. Paralytic Shellfish Poisoning in the Canadian Atlantic Coast. Fish. Res. Bd. Canad., *Bull.* 75. 1947.
1088. Meissner, H., and G. Schoop. Über den Pilzbefall amerikanischer "Giftgerste." *Deutsche Tierärztl. Wochenschr.,* **37**: 167. 1929.
1089. Menaul, P. The Poisonous Substance in Cottonseed. *Proc. Oklahoma Acad. Sci.,* **2**: 68. 1922.

1090. Menaul, P. The Physiological Effect of Gossypol. *J. Agr. Res.*, **26**: 233. 1923.
1091. Mercier, F., and S. Macary. Sur le dosage biologique des glucosides de l'*Adonis vernalis* chez le cobaye. *Compt. Rend. Séances Soc. Biol.* (Paris), **131**: 378. 1900.
1092. Merrill, S. D. Apple Poisoning in Dairy Cows. *Vet. Med.*, **47**: 405. 1952.
1093. Merriman, G. M. Fescue Poisoning. Tennessee Agr. Expt. Sta., *Tennessee Farm and Home Science*, **16**: 8. 1955.
1094. Mershon, M. M. and F. D. Custer. Tetany in Cattle on Winter Rations. I. *J. Am. Vet. Med. Assoc.*, **132**: 396. 1958.
1095. Mettler, F. A., and G. M. Stern. Observations on the Toxic Effects of Yellow Star Thistle. *J. Neuropath. Expt. Neurol.*, **22**: 164. 1963.
1096. Metzger, H. J. A Case of Tetany with Hypomagnesemia in a Dairy Cow. *Cornell Vet.*, **26**: 353. 1936.
1097. Meyer, K. F. Food Poisoning (Concluded). *New Engl. J. Med.*, **249**: 843. 1953.
1098. Meyer, K. F., H. Sommer, and P. Schoenholz. Mussel Poisoning. *J. Prevent. Med.*, **2**: 365. 1928.
1099. Michael, D. T. Rape or Cole: Some Observations on its Management in Relation to the Health of Sheep Grazing on it. *Vet. Rec.*, **65**: 231. 1953.
1100. Michael, P. W. Oxalate Ingestion Studies in the Sheep. *Austral. Vet. J.*, **35**: 431. 1959.
1101. Michener, D. V. S. Cerebro-spinal Meningitis—Fungosus Toxicum Paralyticus. *Am. Vet. Rev.*, **6**: 345. 1882.
1102. Miller, E., O. N. Massengale, and M. A. Barnes. Some Effects Resulting from Eating Velvet Beans. *J. Am. Pharm. Assoc.*, **14**: 1113. 1925.
1103. Miller, E. V. *The Chemistry of Plants.* Reinhold Publ. Corp., New York. 1957.
1104. Miller, M. R. Alkaloidal Assays of *Delphinium andersonii* Gray. *J. Am. Pharm. Assoc.*, **12**: 492. 1923.
1105. Miller, M. R. The Toxicity of *Corydalis caseana*. *J. Agr. Research*, **42**: 239. 1931.
1106. Miller, M. R. *Halogeton glomeratus*, Poisonous to Sheep. *Science*, **97**: 262. 1943.
1107. Miller, W. T., and K. T. Williams. The Minimum Lethal Dose of Selenium as Sodium Selenite for Horses, Cattle, and Swine. *J. Agr. Res.*, **60**: 163. 1940.
1108. Millspaugh, C. F. *American Medical Plants.* Boericke and Tafel, New York. 1887.
1109. Millspaugh, C. F. *Medicinal Plants.* John C. Yorston & Co., Philadelphia. Vol. I, 1892.
1110. Minyard, J. A., C. A. Dinkel, and O. E. Olson. Effect of Arsanilic Acid in Counteracting Selenium Poisoning in Beef Cattle. *J. Anim. Sci.*, **19**: 260. 1960.
1111. Mitchell, H. H., and J. R. Beadles. The Impairment in Nutritive Value of Corn Grain Damaged by Specific Fungi. *J. Agr. Res.*, **61**: 135. 1940.

1112. Mitchell, J. E., and F. N. Mitchell. Jimson Weed (*Datura stramonium*) Poisoning in Childhood. *J. Pediatrics,* **47**: 227. 1955.
1113. Mitchell, P. H., and G. Smith. The Physiological Effects of Alkaloids of *Zygadenus intermedius. Am. J. Physiology,* **28**: 318. 1911.
1114. Mohler, J. R. Cerebrospinal Meningitis ("Forage Poisoning"). USDA, *Dept. Bull.* 65. 1914.
1115. Monlux, W., J. Fitte, G. Kendrick, and H. Dubuisson. Progressive Pulmonary Adenomatosis in Cattle. *Southw. Vet.,* **6**: 267. 1953.
1116. Monlux, W. S., P. C. Bennett, and B. W. Kingrey. Pulmonary Adenomatosis in Iowa Cattle. *Iowa Vet.,* **26**: 11. 1955.
1117. Montgomerie, R. F. Hydrocyanic Acid Generated from Linseed Cake Meal. A Case of Poisoning in Calves. *Vet. J.,* **80**: 311. 1924.
1118. Moon, F. E., and J. M. McKeand. Observations on the Vitamin C Status and Haematology of Bracken-fed Animals. *Brit. Vet. J.,* **109**: 321. 1953.
1119. Moon, F. E., and A. K. Pal. The Composition and Nutritive Value of Bracken. *J. Agr. Sci.,* **39**: 296. 1949.
1120. Moon, F. E., and M. A. Raafat. The Experimental Production of Bracken "Poisoning" in Sheep. *J. Comp. Path.,* **61**: 88. 1951.
1121. Moore, C. C. Cassava: Its Content of Hydrocyanic Acid and Starch and Other Properties. USDA, Bur. Chem., *Bull.* 106. 1907.
1122. Moore, C. W. The Constituents of the Rhizome of *Apocynum androsaemifolium. J. Chem. Soc.* (London), *Trans.,* **95**: 734. 1909.
1123. Moore, J. Prussic Acid Poisoning from the Use of Linseed Cake. *Vet. J.,* **80**: 33. 1924.
1124. Moore, V. A. Cornstalk Disease (Toxaemia Maidis) in Cattle. USDA, Bur. Anim. Ind., *Bull.* 10. 1896.
1125. Moran, E. A. Cyanogenetic Compounds in Plants and Their Significance in Animal Industry. *Am. J. Vet. Res.,* **15**: 171. 1954.
1126. Moran, E. A. Feedings of Small-flowered Buttercup not Noticeably Poisonous to a Steer and Sheep. *J. Am. Vet. Med. Assoc.,* **129**: 426. 1956.
1127. Moran, E. A., J. F. Couch, and A. B. Clawson. *Peganum harmala,* A Poisonous Plant in the Southwest. *Vet. Med.,* **35**: 234. 1940.
1128. Morgan, H. A., and M. Jacob. Alsike Clover; Ill Effect Sometimes Produced on Horses and Mules Pastured Exclusively upon Alsike. Tennessee Agr. Expt. Sta., *Bull.* 18 (3): 1. 1905.
1129. Morrill, C. C. Clover Sickness or Trifoliosis. *North Am. Vet.,* **24**: 731. 1943.
1130. Morris, M. D. Nuttall Death Camas Poisoning in Horses. *Vet. Med.,* **39**: 462. 1944.
1131. Morris, M. P., and J. Garcia-Rivera. The Destruction of Oxalates by the Rumen Contents of Cows. *J. Dairy Sci.,* **38**: 1169. 1955.
1132. Morrison, F. R. A Contribution to the Chemistry of the Fruit Obtained from the White Cedar Tree (*Melia azedarach* L. var. *australasica* C.DC.; syn. *Melia australasica* A. Juss.) Growing in New South Wales, with Notes on its Reputed Toxicity. *J. & Proc. Roy. Soc. New S. Wales,* **65**: 153. 1932.

1133. Morse, F. W., and C. D. Howard. Poisonous Properties of Wild Cherry Leaves. New Hampshire Agr. Expt. Sta., *Bull.* 56: 113. 1898.

1134. Morton, H. L., R. H. Haas, and L. C. Erickson. Oxalate and Mineral Contents of *Halogeton glomeratus*. *Weeds,* 7: 255. 1959.

1135. Morton, H. L., R. H. Haas, and L. C. Erickson. Halogeton and its Control. Idaho Agr. Expt. Sta., *Bull.* 307. 1959.

1136. Morton, J. F. Ornamental Plants with Poisonous Properties. *Proc. Florida State Hort. Soc.,* 71: 372. 1958.

1137. Moseley, E. L. The Cause of Trembles in Cattle, Sheep, and Horses, and of Milksickness in People. *Ohio Naturalist,* 6: 463. 477. 1906.

1138. Moseley, E. L. *Milk Sickness Caused by White Snakeroot.* Publ. jointly by the author & Ohio Acad. Sci., Bowling Green, Ohio. 1941.

1139. Moxon, A. L., and M. Rhian. Selenium Poisoning. *Physiol. Revs.,* 23: 305. 1943.

1140. Mundkur, B. B. Some Preliminary Feeding Experiments with Scabby Barley. *Phytopath.,* 24: 1237. 1934.

1141. Mundkur, B. B., and R. L. Cochran. Some Feeding Tests with Scabby Barley. *Phytopath.,* 20: 132. 1930.

1142. Muenscher, W. C. Leafy Spurge and Related Weeds. New York State Col. Agr., *Cornell Extension Bull.* 192. 1930; rev. 1935.

1143. Muenscher, W. C. *Poisonous Plants of the United States.* Macmillan, New York. 2nd ed., 1951.

1144. Muenscher, W. C. *Weeds.* Macmillan, New York. 2nd ed., 1955.

1145. Muhrer, M. E. and R. F. Gentry. A Hemorrhagic Factor in Moldy Lespedeza Hay. Missouri Agr. Expt. Sta., *Res. Bull.* 429. 1948.

1146. Mullenax, C. H. Observations on *Leucaena glauca. Austral. Vet. J.,* 39: 88. 1963.

1147. Mullenax, C. H. and P. B. Mullenax. Mushroom Poisoning in Cats—Two Possible Cases. *Mod. Vet. Pract.,* 43(1): 61. 1962.

1148. Mullins, J. Acorn Poisoning in Sheep. *New Zealand Vet. J.,* 3: 159. 1955.

1149. Munz, P. A., and D. D. Keck. *A California Flora.* Univ. of California Press, Berkeley. 1959.

1150. Murnane, D. Ragwort Poisoning in Cattle in Victoria. *J. Counc. for Sci. and Ind. Res., Australia,* 6: 108. 1933.

1151. Murphy, A. L. Mussel Poisoning in Nova Scotia. *Canad. Med. Assoc. J.,* 35: 418. 1936.

1152. Murrill, W. A. A New Poisonous Mushroom. *Mycologia,* 1: 211. 1909.

1153. Murrill, W. A. Poisonous Mushrooms. *Mycologia,* 2: 255. 1910.

1154. Murrill, W. A. *Edible and Poisonous Mushrooms.* Publ. by the author, New York. 1916.

1155. Murrill, W. A. A Very Dangerous Mushroom. *Mycologia,* 8: 186. 1916.

1156. Murtha, E. F. Pharmacological Study of Poisons from Shellfish and Puffer Fish. *Ann. N. Y. Acad. Sci.,* 90: 820. 1960.

1157. Mushett, C. W., K. L. Kelley, G. E. Boxer, and J. C. Rickards. Antidotal Efficacy of Vitamin B_{12a} (Hydroxo-cobalamin) in Experimental Cyanide Poisoning. *Proc. Soc. Exptl. Med.,* 81: 234. 1952.

1158. Musson, E. H. Oil of Tansy Poisoning. *J. Am. Med. Assoc.,* **47:** 1917. 1906.

1159. Muth, O. H. An Attempt to Determine the Toxicity of *Amsinckia intermedia* (Tarweed) for Fattening Lambs. *J. Am. Vet. Med. Assoc.,* **99:** 145. 1941.

1160. Muth, O. H. Chronic Copper Poisoning in Sheep. *J. Am. Vet. Med. Assoc.,* **120:** 148. 1952.

1161. Muth, O. H. Bracken Poisoning. *Proc. Am. Col. Vet. Toxicol.,* **1961:** 25. 1961.

1162. Muth, O. H., and J. R. Haag. Disease of Oregon Cattle Associated with Hypomagnesemia and Hypocalcemia. *N. Am. Vet.,* **26:** 216. 1945.

1163. Naftalin, J. M., and G. H. Cushnie. Pathology of Bracken Poisoning. *Vet. Rec.,* **63:** 332. 1951.

1164. Naftalin, J. M., and G. H. Cushnie. Pathology of Bracken Poisoning in Cattle. *J. Comp. Path.,* **64:** 54. 1954.

1165. Naftalin, J. M., and G. H. Cushnie. Experimental Bracken Poisoning in Calves. *J. Comp. Path.,* **64:** 75. 1954.

1166. Naftalin, J. M., and G. H. Cushnie. Haematology of Experimental Bracken Poisoning of Cattle. I, II. *J. Comp. Path.,* **66:** 354. 1956.

1167. National Clearinghouse for Poison Control Centers, *Bull.,* July-August, **1961:** 1.

1168. Neale, R. C. Personal communication. 1962.

1169. Neal, F. C., F. R. Ramsey, K. S. Preston, and R. Creel. Polioencephalomalacia in Iowa Cattle. *Iowa State Univ. Vet.,* **23:** 15. 1960.

1170. Neal, W. M., L. L. Rusoff, and C. F. Ahman. The Isolation and Some Properties of an Alkaloid from *Crotalaria spectabilis* Roth. *J. Am. Chem. Soc.,* **57:** 2560. 1935.

1171. Neill, J. C. The Endophyte of Rye-grass (*Lolium perenne*). *New Zealand J. Sci. and Tech.* (Sect. A), **21:** 280A. 1940.

1172. Neill, J. C. The Endophytes of Lolium and Festuca. *New Zealand J. Sci. and Tech.* (Sect. A), **23:** 185A. 1941.

1173. Nelson, A. Squirrel-tail Grass. Wyoming Agr. Expt. Sta., *Bull.* 19. 1894.

1174. Nelson, D. A. Accidental Poisoning by *Veratrum japonicum. J. Am. Med. Assoc.,* **156:** 33. 1954.

1175. Newberne, J. W. Bladderpod Poisoning in Cattle. *Auburn Vet.,* **9:** 169. 1953.

1176. Newsom, I. E. *Sheep Diseases.* Williams and Wilkins, Baltimore. 1952.

1177. Newsom, I. E., F. Cross, B. R. McCrory, A. H. Groth, J. W. Tobiska, E. Balis, L. W. Durrell, E. C. Smith, and E. N. Stout. Timber Milk Vetch as a Poisonous Plant. Colorado Agr. Expt. Sta., *Bull.* 425. 1936.

1178. Newsom, I. E., E. N. Stout, F. Thorp, C. W. Barber, and A. H. Groth. Oat Hay Poisoning. *J. Am. Vet. Med. Assoc.,* **90:** 66. 1937.

1179. Niemann, K. W. Report of an Outbreak of Poisoning in the Domesticated Fowl, Due to Death Camas. *J. Am. Vet. Med. Assoc.,* **73:** 627. 1928.

1180. Nolan, A. F., and F. E. Hull. Grass Tetany in Cattle. *Am. J. Vet. Res.,* **2:** 41. 1941.

1181. Nordfeldt, S., N. Gellerstedt, and S. Falkmer. Studies on Rapeseed Meal and its Goitrogenic Effects on Pigs. *Acta Path. et Microbiol. Scandinavica,* **35**: 217. 1954.

1182. Nordfeldt, S., L. A. Henke, F. Morita, H. Matsumoto, M. Takahashi, O. R. Younge, E. H. Willers, and R. F. Cross. Feeding Tests with *Indigofera endecaphylla* Jacq. (Creeping Indigo) and Some Observations on its Poisonous Effects. Hawaii Agr. Expt. Sta., *Tech. Bull.* 15. 1952.

1183. Nordfeldt, S., and O. R. Younge. Toxicity of Creeping Indigo to Livestock. Hawaii Agr. Expt. Sta., *Prog. Note* 55. 1949.

1184. Nordskog, A. W., and R. T. Clark. Ergotism in Pregnant Sows, Female Rats, and Guinea Pigs. *Am. J. Vet. Res.,* **6**: 107. 1945.

1185. Norris, J. J., and K. A. Valentine. Principal Livestock-poisoning Plants of New Mexico Ranges. New Mexico Agr. Expt. Sta., *Bull.* 390. 1954.

1186. Nuessle, N. O., and W. M. Lauter. Isolation of Constituents of *Glottidium vesicarium. Econ. Bot.,* **12**: 307. 1958.

1187. O'Dell, B. L. A Study of the Toxic Principle in Red Clover. Missouri Agr. Expt. Sta., *Res. Bull.* 702. 1959.

1188. O'Donoghue, J. G., and G. S. Wilton. Algal Poisoning in Alberta. *Canad. J. Comp. Med. Vet. Sci.,* **15**: 193. 1951.

1189. O'Driscoll, J. Rape Poisoning in Cattle. *Irish Vet. J.,* **12**: 82. 1958.

1190. Oelrichs, P. B. and T. McEwan. The Toxic Principle of *Acacia georginae. Queensl. J. Agr. Sci.,* **19**: 1. 1962.

1191. Office of Commissioner of Narcotics, Bureau of Narcotics, Treasury Department.

1192. Ogilvie, D. D. Atropine Poisoning in the Goat. *Vet. Rec.,* **15**: 1415. 1935.

1193. O'Hara, J. L. Molybdenosis—Its Treatment and Control by Injection of Copper Cyclinates. Am. Col. Vet. Toxicologists, *Minutes,* Jan. 1960: 8. 1960.

1194. Olafson, P. Hyperkeratosis (X Disease) of Cattle. *Cornell Vet.,* **37**: 279. 1947.

1195. Olcott, H. S., and T. D. Fontaine. The Effect of Autoclaving on the Nutritive Value of the Protein in Cottonseed Meal. *J. Nutr.,* **22**: 431. 1941.

1196. Oliver, H. Supposed Poisoning of Pigs by *Convolvulus. The Vet.,* **45**: 727. 1872.

1197. Olson, C. A Possible Relation Between Bracken Fern and Enzootic Hematuria of Cattle. *Proc. Am. Col. Vet. Toxicol.,* **1961**: 47. 1961.

1198. Olson, O. E., C. A. Dinkel, and L. D. Kamstra. New Aid in Diagnosing Selenium Poisoning. *South Dakota Farm and Home Res.,* **6**: 12. 1954.

1199. Olson, O. E., and A. L. Moxon. Nitrate Reduction in Relation to Oat Hay Poisoning. *J. Am. Vet. Med. Assoc.,* **100**: 403. 1942.

1200. Olson, O. E., and E. Whitehead. Nitrate Content of Some South Dakota Plants. *Proc. S. Dakota Acad. Sci.,* **20**: 95. 1940.

1201. Olson, O. E., and E. I. Whitehead. Cornstalk Poisoning. *South Dakota Farm and Home Res.,* **5**: 8. 1953.

1202. Olson, O. E., E. I. Whitehead, and A. L. Moxon. Occurrence of Soluble Selenium in Soils and its Availability to Plants. *Soil Sci.,* **54**: 47. 1942.

1203. Olson, T. A. Toxic Phytoplankton. *Water Sewage Wk.*, **99**: 75. 1952.

1204. Olson, T. A. Water Poisoning—A Study of Poisonous Algae Blooms in Minnesota. *Am. J. Publ. Health*, **50**: 883. 1960.

1205. O'Moore, L. B. The Treatment with Vitamin B_1 of Bracken Staggers in the Bovine. *Vet. Rec.*, **61**: 768. 1949.

1206. Orfila, M. J. B. *A General System of Toxicology*. Trans. from the 2nd French ed. by J. A Waller. Cox, Butterworth and Burgess, London. Vol. II, 1819.

1207. Orgell, W. H., K. A. Vaidya, and P. A. Dahm. Inhibition of Human Plasma Cholinesterase *in Vitro* by Extracts of Solanaceous Plants. *Science*, **128**: 1136. 1958.

1208. Osebold, J. W. An Approach to the Pathogenesis of Fern Poisoning in the Bovine Species. *J. Am. Vet. Med. Assoc.*, **119**: 440. 1951.

1209. Osebold, J. W. Bracken Fern Poisoning. *M.S.C.* (Michigan State Coll.) *Vet.*, **12**(2): 74. 1952.

1210. Pace, N. The Etiology of Hypericism, a Photosensitivity Produced by St. Johnswort. *Am. J. Physiology*, **136**: 650. 1942.

1211. Pace, N., and G. MacKinney. Hypericin, the Photodynamic Pigment from St. Johnswort. *J. Am. Chem. Soc.*, **63**: 2570. 1941.

1212. Painter, E. P. The Chemistry and Toxicity of Selenium Compounds, with Special Reference to the Selenium Problem. *Chem. Rev.*, **28**: 179. 1941.

1213. Palmer, R. L. An Outbreak of Oak Leaf Poisoning in Cattle. *Mod. Vet. Pract.*, **43**(10): 1962.

1214. Palotay, J. L. "Crooked Calves." *Western Vet.*, **6**: 16. 1959.

1215. Palsson, P. A., and H. Grimsson. Demyelination in Lambs from Ewes which Feed on Seaweeds. *Proc. Soc. Exp. Biol. Med.*, **83**: 518. 1953.

1216. Pammel, L. H. Poisoning from Cowbane (*Cicuta maculata* L.). Iowa Agr. Exp. Sta., *Bull.* 28. 1895.

1217. Pammel, L. H. *A Manual of Poisonous Plants*. Torch Press, Cedar Rapids, Iowa. 1911.

1218. Pammel, L. H. Poisoning from Oaks. *Am. J. Vet. Med.*, **12**: 323. 1917.

1219. Pammel, L. H. Young Sneezeweed Poisonous. *Am. J. Vet. Med.*, **12**: 461. 1917.

1220. Pammel, L. H. More Cases of Poisoning from Oak. *Am. J. Vet. Med.*, **12**: 712. 1917.

1221. Pammel, L. H. Poisoning from Lima Bean. *Am. J. Vet. Med.*, **12**: 787. 1917.

1222. Pammel, L. H. Poisoning from Sorghum and Sudan Grass. *Am. J. Vet. Med.*, **14**: 30. 1919.

1223. Pammel, L. H. Notes on Poisonous Plants. *Am. J. Vet. Med.*, **14**: 244. 1919.

1224. Pammel, L. H. Sesban or Mole Bean Poisonous. *Am. J. Vet. Med.*, **14**: 246. 1919.

1225. Pammel, L. H. Poison Hemlock. *Am. J. Vet. Med.*, **14**: 513. 1919.

1226. Pammel, L. H. Ground Cherry Leaves Supposed to be Poisonous. *Am. J. Vet. Med.*, **14**: 606. 1919.

1227. Pammel, L. H. Castor Seed Poisonous. *Am. J. Vet. Med.*, **15**: 171. 1920.

1228. Pammel, L. H. Alsike Clover Poisoning. *Am. J. Vet. Med.*, **15**: 437. 1920.
1229. Pammel, L. H. Darnel Poisonous. *Am. J. Vet. Med.*, **15**: 491. 1920.
1230. Pammel, L. H. Three-flowered Nightshade Poisonous. *Vet. Med.*, **16**(2): 46. 1921.
1231. Pammel, L. H. Equisetosis or Horsetail Poisoning. *Vet. Med.*, **16**(4): 43. 1921.
1232. Pammel, L. H. Some Forms of Lima Beans Poisonous. *Vet. Med.*, **16**(5): 45. 1921.
1233. Pammel, L. H. Is Common Sorrel (*Rumex acetosa*) Poisonous? *Vet. Med.*, **16**(8): 47. 1921.
1234. Pammel, L. H. China Tree Poisonous. *Vet. Med.*, **16**(10): 47. 1921.
1235. Pammel, L. H. Western Poison Cowbane. *Vet. Med.*, **16**(11): 33. 1921.
1236. Pammel, L. M. Castor Oil Plant—Poisonous. *Vet. Med.*, **16**(12): 39. 1921.
1237. Pammel, L. H. Golden Glow Poisons. *Vet. Med.*, **16**(12): 50. 1921.
1238. Pammel, L. H. Ergotism. *Vet. Med.*, **17**: 89. 1922.
1239. Pammel, L. H. Alleged Sweet Clover Poisoning: Its Relation to Hemorrhagic Septicemia. *Vet. Med.*, **18**: 245. 1923.
1240. Pammel, L. H. Worm Seed or Mexican Tea Poisonous to Geese. *Vet. Med.*, **18**: 736. 1923.
1241. Pammel, L. H. The Toxicity of Black Locust. *N. Am. Vet.*, **8**: 41. 1927.
1242. Pammel, L. H. Golden Glow is Injurious. *Vet. Med.*, **23**: 28. 1928.
1243. Pammel, L. H. Probably a Cryptogam Poisoning Due to Mold on the Corn. *Vet. Med.*, **23**: 29. 1928.
1244. Pammel, L. H. Buttercup or Crowfoot Poisoning. *Vet. Med.*, **24**: 540. 1929.
1245. Pammel, L. H. Horses and Milkwort. *Vet. Med.*, **24**: 514. 1929.
1246. Pammel, L. H., J. B. Weems, and W. H. Heileman. Squirrel-tail Grass or Wild Barley. Iowa Agr. Expt. Sta., *Bull.* 30. 1895.
1247. Parker, K. W. Prevention of Death Losses in Sheep in Areas Infested with Pingue (*Actinea richardsoni*). New Mexico Agr. Expt. Sta., *Bull.* 241. 1936.
1248. Parker, W. H. Foxglove (*Digitalis purpurea*) Poisoning in Turkeys. *Vet. Rec.*, **63**: 416. 1951.
1249. Parkinson. B., and A. K. Sutherland. Post-parturient Haemoglobinuria of Dairy Cows. *Austral. Vet. J.*, **30**: 232. 1954.
1250. Passenger, R. E., W. C. Spain, and M. B. Strauss. Aqua Ivy. Toxicity Studies on the Guinea Pig and Treatment of Sensitive Cases. *J. Allergy*, **27**: 409. 1956.
1251. Patterson, F. D. Pokeweed Causes Heavy Losses in Swine Herd. *Vet. Med.*, **24**: 114. 1929.
1252. Pauhlman, V. C. Blackberry Vines in Nasal Tracts of Cattle. *J. Am. Vet. Med. Assoc.*, **131**: 94. 1957.
1253. Paulman, V. C. Poisoning from Burned, Sweet-clover Hay. *Vet. Med.*, **18**: 8. 1923.

1254. Pearson, L. A Preliminary Report Upon Forage-poisoning of Horses (So-called Cerebro-spinal Meningitis). *J. Comp. Med. and Vet. Arch.,* **21:** 654. 1900.

1255. Pease, H. T. Poisoning of Cattle by *Andropogon sorghum. J. Comp. Med. and Vet. Arch.,* **18:** 679. 1897.

1256. Peck, C. H. Edible and Poisonous Fungi of New York. State Botanist of New York, *Ann. Rept.,* **1894:** 203. 1894.

1257. Peck, C. H. Report of the State Botanist for 1911. New York State Museum, *Bull.* 157. 1912.

1258. Penberthy, J. Vegetable Poisoning (?) Simulating Anthrax in Cattle. *J. Comp. Path. and Therapeut.,* **6:** 266. 1893.

1259. Penny, R. H. C. Hemlock Poisoning in Cattle. *Vet. Rec.,* **65:** 669. 1953.

1260. Penny, R. H. C. Suspected Poisoning by Fodder-beet in the Bovine. *Vet. Rec.,* **66:** 134. 1954.

1261. Perkins, L. E. Experiments in Bracken Poisoning. *Brit. Vet. J.,* **106:** 377. 1950.

1262. Peters, A. T. Cornstalk Disease. Nebraska Agr. Expt. Sta., *Bull.* 52, 1898.

1263. Peters, A. T., H. B. Slade, and S. Avery. Poisoning of Cattle by Common Sorghum and Kafir Corn. Nebraska Agr. Expt. Sta., *Bull.* 77. 1903.

1264. Peters, R. A., R. J. Hall, P. F. V. Ward, and N. Sheppard. The Chemical Nature of the Toxic Compounds Containing Fluorine in the Seeds of *Dichapetalum toxicarium. Biochem. J.,* **77:** 17. 1960.

1265. Peterson, W. H., R. H. Burris, H. Sant, and H. N. Little. Production of Toxic Gas (Nitrogen Oxides) in Silage Making. *J. Agr. & Food Chem.,* **6:** 121. 1958.

1266. Peterson, W. H., R. W. Thoma, and R. F. Anderson. Yellow Gas from Corn Silage. *Hoard's Dairyman,* **94:** 870. 1949.

1267. Pethick, W. H. Pictou Cattle Disease, with Special Reference to the Symptomology. *Canad. Vet. Rec.,* 2(3): 13. 1921.

1268. Pfander, W. H., G. B. Garner, W. C. Ellis, and M. E. Muhrer. The Etiology of "Nitrate Poisoning" in Sheep. Missouri Agr. Expt. Sta., *Res. Bull.* 637. 1957.

1269. Phares, D. L. Bitterweed (*Helenium autumnale*). Mississippi Agr. Expt. Sta., *Bull.* **9:** 11. 1889.

1270. Phillips Petroleum Company. Pasture and Range Plants. IV. *Poisonous Grassland Plants.* Phillips Petroleum Company, Bartlesville, Oklahoma. 1957.

1271. Phillipson, A. T., and R. S. Reid. Studies on the Toxicity of Bracken (*Pteris aquilina*). *J. Comp. Path.,* **64:** 243. 1954.

1272. Piercy, P. L., G. Hargis, and C. A. Brown. Mushroom Poisoning in Cattle. *J. Am. Vet. Med. Assoc.,* **105:** 206. 1944.

1273. Piercy, P. L., and L. L. Rusoff. Livestock Poisoning by *Crotalaria spectabilis.* Louisiana Agr. Expt. Sta., *Circ.* 36. 1945.

1274. Piercy, P. L., and L. L. Rusoff. *Crotalaria spectabilis* Poisoning in Louisiana Livestock. *J. Am. Vet. Med. Assoc.,* **108:** 69. 1946.

1275. Pigeon, R. F., B. J. Camp, and J. W. Dollahite. Oral Toxicity and Polyhydroxyphenol Moiety of Tannin Isolated from *Quercus havardi* (Shin Oak). *Am. J. Vet. Res.*, **23**: 1268. 1962.

1276. Pijoan, M. Cyanide Poisoning from Choke Cherry Seed. *Am. J. Med. Sci.*, **204** (n.s.): 550. 1942.

1277. Pilat, A. and O. Usak. *A Handbook of Mushrooms.* Spring Books, London. (Undated.)

1278. Pipal, F. J. A Suspected Case of Stock Poisoning by Wild Onion (*Allium canadense*). *Proc. Indiana Acad. Sci.*, **1917**: 139. 1918.

1279. Pinckney, R. M. Effects of Nitrate Application upon the Hydrocyanic Acid Content of Sorghum. *J. Agr. Res.*, **27**: 717. 1924.

1280. Pistor, W. J. Johnson Grass (*Sorghum halepense*) Poisoning. Arizona Agr. Ext. Serv., *Circ.* 168. 1950.

1281. Pistor, W. J. Poisoning by Pig Weed or Careless Weed. *Arizona Cattlelog,* **7**: 55. 1952.

1282. Pohl, R. W., Iowa State University. Personal communication of a case in the practice of L. B. Anderson, Billings, Montana. 1961.

1283. Pohl, R. W. Poisoning by Dieffenbachia. *J. Am. Med. Assoc.* **177**: 812. 1961.

1284. Pollard, E. F., H. L. E. Vix, and J. J. Spadaro. Separating the Fractions of Cottonseed. USDA, *Yearbook of Agr.,* **1950–1951**: 561. 1951.

1285. Pominski, C. H., L. E. Castillion, and J. M. Dechary. Removing the Glands from Cottonseed. USDA, *Yearbook of Agr.,* **1950–1951**: 558. 1951.

1286. Ponseti, I. V., and W. A. Baird. Scoliosis and Dissecting Aneurysm of the Aorta in Rats Fed with *Lathyrus odoratus* (Sweet Pea) Seeds. *Am J. Path.,* **28**: 1059. 1952.

1287. Ponseti, I. V., S. Wawzonek, R. S. Shepard, T. C. Evans, and G. Stearns. Further Studies on Lathyrism in the Rat. *Proc. Soc. Exptl. Biol. and Med.,* **92**: 366. 1956.

1288. Porter, C. L. *Astragalus* and *Oxytropis* in Colorado. *Univ. Wyoming Publ.,* **16**: 1. 1951.

1289. Poulsen, E. Forgifning med myrosinasefri sennepsskro hos kvaeg. *Nordisk Veterinaermedicin,* **10**: 487. 1958.

1290. Poulsson, E. Untersuchungen über *Caltha palustris.* (*Naunyn-Schmiedeberg's*) *Archiv f. Expt. Path.,* **80**(3): 173. 1916.

1291. Power, F. B. The Chemistry of the Bark of *Robinia pseudo-acacia,* Linné. *Pharmaceut. J.,* 1901.

1292. Prelog, V., and O. Jeger. The Chemistry of Solanum and Veratrum Alkaloids. *In* Manske, R. H. F., and H. L. Holmes, eds., *The Alkaloids.* Academic Press, New York. Vol. III, 1953.

1293. Prelog, V., and O. Jeger. Steroid Alkaloids: The Solanum Group. *In* Manske, R. H. F., ed., *The Alkaloids.* Academic Press, New York. Vol. VII, 1960.

1294. Prescott, G. W. Objectionable Algae with Reference to the Killing of Fish and Other Animals. *Hydrobiol.,* **1**: 1. 1948.

1295. Preston, T. R. Acute Overeating with Cereals in Ruminants. *Vet. Rec.,* **75**: 125. 1963.

1296. Price, D. A., and W. T. Hardy. Guajillo Poisoning of Sheep. *J. Am. Vet. Med. Assoc.,* **122:** 223. 1953.

1297. Price, T. M. Enzymes in Cornstalks and Their Relation to Cornstalk Disease. USDA, Bur. Anim. Ind., *Ann. Rept.,* **21:** 66. 1904.

1298. Prien, O. L. Woody Aster (*Xylorrhiza parryi* Gray). Wyoming Agr. Expt. Sta., *Prelim. Bull.* 88. 1911.

1299. Priouzeau, M. M. Fagopyrisme chez les Bovidés. *Rec. Méd. Vét.,* **118:** 160. 1942.

1300. Pritchard, W. R. Bracken Poisoning. *Vet. Sci. News, Univ. Wisconsin,* **2:** 4. 1948.

1301. Pritchard, W. R. Laurel (*Kalmia angustifolia*) Poisoning of Sheep. *N. Am. Vet.,* **37:** 461. 1956.

1302. Pritchard, W. R., R. Hammer, J. H. Sautter, and M. O. Schultze. Studies on Trichloroethylene-extracted Feeds. IV. Suspectibility of the Horse to the Toxic Factor in Trichloroethylene-extracted Soybean Oil Meal. *Am. J. Vet. Res.,* **17:** 441. 1956.

1303. Pritchard, W. R., W. E. Mattson, J. H. Sautter, and M. O. Schultze. *Ibid.* III. The Use of Young Calves for Study of Various Aspects of Toxicity of Trichloroethylene-extracted Soybean Oil Meal. *Am. J. Vet. Res.,* **17:** 437. 1956.

1304. Pritchard, W. R., W. E. Mattson, J. H. Sautter, and M. O. Schultze. *Ibid.* V. Failure to Demonstrate the Presence of a Toxic Factor in the Milk of Cows Being Fed Toxic Specimens of Trichloroethylene-extracted Soybean Oil Meal. *Am. J. Vet. Res.,* **17:** 444. 1956.

1305. Pritchard, W. R., V. Perman, W. E. Mattson, J. H. Sautter, and M. O. Schultze. *Ibid.* VI. The Effects of Feeding Trichloroethylene-extracted Soybean Oil Meal to Sheep. *Am. J. Vet. Res.,* **17:** 446. 1956.

1306. Pritchard, W. R., C. E. Rehfeld, W. E. Mattson, J. H. Sautter, and M. O. Schultze. *Ibid.* II. The Effect of Feeding Different Levels of Trichloroethylene-extracted Soybean Oil Meal to Young Heifers—Experimental Production of Chronic Aplastic Anemia. *Am. J. Vet. Res.,* **17:** 430. 1956.

1307. Pritchard, W. R., C. E. Rehfeld, N. S. Mizuno, J. H. Sautter, and M. O. Schultze. *Ibid.* I. Experimental Production of Acute Aplastic Anemia in Young Heifers. *Am. J. Vet. Res.,* **17:** 425. 1956.

1308. Pritchard, W. R., C. E. Rehfeld, and J. H. Sautter. Aplastic Anemia of Cattle Associated with Ingestion of Trichloroethylene-extracted Soybean Oil Meal (Stockman Disease, Duren Disease, Brabant Disease). I. Clinical and Laboratory Investigation of Field Cases. *J. Am. Vet. Med. Assoc.,* **121:** 1. 1952.

1309. Pritchard, W. R., F. Sauer, C. E. Rehfeld, V. Perman, J. H. Sautter, S. Wada, and M. O. Schultze. Studies on Trichloroethylene-extracted Feeds. VII. Observations with Laboratory Animals Fed Trichloroethylene-extracted Soybean Oil Meal. *Am. J. Vet. Res.,* **17:** 448. 1956.

1310. Pryor, W. J. An Outbreak of Copper Poisoning in Sheep Following Copper Topdressing of Pastures. *Austral. Vet. J.,* **35:** 366. 1959.

1311. Przybylska, M., and L. Marion. The Absolute Configuration of (+)- des-(oxymethylene)-Lycoctonine Hydriodide Monohydrate and (+)-Demethanolaconine Hydriodide Trihydrate. *Canad. J. Chem.*, **37**: 1843. 1959.

1312. Pullar, E. M. Studies on Five Suspected Poisonous Plants. *Austral. Vet. J.*, **15**: 19. 1939.

1313. Pullar, E. M., and W. M. Larew. Vulvovaginitis in Swine. *Austral. Vet. J.*, **13**: 28. 1937.

1314. Quick, A. J. The Coagulation Defect in Peptone Shock and in Sweet Clover Disease. *J. Biol. Chem.*, **114**: 1. 1936.

1315. Quick, A. J. The Coagulation Defect in Sweet Clover Disease and in the Hemorrhagic Chick Disease of Dietary Origin. *Am. J. Physiol.*, **118**: 260. 1937.

1316. Quigley, G. D., and R. H. Waite. Miscellaneous Feeding Trials with Poultry. I. The Effects of Corn Cockle on Poultry. Maryland Agr. Expt. Sta., *Bull.* **325**: 343. 1931.

1317. Quin, A. H. Sheep Poisoned by Algae. *J. Am. Vet. Med. Assoc.*, **102**: 299. 1943.

1318. Quortrup, E. R., and R. J. McFarland. Animal Losses Involving Noxious Weeds in San Diego County. *California Vet.*, 9(5): 14. 1956.

1319. Ramsbottom, J. *Poisonous Fungi*. Penguin Books, Ltd., New York. 1945.

1320. Ramsbottom, J. *Mushrooms and Toadstools*. Collins, London. 1953.

1321. Randall, J. A. Twenty-two Cases of Poisoning by the Seed of *Jatropha curcas*. *U.S. Naval Med. Bull.*, **8**: 290. 1914.

1322. Ransohoff, J. N., ed. Abrin, Lethal Jewelry. *A.M.A. Arch. Indust. Health,* **12**: 468. 1955.

1323. Rapp, W. F., Jr. The Toxicity of Equisetum. *Am. Fern J.*, **44**: 148. 1954.

1324. Ratigan, W. J. Oleander Poisoning in a Bear. *J. Am. Vet. Med. Assoc.*, **60**: 96. 1921.

1325. Ratnoff, O. D., and G. S. Mirick. Influence of Sex upon the Lethal Effects of an Hepatotoxic Alkaloid, Monocrotaline. *Bull. Johns Hopkins Hosp.*, **84**: 507. 1949.

1326. Rautavaara, T. Poisonous Fungi and Fungi Believed to be Poisonous. *Karstenia*, **1**: 37–47. 1950.

1327. Raynor, R. N. The Chemical Control of St. Johnswort. California Agr. Expt. Sta., *Bull.* 615. 1937.

1328. Redmond, H. E. Wheat Poisoning in Cattle. *Southw. Vet.*, 3(3): 22. 1950.

1329. Reeks, H. C. Poisoning of Cattle by Common Celandine. *J. Comp. Path.*, **16**: 367. 1903.

1330. Reid, T. L., and A. G. Smith. The Alkaloids of *Zygadenus gramineus*. *Proc. South Dakota Acad. Sci.*, **35**: 124. 1956.

1331. Reiser, R. and H. C. Fu. The Mechanism of Gossypol Detoxification by Ruminant Animals. *J. Nutr.*, **76**: 215. 1962.

1332. Ressler, C. Isolation and Identification from Common Vetch of the Neurotoxin β-Cyano-L-alanine, A Possible Factor in Neurolathyrism. *J. Biol. Chem.*, **237**: 733. 1962.

1333. Ressler, C., P. A. Redstone, and R. H. Erenberg. Isolation and Identification of a Neuroactive Factor from *Lathyrus latifolius*. *Science,* **134**: 188. 1961.

1334. Retief, G. P. The Use of Crystalline Methionine as a Treatment for Liver Damage in Racehorses. *J. S. Africa Vet. Med. Assoc.,* **33**: 405. 1962.

1335. Reynard, G. B., and J. B. S. Norton. Poisonous Plants of Maryland in Relation to Livestock. Maryland Agr. Expt. Sta., *Tech. Bull.* A10. 1942.

1336. Reynolds, A. K. Uterine Stimulants. *In* R. H. F. Manske, ed., *The Alkaloids.* Academic Press, Inc., New York. Vol. V, 1955.

1337. Rhian, M., and A. L. Moxon. Chronic Selenium Poisoning in Dogs and its Prevention by Arsenic. *J. Pharm. and Exptl. Therapeut.,* **78**: 249. 1943.

1338. Rich, F. A. Equisetum Poisoning. *Am. Vet. Rev.,* **26**: 944. 1902.

1339. Rich, F. A., and L. R. Jones. A Poisonous Plant, the Common Horsetail. Vermont Agr. Expt. Sta., *Bull.* 95. 1902.

1340. Richmond, J. W., N. H. Sutcliffe, N. W. R. Daniels, P. W. Russell Eggitt, and J. B. M. Coppock, Factors Other than Groundnut Relating to "Turkey X Disease." *Vet. Rec.,* **74**: 544. 1962.

1341. Riegel, B. D., W. Stanger, D. M. Wilholm, J. D. Mold, and H. Sommer. Paralytic Shellfish Poison. V. Primary Source of Poison, Marine Plankton Organism *Gonyaulax catenella. J. Biol. Chem.,* **177**: 7. 1949.

1342. Rigdon, R. H., G. Crass, T. M. Ferguson, and J. R. Couch. Effects of Gossypol in Young Chickens with the Production of a Ceroid-like Pigment. *A.M.A. Arch. Path.,* **65**: 228. 1958.

1343. Riggs, C. W. Nitrite Poisoning from Ingestion of Plants High in Nitrate. *Am. J. Vet. Res.,* **5**: 194. 1945.

1344. Rimington, C., J. I. Quin, and G. C. S. Roets. The Icterogenic Factor in Geel-dikkop. Isolation of Active Principles from *Lippia rehmanni* Pears. *Onderstepoort J. Vet. Sci. and Anim. Ind.,* **9**: 225. 1937.

1345. Ritchey, G. E., R. McKee, R. B. Becker, W. M. Neal, and P. D. Dix Arnold. Crotalaria for Forage. Florida Agr. Expt. Sta., *Bull.* 361. 1941.

1346. Robb, H. F. Death From Rhubarb Leaves Due to Oxalic Acid Poisoning. *J. Am. Med. Assoc.,* **73**: 627. 1919.

1347. Roberts, G. A. Paraplegia (Wobbles) in Cattle. *Vet. Med.,* **36**: 507. 1941.

1348. Roberts, H. E., E. T. R. Evans, and W. C. Evans. The Production of "Bracken Staggers" in the Horse and its Treatment by Vitamin B$_1$ Therapy. *Vet. Rec.,* **61**: 549. 1949.

1349. Robinson, B. B. Marihuana Investigations. IV. A Study of Marihuana Toxicity on Goldfish Applied to Hemp Breeding. *J. Am. Pharm. Assoc.* (Sci. ed.), **30**: 616. 1941.

1350. Robinson, M. E. Cyanogenesis in Plants. *Biol. Rev.,* **5**: 126. 1930.

1351. Robinson, T. Alkaloids. *Sci. Am.,* **201**(1): 113. 1959.

1352. Roche, B. H., and G. Bohstedt. Scabbed Barley and Oats and Their Effect on Various Classes of Livestock. *Proc. Am. Soc. Anim. Prod.,* **23**(1930): 219. 1931.

1353. Roche, B. H., G. Bohstedt, and J. G. Dickson. Feeding Scab-infected Barley. *Phytopath.,* **20**: 132. 1930.

1354. Roderick, L. M. The Pathology of Sweet Clover Disease in Cattle. *J. Am. Vet. Med. Assoc.*, **74**: 314. 1929.

1355. Roderick, L. M. A Problem in the Coagulation of the Blood. "Sweet Clover Disease of Cattle." *Am. J. Physiol.*, **96**: 413. 1931.

1356. Roderick, L. M., and A. F. Schalk. Studies on Sweet Clover Disease. North Dakota Agr. Expt. Sta., *Bull.* 250. 1931.

1357. Rogers, C. F., and O. C. Frykolm. Observations on the Variations in Cyanogenetic Power of White Clover Plants. *J. Agr. Res.*, **55**: 533. 1937.

1358. Rogers, C. F., A. H. Larson, and M. L. Spracher. Variation of the Hydrocyanic Acid Content of Sudan Grass from a Single Lot of Seed. *J. Am. Soc. Agron.*, **29**: 865. 1937.

1359. Rogers, T. B. On the Action of St. Johnswort as a Sensitizing Agent for Non-pigmented Skin. *Am. Vet. Rev.*, **46**: 145. 1914.

1360. Rose, E. T. Toxic Algae in Iowa Lakes. *Proc. Iowa Acad. Sci.*, **60**: 738. 1953.

1361. Rosen, A. P., and J. J. Scanlan. Favism. *New England J. Med.*, **239**: 367. 1948.

1362. Rosenberg, M. M., and A. L. Palafox. The Effect of Creeping Indigo (*Indigofera endecaphylla*) When Fed to Growing Chickens. *World's Poultry Sci. J.*, **6**: 284. 1950.

1363. Rosenberg, M. M., and A. L. Palafox. The Effect of Creeping Indigo (*Indigofera endecaphylla*) on Laying Chickens. *World's Poultry Sci. J.*, **7**: 9. 1951.

1364. Rosenberg, M. M., and O. C. Zoebisch. A Chick Text for Toxicity in Forage Legumes. *Agron. J.*, **44**: 315. 1952.

1365. Rosenfeld, I., and O. A. Beath. Tissue Changes Induced by *Senecio riddellii*. *Am. J. Clin. Path.*, **15**: 407. 1945.

1366. Rosenfeld, I., and O. A. Beath. Pathology of Selenium Poisoning. Wyoming Agr. Expt. Sta., *Bull.* 275. 1946.

1367. Rosenfeld, I., and O. A. Beath. The Influence of Protein Diets on Selenium Poisoning. I. II. *Am. J. Vet. Res.*, **7**: 52. 1946.

1368. Rosenfeld, I. and O. A. Beath. Congenital Malformations of Eyes of Sheep. *J. Agr. Res.*, **75**: 93. 1947.

1369. Rosenfeld, I., and O. A. Beath. Toxic Effects of Crude Ergot. *J. Am. Vet. Med. Assoc.*, **116**: 308. 1950.

1370. Rottgardt, A. A. Fotosensibilizacion. Fac. Med. Vet., Univ. Nat de La Plata, *Anuario*, **7**: 49, 1944.

1371. Roueché, B. Annals of Medicine: The Most Delicate Thing in the World. *The New Yorker*, May 4, 1957: 144. 1957.

1372. Roy, D. N., S. H. Lipton, H. R. Bird, and F. M. Strong. Relation of Semicarbazide, Nitrofurazone and Related Compounds to Beta-Aminopropionitrile Toxicity in Turkey Poults. *Poultry Sci.*, **40**: 55. 1961.

1373. Ruby, E. S., J. Beasley, and E. L. Stephenson. Prussic Acid Poisoning in Common Vetch (*Vicia sativa*) Seed. *Proc. Arkansas Acad. Sci.*, **7/8**: 18. 1955.

1374. Rusby, H. H. How Goldenrods May be Poisonous. *Am. Vet. Rev.*, **20**: 5. 1896.

1375. Rusby, H. H. The Poisonous Properties of Mountain Laurel. *Druggist's Circ. and Chem. Gaz.,* **46:** 27. 1902.

1376. Rusk, H. P., and H. S. Grindley. Field Investigations of Forage Poisoning in Cattle and Horses. Illinois Agr. Expt. Sta., *Bull.* 210. 1918.

1377. Rusoff, L. L., N. R. Mehrhof, and R. S. McKinney. Chick Feeding Experiments with Solvent-extracted Tung Oil Meal. *Poultry Sci.,* **21:** 451. 1942.

1378. Ruthruff, R. F. The Occurrence of Alkaloids in the Amaryllidaceae. *Herbertia* (Yearbook Am. Amaryllis Soc.), **2:** 89. 1935.

1379. Rydberg, P. A. Two New Species from the Mountains of West Virginia. *Torreya,* **26:** 29. 1926.

1380. Sackett, W. G. The Connection of Milksickness with the Poisonous Qualities of White Snakeroot (*Eupatorium urticaefolium*) *J. Infect. Diseases,* **24:** 231. 1919.

1381. Salmon, D. E. Enzootics of Ergotism. USDA, *Report,* **1884:** 212. 1884.

1382. Salmon, W. D., and W. E. Sewell. Lameness in Hogs Produced by Austrian Pea (*Pisum arvense*) Forage. Alabama Agr. Expt. Sta., *Ann. Rept.,* **47:** 17. 1936.

1383. Sampson, A. W., and H. E. Malmsten. Stock-poisoning Plants of California. California Agr. Expt. Sta., *Bull.* 593. Rev. 1942.

1384. Sampson, A. W., and K. W. Parker. St. Johnswort on Range Lands in California. California Agr. Expt. Sta., *Bull.* 503. 1930.

1385. Sanders, D. A. Lantana Poisoning in Cattle. *J. Am. Vet. Med. Assoc.,* **109:** 139. 1946.

1386. Sanders, D. A. Lantana Poisoning in Cattle. Florida Agr. Expt. Sta., *Press Bull.* 620. 1946.

1387. Sanders, D. A., M. W. Emmel, and L. E. Swanson. Tung Tree (*Aleurites Fordi* Hemsl.) Foliage Poisoning of Cattle. Florida Agr. Expt. Sta., *Bull.* 376. 1942.

1388. Sanders, D. A., A. L. Shealy, and M. W. Emmel. The Pathology of *Crotalaria spectabilis* Roth Poisoning in Cattle. *J. Am. Vet. Med. Assoc.,* **89:** 150. 1936.

1389. Sanghri, L. M., S. N. Misra, and T. K. Bose. Cardiovascular Manifestations in *Argemone mexicana* Poisoning (Epidemic Dropsy). *Circulation,* **21:** 1096. 1960.

1390. Santos, A. C., and P. Adkilen. The Alkaloids of *Argemone mexicana. J. Am. Chem. Soc.,* **54:** 2923. 1932.

1391. Sapiro, M. L., S. Hoflund, R. Clark, and J. I. Quin. Studies on the Alimentary Tract of the Merino Sheep in South Africa. XVI. The Fate of Nitrate in Ruminal Ingesta as Studied in Vitro. *Onderstepoort J. Vet. Sci. Anim. Ind.,* **22:** 357. 1949.

1392. Sarkar, S. N. Isolation from Argemone Oil of Dihydrosanguinarine and Sanguinarine: Toxicity of Sanguinarine. *Nature* (London), **162:** 265. 1948.

1393. Sauer, J. D. Pokeweed, an Old American Herb. Missouri Bot. Gard., *Bull.* **38:** 82. 1950.

1394. Sautter, J. H., C. E. Rehfeld, and W. R. Pritchard. Aplastic Anemia of Cattle Associated with Ingestion of Trichloroethylene-extracted Soybean

Meal. (Stockman Disease, Duren Disease, Brabant Disease). II. Necropsy Findings in Field Cases. *J. Am. Vet. Med. Assoc.,* **121:** 73. 1952.

1395. Savage, A. Nitrate Poisoning from Sugar Beet Tops. *Canad. J. Comp. Med. and Vet. Sci.,* **13:** 9. 1949.

1396. Saxton, J. E. The Indole Alkaloids. *In* Manske, R. H. F., ed., *The Alkaloids.* Academic Press, New York. Vol. VII, 1960.

1397. Scarisbrick, R. Acid Indigestion in a Sheep Fed on Mangolds. *Vet. Rec.,* **66:** 131. 1954.

1398. Schaeffer, H. J., W. M. Lauter, and P. A. Foote. A Preliminary Phytochemical Study of *Hippomane mancinella* L. *J. Am. Pharm. Assoc.* (Sci. ed.), **43:** 43. 1954.

1399. Schaffner, J. H. Poisonous and Other Injurious Plants of Ohio. *Ohio Naturalist,* **4:** 32. 1903.

1400. Schalk, A. F. Cattle Disease Resulting from Eating Damaged or Spoiled Sweet Clover Hay or Silage. North Dakota Agr. Expt. Sta., *Circ.* 27. 1926.

1401. Schantz, E. J. Biochemical Studies on Paralytic Shellfish Poisons. *Ann. N.Y. Acad. Sci.,* **90:** 843. 1960.

1402. Schantz, E. J., J. D. Mold, D. W. Stanger, J. Shavel, F. J. Riel, J. P. Bowden, J. M. Lynch, R. S. Wyler, B. Riegel, and H. Sommer. Paralytic Shellfish Poison. VI. A Procedure for the Isolation and Purification of the Poison from Toxic Clam and Mussel Tissues. *J. Am. Chem. Soc.,* **79:** 5230. 1957.

1403. Schilling, E. D., and F. M. Strong. Isolation, Structure, and Synthesis of Lathyrus Factor from *L. odoratus. J. Am. Chem. Soc.,* **77:** 2843. 1955.

1404. Schmidt, H. Swellhead in Sheep and Goats. Texas Agr. Expt. Sta., *Ann. Rept.,* **44:** 11. 1931.

1405. Schmidt, H. Poisonous Plants Investigations. Texas Agr. Expt. Sta., *Ann. Rept.,* **45:** 11. 1932.

1406. Schmittle, S. C., D. J. Richey, and J. T. Tumlin. Toxicity of *Crotalaria spectabilis* Seed in Poultry. *Poultry Sci.,* **38:** 1244. 1959.

1407. Schoental, R. Blood Changes in Rats Treated with Senecio Alkaloids. *Biochem. J.,* **60:** (Proc.) i. 1955.

1408. Schoental, R. Hepatotoxic Action of Pyrrolizidine (Senecio) Alkaloids in Relation to their Structure. *Nature* (London), **179:** 361. 1957.

1409. Schoental, R. The Chemical Aspect of Seneciosis. *Proc. Roy. Soc. Med.,* **58:** 284. 1960.

1410. Schoental, R., and P. N. Magee. Chronic Liver Changes in Rats after a Single Dose of Lasiocarpine, a Pyrrolizidine (Senecio) Alkaloid. *J. Path. and Bact.,* **74:** 305. 1957.

1411. Schoental, R., and P. N. Magee. Further Observations on the Subacute and Chronic Liver Changes in Rats after a Single Dose of Various Pyrrolizidine (*Senecio*) Alkaloids. *J. Path. and Bact.,* **78:** 471. 1959.

1412. Schofield, F. W. A Brief Account of a Disease in Cattle Simulating Hemorrhagic Septicaemia Due to Feeding Sweet Clover. *Canad. Vet. Rec.,* **3:** 74. 1922.

1413. Schofield, F. W. Damaged Sweet Clover: The Cause of a New Disease

Simulating Hemorrhagic Septicemia and Blackleg. *J. Am. Vet. Med. Assoc.*, **64**: 553. 1924.

1414. Schofield, F. W. Liver Disease of Horses (Big Liver) Caused by the Feeding of Alsike Clover. Ontario Vet. Col., *Circ.* 52. 1933.

1415. Schofield, F. W. Acute Pulmonary Emphysema in Cattle. Ontario Vet. Col., *Rept.*, **1946–1947**: 45. 1947.

1416. Schofield, F. W. Acute Pulmonary Emphysema of Cattle. *J. Am. Vet. Med. Assoc.*, **112**: 254. 1948.

1417. Schroeder, E. C. "Bottom Disease" Among Horses in South Dakota. USDA, Bur. Anim. Ind., *Ann. Rept.*, **8/9**: 371. 1892.

1418. Schroeder, H. A., and J. J. Balassa. Cadmium: Uptake by Vegetables from Superphosphate in Soil. *Science*, **140**: 819. 1963.

1419. Schulert, A. R., and H. B. Lewis. Experimental Lathyrism. *Proc. Soc. Exptl. Biol. and Med.*, **81**: 86. 1952.

1420. Schwarte, L. H. Moldy Corn Poisoning in Horses. *J. Am. Vet. Med. Assoc.*, **92**: 152. 1938.

1421. Schwarte, L. H., H. E. Biester, and C. Murray. A Disease of Horses Caused by Feeding Moldy Corn. *J. Am. Vet. Med. Assoc.*, **90**: 76. 1937.

1422. Schwarte, L. H., D. F. Eveleth, and H. E. Biester. Studies on the So-called Corn Stalk Poisoning in Cattle. *Vet. Med.*, **34**: 648. 1939.

1423. Schwarting, A. E. Poisonous Plants. *In* Stewart, C. P., and A. Stolman, eds., *Toxicology*. Academic Press, New York. Vol. II, 1961.

1424. Schwartze, E. W., and C. L. Alsberg. Quantitative Variation of Gossypol and its Relation to the Oil Content of Cottonseed. *J. Agr. Res.*, **25**: 285. 1923.

1425. Schwartze, E. W., and C. L. Alsberg. Relation Between Toxicity of Cottonseed and its Gossypol Content. *J. Agr. Res.*, **28**: 173. 1924.

1426. Schwartze, E. W., and C. L. Alsberg. Pharmacology of Gossypol. *J. Agr. Res.*, **28**: 191. 1924.

1427. Schwimmer, M., and D. Schwimmer. *The Role of Algae and Plankton in Medicine.* Grune & Stratton, New York. 1955.

1428. Science Service. Some Papers Read at the Boston Meeting of the American Association for the Advancement of Science. *Science (Suppl.)*, **79**(2041): 5. 1934.

1429. Scott, J. L. Goldenrod Killing Horses. *Garden and Forest*, **8**: 477. 1895.

1430. Seaton, V. A. Pulmonary Adenomatosis in Cattle Produced by Nitrogen Dioxide Poisoning. *North Am. Vet.*, **38**: 109. 1957.

1431. Sebrell, W. H. An Anemia of Dogs Produced by Feeding Onions. *U.S. Public Health Reports*, **24**: 1175. 1930.

1432. Seddon, H. R., and H. G. Belschner. The Effect of Immature St. John's Wort (*Hypericum perforatum*) on Sheep. *J. Counc. Sci. and Industr. Res.*, **2**: 229. 1929.

1433. Seibold, H. R. Crotalaria Poisoning in a Horse. *J. Am. Vet. Med. Assoc.*, **130**: 336. 1957.

1434. Selye, H., and P. Bois. Effect of Cortisoids upon Experimental Lathyrism. *Endocrinology*, **60**: 507. 1957.

1435. Selye, H., and P. Bois. Effect of STH on Experimental Lathyrism. *Proc. Soc. Exptl. Biol. and Med.,* **94:** 133. 1957.
1436. Selzer, G., and R. G. F. Parker. Senecio Poisoning Exhibiting as Chiari's Syndrome, A Report on Twelve Cases. *Am. J. Path.,* **27:** 885. 1951.
1437. Selzer, G., R. G. F. Parker, and N. Sapeika. An Experimental Study of Senecio Poisoning in Rats. *Brit. J. Exptl. Path.,* **32:** 14. 1951.
1438. Senior, V. E. Algal Poisoning in Saskatchewan. *Canad. J. Comp. Med.,* **24:** 26. 1960.
1439. Setchell, B. P. and A. J. Williams. Plasma Nitrate and Nitrite Concentration in Chronic and Acute Nitrate Poisoning in Sheep. *Austral. Vet. J.,* **38:** 58. 1962.
1440. Seven, M. J. Mussel Poisoning. *Ann. Int. Med.,* **48:** 891. 1958.
1441. Sewell, W. E. Detoxification of Cottonseed Meal for Hogs. Alabama Agr. Expt. Sta., *Bull.* 259. 1943.
1442. Sewell, W. E., and D. M. Turney. Further Experiments with Detoxification of Cottonseed Meal for Hogs. Alabama Agr. Expt. Sta., *Prog. Rept.* 25. 1946.
1443. Shand, A. The Goitrogenic Factor in Kale. Proc. Conf. on Metabolic Disorders, Brit. Vet. Assoc., *Publ.* **23:** 58. 1953.
1444. Shaw, J. N., and O. H. Muth. Some Types of Forage Poisoning in Oregon Cattle and Sheep. *J. Am. Vet. Med. Assoc.,* **114:** 315. 1949.
1445. Shealy, A. L., and E. F. Thomas. *Daubentonia* Seed Poisoning of Poultry. Florida Agr. Expt. Sta., *Bull.* 196. 1928.
1446. Sheard, C., H. D. Caylor, and C. Schlotthauer. Photosensitization of Animals after the Ingestion of Buckwheat. *J. Exptl. Med.,* **47:** 1013. 1928.
1447. Shearer, G. D. Some Observations on the Poisonous Properties of Buttercups. *Vet. J.,* **94:** 22. 1938.
1448. Shearer, G. D. Some Observations on the Poisonous Properties of Bracken (*Pteris aquilina*). *J. Comp. Path.,* **55:** 301. 1945.
1449. Shelubsky, M. Observations on the Properties of a Toxin Produced by *Microcystis. Proc. Internat. Assoc. Limnol. (Internat. Verein. f. Theoret. u. Angew. Limnol.),* **11:** 362. 1951.
1450. Shenstone, F. S. and J. R. Vickery. Substances in Plants of the Order Malvale Causing Pink Whites in Stored Eggs. *Poultry Sci.,* **38:** 1055. 1959.
1451. Shone, D. K. Toxicity of the Jack Bean. *Rhodesia Agr. J.,* **58:** 18. 1961.
1452. Shrift, A. Biological Activities of Selenium Compounds. *Bot. Rev.,* **24:** 550. 1958.
1453. Siegmund, O. H., ed. *Merck Veterinary Manual.* Merck & Co., Rahway, N.J. 2nd ed., 1961.
1454. Simic, W. J. Solanine Poisoning in Swine. *Vet. Med.,* **38:** 353. 1943.
1455. Simmons, J. S., and Z. E. Bolin. Dermatitis Venenata Produced by an Irritant Present in the Stem Sap of the Mango (*Mangifera indica* L.). *Am. J. Trop. Med.,* **1:** 351. 1921.
1456. Simms, B. T. Dallis Grass Poisoning. *Auburn Vet.,* **8:** 22. 1951.

1457. Simon, J., J. M. Sund, F. D. Douglas, M. J. Wright, and T. Kowalczyk. The Effect of Nitrate or Nitrite when Placed in the Rumens of Pregnant Dairy Cattle. *J. Am. Vet. Med. Assoc.,* 135: 311. 1959.

1458. Simon, J., J. M. Sund, M. J. Wright, and F. D. Douglas. Prevention of Noninfectious Abortion in Cattle by Weed Control and Fertilization Practices on Lowland Pastures. *J. Am. Vet. Med. Assoc.,* 135: 315. 1959.

1459. Simpson, C. F., and E. West. Ergot Poisoning in Cattle. Florida Agr. Expt. Sta., *Circ.* S43, 1952.

1460. Simpson, C. F., and E. West. Coffee-weed (Bagpod) Seed Poisoning of Cattle. Florida Agr. Expt. Sta., *Circ.* S58. 1953.

1461. Simpson, K. R., and P. C. Banerjee. Cases of Poisoning in the Horse with Ratti Seeds (*Abrus precatorius*), by Oral Administration. *Indian Vet. Sci. and Animal Husbandry,* 2: 59. 1932.

1462. Sims, F. H., and H. R. Crookshank. Wheat Pasture Poisoning in Cattle. Texas Agr. Expt. Sta., *Prog. Rept.* 1739. 1954.

1463. Sims, F. H., and H. R. Crookshank. Wheat Pasture Poisoning. Texas Agr. Expt. Sta., *Bull.* 842. 1956.

1464. Sims, F. H., and H. R. Crookshank. Wheat Pasture Poisoning in Cows. *Southw. Vet.,* 10: 277. 1957.

1465. Sinclair, D. P., and E. D. Andrews. Goitre in New-Born Lambs. *New Zealand Vet. J.,* 2: 72. 1954.

1466. Singer, R., and A. H. Smith. About the Identity of the Weed Panaeolus or Poisonous Panaeolus. *Mycopath. et Mycologia Applic.,* 9: 280. 1958.

1467. Singer, R. H., R. B. Grainger, and F. H. Baker. Investigations on a Complicated Grass Tetany Syndrome in Ruminants of Kentucky. I. Preliminary Observations. Kentucky Agr. Expt. Sta., *Bull.* 658. 1958.

1468. Sippel, W. L. Prevention of Bracken Fern Poisoning. *J. Am. Vet. Med. Assoc.,* 118: 384. 1951.

1469. Sippel, W. L. Bracken Fern Poisoning. *J. Am. Vet. Med. Assoc.,* 121: 9. 1952.

1470. Sippel, W. L. New Treatment for Bracken Fern Poisoning Tried. *Georgia Vet.,* 6(4): 15. 1954.

1471. Sippel, W. L. Mold Intoxication of Livestock. *Iowa Vet.,* 28(5): 15. 1957.

1472. Sippel, W. L., and J. E. Burnside. Oat Dermatitis. *Georgia Vet.,* 6(2): 3–4. 1954.

1473. Sippel, W. L., J. E. Burnside, and M. B. Atwood. A Disease of Swine and Cattle Caused by Eating Moldy Corn. *Am. Vet. Med. Assoc., Proc.,* 90: 174. 1954.

1474. Skidmore, L. V. Water Hemlock (*Cicuta maculata* L.) Poisoning in Swine. *Vet. J.,* 89: 76. 1954.

1475. Skidmore, L. V., and N. F. Peterson. Observations on the Toxicity of Golden Glow (*Rudbeckia laciniata*) to Swine and Other Animals. *J. Am. Vet. Med. Assoc.,* 81: 655. 1932.

1476. Slade, H. B. Prussic Acid in Sorghum. *J. Am. Chem. Soc.,* 25: 55. 1903.

1477. Small, J. K. *Manual of the Southeastern Flora.* Univ. of North Carolina Press, Chapel Hill. 1933.

1478. Smit, J. D. Experimental Cases of Algae Poisoning in Small Animals. *South African Ind. Chem.,* **4**: 66. 1950.

1479. Smith, A. H. *Mushrooms in Their Natural Habitats.* Sawyer's Inc., Portland, Oregon. 2 vols. 1949.

1480. Smith, A. H. New Species of Galerina from North America. *Mycologia,* **45**: 893. 1953.

1481. Smith, C. P. Lupinus. *In* Abrams, L., *Illustrated Flora of the Pacific States.* Stanford Univ. Press, Stanford Univ., California. Vol. II, 1944.

1482. Smith, D., and F. Rauchfuss. Effects of Aqueous Extracts of Halogeton Tissue on Germination of Seeds and Growth of Seedlings. *J. Range Management,* **11**: 300. 1958.

1483. Smith, E. V. Poisonous Plants as a Problem in Southern Livestock Production. *Assoc. Southern Agr. Workers, Ann. Proc.,* **41**: 104, 1940.

1484. Smith, F. H. and J. C. Orsborne. Toxic Effects of Crotalaria Seed. *Vet. Med.,* **57**: 234. 1962.

1485. Smith, F. J. Poisoned by Castor Beans. *Am. Vet. Rev.,* **10**: 367. 1886.

1486. Smith, H. A. The Pathology of Gossypol Poisoning. *Am. J. Path.,* **33**: 353. 1957.

1487. Smith, H. A. The Diagnosis of Oak Poisoning. *Southw. Vet.,* **13**: 34. 1959.

1488. Smith, H. A., and T. C. Jones. *Veterinary Pathology.* Lea and Febiger, Philadelphia. 1957.

1489. Smith, H. A., and T. C. Jones. *Veterinary Pathology.* Lea & Febiger, Philadelphia. 2nd ed. 1961.

1490. Smith, H. C., V. E. Lovell, R. Reppert, and D. Griswold. Nitrate Poisoning in Swine. *Vet. Med.,* **54**: 547. 1959.

1491. Smith, M. I., and E. F. Stohlman. Further Observations on the Influence of Dietary Protein on the Toxicity of Selenium. *J. Pharm. and Exptl. Therapeut.* **70**: 270. 1960.

1492. Smith, T. Two Cases of Cirrhosis of the Liver. USDA, Bur. Anim. Ind., *Ann. Rept.,* **12/13**: 179. 1896.

1493. Smith, W. K., and R. A. Brink. Relation of Bitterness to the Toxic Principle in Sweetclover. *J. Agr. Res.,* **56**: 145. 1938.

1494. Soria, J., and C. B. Heiser. The Garden Huckleberry and the Sunberry. *Baileya,* **7**: 33. 1959.

1495. Soria, J. and C. B. Heiser, Jr. A Statistical Study of the Relationships of Certain Species of the *Solanum nigrum* Complex. *Econ. Bot.,* **15**: 245. 1961.

1496. Sommer, H., and K. F. Meyer. Paralytic Shellfish Poisoning. *Arch. Path.,* **24**: 560. 1937.

1497. Sommer, H., and K. F. Meyer. Mussel Poisoning. *Hygeia,* **19**: 620. 1941.

1498. Sommer, H., W. F. Whedon, C. A. Kofoid, and R. Stohler. Relation of Paralytic Shellfish Poison to Certain Plankton Organisms of the Genus *Gonyaulax. Arch. Path.,* **24**: 537. 1937.

1499. Spector, W. S., ed. *Handbook of Toxicology.* Wright Air Development Center, Wright-Patterson Air Force Base, Ohio. Vol. 1, 1955.

1500. Sperry, O. E. Rayless Goldenrod—A Poisonous Range Plant in Texas. *J. Range Management*, **6**: 6. 1953.

1501. Sperry, O. E., J. W. Dollahite, J. Morrow, and G. O. Hoffman. Texas Range Plants Poisonous to Livestock. Texas Agr. Expt. Sta., *Bull*. 796. 1955.

1502. Sperry, O. E., and F. W. Pond. Buckeye—Its Distribution and Control. Texas Agr. Expt. Sta., *Misc. Publ*. MP188. 1957.

1503. Sperry, O. E. and E. D. Robison. Chemical Control of Perennial Broomweed. Texas Agr. Expt. Sta., *Prog. Rept*. 2273. 1963.

1504. Sperry, O. E., D. E. Ryerson, and H. A. Pearson. Distribution and Chemical Control of Coyotillo, a Range Shrub Poisonous to Livestock. Texas Agr. Expt. Sta., *Misc. Publ*. MP594. 1962.

1505. Sperry, O. E., R. D. Turk, G. O. Hoffman, and F. B. Stroud. Photosensitization of Cattle in Texas. Texas Agr. Expt. Sta., *Bull*. 812. 1955.

1506. Sperry, O. E., P. H. Vardiman, and R. G. Gray. Peavine, a Poisonous Plant in Texas. Texas Agr. Expt. Sta., *Prog. Rept*. 1474. 1952.

1507. Stahler, L. M., and E. I. Whitehead. The Effect of 2,4-D on Potassium Nitrate Levels in Leaves of Sugar Beets. *Science*, **112**: 749. 1950.

1508. Stahman, M. A., C. F. Huebner, and K. P. Link. Studies on the Hemorrhagic Sweet Clover Disease. V. *J. Biol. Chem.*, **138**: 513. 1941.

1509. Stalker, M. Crotalism. *Am. Vet. Rev.*, **8**: 342. 1884.

1510. Stalker, M. Ergotism Again. Iowa Agr. Expt. Sta., *Bull*. 17: 453. 1892.

1511. Stamp, J. T. A Review of Bracken Poisoning in Cattle. *J. Brit. Grassland Soc.*, **2**: 191. 1947.

1512. Stamp, J. T., and J. Stewart. Haemolytic Anemia with Jaundice in Sheep. *J. Comp. Path. and Exptl. Therapeut.*, **63**: 48. 1953.

1513. Standley, H. P. Poisoning by Ragwort (*Senecio jacobaea*). *Vet. J.*, **80**: 35. 1924.

1514. Standley, P. C. Trees and Shrubs of Mexico. *Contrib. U.S. Natl. Herbarium*, **23**: 435. 1922.

1515. Stange, C. H. Forage Poisoning or Cryptogamic Poisoning. *Am. Vet. Rev.*, **38**: 473. 1911.

1516. Sterns, T. J. Fescue Foot or Ergot-like Disease in Cattle in Kentucky. *J. Am. Vet. Med. Assoc.*, **122**: 388. 1953.

1517. Stein, S. I. An Unusual Effect from a Species of Mexican Mushroom *Psilocybe cubensis. Mycopath. et Mycologia Applic.*, **9**: 263. 1958.

1518. Stein, S. I. Clinical Observations on the Effects of *Panaeolus venenosus* versus *Psilocybe caerulescens* Mushrooms. *Mycologia*, **51**: 49. 1959.

1519. Stein, S. I., G. L. Closs, and N. W. Gabel. Observations on Psychoneurophysiologically Significant Mushrooms. *Mycopath. et Mycologia Applic.*, **11**: 205. 1959.

1520. Stephens, E. L. *Microcystis toxica* sp. nov.: A Poisonous Alga from the Transvaal and Orange Free State. *Trans. Roy. Soc. South Africa*, **32**: 105. 1949.

1521. Stephenson, N. R., H. I. Edwards, B. F. MacDonald, and L. I. Pugsley. Biological Assay of the Toxin from Shellfish. *Canad. J. Biochem. Physiol.*, **33**: 849. 1955.

1522. Stern, E. S. The Aconitum and Delphinium Alkaloids. *In* Manske, R. H. F., and H. L. Holmes, eds., *The Alkaloids.* Academic Press, New York. Vol. IV, 1954.

1523. Stern, E. S. The Diterpenoid Alkaloids from Aconitum, Delphinium, and Garrya Species. *In* Manske, R. H. F., ed., *The Alkaloids.* Academic Press, New York. Vol. VII, 1960.

1524. Stevens, O. A. Poisonous Plants and Plant Products. North Dakota Agr. Expt. Sta., *Bull.* 265. 1933.

1525. Stevenson, J. A. and C. R. Benjamin. Scleroderma Poisoning. *Mycologia,* **53:** 438. 1961.

1526. Stewart, A. G., D. A. Barnum, and J. A. Henderson. Algal Poisoning in Ontario. *Canad. J. Comp. Med. Vet. Sci.,* **14:** 197. 1950.

1527. Stewart, G. A., and C. P. Merilan. Effect of Potassium Nitrate Intake on Lactating Dairy Cows. Missouri Agr. Expt. Sta., *Res. Bull.* 650. 1958.

1528. Stewart, J., and J. W. S. Reith. The Effects of Magnesium Liming on the Magnesium Content of Pasture and the Blood Level of Magnesium in Cows. *J. Comp. Path. and Exptl. Therapeut.,* **66:** 1. 1956.

1529. Steyn, D. G. Fungi in Relation to Health in Man and Animal. *Onderstepoort J. Vet. Sci. and Anim. Ind.,* **1:** 183. 1933.

1530. Steyn, D. G. Poisoning of Human Beings by Weeds Contained in Cereals (Bread Poisoning). *Onderstepoort J. Vet. Sci. and Anim. Ind.,* **1:** 219. 1933.

1531. Steyn, D. G. The Poisoning in Human Beings by Weeds Contained in Wheat (Bread Poisoning). *Farming in S. Africa,* **9:** 45. 1934.

1532. Steyn, D. G. Senecio Poisoning in Animals. *Farming in S. Africa,* **9:** 97. 1934.

1533. Steyn, D. G. *The Toxicology of Plants in South Africa.* Central News Agency, Ltd., Johannesburg. 1934.

1534. Steyn, D. G. Fungus-infected and Fermented Feeds Dangerous to Stock. *Farming in S. Africa,* **16:** 197. 1941.

1535. Steyn, D. G. Poisoning of Animals and Human Beings by Algae. *South African J. Sci.,* **41:** 243. 1944.

1536. Steyn, D. G., and S. J. Van Der Walt. Recent Investigations into the Toxicity of Known and Unknown Poisonous Plants. *Onderstepoort J. Vet. Sci. and Anim. Ind.,* **16:** 121. 1941.

1537. Stiles, F. C. Stramonium Poisoning. *J. Pediatrics,* **39:** 354. 1951.

1538. Stiles, G. W. Poisoning of Turkey Poults from Whorled Milkweed (*Asclepias galioides*). *Poultry Sci.,* **21:** 263. 1942.

1539. Stirling, G. A. and A. E. Urquhart. The Toxic Effect of Crotalaria Extract on the Liver of Rats. *Brit. J. Expt. Path.,* **43:** 441. 1962.

1540. Stockman, R. Lathyrism. *J. Pharm. and Exptl. Therapeut.,* **37:** 43. 1929.

1541. Stockman, S. Cases of Poisoning in Cattle Feeding on Meal from the Soya Meal after Extraction of the Oil. *J. Comp. Path. and Exptl. Therapeut.,* **29:** 95. 1916.

1542. Stockman, S. Bracken Poisoning in Cattle in Great Britain. *J. Comp. Path. and Exptl. Therapeut.,* **30:** 311. 1917.

1543. Stockman, S. Bracken Poisoning in Cattle in Great Britain. *J. Comp. Path. and Exptl. Therapeut.,* **35**: 273. 1922.

1544. Stoddart, L. A., G. T. Baird, G. Stewart, B. S. Markham, and H. Clegg. The Halogeton Problem in Utah. Utah Agr. Ext. Serv., *Bull.* 250. 1951.

1545. Stoddart, L. A., H. Clegg, B. S. Markham, and G. Stewart. The Halogeton Problem On Utah's Ranges. *J. Range Management,* **4**: 223. 1951.

1546. Stoddart, L. A., A. H. Holmgren, and C. W. Cook. Important Poisonous Plants of Utah. Utah Agr. Expt. Sta., *Special Rept.* 2. 1949.

1547. Stoll, A. Les alcaloides de l'ergot. *Experientia,* **1**: 250. 1945.

1548. Stormorken, H. Methemoglobinemia in Domestic Animals. *Proc. Internat. Vet. Congr.,* **15**(I): 501. 1953.

1549. Storrar, D. M. Cases of Vegetable Poisoning in Cattle. *J. Comp. Path. and Exptl. Therapeut.,* **6**: 276. 1893.

1550. Stout, E. N. *Suckleya suckleyana,* a Poisonous Plant. Colorado Agr. Ext. Serv., *Bull.* 359a. 1939.

1551. Sugg, R. S., B. T. Sims, and K. F. Baker. Studies of Toxicity of Wild Winter Peas (*Lathyrus hirsutus*) for Cattle. *Vet. Med.,* **39**: 308. 1944.

1552. Sund, J. M. Nitrate Poisoning Can Kill your Cows. *Hoard's Dairyman,* **105**: 453. 1960.

1553. Sund, J. M., M. J. Wright, and J. Simon. Weeds Containing Nitrates Cause Abortion in Cattle. *Agron. J.* **49**: 278. 1957.

1554. Sunthankar, S. V., and C. R. Dawson. The Structural Identification of the Olefinic Components of Japanese Lac Urushiol. *J.A.C.S.,* **76**: 5070. 1954.

1555. Swanson, C. O. Hydrocyanic Acid in Sudan Grass and its Effect on Cattle. *J. Am. Soc. Agron.,* **13**: 33. 1921.

1556. Swanson, C. O. Hydrocyanic Acid in Sudan Grass. *J. Agr. Res.,* **22**: 125. 1921.

1557. Swanson, E. E., H. W. Youngken, C. J. Zufall, W. J. Husa, J. C. Munch, and J. B. Wolffe. Aconitum. Am. Pharmaceut. Assoc., *Monogr.* 1. 1938.

1558. Symes, W. F., and C. R. Dawson. Cashew Nut Shell Liquid. IX. The Chromatographic Separation and Structural Investigation of the Olefinic Components of Methylcardanol. *J.A.C.S.,* **75**: 4952. 1953.

1559. Tailhardat, B. Les Intoxications animales par le Gland. *Rev. de Méd. Vét.,* **103**: 853. 1952.

1560. Takahashi, M., and J. C. Riperton. Koa Haole (*Leucaena glauca*). Hawaii Agr. Expt. Sta., *Bull.* 100. 1949.

1561. Talapatra, S. K., S. C. Ray, and K. C. Sen. Calcium Assimilation in Ruminants on an Oxalate-rich Diet. *J. Agr. Sci.,* **38**: 163. 1948.

1562. Talbot, P. R., J. C. Hooper, and E. E. Ballantyne. *Weeds Poisonous to Livestock.* Alberta Dept. Agr. Alberta, Canada. 1951.

1563. Tasaki, B. and U. Tanaka. On the Toxic Constituents in the Bark of *Robinia pseudoacacia* L. *J. Col. Agr. Imperial Inst. Tokyo,* **3**: 337. 1918.

1564. Taylor, C. A. The Culture of False Hellebore. *Econ. Bot.,* **10**: 155. 1956.

1565. Taylor, H. Poisoning by the Aconite Plant. *Vet. Rec.,* **5**: 533. 1925.

1566. Tehon, L. R., C. C. Morril, and R. Graham. Illinois Plants Poisonous to Livestock. Illinois Ext. Serv., *Circ.* 599. 1946.

1567. Tennant, A. D., J. Naubert, and H. E. Corbeil. An Outbreak of Paralytic Shellfish Poisoning. *Canad. Med. Assoc. J.*, **72:** 436. 1955.

1568. The Congress (U.S.). Opium Poppy Control Act of 1942. Public Law 797, 77th Congress, 2nd Session. 1942.

1569. Thomas, A. J., I. A. Evans, and W. C. Evans. Bracken Poisoning of Cattle—Nature of the Poison. *Biochem. J., Proc.*, **65:** 5P. 1957.

1570. Thomas, A. J., J. E. Watkin, I. A. Evans, and W. C. Evans. The Bracken Poisoning of Ruminants. *Biochem. J., Proc.*, **61:** viii. 1955.

1571. Thomas, B., and A. F. Walker. The Inactivation of Thiamine by Bracken. *J. Soc. Chem. Ind.*, **68:** 6. 1949.

1572. Thomas, E. F. The Toxicity of Certain Species of Crotalaria Seed to the Chicken, Quail, Turkey, and Dove. *J. Am. Vet. Med. Assoc.*, **85:** 617. 1934.

1573. Thomas, E. W., W. M. Neal, and C. F. Ahman. The Toxicity of *Crotalaria spectabilis* Roth to Livestock and Poultry. *J. Am. Soc. Agron.*, **27:** 499. 1935.

1574. Thomson, R. B., and H. B. Sifton. *A Guide to the Poisonous Plants and Weed Seeds of Canada and the Northern United States.* Univ. of Toronto Press, Toronto. 1922.

1575. Thornber, J. J. Work on Poison Plants. Arizona Agr. Expt. Sta., *Ann. Rept.*, **30:** 428. 1919.

1576. Thorp, F. Further Observations on Oat Hay Poisoning. *J. Am. Vet. Med. Assoc.*, **92:** 159. 1938.

1577. Thorp, F., and G. S. Harshfield. Onion Poisoning in Horses. *J. Am. Vet. Med. Assoc.*, **94:** 52. 1939.

1578. Throp, F., Jr., and A. W. Deem. *Suckleya suckleyana,* a Poisonous Plant. *J. Am. Vet. Med. Assoc.*, **94:** 192. 1939.

1579. Throp, F., Jr., A. W. Deem, H. D. Harrington, and J. W. Tobiska. *Suckleya suckleyana,* a Poisonous Plant. Colorado Agr. Expt. Sta., *Tech. Bull.* 22. 1937.

1580. Thorp, F., Jr., L. W. Durrell, G. S. Harshfield, and C. G. Barr. Oxytenia Found to be Poisonous to Livestock. *Colorado* (Agr. Expt. Sta.) *Farm Bull.*, **2(2):** 18. 1940.

1581. Throp, F., Jr., G. S. Harshfield, L. W. Durrell, and C. G. Barr. *Oxytenia acerosa*—A Plant Poisonous to Livestock. *J. Am. Vet. Med. Assoc.*, **96:** 97. 1940.

1582. Tinker, R. B., and W. M. Lauter. Constituents of *Crotalaria spectabilis* Roth. *Econ. Bot.* **10:** 254. 1956.

1583. Tisdale, E. S. Epidemic of Intestinal Disorders in Charleston, W. Va., Occurring Simultaneously with Unprecedented Water Supply Conditions. *Am. J. Publ. Health*, **21:** 198. 1931.

1584. Tisdale, E. W., and G. Zappettini. Halogeton Studies of Idaho Ranges, *J. Range Management*, **6:** 225. 1953.

1585. Todd, A. R. The Hemp Drugs. *Endeavour* (London), **2:** 69. 1943.

1586. Tokarnia, C. H., J. Dobereiner, and C. F. C. Canella. Estudo Experimental Sobre a Toxidez do "Canudo" (*Ipomoea fistulosa* Mart.) em Ruminantes. *Arq. Inst. Biol. Animal*, **3:** 59. 1960.

1587. Tolmas, H. C. Favism. *J. Pediatrics,* 51: 445. 1957.

1588. Torell, P. J., and R. E. Higgins. Tall Larkspur and its Control. Idaho Agr. Expt. Sta., *Bull.* 407. 1963.

1589. Torlone, V., and L. Rampichini. Contributo allo Studio delle Malattie da Fotosensibilità Negli Animali Domestici. *Arch. Vet. Ital.,* 10: 501. 1959 (English summary).

1590. Towers, K. G. Acorn Poisoning in Heifers. *Vet. Rec.,* 62: 74. 1950.

1591. Trelease, S. F., and O. A. Beath. *Selenium.* Publ. by the authors, New York. 1949.

1592. Trelease, S. F., A. A. DiSomma, and A. L. Jacobs. Seleno-amino Acid Found in *Astragalus bisulcatus. Science,* 132: 618. 1960.

1593. Trenchi, H. Ingestion of *Ammi visnaga* Seeds and Photosensitization— The Cause of Vesicular Dermatitis in Fowls. *Avian Diseases,* 4: 275. 1960.

1594. Trethewie, E. R., F. M. Gaffney, and P. J. Gladwell. Pharmacological Studies of Grasses Obtained from a Property Where "Tall Fescue Lameness" in Cattle Occurs. *Austral. J. Exptl. Biol. and Med. Sci.,* 32: 207. 1954.

1595. Trouche, Dr. Intoxication d'un troupeau d'agnelles par suite d'une absorption abondante de ravenelles. *Rev. Vét.* (Toulouse), 88: 682. 1936.

1596. Trum, B. F. Grass Intoxication and Tetany. *U.S. Army Vet. Bull.,* 36: 110. 1942.

1597. Tryon, R. M. A Revision of the Genus *Pteridium. Rhodora,* 43: 1;37. 1941.

1598. Tucker, J. M., D. R. Cordy, L. J. Berry, W. A. Harvey, and T. C. Fuller. Nitrate Poisoning in Livestock. California Agr. Expt. Sta., *Circ.* 506. 1961.

1599. Tucker, J. O. Preliminary Report of Selenium Toxicity in Sheep. *Proc. Am. Coll. Vet. Toxicol.,* 1960: 41. 1961.

1600. Tucker, J. O. Pine Needle Abortion in Cattle. *Proc. Am. Coll. Vet. Toxicol.,* 1961: 35. 1961.

1601. Tumlin, J. T. Crotalaria Poisoning in Chickens. *Southeastern Vet.,* 10: 60. 1959.

1602. Tunnicliff, E. A., and V. L. Cory. Broad-leafed Milkweed (*Asclepias latifolia*) Poisonous for Sheep and Goats. *J. Am. Vet. Med. Assoc.,* 77: 165. 1930.

1603. Turner, C. W. Effect of Rapeseed on the Thyroid of the Chick. *Poultry Sci.,* 25: 186. 1946.

1604. Turney, D. M., D. H. Copeland, and W. D. Salmon. Lathyrism in Relation to the Use of Caley Peas (*Lathyrus hirsutus*) for Livestock. Alabama Agr. Expt. Sta., *Ann. Rept.,* 54–55: 18. 1943.

1605. Turney, D. M., W. D. Salmon, and D. H. Copeland. Lathyrism in Relation to the Use of *Lathyrus hirsutus* for Livestock. Alabama Agr. Expt. Sta., *Ann. Rept.,* 56–57: 18. 1944.

1606. Twiehaus, M. J., and E. E. Leasure. The Presence of a Hemorrhagenic Factor in Soybean Pellets Extracted with Trichloroethylene as a Solvent When Fed to Cattle. *Vet. Med.,* 46: 428. 1951.

1607. Udall, R. H. Low Blood Magnesium and Associated Tetany Occurring in Cattle in the Winter. *Cornell Vet.,* **37:** 314. 1947.

1608. Uraguchi, K., T. Tatsuno, M. Tsukioka, Y. Sakai, F. Sakai, Y. Kobayashi, M. Saito, M. Enomoto, and M. Miyake. Toxicological Approach to the Metabolites of *Penicillium islandicum* Sopp Growing on the Yellowed Rice. *Japan. J. Exp. Med.,* **31:** 1. 1961.

1609. Valeri, H., and N. Gimeno. F. Estudio Fito-quimico Toxicologico de los Frutos de Aguacate (*Persea americana*—C. Bauhin, Pinax 441, 1623). *Rev. de Med. Vet. y Parasit.* (Caracas), **12:** 131. 1953.

1610. VanderVeer, J. B., and D. L. Farley. Mushroom Poisoning (Mycetismus). *Arch. Intern. Med.,* **55:** 773. 1935.

1611. VanDerWalt, S. J. Some Aspects of the Toxicology of Hydrocyanic Acid in Ruminants. *Onderstepoort J. Vet. Sci. and Anim. Ind.,* **19:** 79. 1944.

1612. Van Es, L., L. R. Cantwell, H. M. Martin, and J. Kramer. On the Nature and Cause of the "Walking Disease" of Northwestern Nebraska. Nebraska Agr. Expt. Sta., *Res. Bull.* 43. 1929.

1613. Vardiman, P. H. Experimental Feeding of Senecio Silage to Calves. *J. Am. Vet. Med. Assoc.,* **121:** 397. 1952.

1614. Vardiman, P. H. The Bromsulfalein Liver Function Test and Biopsy of the Liver in the Diagnosis of Senecio Poisoning in Cattle. *Am. J. Vet. Res.,* **14:** 175. 1953.

1615. Vaughan, K. L. The Treatment with Vitamin B_1 of Bracken Staggers in the Bovine. *Vet. Rec.,* **61:** 693. 1949.

1616. Vawter, L. R. Halogeton Glomeratus. A Range Plant Poisonous to Sheep and Cattle. *California Vet.,* 3(6): 12. 1950.

1617. Vawter, L. R. Halogeton Poisoning in Sheep. *Natl. Wool Grower,* 41(2): 24. 1951.

1618. Vedder, C. D., Jr. Personal communication. 1957.

1619. Veldee, M. V. Epidemological Study of Suspected Water-borne Gastroenteritis. *Am. J. Publ. Health,* **21:** 1227. 1931.

1620. Venek, J. Vergiftung mit Kreuzkraut (Senecio) als Ursache der Zdarer Pferdeseuche. *Schweiz. Z. Path. Bakt.,* **21:** 821. 1958.

1621. Verhulst, H. L., and L. A. Page. Lantana. (Bull. of) *Natl. Clearinghouse Pois. Contr. Cent.,* Feb.-Mar. **1962:** 6. 1962.

1622. Verrill, A. E. A Recent Case of Mushroom Intoxication. *Science* **40:** 408. 1914.

1623. Viehoever, A. Edible and Poisonous Beans of the Lima Type (*Phaseolus lunatus* L.). *Thai Sci. Bull.,* **2:** 1. 1940.

1624. Viehoever. A., and I. Cohen. Physiological Evaluation of *Veratrum viride* and *V. album.* I. Toxicity. *Am. J. Pharmacy,* **111:** 86. 1939.

1625. Vinall, H. N. Sudan Grass. USDA, *Farmers' Bull.* 1126. 1920; rev. 1922, 1925, 1931, 1935, 1957 (by Hein, M.A.).

1626. Vinall, H. N. A Study of the Literature Concerning Poisoning of Cattle by the Prussic Acid in Sorghum, Sudan Grass, and Johnson Grass. *J. Am. Soc. Agron.,* **13:** 267. 1921.

1627. Vinberg, G. G. Toksicheskii Fitoplankton (Toxic Phytoplankton). *Uspek.*

Sovr. Biol., **38:** 216. 1954. (Also Nat. Res. Counc. Canad., *Tech. Transl.* TT549. 1955.)

1628. Volker, R. *Eugen Fröhner's Lehrbuch der Toxikologie.* Ferdinand Enke Verlag, Stuttgart. 6th ed., 1950.

1629. Von Oettingen, W. F. *Poisoning.* W. B. Saunders Co., Philadelphia. 2nd. ed., 1958.

1630. Wagnon, K. A. A Study of Bracken Fern Poisoning of Cattle on a California Forest Range. *J. Range Management,* **12:** 249. 1959.

1631. Wagnon, K. A. Lupine Poisoning as a Possible Factor in Congenital Deformities in Cattle. *J. Range Management,* **13:** 89. 1960.

1632. Wagnon, K. A., and G. H. Hart. Durango Root (*Datisca glomerata*) Poisoning of Range Stock. *J. Am. Vet. Med. Assoc.,* **107:** 3. 1945.

1633. Wahlstrom, R. C., L. D. Kamstra, and O. E. Olson. Preventing Selenium Poisoning in Growing and Fattening Pigs. South Dakota Agr. Expt. Sta., *Bull.* 456. 1956.

1634. Walstrom, R. C., and O. E. Olson. The Relation of Pre-natal and Pre-weaning Treatment to the Effect of Arsanilic Acid on Selenium Poisoning in Weanling Pigs. *J. Anim. Sci.,* **18:** 578. 1959.

1635. Wakefield, E. M. Edible and Poisonous Fungi. Ministry of Agr., Fisheries, and Food (Britain), *Bull.* 23. 6th ed., 1945.

1636. Waldron, C. A. Poisoning from Locust Bark. *Am. Vet. Rev.,* **33:** 456. 1908.

1637. Walker, D. G., and Z. T. Wirtschafter. Resorption of Embryos in Rats on *Lathyrus odoratus* Diet. *J. Nutrition,* **58:** 147. 1956.

1638. Walker, D. G., and Z. T. Wirtschafter. Estrogenic Inhibition of Fetal Resorption in Lathyrism. *J. Nutrition,* **58:** 161. 1956.

1639. Wall. M. C., C. R. Eddy, M. C. McClennan, and M. E. Klumpp. Detection and Estimation of Steroidal Sapogenins in Plant Tissue. *Anal. Chem.,* **24:** 1337. 1952.

1640. Wall, M. E., B. H. Warnock, and J. J. Willaman. Steroidal Sapogenins. 48. Their Occurrence in *Agave lecheguilla. Econ. Bot.,* **16:** 266. 1962.

1641. Waller, C. W. A Poisonous Pea Contaminate. *Science,* **99:** 80. 1944.

1642. Waller, E. F., F. S. Prince, A. R. Hodgdon, and N. S. Colovos. Sensitive Fern Poisoning of Horses. New Hampshire Agr. Expt. Sta., *Tech. Bull.* 83. 1944.

1643. Walter, E. D., G. R. Van Atta, C. R. Thompson, and W. D. Maclay. Alfalfa Saponin. *J. Am. Chem. Soc.,* **76:** 2271. 1954.

1644. Warmke, H. E. Discussion of "Assaying Toxicity in Legumes by the Chick Tests." *Proc. 6th Internat. Grasslands Congr.,* **2:** 1532. 1952.

1645. Warren, L. E. A Note on the Poisonous Properties of *Parthenocissus quinquefolia. Merck's Rept.,* **21:** 123. 1912.

1646. Warren, R., and V. Freed, Tansy Ragwort, a Poisonous Weed. Oregon Agr. Ext. Serv., *Bull.* 717. 1951.

1647. Washko, F. V., and C. W. Mushett. Some Observations on the Pathology of the Hemorrhagic Condition of Chickens. *Am. Vet. Med. Assoc., Proc.,* **92:** 360. 1955.

1648. Watkin, J. E., A. J. Thomas, and W. C. Evans. Identity of the Natural "Cofactor" of Bracken Thiaminase. *Biochem. J., Proc.,* **54**: xiii. 1953.
1649. Watson, D. F., J. R. Rooney, and W. G. Hoag. Fescue Foot Lameness in Cattle—Some Observations in the Disease in Virginia. *J. Am. Vet. Med. Assoc.,* **130**: 217. 1957.
1650. Watt, J. M., and M. G. Breyer-Brandwijk. *The Medicinal and Poisonous Plants of Southern Africa.* Livingstone, Edinburgh. 1932.
1651. Waud, R. A. The Action of *Kalmia angustifolia* (Lambkill). *J. Pharm. and Exptl. Therapeut.,* **69**: 103. 1940.
1652. Wawzonek, S., I. V. Ponseti, R. S. Shepard, and L. G. Wiedermann. Epiphyseal Plate Lesions, Degenerative Arthritis, and Dissecting Aneurysm of the Aorta Produced by Aminonitriles. *Science,* **121**: 63. 1955.
1653. Webb, L. J. Guide to the Medicinal and Poisonous Plants of Queensland. Australia Counc. Sci. Industr. Res., *Bull.* 232. 1948.
1654. Webster, H. A Rash Mycophagist. *Rhodora,* **17**: 30. 1915.
1655. Welch, H., and H. E. Morris. Range Plants Poisonous to Livestock in Montana. Montana Agr. Expt. Sta., *Circ.* 197. 1952.
1656. Wells, H. E. Bracken Poisoning. *Agriculture* (Britain), **56**: 204. 1949.
1657. Wender, S. H. The Action of Photosensitizing Agents Isolated from Buckwheat. *Am. J. Vet. Res.,* **7**: 486. 1946.
1658. Wender, S. H., R. A. Gortner, and O. L. Inman. The Isolation of Photosensitizing Agents from Buckwheat. *J. Am. Chem. Soc.,* **65**: 1733. 1943.
1659. Weniger, W. Ergot and its Control. North Dakota Agr. Expt. Sta., *Bull.* 176. 1924.
1660. West, E. Poisonous Plants Around the Home. Florida Agr. Expt. Sta., *Circ.* S-100. 1957.
1661. West, E., and M. W. Emmel. Poisonous Plants in Florida. Florida Agr. Expt. Sta., *Bull.* 510. 1952.
1662. West, J. L. Lesions of Gossypol Poisoning in the Dog. *J. Am. Vet. Med. Assoc.,* **96**: 74. 1940.
1663. Weswig, P. H., A. M. Freed, and J. R. Haag. Antithiamine Activity of Plant Materials. *J. Biol. Chem.,* **165**: 737. 1946.
1664. Wetter, L. R. The Determination of Mustard Oils in Rapeseed Meal. *Canad. J. Biochem. and Physiol.,* **33**: 980. 1955.
1665. Wheeler, R. E., J. B. Lackey, and S. Schott. A Contribution on the Toxicity of Algae. *U.S. Publ. Health Rept.,* **57**: 1695. 1942.
1666. Whitehair, C. K., H. C. Young, Jr., M. E. Gibson, and G. E. Short. A Nervous Disturbance in Cattle Caused by a Toxic Substance Associated with Mature Bermuda Grass. Oklahoma Agr. Expt. Station, *Misc. Publ.* MP-22: 57. 1951.
1667. Whitehead, E. I., and A. L. Moxon. Nitrate Poisoning by Corn Stalks. *South Dakota Farm and Home Research.* **1**: 3. 1949.
1668. Whitehead, E. I., and A. L. Moxon. Nitrate Poisoning. South Dakota Agr. Expt. Sta., *Bull.* 424. 1952.
1669. Whitehead, E. I., F. G. Viets, Jr., and A. L. Moxon. Nitrogen Distribution in the Corn Plant. South Dakota Agr. Expt. Sta., *Tech. Bull.* 7. 1948.
1670. Whiting, F., R. Connell, P. J. G. Plummer, and R. D. Clark. Incoordina-

tion (Cerebellar Ataxia) Among Lambs From Ewes Fed Peavine Silage. *Canad. J. Comp. Med. and Vet. Sci.,* **21:** 77. 1957.
1671. Whittem, J. H., and L. R. Murray. The Chemistry and Pathology of Georgina River Poisoning. *Austral. Vet. J.,* **39:** 168. 1963.
1672. Wicktor, C. E. Molybdenum Poisoning. Los Angeles County Livestock Dept., *Ann. Rept.,* **1951–1952:** 22. 1952.
1673. Wicktor, C. E. Poisonous Plants. Los Angeles County Livestock Dept., *Ann. Rept.,* **1951–1952:** 23. 1952.
1674. Wiesner. K., M. Götz, D. L. Simmons, L. F. Flowler, F. W. Bachelor, R. F. C. Brown, and G. Büchi. The Structure of Aconitine. *Tetrahedron Letters* **1959**(2): 15. 1959.
1675. Wiesner, K., D. L. Simmons, and L. R. Fowler. Direct Correlation of Aconitine and Delphinine. *Tetrahedron Letters.* **1959**(18): 1. 1959.
1676. Wiggins, A. M. Johnsongrass Poisoning. *Auburn Vet.,* **9:** 77. 1953.
1677. Wiggins, A. M. Crotalaria Poisoning in Cattle. *Auburn Vet.,* **15:** 84. 1959.
1678. Wilcox, E. V. Larkspur Poisoning of Sheep. Montana Agr. Expt. Sta., *Bull.* 15: 37. 1897.
1679. Wilcox, E. V. Lupins as Plants Poisonous to Stock. *J. Comp. Med. and Vet. Archives,* **20:** 766. 1899.
1680. Wilcox, E. V. Cattle Poisoning by the Tall Larkspur. Montana Agr. Expt. Sta., *Bull.* 22: 45. 1899.
1681. Wilcox, E. V. The Poisoning of Cattle by Smutty Oat Hay. Montana Agr. Expt. Sta., *Bull.* 22: 51. 1899.
1682. Wilcox, E. V. List of Plants of Known or Suspected Poisonous Properties Which Occur Within the State. Montana Agr. Expt. Sta., *Bull.* 22. 1899.
1683. Wilcox, E. V. Ergotism in Horses. Montana Agr. Expt. Sta., *Bull.* 22: 49. 1899.
1684. Wilcox, F. P. Poisoning—Castor Bean. Los Angeles County Livestock Dept., *Ann. Rept.,* **1954–1955:** 38. 1955.
1685. Wilde, J. K. H. Post-mortem Lesions Noted in Pigs Used in Cottonseed Feeding Trials. *Vet. J.,* **100:** 209. 1944.
1686. Wildman, W. C. Colchicine and Related Compounds. *In* Manske, R. H. F., ed., *The Alkaloids.* Academic Press, New York. Vol. VI, 1960.
1687. Willaman, J. J. The Estimation of Hydrocyanic Acid and the Probable Form in Which it Occurs in *Sorghum vulgare. J. Biol. Chem.,* **29:** 25. 1917.
1688. Willaman, J. J., and B. G. Schubert. Alkaloid Hunting. *Econ. Bot.,* **9:** 141. 1955.
1689. Willaman, J. J., and B. G. Schubert. Alkaloid-bearing Plants and Their Contained Alkaloids. USDA, *Tech. Bull.* 1234. 1961.
1690. Willaman, J. J., and R. M. West. Notes on the Hydrocyanic Acid Content of Sorghum. *J. Agr. Res.,* **4:** 179. 1915.
1691. Willaman, J. J., and R. M. West. Effect of Climatic Factors on the Hydrocyanic-acid Content of Sorghum. *J. Agr. Res.,* **6:** 261. 1916.
1692. Williams, T. A. Some Plants Injurious to Stock. South Dakota Agr. Expt. Sta., *Bull.* 33. 1893.

1693. Willson, V. A. Toxic Properties of Greasewood, with a brief Discussion of the Physiological Action of Oxalic Acid and its Soluble Salts. *J. Am. Vet. Med. Assoc.,* **85:** 76. 1934.

1694. Wilson, B. J., and C. H. Wilson. Oxalate Formation in Moldy Feedstuffs as a Possible Factor in Livestock Toxic Disease. *Am. J. Vet. Res.,* **22:** 961. 1961.

1695. Wilson, F. W. Oleander Poisoning of Livestock. Arizona Agr. Expt. Sta., *Bull.* 59: 381. 1909.

1696. Wilson, J. K. Nitrate in Plants: Its Relation to Fertilizer Injury, Changes During Silage Making, and Indirect Toxicity to Animals. *J. Am. Soc. Agron.,* **35:** 279. 1943.

1697. Wilson, R. K. An Attempt to Induce Hypomagnesaemia in Wethers by Feeding High Levels of Urea. *Vet. Rec.,* **75:** 698. 1963.

1698. Wilson, T. See: Poisoning Caused by Eating Daffodil Bulbs. *Bull. Missouri Bot. Gard.,* **12:** 52. 1924.

1699. Winter, A. J. Studies on Nitrate Metabolism in Cattle. *Am. J. Vet. Res.,* **23:** 500. 1962.

1700. Withers, W. A., and F. E. Carruth. Gossypol, the Toxic Substance in Cottonseed Meal. *J. Agr. Res.,* **5:** 261. 1915.

1701. Withers, W. A., and F. E. Carruth. Comparative Toxicity of Cottonseed Products. *J. Agr. Res.,* **14:** 425. 1918.

1702. Wolf, F. A., R. S. Curtis, and B. F. Kaupp. A Monograph on Trembles or Milksickness and White Snakeroot. North Carolina Agr. Expt. Sta., *Tech. Bull.* 15. 1918.

1703. Wood, W. E., Jr. Charlottesville, Va. Personal communication, 1958.

1704. Woodson, R. E., Jr. The North American Species of *Asclepias* L. *Ann. Missouri Bot. Gard.,* **41:** 1. 1954.

1705. Woolsey, J. H., Jr., D. E. Jasper, D. R. Cordy, and J. F. Christensen. Two Outbreaks of Hepatic Cirrhosis in Swine in California, with Evidence Incriminating the Tarweed, *Amsinckia intermedia. Vet. Med.* **47:** 55. 1952.

1706. Woolsey, J. H., Jr., and M. H. Shaffer. A Suspected Plant Poisoning in Cattle. *California Vet.,* **5**(3)**:** 21. 1952.

1707. Worden, A. N., J. Bunyan, and J. Pickup. A Fatal Hypocalcemia-like Syndrome in Dairy Cows Following the Excess Consumption of Fodderbeet. *Vet. Rec.,* **66:** 133. 1954.

1708. Wyngaarden, J. B., B. M. Wright, and P. Ways. The Effect of Certain Anions Upon the Accumulation and Retention of Iodide by the Thyroid Gland. *Endocrinology,* **50:** 537. 1952.

1709. Yates, S. G. Toxicity of Tall Fescue Forage: A Review. *Econ. Bot.,* **16:** 295. 1962.

1710. Yelf, J. D. The Toxicity of Creeping Indigo in Fiji. *Fiji Agr. J.,* **29:** 9. 1959.

1711. Yoshida, R. A Chemical and Physiological Study of the Nature and Properties of *Leucaena glauca* (Koa Haole). *Proc. Hawaiian Acad. Sci.,* **19–20:** 5. 1945.

1712. Youngken, H. W., Jr. Ergot—A Blessing and a Scourge. *Econ. Bot.,* 1: 372. 1947.

1713. Zinkham, W. H., R. E. Lenhard, Jr., and B. Childs. Erythrocyte Glutathione Metabolism and Drug Sensitivity. *J. Pharm. and Exptl. Therapeut.,* **122**: 85A. 1958.

1714. ZoBell, R. S., and B. W. Silcock. Another Russian Invades U.S. *Natl. Wool Grower,* **40**(4): 22. 1950.

1715. Zoebisch, O. C., M. Rosenberg, and M. Takahashi. Assaying Toxicity in Legumes by Chick Test. *Proc. 6th Internat. Grasslands Congr.,* **2**: 1526. 1952.

INDEX

For practical reasons, signs, lesions, and treatments have been indexed only when they are unique to one or at most a few syndromes. Boldface page numbers indicate that this is the major reference in the text.

I

M

O

X

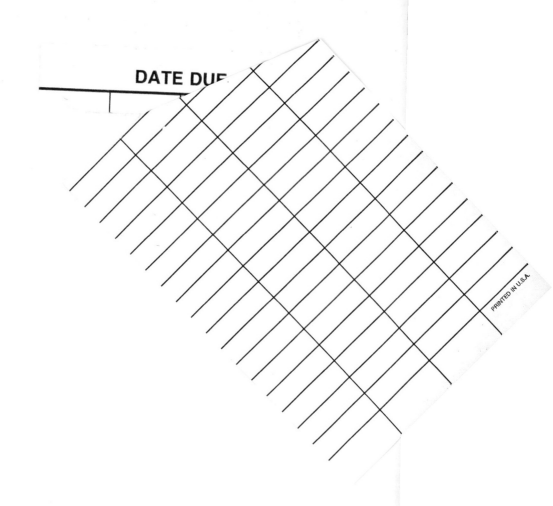

DATE DUE

PRINTED IN U.S.A.